Introduction to
Linear Models and

The Design and Analysis
of Experiments

William Mendenhall
University of Florida

Duxbury Press, A Division of
Wadsworth Publishing Company, Inc., Belmont, California

Duxbury Press, A Division
of Wadsworth Publishing Company,
Inc.

L.C. Cat. Card No.: 67–14246
Printed in the United States of America

4 5 6 7 8 9 10   74 73 72

Preface

A course on the design of experiments must necessarily be preceded by one concerned with basic concepts and inference. Thus we must know how to use information to make inferences and how to measure it in order to understand how experimental design affects the quantity of information in an experiment. This text is written for the large number of students who have had an introductory course in statistics and are faced with the problem of designing and analyzing experiments in their field of study. It is also written for engineers and scientific personnel in industry and for research workers in the social and biological sciences who must design and analyze experiments and sometimes attempt to extract information from masses of process data.

The design and analysis of experiments can be introduced using one of two points of view. The traditional method and the one employed in almost all texts currently on the market is to introduce the subject using the analysis of variance. Underlying each of these analyses is an oft-forgotten linear model of fixed and random components. Our approach is to commence with the underlying model and to fit it to the experimental data using the

v

method of least squares. Thus the analysis of variance is usually taught with the major emphasis on tests of hypotheses, while least-squares analysis stresses estimation. Both methods should eventually arrive at the same point. I favor the least-squares approach in introducing the design and analysis of experiments for a number of reasons.

The notion of fitting a linear statistical model to experimental data is easy for the beginner to visualize because he has considered the simple problem of fitting a straight line in an introductory course. Thus the approach is familiar, intuitively appealing, and very easily extended to a multidimensional space of independent variables. Introducing the sums of squares for the analysis of variance as the difference in sums of squares for error for two linear models is meaningful and provides an easily understood intuitive justification for the F-test. Once the student sees how the sums of squares are obtained for a few examples, he is content to memorize the formulas for various types of designs. In contrast, the sums of squares for the analysis of variance are often presented in a cookbook manner and appear to most beginners to have been acquired out of the blue. This fact is not difficult to explain because proof of expectations is usually omitted. Some authors give the tedious algebraic proof of additivity of sums of squares, but this by itself does not give intuitive justification to the F-test.

Other advantages to the least-squares approach are numerous. It forces the student to think about the probabilistic model for his conceptual population when he designs his experiment, not after. Thus he realizes that he must in some way relate the practical question that he wishes to answer to an inference about one or more parameters in the probabilistic model. He early achieves a single and powerful method of analysis that, unlike the analysis of variance, can be applied to data from undesigned (or badly designed) experiments. It leads early and easily into the analysis of variance, and from that point on the student possesses two powerful methods of analysis. This, along with unity of presentation and intuitive appeal, is perhaps the most important advantage to the approach. It is not proposed that least squares be *substituted* for the analysis of variance. Rather, the least-squares approach can be used as a powerful tool for estimation that will unify and *supplement* the analysis of variance.

The previous paragraph disposes of the criticism that the least-squares approach is computationally tedious. We give the student both tools—least squares and the analysis of variance—and he should employ the method that answers the objective of the experiment with the least computation. (Actually, it is well known that the least-squares equations assume a simple form for designed experiments.)

Another point that may initially be disturbing is that we always use linear models of full rank. The student need not concern himself with the problem of reparametrizing because the difficulty is eliminated at its source —that is, when the model is written. The traditional analysis of variance model is more convenient when dealing with mixed models. Consequently, it is introduced in Chapter 9 (in an example) and is employed in the analysis of experiments for which mixed models are appropriate, Chapter 13.

The text can be adapted to students at various levels, depending on the speed of presentation. The material in the first eight chapters is presented in a very elementary manner and, consequently, can be used for a second-semester course at the undergraduate level for students in the biological, physical, or social sciences. More rapid presentation and greater emphasis on the mathematical aspects of the material would make the first eight chapters suitable for a second course for undergraduate engineers. The complete text has been used in a course on the design of experiments for graduate students in the applied fields of science and for seniors or first-year graduate students majoring in statistics at the University of Florida. Proof of theorems, references, and journal articles are used to supplement the text material for this latter group.

I would like to acknowledge the very kind assistance of the many TAPPI members, Bureau of Mines, and Armstrong Cork Company research personnel to whom this material was presented in lectures, and to the graduate students and colleagues who aided in the preparation of the original manuscript. I am particularly indebted to Professor P. V. Rao of the Department of Statistics, University of Florida, who reviewed the rough drafts of the material, chapter by chapter, as it was prepared, to Professors Paul D. Minton of Southern Methodist University, Paul Meyer of Washington State University, and John Thornby of Bucknell University, who reviewed and offered many helpful comments on the completed manuscript, to Professors John Saw and Fred Barnett, who reviewed the first half of the manuscript, to Dr. Donald Gardiner of the Oak Ridge National Laboratories for his helpful comments on Chapter 10, and to Professor Paul Benson of Bucknell University, who used and tested the material for several years in a course for undergraduates in the social, biological, and physical sciences. I wish to express my appreciation for the assistance of Michael Braddock, William Blot, Robert Beaver and David Hughes, who, along with other graduate students at the University of Florida, assisted in the preparation and solution of the exercises. They will be pleased to note that I credit them for both the correct and incorrect solutions to the exercises. I wish to thank Professor E. S. Pearson for permission to reprint tables from *Biometrika* and Dr. W. H. Beyer and the Chemical Rubber Company for permission to reprint Table 9 in Appendix III. Finally, I wish to acknowledge the very valuable assistance of a succession of secretaries, without whose assistance this text could never have been written: Mrs. Pat Germann, Patsy Bragg, Mrs. Angie Anastasia, and Mrs. Gay Midelis. In an age of labor difficulties, inflation, and low secretarial salaries, they are to be commended for their devotion to duty.

William Mendenhall

Contents

**9   The Effect of Coding
on the Analysis   221**

**10   Seeking a Maximum
or Minimum Response   267**

14 A Brief Summary   403

1

Introduction and
Review

1.1 Introduction

The reader acquainted with statistics will recall that statistics is a theory of information and that the objective of statistics is to make inferences about a *population* of measurements based upon information contained in a *sample.* The population of interest is a set of responses, usually quantitative, that either exists in fact or is conceptual. For example, the population may consist of the diameter measurements for a carton of one thousand bolts; thus it contains a finite number of measurements and does exist. On the other hand, the experimenter may study the strength of a new plastic by testing several pieces in the laboratory. In this case he seeks information on the conceptual population that would be created if the experiment were repeated a very large number of times under similar experimental conditions.

The sample drawn from the population of interest represents a subset of the population and consequently contains information, albeit partial, concerning the population.

The sampling of the population by means of a survey, a series of controlled experiments, or simply the recording of data in an uncontrolled situation requires an expenditure of money and time, and hence the purchase of a quantity of information. Indeed, business corporations, foundations, and the federal government budget large sums of money for research with information as the sole immediate goal. Thus information is purchased and utilized by the experimenter to make inferences about the population of interest. A suit of clothes may vary in price depending on where it is purchased. Similarly, the cost of information may vary over a very wide range, depending upon the sampling procedure. Hence the statistician is concerned with the economics of the purchase of information and, especially, with the design of sample surveys and experiments. We will concentrate in this text on some of the elementary aspects of the design and analysis of experiments, emphasizing the role of experimental design in the economics of experimentation.

1.2 Variability

In order to understand the fundamentals of the design of experiments, one must be familiar with the way in which information is used in inference making. Although it will be assumed that the reader has been exposed to an introductory course in statistics, we will review a few of the basic ideas in this introductory chapter.

Sets of measurements are described by frequency distributions. These, in turn, are described by numerical descriptive measures with a measure of central tendency locating the center of the distribution and a measure of variability indicating its spread.

The notion of variability is one of the most important concepts in statistics because it is one of the basic reasons for the existence of the subject. If one always observed identically the same result when conducting an experiment under standard conditions—that is, if no random variability were present in the experimental results—then one could always predict, presumably, the outcome of an experiment without error and there would be no need for statistical procedures. For example, suppose that an experimenter wished to estimate the average strength of a new plastic by conducting breaking tests on ten experimental pieces of the material. If all ten pieces broke under exactly the same compressive load, then all of the strength measurements would be identical and we would predict the average strength of the plastic to be the same as that observed for the ten measurements. On the other hand, if the ten strength measurements differed, we would have greater difficulty in estimating the true average strength of the plastic. Furthermore, we can see, intuitively, that this difficulty would increase with an increase in the variability of the individual measurements.

The variability of a set of measurements may be described in a number of ways. In this text we will use the following measures of variability:

(1) *Range:* The difference between the largest and smallest measurements in the set.

(2) *Variance:* The average of the square of the deviations of the measurements about their mean.

  (a) The variance of a population will be denoted by the symbol σ^2. (Note: the population mean will be denoted by the symbol μ.)

  (b) The variance of a sample of n measurement is

$$\frac{\sum_{i=1}^{n} (y_i - \bar{y})^2}{n},$$

where $y_1, y_2, y_3, \ldots, y_n$ represent the n measurements in the sample and

$$\bar{y} = \frac{\sum_{i=1}^{n} y_i}{n}$$

denotes the sample mean.

  (c) The unbiased estimator of σ^2, computed from a sample of n measurements, is

$$s^2 = \frac{\sum_{i=1}^{n} (y_i - \bar{y})^2}{n - 1}.$$

To simplify our terminology and since we will most often need s^2 for our inferential procedures, we will calculate s^2 and refer to it as the "sample variance"; it will not differ greatly from the actual sample variance if n is not too small.

(3) The *standard deviation* of a set of measurements is equal to the positive square root of the variance.

  (a) The population standard deviation is σ.

  (b) The sample standard deviation of a sample of n measurements is

$$\sqrt{\frac{\sum_{i=1}^{n} (y_i - \bar{y})^2}{n}}.$$

We will prefer the use of $s = \sqrt{s^2}$, an estimator of σ, and will refer to it as the "sample standard deviation." Thus

$$s = \sqrt{\frac{\sum_{i=1}^{n} (y_i - \bar{y})^2}{n - 1}}$$

For our purposes the most important measure of variability of a set of measurements is the standard deviation. In order to interpret the standard deviation as a measure of variability, one might use either Tchebysheff's theorem or a rule of thumb which we will call the *empirical rule*. [See Mendenhall (1967).][†]

Theorem 1.1 *Tchebysheff's theorem: Given a number k greater than or equal to 1 and a set of n measurements $y_1, y_2, \ldots, y_n$, then at least $(1 - 1/k^2)$ of the measurements will lie within k standard deviations of their mean.*

Example When $k = 2$, $(1 - 1/k^2) = \frac{3}{4}$. Hence, at least three-fourths of a set of measurements will lie within two standard deviations of their mean.

Empirical Rule *Given a distribution of measurements that is approximately normal, the interval*

(1) *$\mu \pm \sigma$ will contain approximately 68 per cent of the measurements,*
(2) *$\mu \pm 2\sigma$ will contain approximately 95 per cent of the measurements,*
(3) *$\mu \pm 3\sigma$ will contain approximately 99.7 per cent of the measurements.*

The symbols for the sample mean and standard deviation, $\bar{y}$ and s, could have been employed in the statement of the empirical rule because the rule will hold fairly well for samples that possess a mound-shaped frequency distribution.

The reader will note several important points regarding Tchebysheff's theorem and the empirical rule. The "at least" appearing in Tchebysheff's theorem is important and would imply that $(1 - 1/k^2)$ is a lower bound. Thus Tchebysheff's theorem applies to *any* set of measurements and is a conservative statement of the fraction of the total number of measurements falling within a specified number, k, standard deviations of the mean. The empirical rule applies rather well to mound-shaped distributions of data, the accuracy of the statement increasing as the distribution of the data approaches the normal distribution. In attempting to be more specific, the empirical rule tends to be less conservative than Tchebysheff's theorem.

It follows from Tchebysheff's theorem and the empirical rule that we would expect most of the measurements in a set to lie within two standard deviations of their mean (Tchebysheff states "at least three-fourths"; the empirical rule indicates "approximately 95 per cent"). Secondly, we note that "plus or minus two standard deviations" spans an interval four standard deviations in width. Thus we might expect the standard deviation to be roughly equal to one-fourth of the range of a set of measurements. A large number of measurements may spread over a range of nearly six standard deviations, while a small number might have a range of only two or three

†Consult the list of references at the end of this chapter.

standard deviations. These statements are not exact but they give a rough rule of thumb for guessing the value of the standard deviation, based upon the range of the measurements, as a check on the calculation of s.

Example 1.1 Given the measurements 1, 3, 1, 7, 2, 4, guess the value of s and then calculate its value.

Solution: The range is equal to $(7 - 1) = 6$. We guess that s equals roughly one-third of the range (since n, the sample size, is small). Therefore we expect s to fall somewhere near 2.

The actual value of s may be calculated as follows:

$$\sum_{i=1}^{6} y_i^2 = (1)^2 + (3)^2 + (1)^2 + \cdots + (4)^2 = 80,$$

$$\sum_{i=1}^{6} y_i = 1 + 3 + 1 + 7 + 2 + 4 = 18.$$

Then

$$\sum_{i=1}^{n} (y_i - \bar{y})^2 = \sum_{i=1}^{n} y_i^2 - \frac{\left(\sum_{i=1}^{n} y_i\right)^2}{n}$$

$$= 80 - \frac{(18)^2}{6}$$

$$= 26,$$

$$s^2 = \frac{\sum_{i=1}^{n} (y_i - \bar{y})^2}{n - 1} = \frac{26}{5} = 5.2,$$

and

$$s = \sqrt{s^2} = \sqrt{5.2} = 2.28.$$

Note that the resulting answer is near our guessed value of $s = 2$.

1.3 Expectations

We may recall that random variables may be either discrete or continuous and that the probabilistic model leading to a probability distribution for these two types of random variables will differ.† The probability distribution may be an exact representation of the frequency distribution for a random variable but most often it represents a model for some actual population frequency distribution.

†A unified theory appropriate for both discrete and continuous random variables, based on measure theory, exists but is not usually presented in introductory texts on statistical theory.

The mean value of the probability distribution of a random variable y is called its expected value and is denoted by the symbol $E(y)$. If the probability distribution is an accurate model of the population frequency distribution, then $E(y) = \mu$. For a discrete random variable with probability distribution $p(y)$, the expected value of y is defined to be

$$E(y) = \sum_y y\, p(y),$$

where the summation is over all values of y. The expected value of continuous random variables is obtained by the use of the integral calculus.

Similarly, we may wish to find the expected value of some function of one or more random variables. Thus we might denote the variance of a random variable, y, as

$$\sigma^2 = V(y) = E[(y - \mu)^2].$$

The process of finding expected values of particular random variables is explained in introductory courses in statistical theory and will not be discussed here. We primarily wish to understand the practical implication of an expectation and to use expectation notation. Thus the symbol $E[\ \ ]$ will imply the expected value (average over a population) of the quantity in brackets or parentheses.

The reader is referred to the Glossary of Symbols, Appendix I.

1.4 Simple Linear Correlation

It is not unusual for an experiment to yield more than one random variable of interest. For example, suppose that an experimenter produced ten test pieces of a new plastic and was interested in measuring tensile strength, compressive strength, and hardness, designated as y_1, y_2, and y_3, respectively, for each test piece. Particularly, he might be interested in determining whether the tensile strength of the plastic, y_1, is related to its hardness, y_3.

Similarly, the psychologist measures more than one characteristic per individual in a study of human behavior. Typical variables might be a measure of intelligence, y_1, a personality measure, y_2, and other variables representing test scores or measures of physical characteristics. As in the case of the plastic, often we are interested in the simple dependence of pairs of variables such as the relationship between personality and intelligence. Particularly, we ask whether data representing paired observations of y_1 and y_2 on a number of people imply a dependence between the two variables. If so, how strong is the dependence?

Intuitively, we think of the dependence of two random variables, y_1 and

y_2, as implying that one, say y_1, either increases or decreases as y_2 changes. We will confine our attention to two measures of dependence, the *covariance* and the *simple coefficient of linear correlation,* and will utilize Figs. 1.1(a) and (b) to justify their choice as measures of dependence. Figures 1.1(a) and (b) represent plotted points for two random samples of $n = 10$ experimental units drawn from a population. Measurements on y_1 and y_2 were made on each experimental unit. If all of the points fell along a straight line as indicated in Fig. 1.1(a), y_1 and y_2 are obviously dependent. In contrast, Fig. 1.1(b) would indicate little or no dependence between y_1 and y_2.

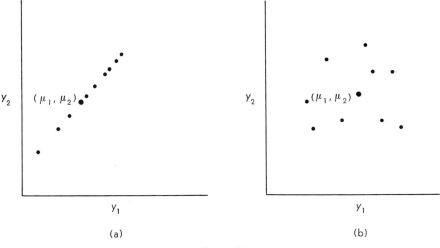

Figure 1.1

Suppose that one really knew the values of μ_1 and μ_2 and located this point on the graphs, Fig. 1.1. Now locate a plotted point on Fig. 1.1(a) and measure the deviations, $(y_1 - \mu_1)$ and $(y_2 - \mu_2)$. Note that both deviations will assume the same algebraic sign for a particular point and hence that their product, $(y_1 - \mu_1)(y_2 - \mu_2)$, will be positive. This will be true for *all* plotted points on Fig. 1.1(a). Points to the right of μ_1 will yield pairs of positive deviations, points to the left will produce pairs of negative deviations, and the average of the product of the deviations, $(y_1 - \mu_1)(y_2 - \mu_2)$, will be "large" and positive. If the linear relation indicated in Fig. 1.1(a) had sloped downward to the right, all corresponding pairs of deviations would have been of the opposite sign and the average value of $(y_1 - \mu_1)(y_2 - \mu_2)$ would have been a large negative number.

The situation described above will not occur for Fig. 1.1(b), where little dependence exists between y_1 and y_2. Corresponding deviations, $(y_1 - \mu_1)$

and $(y_2 - \mu_2)$, will assume the same algebraic sign for some points and opposite signs for others. Thus the product

$$(y_1 - \mu_1)(y_2 - \mu_2)$$

will be positive for some points, negative for others, and will average to some value near zero.

It is clear from the foregoing discussion that the average value of $(y_1 - \mu_1)(y_2 - \mu_2)$ will provide a measure of the linear dependence of y_1 and y_2. This quantity, defined over the two corresponding populations associated with y_1 and y_2, is called the *covariance* of y_1 and y_2. It is defined as follows:

Definition *The covariance of y_1 and y_2 is defined to be the expected value of $(y_1 - \mu_1)(y_2 - \mu_2)$. In the notation of expectation, the covariance will equal*

$$\text{Cov } (y_1, y_2) = E[(y_1 - \mu_1)(y_2 - \mu_2)].$$

The larger the absolute value of the covariance of y_1 and y_2, the greater the linear dependence between y_1 and y_2. Positive values indicate that y_1 increases as y_2 increases; negative values indicate that y_1 decreases as y_2 increases. A zero value of the covariance would indicate no linear dependence between y_1 and y_2.

Unfortunately, it is difficult to employ the covariance as an absolute measure of dependence because its value depends upon the scale of measurement and so it is difficult to determine whether a particular covariance is "large" at first glance. This difficulty can be eliminated by standardizing its value, using the familiar simple coefficient of linear correlation. Thus the population linear coefficient of correlation, ρ, is related to the covariance,

$$\rho = \frac{\text{Cov } (y_1, y_2)}{\sigma_1 \sigma_2},$$

where σ_1 and σ_2 are the standard deviations of y_1 and y_2, respectively. Supplemental discussion of correlation may be found in Mendenhall (1967).

Of particular interest is the question of correlation of two random variables, say y_1 and y_2, that are known to be independent in a probabilistic sense. That is, they represent independent numerical events. Although proof is omitted, it can be easily shown that the covariance (and hence correlation) of two independent random variables will equal zero. For example, random sampling (see Sec. 1.5) from large populations produces measurements that, for all practical purposes, are observations on random variables that are independent and hence possess a zero covariance. As a final comment, it is interesting to note that the converse is not generally true. If two random variables are uncorrelated, they *may or may not* be independent.

1.5 Random Sampling

Many statistical estimation and testing procedures are based upon the assumption of random sampling. Others tend to place some restrictions on the manner in which the sample is drawn.

Suppose that we wish to draw a sample of n measurements from a population consisting of N measurements $(n < N)$. Recalling combinatorial methods, the reader will observe that one may select a total of C_n^N different samples (combinations) of the N measurements taking them n at a time. A sample selected from the population such that each of the C_n^N different samples has an equal probability of being drawn is said to be a *random sample*. The sampling procedure employed is called *random sampling.*

True random sampling is difficult to achieve. One might approximate random sampling by numbering the elements in the population, for purposes of identification, and then selecting the sample by consulting a table of random numbers. Tables of random numbers are constructed so that specific numbers appear with approximately the same frequency during the generation of a long series. A selection of a set of n numbers from the table would identify the population elements to be included in the sample and would, for all practical purposes, provide a random sample. See Hald (1952) for a table of random numbers.

1.6 Two Important Theorems on Distributions

One must know the exact form of the distribution of a particular estimator in repeated sampling in order to make exact statements concerning the error of estimation. The following two theorems justify the assumption that many estimators employed in statistical inference possess approximately a normal distribution when certain conditions are satisfied. The first of these is the familiar central limit theorem and the second deals with linear functions of normally distributed random variables. The theorems as presented here are not the rigorous statements employed in a theoretical presentation of statistics but represent a translation for the convenience of the reader.

Theorem 1.2 *The Central Limit Theorem:* *If random samples of n observations are drawn from a population with finite mean, μ, and standard deviation,*

σ, *then, when n is large, the sample mean, $\bar{y}$, will be approximately normally distributed with mean equal to μ and standard deviation $\sigma/\sqrt{n}$. The approximation will become more and more accurate as n becomes large.*

The Central Limit Theorem essentially states that the distribution of either the sums or averages of n measurements drawn from a population tend to possess, approximately, a normal distribution in repeated sampling when n is large. It is interesting to note that "large" may be as small as $n = 5$ or $n = 10$ in many cases. Hence we would expect the sample mean, $\bar{y}$, to be approximately normally distributed in repeated sampling. Furthermore, the central limit theorem justifies the approach to normality of the binomial probability distribution as n becomes large.

The second theorem deals with linear functions of normally distributed random variables. Let $y_1, y_2, y_3, \ldots, y_n$ be random variables, each of which possesses a normal distribution in repeated sampling. Further, suppose that these distributions have different means and variances (they may be equal as a special case) and that they may or may not be correlated. The quantity

$$l = a_1y_1 + a_2y_2 + a_3y_3 + \cdots + a_ny_n,$$

where $a_1, a_2, a_3, \ldots, a_n$ are constants, is called a *linear function* of $y_1, y_2, y_3, \ldots, y_n$.

Theorem 1.3 *A linear function of normally distributed random variables will be normally distributed in repeated sampling.*[†]

Once again, note that the only requirement placed upon the measurements $y_1, y_2, y_3, \ldots, y_n$ is that they be normally distributed. The means and variances of the distributions may be different, the measurements may be correlated, and the number of measurements, n, may be of any size.

Many estimators and decision-makers are linear functions of random variables that are either exactly or approximately normally distributed. Applying Theorem 1.3, we would expect the distributions of these estimators to be exactly or approximately normally distributed. Theorem 1.3, along with the central limit theorem, provides some justification for the very common occurrence of inference-makers that approximately possess normal distributions in repeated sampling.

1.7 A Theorem Concerning the Means and Variances of Linear Functions

Since we will frequently be concerned with estimators that are linear functions of random variables, we want to be able to determine their means

[†]This assumes that the random variables, $y_1, y_2, \ldots, y_n$, possess a multivariate normal distribution.

and variances. The following theorem gives a formula for the mean and variance of a linear function of random variables.

Let $y_1, y_2, \ldots, y_n$ be random variables with means and variances that may be unequal and that may be dependent upon one another. Specifically, let:

$$E(y_1) = \mu_1, \quad E(y_2) = \mu_2, \quad E(y_3) = \mu_3, \quad \ldots, \quad E(y_n) = \mu_n,$$
$$V(y_1) = \sigma_1^2, \quad V(y_2) = \sigma_2^2, \quad V(y_3) = \sigma_3^2, \quad \ldots, \quad V(y_n) = \sigma_n^2,$$

and assume that the pairs of random variables possess covariances:

$$\text{Cov }(y_1, y_2) = \sigma_{12}, \quad \text{Cov }(y_1, y_3) = \sigma_{13}, \quad \ldots.$$

In general, let the covariance of any pair, y_i, y_j, be designated by the symbol

$$\text{Cov }(y_i, y_j) = \sigma_{ij}$$

for all i and j, $i \neq j$. Finally, let

$$l = a_1 y_1 + a_2 y_2 + a_3 y_3 + \cdots + a_n y_n$$

be a linear function of $y_1, y_2, \ldots, y_n$, where $a_1, a_2, \ldots, a_n$ are constants. Note that no assumptions are made regarding the distributions of $y_1, y_2, \ldots, y_n$.

The following theorem expresses the expected value and variance of l as a function of the means, variances, and covariances of

$$y_1, y_2, \ldots, y_n.$$

Theorem 1.4 *Let $y_1, y_2, y_3, \ldots, y_n$ be random variables satisfying the restrictions stated above and let*

$$l = a_1 y_1 + a_2 y_2 + a_3 y_3 + \cdots + a_n y_n.$$

Then it can be shown that

$$E(l) = a_1 \mu_1 + a_2 \mu_2 + a_3 \mu_3 + \cdots + a_n \mu_n$$
$$= \sum_{i=1}^{n} a_i \mu_i$$

and

$$V(l) = a_1^2 \sigma_1^2 + a_2^2 \sigma_2^2 + a_3^2 \sigma_3^2 + \cdots + a_n^2 \sigma_n^2$$
$$+ 2a_1 a_2 \sigma_{12} + 2a_1 a_3 \sigma_{13} + 2a_2 a_3 \sigma_{23} + \cdots + 2a_{n-1} a_n \sigma_{n-1, n}$$

or

$$V(l) = \sum_{i=1}^{n} a_i^2 \sigma_i^2 + 2 \sum_{i=1}^{n} \sum_{j=i+1}^{n} a_i a_j \sigma_{ij}.$$

Example 1.2 Let $y_1, y_2, y_3, \ldots, y_n$ be independent measurements drawn from a population with mean μ and variance σ^2. This implies that all of the measurements would possess the same mean and variance in repeated sampling and that their covariances would equal zero because of their independence. Random sampling of n measurements from a very large (infinitely large) population would possess these characteristics. Find the expected value and variance of the sample mean $\bar{y}$.

Solution: Note that $\bar{y}$ is a linear function of $y_1, y_2, \ldots, y_n$, where

$$l = \bar{y} = \frac{\sum\limits_{i=1}^{n} y_i}{n}$$

$$= \frac{y_1}{n} + \frac{y_2}{n} + \frac{y_3}{n} + \cdots + \frac{y_n}{n}.$$

Note that

$$a_1 = \frac{1}{n}, \quad a_2 = \frac{1}{n}, \quad a_3 = \frac{1}{n}, \quad \ldots, \quad a_n = \frac{1}{n}.$$

Applying Theorem 1.4,

$$E(l) = E(\bar{y}) = \left(\frac{1}{n}\right)(\mu) + \left(\frac{1}{n}\right)(\mu) + \left(\frac{1}{n}\right)(\mu) + \cdots + \left(\frac{1}{n}\right)(\mu)$$

$$= \frac{n\mu}{n} = \mu,$$

$$V(l) = V(\bar{y}) = \left(\frac{1}{n}\right)^2 \sigma^2 + \left(\frac{1}{n}\right)^2 \sigma^2 + \left(\frac{1}{n}\right)^2 \sigma^2 + \cdots + \left(\frac{1}{n}\right)^2 \sigma^2$$

$$+ \text{(all covariances equal zero)},$$

or

$$V(\bar{y}) = n\left(\frac{1}{n}\right)^2 \sigma^2 = \frac{\sigma^2}{n}.$$

The above proves a result well known to the reader, namely, that the expected value and variance of a sample mean, $\bar{y}$, based upon a random sample from a large population, are equal to μ and σ^2/n, respectively.

Example 1.3 Suppose we possess independent random samples of n_1 and n_2 measurements from populations with means and variances equal to (μ_1, σ_1^2) and (μ_2, σ_2^2), respectively. In order to make inferences regarding the difference in the population mean, $\mu_1 - \mu_2$, we would be interested in the linear function, $l = \bar{y}_1 - \bar{y}_2$. Find the expected value and variance of l.

Solution: It would follow from Example 1.3 that

$$E(\bar{y}_1) = \mu_1, \qquad V(\bar{y}_1) = \sigma_1^2/n_1,$$

$$E(\bar{y}_2) = \mu_2, \qquad V(\bar{y}_2) = \sigma_2^2/n_2.$$

Then, from Theorem 1.4, the expected value and variance of l will be

$$E(l) = \mu_1 - \mu_2$$

(where we note that $a_1 = 1$ and $a_2 = -1$),

$$V(l) = (1)^2 V(\bar{y}_1) + (-1)^2 V(\bar{y}_2) + 2(1)(-1) \operatorname{Cov}(\bar{y}_1, \bar{y}_2).$$

Since $\bar{y}_1$ and $\bar{y}_2$ were based upon independent random samples, the covariance of $\bar{y}_1$ and $\bar{y}_2$ will equal zero and

$$V(l) = \frac{\sigma_1^2}{n_1} + \frac{\sigma_2^2}{n_2}.$$

Note that this is the familiar expression for the variance of the difference between a pair of sample means.

1.8 Inference Making

As previously noted, the measurements in the population are characterized by a frequency distribution which, in turn, is described by numerical descriptive measures. The population mean, μ, and the standard deviation, σ, are examples of some of the numerical descriptive measures of the population. Since these numerical descriptive measures (called *parameters*) describe the population, we are interested in making inferences concerning their values.

Inferences concerning population parameters may be phrased in one of two ways. We may wish either to estimate or to test some hypothesis concerning their values. Testing requires that the inference result in a decision either to accept or to reject the proposed hypothesis. While some statisticians like to view inference making as solely a decision-making problem, we will divide the procedures into two categories, *estimation* and *tests of hypotheses*.

1.9 Estimation

As noted, the objective of estimation as an inference-making procedure is to estimate (or predict) the values of one or more parameters of the population. An *estimator* of a parameter is defined to be a rule which specifically states how one may calculate the estimate based upon information contained in a sample. When a value of a parameter is predicted based upon the information contained in a particular sample, the resulting predicted value is called an *estimate*.

A parameter may be estimated by using either a *point estimator* or an *interval estimator*.

Point estimation implies the calculation of a single number that would determine a point on a line and that would provide an estimate of the parameter of interest. Many different point estimators may be constructed for estimating a parameter based upon identically the same information. Hence it becomes necessary to evaluate the goodness of an estimator so that we may choose the "best" one for a given situation. Secondly, we would like to know "how good" a particular estimate is when the estimator is used in some practical situation.

A useful analogy may be drawn between estimation and firing a revolver at a target. The bullseye corresponds to the parameter estimated. The estimate based upon the information contained in a sample corresponds to the bullet. The revolver-marksman combination corresponds to the estimator. Estimation, like target shooting, involves a single shot fired at an unknown bullseye. Naturally we would like our single shot to hit the bullseye, but for most estimators this seldom occurs. Most of the time we overestimate or underestimate by an amount which we would regard as the *error of estimation*.

The goodness of a point estimator is associated with the *error of estimation* which varies from shot to shot. If the sample size were held constant and repeated samples drawn from the population, one could test the estimator (revolver) by firing over and over again at the parameter (bullseye). Some of the estimates would hit very near the parameter while others would strike above or below. Thus the goodness of a particular estimator could be evaluated by testing it by repeatedly sampling a very large number of times from a population where the parameters were known and obtaining a distribution of estimates about the true value of the parameter. This distribution of estimates would be referred to as the *distribution of the estimator*.

In theory, this sampling is repeated an "infinitely" large number of times. Much as we would compare different revolver-marksman combinations by comparing their targets after repeated firing, we would compare estimators by comparing their distributions. Those estimators possessing distributions that grouped most closely about the parameter would be regarded as "best." The reader will recall that two of the important properties desired in good estimators are that:

(1) They are unbiased. An unbiased estimator is one whose expected value is equal to the parameter estimated—that is, the mean of the distribution of estimates is equal to the true value of the parameter.

(2) The variance of the estimator is a minimum—that is, it is smaller than that of any other estimator. If this were true, the distribution of estimates would possess minimum variability and would group closely about the parameter in comparison with other estimators, assuming that the estimators were unbiased.

Hence, the relative "goodness" of estimators may be evaluated by comparing their biases and their variances. Furthermore, we would characterize the "goodness" of a particular estimator by giving its bias and standard deviation. Since we will be dealing exclusively with unbiased estimators in this text, we will be concerned only with the variance (and standard deviation) of the estimator.

The material of Sec. 1.2 becomes very useful when we wish to make a statement concerning the goodness of a particular estimate based upon a sample of n measurements. Suppose that the parameter is denoted as θ, its estimator as $\hat{\theta}$, and its standard deviation as $\sigma_{\hat{\theta}}$. Further, assume that $\hat{\theta}$ is an unbiased estimator of θ and that the distribution of $\hat{\theta}$ in repeated sampling of n measurements from the population might appear as in Fig. 1.2.

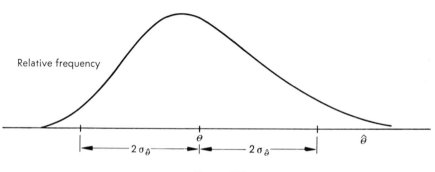

Figure 1.2

Observing the history of repeated use of the estimator as shown in Fig. 1.2, we now wish to make a statement regarding the goodness of an estimate based upon a single sample. Naturally we cannot state whether our particular estimate will be greater than θ or less than θ (since θ is unknown in a practical problem). However, looking at the distribution and recalling Tchebysheff's theorem and the empirical rule, we can be reasonably confident that our estimate lies within $2\sigma_{\hat{\theta}}$ of the true value of θ. Tchebysheff's theorem states that *at least* three-fourths of the estimates lie within $2\sigma_{\hat{\theta}}$ of their mean (which is θ) and the empirical rule states approximately 95 per cent.

Translated into the terminology of probability, we would say that the probability that the error of estimation is less than $2\sigma_{\hat{\theta}}$ is at least .75 and perhaps as large as .95. Hence we would be reasonably confident that on this particular occasion our error of estimation is less than $2\sigma_{\hat{\theta}}$.

The bound on the error of estimation stated above is not very precise but is very practical. Exact knowledge of the shape of the distribution of the estimator would permit a more exact statement of the probability that the error of estimation will be less than $2\sigma_{\hat{\theta}}$. These refinements appear as special techniques appropriate for specific sampling procedures and for specific populations and are those with which the reader is familiar. When available, the appropriate probability statement should be used for a given situation, but we reiterate that $2\sigma_{\hat{\theta}}$ would provide a rough but useful bound on the error of estimation if a reasonably accurate estimate of $\sigma_{\hat{\theta}}$ were available.

Example 1.4 Suppose that one wished to estimate the average length of reaction time for a human subjected to a stimulus in a psychological experiment. A random sample of $n = 36$ people were subjected to the stimulus and the reaction time recorded for each. The sample mean and standard deviation, $\bar{y}$ and s, were equal to 18 and 4.2 seconds, respectively. Then the estimate of μ would be $\bar{y} = 18$ seconds.

The reader will recall that the standard deviation of a sample mean, $\bar{y}$, based upon a random sample of n measurements is

$$\sigma_{\bar{y}} = \frac{\sigma}{\sqrt{n}}.$$

Then

$$2\sigma_{\bar{y}} = 2\frac{\sigma}{\sqrt{n}} \approx 2\frac{s}{\sqrt{n}} = 2\frac{4.2}{\sqrt{36}} = 1.4.$$

(Note: $\approx$ means "approximately equal to.") Hence we would conclude that the probability is at least .75 and most likely near .95 that $\bar{y}$ will lie within 1.4 seconds of the true reaction time, μ.

An *interval estimator* requires the calculation of two numbers (points) based upon the information contained in a sample. The two points form an interval; the objective, of course, is to choose the interval in such a way that with high probability it will enclose the value of the parameter estimated. The goodness of the confidence interval is evaluated by observing its behavior in repeated sampling. Each of the end points of the interval, called *confidence limits* (lower confidence limit, LCL, and upper confidence limit, UCL), will possess distributions in repeated sampling and, generally speaking, the width and position of the interval will shift from sample to sample. One measure of the goodness of the interval estimator is the confidence coefficient, which is the probability that the interval will enclose the parameter of interest. Other measures of goodness might be the average width of the interval (preferably small), the variance of the width, and the expected location of the center of the interval. The interval estimator is often called a *confidence interval* (because the confidence coefficient gives the probability of enclosing the parameter of interest).

Interval estimators of particular interest are those which employ statistics having a normal distribution. For example, let θ be a parameter of interest and let $\hat{\theta}$ be an unbiased normally distributed estimator of θ. Then a $(1 - \alpha)$ confidence interval† for θ is

$$\hat{\theta} \pm z_{\alpha/2}\sigma_{\hat{\theta}}.$$

Note that the symbol z will be used to denote a normally distributed random variable with mean zero and standard deviation equal to one.

The quantity $z_{\alpha/2}$ can be determined from a table of areas under the normal curve (Table 1, Appendix III) using the relation

$$p[z > z_{\alpha/2}] = \frac{\alpha}{2}.$$

Thus it is the value of z such that the area exceeding it in the upper tail of the normal distribution is $\alpha/2$. The values of $z_{\alpha/2}$ for various values of α are shown in Table 1.1.

Table 1.1   Values of $z_{\alpha/2}$ for various confidence coefficients

α	Confidence coefficient $1 - \alpha$	$z_{\alpha/2}$
.10	.90	1.645
.05	.95	1.96
.01	.99	2.58

The confidence intervals shown in Table 1.2 are appropriate when the sample size, n, is large enough for the central limit theorem to imply normality of the point estimator $\hat{\theta}$ and when $\sigma_{\hat{\theta}}$ is known or can be estimated with a fair degree of accuracy. The sample sizes indicated as minimum to achieve a good approximation are appropriate when $\sigma_{\hat{\theta}}$ must be estimated.

When the sample size is small, one may use Student's t to construct confidence intervals for the mean of a normal population and the difference between the means of two normal populations when the variances are assumed equal. Thus the confidence interval for a single population mean, based upon a random sample of n measurements, is

$$\bar{y} \pm t_{\alpha/2}\frac{s}{\sqrt{n}},$$

where $t_{\alpha/2}$ is the upper tail value of the t distribution and is chosen such that the area to the right of $t_{\alpha/2}$ is $\alpha/2$. Expressed in probabilistic terms,

$$P[t > t_{\alpha/2}] = \frac{\alpha}{2}.$$

†By a $(1 - \alpha)$ confidence interval, we mean one with confidence coefficient equal to $(1 - \alpha)$. This is often written as a $100(1 - \alpha)$ percent confidence interval.

Table 1.2   Some typical large-sample confidence intervals with confidence coefficient $1 - \alpha$ (see Appendix II)

Population	Parameter of interest	Point estimator	Confidence interval	Assumptions
Binomial with parameters n and p. y = number of successes in n trials. $q = 1 - p$	p	$\hat{p} = \dfrac{y}{n}$	$\hat{p} \pm z_{\alpha/2} \sqrt{\dfrac{\hat{p}\hat{q}}{n}}$	Large n indicated by $np > 2\sqrt{npq}$, $nq > 2\sqrt{npq}$ and $n \geq 10$.
Comparison of two binomial populations with parameters (n_1, p_1) and (n_2, p_2), respectively.	$p_1 - p_2$	$\hat{p}_1 - \hat{p}_2 = \dfrac{y_1}{n_1} - \dfrac{y_2}{n_2}$	$(\hat{p}_1 - \hat{p}_2) \pm z_{\alpha/2} \sqrt{\dfrac{\hat{p}_1\hat{q}_1}{n_1} + \dfrac{\hat{p}_2\hat{q}_2}{n_2}}$	Similar to requirements above.
Population of continuous measurements with finite mean and variance.	μ	$\bar{y}$	$\bar{y} \pm z_{\alpha/2} \dfrac{\sigma}{\sqrt{n}}$	When σ is known, n may be fairly small. If σ is unknown and $n \geq 30$, use s to approximate σ.
Comparison of two populations of continuous measurements	$\mu_1 - \mu_2$	$(\bar{y}_1 - \bar{y}_2)$	$(\bar{y}_1 - \bar{y}_2) \pm z_{\alpha/2} \sqrt{\dfrac{\sigma_1^2}{n_1} + \dfrac{\sigma_2^2}{n_2}}$	When σ_1^2 and σ_2^2 are known, n_1 and n_2 may be small. When unknown, use s_1^2 and s_2^2 to estimate σ_1^2 and σ_2^2 and require $n_1 \geq 30$ and $n_2 \geq 30$.

The implied confidence coefficient is $(1 - \alpha)$. Recorded upper tail values of t are presented in Table 2, Appendix III. Thus for a sample of $n = 8$ $[(n - 1) = 7$ degrees of freedom (d.f.)] and $(1 - \alpha) = .90$, $t_{\alpha/2} = t_{.05} = 1.895$.

Example 1.5 A random sample of $n = 3$ measurements taken on the potency of a batch of antibiotics yielded $\bar{y} = 30$ and $s = 4$. Assuming that the measurements of potency are approximately normally distributed, find a 95 percent confidence interval for the mean potency of the batch.

Solution: For $n = 3$ and $\alpha = .05$, $t_{\alpha/2} = 4.303$. Then the confidence interval for the mean potency, μ, is

$$\bar{y} \pm t_{\alpha/2} \frac{s}{\sqrt{n}}$$

or

$$30 \pm 4.303 \frac{4}{\sqrt{3}}$$

or

$$30 \pm 9.938.$$

Similarly, we may place a confidence interval on the difference in the means of two normal populations, $(\mu_1 - \mu_2)$, where the variances of the two populations are equal. The appropriate confidence interval is

$$(\bar{y}_1 - \bar{y}_2) \pm t_{\alpha/2} s \sqrt{\frac{1}{n_1} + \frac{1}{n_2}},$$

where s^2 is equal to

$$s^2 = \frac{\sum\limits_{i=1}^{n_1} (y_{1i} - \bar{y}_1)^2 + \sum\limits_{i=1}^{n_2} (y_{2i} - \bar{y}_2)^2}{n_1 + n_2 - 2}$$

$$= \frac{(n_1 - 1)s_1^2 + (n_2 - 1)s_2^2}{n_1 + n_2 - 2}.$$

The resulting confidence interval is based on the assumption that independent random samples of n_1 and n_2 measurements, respectively, have been drawn from the two populations. The quantities $\bar{y}_1$, $\bar{y}_2$, s_1^2, and s_2^2 are the sample means and variances calculated from the two samples. The $t_{\alpha/2}$ employed in the calculation of the confidence interval will be based upon $(n_1 + n_2 - 2)$ degrees of freedom (d.f.) and will be appropriate for a confidence coefficient of $(1 - \alpha)$.

The reader will recall that the assumption of normality for both of the confidence intervals described above is not overly restrictive. That is, as long as the populations are approximately normal, the confidence intervals will be appropriate and the confidence coefficient will be approximately the same as for the case when normality exists. Failure to satisfy the assumption of equal population variances would seem to have little effect upon the confidence coefficient when the sample sizes are equal. Unequal sample sizes coupled with unequal population variances will have a marked effect upon the confidence coefficient. In this situation the described procedure must be modified. (See Boneau (1960).)

Example 1.6 An experiment was conducted to estimate the difference in the mean length of life of light bulbs produced by two different manufacturers. Independent random samples of ten light bulbs were drawn from each of the two populations of interest. The resulting sample means and standard deviations were $\bar{y}_1 = 1230$, $s_1^2 = 12{,}030$, $\bar{y}_2 = 1125$, and $s_2^2 = 9880$. Calculate a 90 per cent confidence interval for $(\mu_1 - \mu_2)$. (For all practical purposes, assume both populations to be normal and assume that the population variances are equal.)

Solution: The pooled estimate of the common variance, σ^2, is:

$$s^2 = \frac{(n_1 - 1)s_1^2 + (n_2 - 1)s_2^2}{n_1 + n_2 - 2}$$

$$= \frac{(9)(12{,}030) + (9)(9880)}{10 + 10 - 2} = 10{,}955,$$

$$s = \sqrt{s^2} = \sqrt{10{,}955} = 104.67.$$

The value of $t_{\alpha/2}$ for a 90 per cent confidence interval would imply an $\alpha/2 = .05$ with t based upon $(n_1 + n_2 - 2) = 18$ degrees of freedom. The recorded t-value is 1.734. The 90 per cent confidence interval for $(\mu_1 - \mu_2)$ would then be

$$(\bar{y}_1 - \bar{y}_2) \pm t_{\alpha/2} s \sqrt{\frac{1}{n_1} + \frac{1}{n_2}}$$

or

$$(1230 - 1125) \pm (1.734)(104.67) \sqrt{\frac{1}{10} + \frac{1}{10}}$$

or

$$105 \pm 81.171.$$

We can feel fairly confident that the true $(\mu_1 - \mu_2)$ falls within this interval because, if this procedure were repeated over and over again in repeated sampling, approximately 90 per cent of the intervals constructed would enclose the true value of $(\mu_1 - \mu_2)$.

A summary of some common confidence intervals is given in Appendix II.

1.10 Tests of Hypotheses

The second method for making an inference involves the test of an hypothesis regarding the values of one or more parameters of the population. For example, we might wish to test the hypothesis that the average weight of a box of crackers of a particular brand is equal to eight ounces against the alternative hypothesis that the average weight is less than eight ounces. Presumably, the manufacturer would be interested in obtaining information concerning the loading characteristics of the packaging machine. It could then be set so that the weight of individual packages would meet the minimum weight specified on the package. The hypothesis tested is called the *null hypothesis*, and is indicated by the symbol H_0. In case the null hypothesis is rejected, an alternative hypothesis, indicated by the symbol H_a, is accepted. For our example,

$$H_0: \mu = 8, \qquad H_a: \mu < 8.$$

The information forming the basis for a decision is obtained from a sample drawn from the population of interest. These sample observations are then used to compute the value of a decision-maker, called the *test statistic*, which may assume a range of values that depends upon the sample observations. In order that the test statistic be able to function, the set of values which it may assume is divided into two subsets, one called the *rejection region* and the other called the *acceptance region* for the test. If the test statistic computed from a particular sample assumes a value in the rejection region, the null hypothesis is rejected. Otherwise, it must fall in the acceptance region and the null hypothesis is accepted. An obvious test statistic for our example would be the sample mean, $\bar{y}$, and the rejection region might be $\bar{y} = 7.8$ ounces. Hence if the $\bar{y}$ calculated from our sample were less than or equal to 7.8, we would reject the null hypothesis.

Many different statistical tests may be constructed to test the same hypothesis. One could change either the test statistic or the rejection region and acquire a new statistical test. Specifically, a particular test is defined by stating

(1) the null hypothesis, H_0,
(2) the test statistic,
(3) the rejection region,
(4) the alternative hypothesis, H_a.

A statistical test procedure would be considered "good" if it arrived at the correct decision—that is, it rejected the null hypothesis when it was false and accepted it when true. Since we cannot always reach the correct decision (because the decision is based upon only partial information given by the sample), we measure the goodness of a statistical test procedure by giving the fraction of time that it makes the wrong decision in repeated sampling (that is, in repeated use). Incorrect decisions (errors) can be made in one of two ways. The experimenter may reject the null hypothesis when it is true (*type I error*) or he may accept the null hypothesis when it is false (*type II error*). The probabilities of making the type I and type II errors for a particular test are denoted by the symbols α and β, respectively. One would choose the statistical test for a given practical situation that would provide the minimum values of α and β for a specified sample size, n. Ideally, however, the preferable procedure would be to decide on the values of α and β (measures of the risk of making a false decision) that would be acceptable and then choose the sample size and rejection region necessary to achieve the specified values of α and β.

Example 1.7 Suppose that a sample of $n = 40$ cracker boxes are weighed and found to possess a sample mean of $\bar{y} = 7.9$ ounces. Further suppose that the stability of the loading machine is measured by a standard deviation known to equal $\sigma = .3$ ounces. Do the data present sufficient evidence to indicate that the mean loading weight is less than eight ounces?

Solution: We would use the test statistic,

$$z = \frac{\bar{y} - \mu}{\sigma/\sqrt{n}},$$

which approximately possesses a normal distribution with mean equal to zero and standard deviation equal to one. Specifically, z represents the distance that a normally distributed random variable lies away from its mean expressed in units of its standard deviation. The resulting test is often called a *normal deviate test.*

From the empirical rule, we know that z will be less than or equal to $z = 2$ (actually, $z = 1.96$) with probability equal to .95. Observing the table of areas under the normal curve, Table 1, Appendix III, we note that the probability that z is less than -1.645 is .05. Hence we might choose $z \leq -1.645$ as the rejection region and $z > -1.645$ as the acceptance region. The probability of a type I error will then be $\alpha = .05$.

The null hypothesis is $H_0 : \mu = 8$, the alternative is $H_a : \mu < 8$, and the test statistic is

$$z = \frac{\bar{y} - \mu_0}{\sigma/\sqrt{n}} = \frac{7.9 - 8.0}{.3/\sqrt{40}} = -2.108.$$

Noting that z is less than -1.645 and hence falls in the rejection region, we reject the null hypothesis and conclude that μ is, indeed, less than eight ounces. Furthermore, we would feel fairly confident that we have made the correct decision because our test procedure will reject the null hypothesis when true only $\alpha = .05$ of the time.

The reader will recall that α is usually determined with ease in the process of locating the rejection region for many statistical tests. Hence when an hypothesis is rejected, it is easy to evaluate the risk of making a type I error. However, if the test statistic falls in the "acceptance region," we do not wish to accept the null hypothesis unless we know that β, the probability of making a type II error, is small. The calculation of β is difficult for many statistical tests and, to further complicate matters, for some tests it is difficult to specify an alternative to the null hypothesis that has practical significance. Hence we emphasize that if β is unknown and the test statistic does not fall in the rejection region, we "withhold judgment" rather than "accept," and conclude that the data present insufficient evidence to reject the hypothesis of interest.

The values of β are tabulated for specific alternatives for many statistical tests, thus eliminating the difficulty described above. When these tables are unavailable, an easy and practical procedure is recommended for the beginner. We revert to the process of estimating the parameter of interest and determine whether the bound on the error of estimation is small enough to detect a departure from the null hypothesis that would be of practical value to the experimenter. For example, one would have difficulty detecting a departure of .05 ounce from the hypothesized mean of $\mu = 8$ in Example 1.7 if the bound on the error of estimating μ is, approximately,

$$2 \frac{\sigma}{\sqrt{n}} = \frac{2(.3)}{\sqrt{40}} = .0949.$$

The precision of estimation, measuring the information in the experiment as related to μ, is much less than that needed to estimate μ correct to within .05 ounce. In this situation we would certainly not accept the null hypothesis if $\bar{y}$ fell in the "acceptance region." This point of view is discussed further in Mendenhall (1967).

Some common large-sample normal-deviate statistical tests are presented in Table 1.3. These and other tests are summarized in Appendix II.

The reader will recall that when one is sampling from a normal population, a Student's t, where

$$t = \frac{\bar{y} - \mu_0}{s/\sqrt{n}},$$

may be used as a test statistic to test the hypothesis

$$H_0 : \mu = \mu_0.$$

Table 1.3 Some large-sample normal-deviate tests

Population of interest	H_0	H_a	Test statistic	Assumption	α	Rejection region
(1) Binomial sample based upon n trials.	$p = p_0$	$p \neq p_0$	$z = \dfrac{\hat{p} - p_0}{\sqrt{\dfrac{p_0 q_0}{n}}}$ where $\hat{p} = \dfrac{y}{n}$ and $q_0 = 1 - p_0$	n is large	.05	$\lvert z \rvert \geq 1.96$
(2) Comparison of two binomial populations with parameters p_1 and p_2. Samples of n_1 and n_2 trials, respectively, are drawn from the two populations.	$p_1 - p_2 = 0$	$p_1 - p_2 \neq 0$	$z = \dfrac{(\hat{p}_1 - \hat{p}_2) - D_0}{\sqrt{\hat{p}\hat{q}\left(\dfrac{1}{n_1} + \dfrac{1}{n_2}\right)}}$ where $\hat{p} = \dfrac{y_1 + y_2}{n_1 + n_2}$	n_1 and n_2 are large	.05	$\lvert z \rvert \geq 1.96$
(3) Population with finite mean μ, and standard deviation σ.	$\mu = \mu_0$	$\mu \neq \mu_0$	$z = \dfrac{\bar{y} - \mu_0}{\sigma/\sqrt{n}}$	σ known or $n \geq 30$ and use s to approximate σ	.05	$\lvert z \rvert \geq 1.96$
(4) Comparison of the means of two populations.	$(\mu_1 - \mu_2) = D_0$ (most often we hypothesize $D_0 = 0$)	$\mu_1 - \mu_2 \neq D_0$	$z = \dfrac{(\bar{y}_1 - \bar{y}_2) - D_0}{\sqrt{\dfrac{\sigma_1^2}{n_1} + \dfrac{\sigma_2^2}{n_2}}}$	σ_1^2 and σ_2^2 are known; or, $n_1 \geq 30$ in which case s_1^2 and s_2^2 are used as approximations to σ_1^2 and σ_2^2	.05	$\lvert z \rvert \geq 1.96$

This test, unlike the z-test (Example 1.7), is valid for any sample size. Critical values of t establishing the rejection region for the t-test are given for various sample sizes and degrees of freedom (d.f.) in Table 2, Appendix III.

Example 1.8 A manufacturer of bolts wished to determine whether his machinery was set to produce bolts with an average diameter of .5 inch. Four bolts randomly selected from production were carefully measured and found to possess diameters equal to .496, .496, .502, and .498 inch, respectively. Do these data contradict the hypothesis that $\mu = .5$ inch? Use a probability of a type I error, α, equal to .05.

Solution: The Student's t-statistic,

$$t = \frac{\bar{y} - \mu_0}{s/\sqrt{n}},$$

would be used to test the null hypothesis, $H_0: \mu = .5$ against the alternative, $H_a: \mu \neq .5$. The latter would imply a two-tailed statistical test (in contrast to Example 1.7) with $\alpha = .05$ divided equally between the two tails of the t distribution. The critical value of t based upon a sample of $n = 4$ [$(n - 1)$ $= 3$ degrees of freedom] is recorded as $t = 3.182$ in Table III.2. Hence we would reject the hypothesis $\mu = .5$, if $|t| \geq 3.182$.

For example,

$$\bar{y} = \frac{\sum\limits_{i=1}^{n} y_i}{n} = \frac{1.992}{4} = .498,$$

$$s^2 = \frac{\sum\limits_{i=1}^{n} (y_i - \bar{y})^2}{n - 1} = .000008,$$

and

$$s = \sqrt{.000008} = .0028.$$

The computed value of the test statistic,

$$t = \frac{\bar{y} - \mu_0}{s/\sqrt{n}} = \frac{.498 - .5}{.0028/\sqrt{4}} = -1.43,$$

is negative but is not less than $t = -3.182$. Hence it does not fall in the rejection region.

Do we now accept the null hypothesis that the mean bolt diameter is $\mu = .5$ inch? No, not until we have specified a meaningful alternative to the null hypothesis and have determined β, the probability of falsely accepting H_0 given that the alternative is true. For example, suppose that the manufacturer hoped to detect a .001-inch deviation in the average bolt diameter from the desired setting of .5 inch. What is the probability, β, that our test, based upon $n = 4$ bolt diameters, would fail to reject H_0: $\mu = .5$ when μ really is equal to .499 or .501?

Tables of β for specific alternatives are omitted from this text. However, looking at the 95 per cent confidence interval for estimating μ,

$$\bar{y} \pm t_{\alpha/2} \frac{s}{\sqrt{n}},$$

or

$$\bar{y} \pm 3.182 \frac{.0028}{\sqrt{4}},$$

$$\bar{y} \pm .0045,$$

we note that this confidence interval is rather wide if we wish to detect a deviation from .5 as small as .001 inch. Hence we would not accept H_0. Rather, we would suggest that additional information be obtained by increasing the sample size, n.

A second common statistical test of interest involves the comparison of the means of two normal populations, μ_1, and μ_2, where it is assumed that the population variances, σ_1^2 and σ_2^2, are equal.

The statistic

$$t = \frac{(\bar{y}_1 - \bar{y}_2) - (\mu_1 - \mu_2)}{s \sqrt{\dfrac{1}{n_1} + \dfrac{1}{n_2}}},$$

where

$$s = \sqrt{\frac{(n_1 - 1)s_1^2 + (n_2 - 1)s_2^2}{n_1 + n_2 - 2}},$$

follows a Student's t distribution with $(n_1 + n_2 - 2)$ degrees of freedom. The quantities s_1^2 and s_2^2 are the sample variances calculated from the two samples based upon n_1 and n_2 observations, respectively.

Example 1.9 The gain in weight of rats on two different diets, A and B, was measured for $n_1 = n_2 = 8$ rats for each of the two diets. The means and variances for the two samples were

$$\bar{y}_1 = 3.92, \qquad s_1^2 = .16$$

and

$$\bar{y}_2 = 3.35, \qquad s_2^2 = .20.$$

Do these data present sufficient evidence to indicate a real difference in the gain in weight of rats fed on the two diets?

Solution: The null hypothesis is

$$H_0: (\mu_1 - \mu_2) = D_0 = 0$$

with an alternative

$$H_a: (\mu_1 - \mu_2) \neq 0.$$

The test statistic

$$t = \frac{(\bar{y}_1 - \bar{y}_2) - D_0}{s\sqrt{\frac{1}{n_1} + \frac{1}{n_2}}} = \frac{(3.92 - 3.35) - 0}{.42\sqrt{\frac{1}{8} + \frac{1}{8}}} = 2.69,$$

where

$$s = \sqrt{\frac{(n_1 - 1)s_1^2 + (n_2 - 1)s_2^2}{n_1 + n_2 - 2}} = \sqrt{\frac{(7)(.16) + 7(.20)}{14}}$$

$$= .42.$$

Using a two-tailed test with $\alpha = .05$, we would reject

$$H_0: \text{ if } |t| \geq 2.145.$$

Since the calculated value of t is greater than 2.145, there is sufficient evidence to indicate a difference in the mean gain in weight. The difference in means could be estimated using the confidence interval illustrated in Example 1.6.

1.11 Some Comments

It is very difficult to conclude a review of an introductory course (and a preparation for "what is to come") without a comment and an apology. Notwithstanding our firm belief in probability, the author is convinced that his reader will fall into one of two categories. This review will be entirely too brief for some (we refer these to an introductory text) and will be extremely verbose and boring to others. (We are grateful for the rare individual who will fall between these two categories.)

Admittedly, a review is necessary for most readers because one cannot study the topic of experimental design without a prior knowledge of the basis for inference making. Assuming now that the reader is familiar with the material presented in this chapter, representing some of the material contained in an introductory course, we proceed to a discussion of the design and analysis of experiments.

Exercises

1. Given a sample of $n = 20$ measurements,

16	8	3	5
10	12	10	7
4	0	11	10
−2	6	4	9
7	7	9	8

guess the value of s and then calculate its value. Construct the intervals, $\bar{y} \pm s$, $\bar{y} \pm 2s$ and find the fraction of the total number of measurements in each of these intervals. Compare with Tchebysheff's theorem and the empirical rule. Find the ratio of the range to s.

2. Given a sample of $n = 3$ measurements, 24, 16, and 7, guess the value of s and then calculate its value. Find the ratio of the range to s. (Note that the ratio is small when n is small.)

3. The following data represent the scores on an achievement test for a group of ten high school seniors. Estimate the standard deviation of the scores by observing the range of observations. Then calculate the mean, variance, and standard deviation of the scores.

$$86, \ 72, \ 95, \ 37, \ 58, \ 80, \ 78, \ 73, \ 81, \ 89$$

Do the results agree with Tchebysheff's theorem for $k = 2$ and 3?

4. The average length of bolts produced on a certain machine is three inches, with a standard deviation of .05 inch. Assume that the population of bolt lengths possesses a bell-shaped distribution. What can be said about the lengths of bolts produced by this machine by using Tchebysheff's theorem and by using the empirical rule?

5. Given a random variable y with probability distribution given by

y	$p(y)$
0	1/8
1	1/4
2	3/8
3	1/4

(a) Graph $p(y)$ and guess the value of $E(y)$.

(b) Find $E(y) = \sum_y y\,p(y)$.

(c) Guess σ_y. Then find σ_y^2 using expectations. Compare σ_y with the guessed value.

6. Suppose that a bivariate population for y_1 and y_2 contained only four points with coordinates and probability distribution given below:

y_1, y_2	$p(y_1, y_2)$
2, 2	1/8
1, 4	1/4
3, 3	1/4
4, 5	3/8

Calculate the covariance of y_1 and y_2.

7. Two random variables, y_1 and y_2, possess variances equal to 5 and 7, respectively, and have a covariance equal to 3. Find the value of the simple coefficient of linear correlation, ρ.

8. Let y_1 and y_2 be random variables with

$$E(y_1) = 2, \qquad E(y_2) = 3,$$
$$V(y_1) = 4, \qquad V(y_2) = 5,$$

and

$$\text{Cov}(y_1, y_2) = -3.$$

Find the expected value and variance of

(a) $y_1 + y_2$.
(b) $y_1 - y_2$.
(c) $3y_1 - y_2$.

9. Given the following information:

$$E(y_1) = 2, \qquad E(y_2) = 1, \qquad E(y_3) = 3,$$
$$V(y_1) = 4, \qquad V(y_2) = 1, \qquad V(y_3) = 5.$$

Find the expected value and variance of l where

$$l = 2y_1 - y_2 + 3y_3$$
$$\text{Cov}(y_1, y_2) = -2$$
$$\text{Cov}(y_1, y_3) = 0$$
$$\text{Cov}(y_2, y_3) = 7$$

10. Independent random samples consisting of $n_1 = 10$, $n_2 = 20$, and $n_3 = 30$ are drawn from each of three populations possessing the same mean and with variances equal to 5, 10, and 15, respectively. Find the expected value and variance of $(\bar{y}_1 + \bar{y}_2 + \bar{y}_3)$ where $\bar{y}_1, \bar{y}_2,$ and $\bar{y}_3$ are the three sample means.

11. The mean and variance of a particular type of electrical resistor are 200 and 2 hours, respectively. If four of the resistors are connected in series, the resulting resistance, R, will equal the sum of the resistance of the four individual resistors. Find the expected value and variance of R. (Assume that the individual resistances are independent of each other.)

12. Use the theorem on linear forms to show that the variance of the estimator of the binomial p, is pq/n. Also show that the variance of $\hat{p}_1 - \hat{p}_2$ is

$$p_1 q_1 / n_1 + p_2 q_2 / n_2$$

where $\hat{p}_1$ and $\hat{p}_2$ are independent estimators of the parameters of two binomial populations, p_1 and p_2, based upon samples of n_1 and n_2 trials, respectively. (Hint: The expected value and variance of a binomial random variable, y, representing the number of successes in n trials, are np and npq, respectively. The probability of a success on a single trial is p and $q = 1 - p$.)

13. The lengths of life of a type of transistor are assumed to be normally distributed with mean 500 hours and variance 1764. If one transistor is selected at random from a lot of this type, what is the probability that it lasts more than 600 hours? What fraction of transistors of this type last less than 420 hours?

14. A process for the manufacture of fertilizer has produced, over the full period of time it has been in operation, an average of 20 tons of fertilizer per day, with a variance of 5.76. If the process is observed for a period of five days, what is the probability that the five-day average production will be less than 18 tons?

15. Two assembly lines in a plant which manufactures transistor radios supposedly produce the same fraction of defectives, assumed to be approximately 20 per cent. If fifty radios are taken from each assembly and examined, what is the probability that the difference between the fractions defective in the samples will exceed .1 in absolute value? (Hint: See the results of Exercise 8 and note that $\hat{p}_1$ and $\hat{p}_2$ will be approximately normally distributed by the central limit theorem.)

16. A random sample of 45 pine trees measured on a certain tree farm revealed an average height of 6 feet 4 inches with a standard deviation of 6.8 inches. Estimate the true mean height of all the trees on the farm and place a bound on the error of estimation.

17. A group of fishermen on a certain lake caught 38 fish in a net. Ten of the 38 fish were bass. Estimate the true fraction of bass in the lake with a 98 per cent confidence coefficient.

18. In order to compare two diets of rabbit food, call them diet A and diet B, an apparently homogeneous group of 14 rabbits was used for a test with half of the rabbits receiving diet A and half diet B. After a period of time, the mean weight of the group receiving diet A was 6.2 pounds with a standard deviation of .3 pounds. The mean weight of those receiving diet B was 5.7 pounds with a standard deviation of .4 pounds. Is there evidence of a difference between the average gain in weights for the two diets? Test using $\alpha = .05$.

19. On a question concerning library hours on a college campus, 42 of 50 men interviewed favored the proposal to increase the hours of operation, whereas 78 of 80 women favored the proposal. Is there evidence of a difference between the fractions of all men and women favoring the proposal? Test using $\alpha = .01$.

20. Place a 99 per cent confidence interval on the difference between the

fractions of Exercise 19. What comparison can be drawn between this answer and the answer to Exercise 19?

21. A manufacturer claims that at most 5 per cent of the goods he produces are defective. If out of 200 items randomly selected from his production 14 are found to be defective, check his claim using a statistical test with $\alpha = .10$.

22. In order to be put into full-time operation, a new process for the mining of copper must produce at least 50 tons per day. A five-day trial period gave the following results:

Day	Yield in Tons
1	48
2	45
3	51
4	49
5	50

Do these figures warrant putting the new process in full-time operation? Test using $\alpha = .05$.

23. A comparison of two types of flashlight batteries produced the following results concerning length of life in hours:

	A	B
Sample size	40	50
Mean length of life	375	389
Variance	1400	1250

Estimate the difference in true mean life between the two types of batteries using a 90 per cent confidence interval.

24. A true-false examination consisting of 100 questions was given to a student. The student answered 65 out of the 100 questions correctly. The professor has reason to believe that the student knew none of the answers and was merely guessing. Do the results of the examination contradict the professor's belief?

25. A population of measurements has a mean, μ, of 50 and a variance, σ^2, of 36. Evaluate the following probabilities using Tchebysheff's theorem.
   (a) $P(41 < x < 59)$.
   (b) $P(36 < x < 64)$.
   (c) $P(|x - 50| \geqslant 12)$.

26. It is known that the mean grade point average for the student body of a large university is 2.56 with a standard deviation of .4. If a random sample of 200 students is taken from the above population, what is the probability that the sample average will lie between 2.50 and 2.62?

27. A foreman in a manufacturing plant says that it takes his workmen

on the average at least 29 minutes to assemble a certain article. In order to check his claim, 35 workmen, picked at random from the plant, assembled the device. Their times for assembly of the article revealed a mean of 28.3 minutes with a standard deviation of 3 minutes. Does this information contradict the foreman's claim? Test using $\alpha = .05$.

28. The coded values for the measure of elasticity in plastic prepared by two different processes are given below for samples of size six drawn randomly from each of the two processes (A and B):

A	B
6.1	9.1
9.2	8.2
8.7	8.6
8.9	6.9
7.6	7.5
7.1	7.9

Estimate the difference between the true population means for the two processes using a 95 per cent confidence interval.

29. Using the data in Exercise 28, test to see if a significant difference exists between the means for the two processes using an $\alpha = .05$. Compare the answer obtained here with the answer in Exercise 28, noting that both answer the question of whether or not a significant difference is present.

30. If two parent mammals are of pure-strain, one brown-eyed and one blue-eyed, the ratio of brown-eyed to blue-eyed offspring should be 3 : 1, according to a genetic model. Suppose that two parents for a certain kind of mammal, as described above, have 400 offspring of which 320 have brown eyes. Does this result give sufficient evidence to contradict the genetic model?

31. A doctor is interested in checking to see if the average body temperature of Eskimos is significantly lower than the normal average for man, which is 98.6 degrees Fahrenheit. After selecting 8 Eskimos at random, the following temperatures were recorded:

98.4, 97.8, 98.6, 98.7, 98.3, 97.9, 98.0, 98.4

Do these results give sufficient evidence to reject the claim that the Eskimos have normal body temperatures, on the average? Let $\alpha = .05$.

32. Using the data in Exercise 31, place a 90 per cent confidence interval on the mean body temperature of Eskimos. Compare the result with the result in Exercise 31.

33. A junior high school physical education teacher is interested in comparing the respiration rates, at rest, of his seventh and eighth grade

boys. Seventy-five seventh grade boys had a mean respiration rate of 19.1 times per minute with a standard deviation of 1.6. Seventy eighth grade boys had a mean respiration rate of 17.9 times per minute with a standard deviation of 1.9. Is there evidence of a difference between the two respiration rates? Test using $\alpha = .05$

34. A white mouse is running a maze with three doors of equal size at one end. One of the doors has a piece of cheese behind it, the other two doors have nothing. If the mouse does not "learn" to choose the door with the cheese, he should choose each door with an equal probability. Under the assumption that the mouse does not learn, what is the approximate probability that in 90 runs down the maze he will choose the door with the cheese 40 or more times?

35. Let x be a variate drawn from a normally distributed population with mean equal to 5 and a variance of 4. Let y be a variate drawn from a sample of size 40 from a binomially distributed population with parameter, p, equal to 1/4. Find the expected value and variance of $l = 2x - 3y$.

36. A university administrator made the claim that the percentage of boys at the university who had failed an undergraduate course was at least 3 percent greater than the percentage of girls who failed a course. To check this claim, 400 boys and 400 girls were selected at random from the university. Of the boys selected 14.5 per cent had failed a course, whereas only 10.75 per cent of the girls acquired recorded failure. Do these results substantiate the administrator's claim? Use an $\alpha = .05$.

37. By law, a certain kind of cereal box must contain at least 16 ounces of cereal in order to be marketed. It is known that the machine filling the boxes does so with a standard deviation of .8 ounces. It is also known that the ounces of fill are approximately normally distributed with mean equal to the setting on the machine. At what reading should the machine be set so that only 2 per cent of the filled boxes fall below the stated specifications?

Supplementary Exercises

1. Two independent random samples of n_1 and n_2 measurements are drawn from populations possessing a common variance, σ^2. If s_1^2 and s_2^2 are the two sample variances, show that the expected value of

$$s^2 = \frac{(n_1 - 1)s_1^2 + (n_2 - 1)s_2^2}{n_1 + n_2 - 2},$$

the pooled estimator of σ^2, is unbiased. (Hint: Recall that s_1^2 and s_2^2 are unbiased estimators of σ^2. Then use Theorem 1.4, Chapter 1.)

2. Prove that

$$\sum_{i=1}^{n} (y_i - \bar{y})^2 = \sum_{i=1}^{n} y_i^2 - \frac{(\sum y_i)^2}{n}.$$

3. Prove Tchebysheff's theorem.

4. Suppose that $\hat{\theta}_1$ and $\hat{\theta}_2$ are two independent unbiased estimators of a parameter with variances equal to 2 and 4 respectively. A combined linear estimator that pools the information in $\hat{\theta}_1$ and $\hat{\theta}_2$ is

$$\hat{\theta} = a\hat{\theta}_1 + b\hat{\theta}_2,$$

where a and b are positive constants.

(a) Find the values of a and b such that $\hat{\theta}$ will be unbiased and possess a minimum variance.

(b) Suppose that $\hat{\theta}_1$ and $\hat{\theta}_2$ were correlated with a covariance equal to c. Which will have the effect of reducing the variance of $\hat{\theta}$, a positive or a negative value for c? Prove.

References

Anderson, R. L., and T. A. Bancroft, *Statistical Theory in Research.* New York: McGraw-Hill Book Company, 1952. Chapter 7.

Boneau, C. Alan, "The Effects of Violations of Assumptions Underlying the *t* Test," *Psychological Bulletin*, Vol. 57, No. 1 (1960).

Freund, J. E., *Mathematical Statistics.* Englewood Cliffs, N.J: Prentice-Hall, Inc., 1962.

————, *Modern Elementary Statistics*, 2nd ed. Englewood Cliffs, N.J.: Prentice-Hall, Inc., 1960.

Hald, A., *Statistical Tables and Formulas.* New York: John Wiley & Sons, Inc., 1952. Table XIX.

Hoel, P. G., *Elementary Statistics.* New York: John Wiley & Sons, Inc., 1960.

Huntsberger, D. V., *Elements of Statistical Inference.* Boston: Allyn and Bacon, Inc., 1961.

Li, J. C. R., *Introduction to Statistical Inference.* Ann Arbor, Mich.: J. W. Edwards, Publisher, Inc., 1961. Chapter 10.

Mendenhall, W., *Introduction to Probability and Statistics, Second Edition.* Belmont, Calif.: Wadsworth Publishing Company, Inc., 1967.

Mood, A. M., and F. A. Graybill, *Introduction to the Theory of Statistics.* New York: McGraw-Hill Book Company, 1963.

2

The Information in
an Experiment

2.1 Introduction

Each measurement acquired in an experiment contributes a certain
quantity of information pertinent to the parameter or parameters of interest.
Although we may visualize a situation where the quantity of information
varies from observation to observation, the simplest situation implies
measurements which, in repeated sampling, possess approximately the
same quantity of information. This would be the case for random sampling
from a population.

Since the experimenter purchases information in order to make an inference, he naturally wonders how much information he should buy. Too little
will not permit him to attain his goal and too much may be economically
wasteful. In fact, a purchase of either an inadequate or an excessive amount
of information may result in a loss of labor or of money or both.

In Sec. 2.2 we will consider the problem of choosing the sample size in
random sampling where each observation contains the same quantity of
information. In succeeding sections we will examine the factors affecting

the quantity of information per observation in an experiment and determine the basic principles involved in the design of good experiments.

2.2 Choosing the Sample Size

The quantity of information in an experiment varies with the method of selecting the sample or the design of the experiment. However, suppose that the sampling procedure is specified; how then does one decide upon the sample size necessary to make an inference of specified "goodness"? That is, we would like to answer the question most frequently posed by the experimenter: "How many observations should I include in my sample?"

The answer to this question will depend upon the method of inference —that is, whether one wishes to test an hypothesis or estimate the value of a parameter. However, for either procedure we cannot construct a reply unless the experimenter tells us how much information he wishes to buy.

If the inference is to be a test of an hypothesis, the experimenter must state the magnitude of the deviation from the hypothesized value that he wishes to detect along with the values of α and β, the measures of risk of making an erroneous decision, that he is willing to tolerate. The sample size would be chosen to provide the information necessary to satisfy these requirements.

If he is estimating, the experimenter should specify a bound on his error of estimation, say B, such that

$$P(\text{error of estimation} \leq B) = 1 - \alpha$$

—that is, the probability that the error of estimation is less than or equal to B is equal to some specified value, say $(1 - \alpha)$, that would be acceptable to the experimenter.

Reflecting the author's preference for estimation as a method of inference (when one has a choice), we will discuss the latter procedure. If the estimator possesses a mound-shaped distribution in repeated sampling and is unbiased, one could use Tchebysheff's theorem and the empirical rule to state that the error of estimating a parameter θ should be less than $2\sigma_{\hat{\theta}}$ with probability equal to approximately .95.

Example 2.1   A manufacturer wishes to estimate the difference in the fraction defective of fuses produced by two different production lines correct to within .06 with probability equal to .95. How many fuses should be selected from each production line?

Solution: Let n_1 and n_2 equal the number of observations drawn from the two production lines and let $n_1 = n_2 = n$. Further, let p_1 and p_2 equal the true fraction defective for the two production lines.

The estimator of $(p_1 - p_2)$ is

$$(\hat{p}_1 - \hat{p}_2) = \left(\frac{y_1}{n_1} - \frac{y_2}{n_2}\right),$$

where y_1 and y_2 are the number of defectives observed in the samples drawn from the two production lines. The standard deviation of the estimator is

$$\sqrt{\frac{p_1 q_1}{n_1} + \frac{p_2 q_2}{n_2}}.$$

Since $(\hat{p}_1 - \hat{p}_2)$ is an unbiased estimator of $(p_1 - p_2)$ that will have an approximately normal distribution for large samples, we would expect the error of estimation to be less than $2\sigma_{(\hat{p}_1 - \hat{p}_2)}$ with probability equal to .95. Hence, we would choose n so that

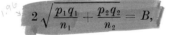

$$2\sqrt{\frac{p_1 q_1}{n_1} + \frac{p_2 q_2}{n_2}} = B,$$

where B is required to equal .06.

Since $n_1 = n_2 = n$, we only need values of p_1 and p_2 to solve for n. Approximate values for p_1 and p_2 may be known in advance. If not, one may obtain a satisfactory solution for n by guessing the values of p_1 and p_2. (The most conservative guess would be to use $p_1 = p_2 = .5$.)

Suppose that, for our example, we expect p_1 and p_2 to be somewhere in the neighborhood of .1. Then

$$\sqrt{\frac{p_1 q_1}{n_1} + \frac{p_2 q_2}{n_2}} = .06$$

or

$$2\sqrt{\frac{(.1)(.9)}{n} + \frac{(.1)(.9)}{n}} = .06$$

or

$$n = 200.$$

Thus one would choose 200 fuses from each production line. We would be fairly confident that the resulting estimate of the difference in fraction defective for the two production lines, $(p_1 - p_2)$, lies within $B = .06$ of the true difference with probability approximately equal to .95.

Example 2.2 Two teaching techniques are to be compared using two groups of children randomly selected from the fourth year of elementary school. An examination at the end of the test period will provide evidence to estimate the difference in the average level of achievement for students taught by the two teaching methods. If the examination is scored from

0 to 800 and if the researcher wishes to estimate the difference in average achievement correct to within 40 units (with probability equal to .90), how many students should be included in each group? Assume that the groups will be of equal size and that prior testing suggests that most students will score in the interval 300 to 700.

Solution: The statement of the problem indicates that the error of estimation is required to be less than 40 with probability equal to .90. Assuming normality for the distribution of $(\bar{y}_1 - \bar{y}_2)$ (which is a very reasonable assumption), we would expect the error of estimation, $(\bar{y}_1 - \bar{y}_2) - (\mu_1 - \mu_2)$, to be less than $1.645\sigma_{(\bar{y}_1 - \bar{y}_2)}$. Hence we wish to choose $n_1 = n_2 = n$ so that

$$1.645\sigma_{(\bar{y}_1 - \bar{y}_2)} = 40$$

 or

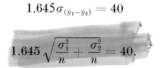

$$1.645\sqrt{\frac{\sigma_1^2}{n} + \frac{\sigma_2^2}{n}} = 40.$$

(Note in Table 1.1 that $z = 1.645$ is the z-value appropriate for a 90 per cent confidence interval.)

A solution of this equation for n requires knowledge of the values for σ_1^2 and σ_2^2. Lacking these, we may obtain an approximate solution by using the guessed value of the range, $(700 - 300)$, and estimating σ_1 and σ_2 roughly as one-fourth of the range.

Solving for n, we have

$$1.645\sqrt{\frac{(100)^2}{n} + \frac{(100)^2}{n}} = 40$$

or

$$n \approx 34.$$

We would acknowledge that this solution is approximate because of the substitution of guessed values for σ_1^2 and σ_2^2. However, for practical purposes the solution should be reasonably near the sample size necessary to acquire the desired quantity of information.

2.3 The Factors Affecting the Quantity of Information in an Experiment

Some very interesting analogies can be drawn between experimentation and phenomena well known to the reader. We may view the researcher as a detective who seeks to learn some fact regarding his field of interest and to reach a conclusion based upon the partial evidence contained in a sample. For example, he may wish to determine whether a real difference exists between the average strengths of two types of steel. This difference either does or does not exist, but the true situation is obscured by the variability of the strength measurements made on test specimens. The more evidence available and the fewer the elements of confusion, the easier it is for the detective to draw a good inference concerning the real and unknown situation confronting him.

For a second analogy, we might compare experimentation and the consequent search for knowledge with the problem of receiving a verbal message from a friend in a small room containing fifty other people. The verbal message corresponds to the true physical phenomenon that the experimenter wishes to detect. Unfortunately, the signal is obscured to some extent by the background noise created by the conversation of the others in the room. The noise in an experiment is created by numerous uncontrolled, and frequently unmeasurable variables, and is exhibited in the random behavior of the measurements in repeated sampling. The message which we seek is obviously affected by two dominating factors that control the quantity of information in the experiment. The first is the level of the background *noise* that tends to obscure the signal. The second is the *volume* of the signal. The measure of noise in an experiment is given by σ^2, the variance of the experimental data. The volume is measured by the sample size, n. We might think of σ^2 as measuring the quantity of information per observation (the greater σ^2, the less the information per observation), while n measures the number of bits of information in the experiment. The amount of information may be increased by either increasing the volume of the signal (n) or by reducing the noise (σ^2). This analogy is well known to the engineer, who often measures the transmissibility of an electrical signal in terms of signal-to-noise ratio (that is, volume to noise).

Referring particularly to estimation, the reader will recall that the bound on the error of estimation is dependent upon the variance of the estimator. For example, the variance of $\bar{y}$, the sample mean, is

$$V(\bar{y}) = \frac{\sigma^2}{n},$$

and is therefore proportional to σ^2 and inversely proportional to the sample size n. Other estimators based upon the same quantity of information per observation exhibit this property.

Therefore we may reduce the variance of the estimator and increase the information in an experiment by either reducing σ^2 (noise) or increasing the sample size (volume of the signal).

The foregoing discussion directs attention to the two basic principles involved in the design of good experiments. Experiments are designed with an attempt to reduce the noise and to increase the volume of the signal in order to maximize the quantity of information obtained at a fixed cost. Some designs (sampling procedures) are constructed primarily for the purpose of increasing information by noise reduction, others concentrate on an increase in volume by shifting information in the experiment to the parameters of interest, and still others employ both principles at the same time.

2.4 An Example of a Designed Experiment

A manufacturer would like to compare two procedures, A and B, for measuring enzyme growth in a fermentation process. The precision of the two methods of measurement appears to be the same, but there is some question as to whether one method produces higher readings than the other.

The experiment could be performed as follows. Samples could be selected at random from the well-mixed vat of fermenting substance. Half of the samples could be measured by method A and half by method B. One could then estimate the difference between the means, $\mu_A - \mu_B$, or could test an hypothesis concerning their equality. Assuming near normality for the two populations of measurements, one would use estimation and test procedures based on the t distribution illustrated in Examples 1.6 and 1.9.

A second design for the experiment would choose only half as many samples. Each sample would be divided into two parts, one randomly assigned for analysis by method A and the other by method B.

While both of the designs described above result in the same number of analyses and approximately the same cost, the second design would be preferable because it might yield a greater amount of information. The variability or noise for the first procedure would be contributed by variability between samples of the fermenting substance in the vat and by measurement error introduced by methods A and B. Admittedly, we expect the within-vat variability of the measurements to be small because the substance is mixed, but lack of homogeneity between samples, however small, will exist and may be considerably larger than the variability within sample and the measurement error. This would then contribute to the variability of the measurements.

We would like to protect against this contingency. If nonhomogeneity exists, we would expect samples of vat contents near each other to be more nearly homogeneous than those far apart. Hence, we would divide each sample and compare A and B within this relatively homogeneous block of experimental material (that is, the substance in the sample). Thus comparisons between A and B would be made in the presence of the reduced noise of the more homogeneous sample.

The experiment, conducted according to the second design, produced the data listed in Table 2.1.

Table 2.1   Data for a paired-difference experiment

Sample	Method A	Method B
1	327.6	327.6
2	327.7	327.7
3	327.7	327.6
4	327.9	327.8
5	327.4	327.4
6	327.7	327.6
7	327.8	327.8
8	327.8	327.7
9	327.4	327.3

$$\bar{y}_A = 327.667 \qquad \bar{y}_B = 327.611$$

The reader will recognize this as a paired-difference experiment where the ith paired difference is

$$d_i = y_{Ai} - y_{Bi},$$
$$i = 1, 2, 3, \ldots, 9.$$

The expected value of the ith paired difference may be found using Theorem 1.4:

$$\mu_d = E(d_i) = E(y_{Ai} - y_{Bi}) = E(y_{Ai}) - E(y_{Bi})$$

or

$$\mu_d = \mu_A - \mu_B.$$

In other words, we may make inferences regarding the difference between the means of the methods of measurement, $\mu_A - \mu_B$, by making inferences regarding the single mean of the differences, μ_d.

The analysis of the paired-difference experiment utilizes the nine paired differences, d_i, $i = 1, 2, \ldots, 9$, shown in Table 2.2.

Table 2.2   The paired differences for the data, Table 2.1

Sample	d_i
1	0
2	0
3	.1
4	.1
5	0
6	.1
7	0
8	.1
9	.1
$\bar{d}$	.056

The sample variance of the $n = 9$ differences is

$$s_d^2 = \sum_{i=1}^{n} \frac{(d_i - \bar{d})^2}{n - 1} = .002778.$$

The null hypothesis,

$$H_0: \mu_A - \mu_B = \mu_d = 0,$$

may be tested using Student's t-statistic,

$$t = \frac{\bar{d} - \mu_d}{s_d/\sqrt{n}}.$$

For our example,

$$t = \frac{.056 - 0}{.053/\sqrt{9}} = 3.17.$$

The critical value of t (Table 2)† based upon $n - 1 = 8$ degrees of freedom and $\alpha = .05$ is $t = 2.306$. Since the calculated t exceeds this value, we reject the hypothesis that $\mu_A - \mu_B = 0$ and conclude that the instruments are not reading at the same mean level. Furthermore we would be reasonably confident that our decision was correct because the probability of a type I error for our test procedure is only $\alpha = .05$.

An indication of the difference in the quantity of information in the unpaired design versus the paired design can be obtained by comparing the relative variability involved in the two resulting methods of analysis. This can most easily be seen by comparing confidence intervals for the two procedures.

The $(1 - \alpha)$ confidence interval for $\mu_A - \mu_B$ using the paired differences is

$$\bar{d} \pm t_{\alpha/2}\frac{s_d}{\sqrt{n}}.$$

Substituting, we obtain a 95 per cent confidence interval,

$$.056 \pm \frac{(2.303)(.053)}{\sqrt{9}}$$

or

$$.056 \pm .041.$$

Unfortunately, we cannot calculate the $(1 - \alpha)$ confidence interval for $\mu_A - \mu_B$ using the unpaired design because the experiment was not conducted in an unpaired manner. While it is difficult to state exactly what might have happened if this design had been employed, one can approximate the confidence interval by using the *between-pairs* variability of the paired-difference data to obtain a pooled estimate of the variance of the experimental error. Specifically, as in Example 1.9, we would assume the population variances to be approximately equal,

†Throughout the text, such table references refer to the tables in Appendix III.

$$\sigma_A^2 = \sigma_B^2 = \sigma^2,$$

and estimate σ^2 by a pooled estimate of variance,

$$s^2 = \frac{\sum_{i=1}^{n_1} (y_{Ai} - \bar{y}_A)^2 + \sum_{i=1}^{n_2} (y_{Bi} - \bar{y}_B)^2}{n_1 + n_2 - 2}.$$

Substituting into this formula, we obtain

$$s^2 = \frac{.2400 + .2289}{16} = .02931$$

and

$$s = .171.$$

The 95 per cent confidence interval for $(\mu_A - \mu_B)$ from this unpaired analysis of the paired data is

$$(\bar{y}_A - \bar{y}_B) \pm t_{\alpha/2} s \sqrt{\frac{1}{n_1} + \frac{1}{n_2}}$$

$$(327.667 - 327.611) \pm (2.12)(.171) \sqrt{\frac{1}{9} + \frac{1}{9}}$$

or

$$.056 \pm .171.$$

We may now compare the 95 per cent confidence intervals for $(\mu_A - \mu_B)$ for the paired and the unpaired analyses of the data for the paired design.

Paired analysis: $.056 \pm .041$

Unpaired analysis: $.056 \pm .171$

We reiterate that a paired design must utilize the paired-difference analysis and that an unpaired analysis of the same data is simply a procedure for calculating a confidence interval that would be a good approximation to what might have been obtained had the experiment been conducted in an unpaired manner.

A comparison of the two intervals reveals the substantial difference in the quantity of information concerning $(\mu_A - \mu_B)$ contained in the two designs. Specifically, the paired analysis produces an interval, and hence a bound on the error of estimation, of less than one-fourth that obtained by the unpaired analysis. Since the standard deviation of $(\bar{y}_A - \bar{y}_B)$ is inversely proportional to the square root of the sample size, it would require approximately $(4)^2 = 16$ times as many observations in the unpaired analysis to reduce the width of the unpaired confidence interval to that obtained from the paired design. In other words, the reduction in noise obtained by the paired design obtains the necessary information at approximately one-sixteenth the cost required for the unpaired design.

The paired design described above, a simple example of a *randomized block design*, illustrates the principle of noise reduction in increasing the information in an experiment.

Before leaving this example, let us dispel the notion that blocking always gives an increase in information. If within-pairs variability is the same as between-pairs variability, then blocking will not produce a reduction in the variability of comparisons. In other words, the variance of $(\bar{y}_A - \bar{y}_B)$ will be identical regardless of whether one conducts the experiment in a paired or an unpaired manner. For this case, pairing actually results in a *loss* in information because the experimenter retains fewer degrees of freedom for the estimation of the variance of the error (reduced from 16 to 8 degrees of freedom) in the calculation of the confidence interval and produces a correspondingly wider interval. Thus blocking may increase the information in an experiment by reducing experimental variability and does decrease the information by reducing the degrees of freedom available for estimating σ^2. The reader will observe that the gain in information obtained by blocking for our example far outweighed the small loss due to the reduction in degrees of freedom. The conditions that dictate a decision to block will be discussed in greater detail in Chapter 4.

Exercises

1. Refer to Example 1.5, Chapter 1. Approximately how many observations would be required to reduce the 95 per cent confidence interval of mean potency to $\bar{y} \pm .6$?

2. Refer to Example 1.6, Chapter 1. If $n_1 = n_2$, approximately how large must n_1 be in order to cut the 90 per cent confidence interval for the estimation of $(\mu_1 - \mu_2)$ in half?

3. Refer to Example 1.7, Chapter 1. Approximately how large a sample would be required to estimate the average load correct to within .01 ounces with a probability of .90? With a probability of .95?

4. Refer to Example 1.8, Chapter 1. Approximately how large a sample would be required to estimate μ correct to within plus or minus .001 with probability equal to .95?

5. Refer to Example 2.1. How many fuses would be required from each production line in order to estimate the difference in the fraction defective correct to within .025?

6. Refer to Example 2.2. How many children must be included in each group to estimate the difference in average achievement correct to

within 30 units with probability equal to .90? With probability equal to .95?

7. A dean of men wished to estimate the average cost of the freshman year at a particular college correct to within $200.00 with a probability of .95. If a random sample of freshmen is to be selected and requested to keep financial data, how many must be included in the sample? Assume that the dean knows only that the range of expenditures will vary from approximately $2200 to $4000.

8. A random sample of voters is to be selected to estimate the percentage favoring a particular candidate in a national election. If the percentage is expected to be near 50 per cent, approximately how many voters must be included in the sample in order that the estimate be correct to within plus or minus .1 per cent with probability equal to .95?

9. A manufacturer of drugs indicated the potency of a new product in treating a disease by producing the results of an experiment. Sixteen of 30 untreated patients recovered versus 22 of 30 treated patients. Do these data present sufficient evidence to indicate that the average per cent recovery for the treated patients is greater than for the untreated? How many patients would have to be included in each group in order to estimate the differences in the average fraction recovered to within .06 with probability equal to .95?

10. What two factors affect the quantity of information in an experiment?

11. How does a paired-difference experiment increase the quantity of information in an experiment?

12. Will a paired-difference experiment always increase the quantity of information in an experiment?

13. Suppose that two independent random samples of $n_1 = n_2$ observations are drawn from two normal populations to make inferences concerning $(\mu_1 - \mu_2)$. Can one increase the quantity of information in the experiment by pairing observations and analyzing as a paired-difference experiment? Explain.

14. Suppose that an experiment conducted to compare two treatments is blocked—that is, paired—but the data are analyzed *as though the experiment were conducted in an unpaired manner*. How does this affect the quantity of information extracted from the experiment?

15. An additive to increase the strength of concrete was evaluated by employing a paired (or blocked) experimental design. Each of five batches of concrete was divided, with half of the batch receiving the additive and the other remaining untreated. The strength measurements

for the experiment are shown below:

Batch	Treated y_1	Untreated y_2
1	16.1	14.8
2	14.7	13.2
3	17.4	15.5
4	13.7	12.3
5	16.9	15.9

Estimate the difference in the average strength between the treated and untreated concrete using a 95 per cent confidence interval.

16. Refer to Exercise 15. Approximately how many test specimens would be required if each test specimen were prepared from a single batch (thus eliminating the pairing)? Analyze the data *as if* it were not paired and obtain a 95 per cent confidence interval for the difference between the mean strengths. Then determine the approximate number of measurements necessary to reduce the width of this interval to that obtained using the paired analysis.

17. Refer to Exercise 15. Approximately how many batches would be required to estimate the difference in mean strength between the treated and untreated concrete correct to within .2 with probability equal to .95? Assume that the experiment is conducted as indicated in Exercise 15.

18. A psychological experiment was conducted to compare the length of response time (in seconds) for two different stimuli. In order to remove natural person-to-person variability in the responses, both stimuli were applied to each of nine subjects, thus permitting an analysis of the difference between stimuli *within* each person.

Subject	Stimulus 1	Stimulus 2
1	9.4	10.3
2	7.8	8.9
3	5.6	4.1
4	12.1	14.7
5	6.9	8.7
6	4.2	7.1
7	8.8	11.3
8	7.7	5.2
9	6.4	7.8

Assume that the response time is approximately normally distributed for each type of stimulus and that the population increases are approximately equal. Do the data present sufficient evidence to indicate a difference in the mean response times for the populations of measurements associated with the two stimuli? Test using $\alpha = .05$.

19. Refer to Exercise 18. Construct a 95 per cent confidence interval for the mean difference in response times.

20. Refer to Exercise 18. Approximately how many individuals would have been required for the experiment to obtain the same quantity of information concerning $(\mu_1 - \mu_2)$ if the experiment had not been conducted in a paired manner? That is, each person would only receive *one* of the stimuli, and equal numbers of subjects would have been assigned to each stimulus group.

21. Refer to Exercise 18. If both stimuli were applied to each individual as indicated in Exercise 18, how many subjects would be required to estimate the difference in mean response time correct to within .3 with probability equal to .95?

22. Suppose that approximately three million people are expected to vote in a particular state during a Presidential election; further, suppose that the early returns represented a random sample from this population (this last supposition, would, of course, rarely be true.) Approximately how many early votes would be required to estimate the fraction of the total vote that one of the candidates will receive correct to within .01 with probability equal to .95?

Reference

Mendenhall, W., *Introduction to Probability and Statistics, Second Edition*. Belmont, Calif.: Wadsworth Publishing Company, Inc., 1967.

3

Linear Statistical Models

3.1 Introduction

At this point it will be advantageous to preface a discussion of experimental design with an introduction to linear models, a topic that is fundamental to our subject for several reasons. First, linear models tend to crystallize one's thinking with regard to the variables operating in an experimental situation. Second, they will be used as a teaching device to describe the mechanics of particular designs. Finally, and most important, they will form the basis for the analysis and interpretation of data generated by the experiments discussed in this text.

3.2 Deterministic and Probabilistic Models

Scientists employ mathematical models to simplify an expression of the relationship between nature's variables. The economist relates the price of commodity to demand and supply, the physicist expresses the interplay between the force of a moving body and its mass and velocity, and the chemist relates the solubility of a solid in a liquid to environmental conditions as well as to the characteristics of the solid and the liquid. All of these models are mathematical equations relating the variables involved; all form a model of reality in much the same way that a photographer attempts to capture an image and, hence, model a subject. All vary in the degree of accuracy with which they depict the true state of nature and all are subject to error in prediction—some large errors and some minute ones.

Accuracy is a relative concept. An error of one tenth of an inch in the manufacture of a basketball is negligible and yet the same error would be woefully large in the finished thickness of a microscopic lens. In other words, a mathematical model is considered accurate—that is, a good model of nature—if it is able to predict some variable and do so with an error that will be negligible for practical purposes. Many mathematical models of phenomena in physics predict with errors that are often extremely small, sometimes so small as to be unobservable by the measuring instrument. Many other models employed in engineering, the physical sciences, business, and the social and the biological sciences predict with a much larger error. Nevertheless, these models possess one common property: they are approximations to reality rather than exact explanations of natural phenomena. In brief, they are models.

Mathematical models may be classified as *deterministic* or *probabilistic*. Newton's law relating the force of a moving body to its mass and acceleration,

$$F = ma,$$

is a deterministic model that predicts with little error of prediction for practical purposes. Similar deterministic models for calculating the strength of a steel beam predict with sizable errors that lead the engineer to multiply the size of a beam by a "safety factor" in order to be fairly certain that the beam will sustain its design load.

For example, suppose that one is interested in relating a response, y, to a variable x based upon the results of n experiments. A plot of the experimental results is shown in Fig. 3.1. Observing the distribution of points, we would be inclined to place a ruler through the points and draw a straight line to model the observed relationship as indicated in Fig. 3.1. In doing so, we have chosen a model of the form,

$$y = \beta_0 + \beta_1 x,$$

the equation of a straight line.

The model, $y = \beta_0 + \beta_1 x$, provides a deterministic mathematical model for the relationship between y and x. Given a value of x, the model predicts a single value of y which is unique and, in this sense, is determined. Although

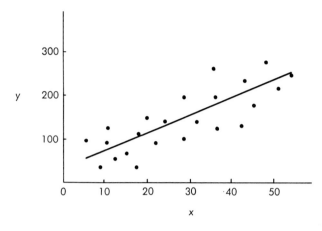

Figure 3.1

our model is deterministic, it is quite obvious from Fig. 3.1 that the model does not provide an exact explanation of the true relationship between y and x.

As previously noted, the lack of fit of a deterministic model does not, in itself, condemn the model. The criterion of goodness of the model is generally whether the model predicts with an error that is negligible for practical purposes. If y is the size of a beam that is to support a bridge, will the model predict y with sufficient accuracy that we need have no concern that the bridge will collapse? If the error of prediction is sizable, then its value must be considered in the selection of the beam size and, as in any statistical estimation problem, we would wish to make a statement with regard to its probable magnitude. For this purpose we would resort to a probabilistic model for y.

Probabilistic models contain one or more random components that are intended to explain the apparent random variability of y for a given value of x. For example, we might use the probabilistic model,

$$y = \beta_0 + \beta_1 x + \epsilon,$$

where ϵ is a random variable representing the variability of y about the basic relationship,

$$\beta_0 + \beta_1 x.$$

To complete the model, one must describe the properties of the random variable ϵ. The simplest set of assumptions would be to state that ϵ has some specific probability distribution with expected value and variance, say,

$$E(\epsilon) = 0, \qquad V(\epsilon) = \sigma^2.$$

Further, assume that repeated values of ϵ are independent of one another in repeated sampling.

The assumptions stated above imply that

$$E(y) = \beta_0 + \beta_1 x.$$

In other words, the average value of y for a given value of x is a linear function of x, with specific values of y oscillating about the line in repeated sampling by a random error, ϵ. These errors are assumed to be independent, sometimes positive, sometimes negative, with an average (expected) value equal to zero. The variance of ϵ is assumed to be constant and equal to σ^2, regardless of the value of x.

This is only one of many probabilistic models that one might concoct to model the data of Fig. 3.1. The random error, ϵ, could have been indicated as a multiplicative error,

$$y = \beta_0 + \beta_1 x \epsilon,$$

or we could change the assumptions regarding its expected value or variance. From the very many probabilistic models that might be employed we would select one that seems to provide the best description of the behavior of y.

3.3 Linear Statistical Models

The reader will note that the estimation problem involved in fitting a probabilistic model to a set of data requires that one estimate unknown parameters in the model. For example, fitting the model

$$y = \beta_0 + \beta_1 x + \epsilon$$

to the data of Fig. 3.1 would require estimation of the two unknown parameters, β_0 and β_1. This estimation might be accomplished by using a ruler, as mentioned in Sec. 3.2, or preferably by a method that we will describe in Chapter 6.

A *linear statistical model* relating a response y to a set of independent variables, $x_1, x_2, x_3, \ldots, x_k$, would be a model of the type

$$y = \beta_0 + \beta_1 x_1 + \beta_2 x_2 + \beta_3 x_3 + \cdots + \beta_k x_k + \epsilon.$$

The independent variables, $x_1, x_2, \ldots, x_k$, are assumed to be measured without error while $\beta_0, \beta_1, \beta_2, \ldots, \beta_k$ represent unknown parameters that, in a sense, measure the weight assigned to the independent variables in the prediction of the random response, y. The random component, ϵ, explains the random fluctuation in y for fixed settings of $x_1, x_2, \ldots, x_k$. We have shown only one random component in the model, but we could have used more than one, associating each random component with some source of variability. The model is called linear because it represents a linear function of the unknown parameters, $\beta_0, \beta_1, \beta_2, \ldots, \beta_k$ (see Sec. 1.7 for definition of "linear function").

The model

$$y = \beta_0 + \beta_1 x_1 + \beta_2 x_2 + \beta_3 x_3 + \cdots + \beta_k x_k + \epsilon$$

will hereafter be referred to as a *general linear model*. Thus the model may contain any number of variables, k, where k may equal $0, 1, 2, \ldots$, or in other words any finite integer. We will usually restrict our attention to those situations for which a single component of variability, ϵ, is appropriate and where

$$E(\epsilon) = 0, \qquad V(\epsilon) = \sigma^2$$

for fixed values of the independent variables. Furthermore, we will assume that every pair of random errors, ϵ_i and ϵ_j, associated with a pair of measurements, y_i and y_j, are independent.

3.4 Response Curves and Surfaces

It is common procedure to graphically represent a variable of interest as a curvilinear function of a single independent variable. The variable y is frequently called a response and the resulting curve is called a *response curve*. A typical response curve is shown in Fig. 3.2. A sketch of the response curve is particularly useful if one is seeking the value of x that will yield a maximum or minimum value of y.

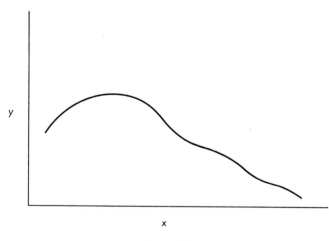

Figure 3.2

When y is a function of two independent variables, say x_1 and x_2, we can no longer employ a single curve on a two-dimensional piece of paper to portray the relationship. For this two-variable case, we geometrically view x_1 and x_2 as the coordinates of a point in a plane. Thus, we indicate the location of a town in reference to our own position as being 10 miles east ($x_1 = 10$) and 4 miles north ($x_2 = 4$). We might be particularly interested in the elevation of the land, y, at a given location indicated by specific values of x_1 and x_2. A three-dimensional graphic representation of the elevation, y, as a function of x_1 and x_2 would be a *response surface*, specifically the surface of the earth. The National Geological Service portrays a response surface on a single graph using a contour map that gives curves of constant elevation above sea level. An example of a contour map is given in Fig. 3.3.

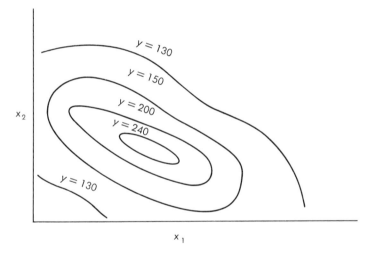

Figure 3.3

Similarly, suppose that x_1 is pressure, x_2 is temperature, and y is the yield of chemical in a manufacturing process. Particular values of temperature and pressure locate a point in the pressure-temperature plane. The yield of chemical, y, would be represented as the elevation of the response and would locate a point on a response surface as indicated in Fig. 3.4.

For the case involving more than two independent variables ($k > 2$), the response, y, could be viewed as a response surface in a ($k + 1$)-dimensional space. Although we cannot visualize surfaces in more than three dimensions, the analogy is useful and the terminology appropriate.

If the reader has been exposed to a course in analytic geometry, he will

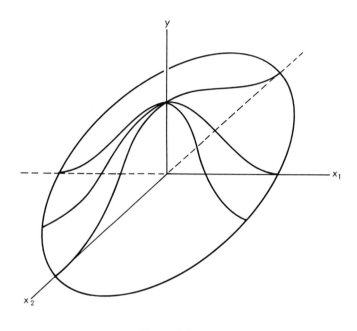

Figure 3.4

recognize the general linear model as the equation of a plane located in a $(k + 1)$-dimensional space. At first glance this would seem to restrict the utility of our model, but further inspection would dispel this notion. We stated that $x_1, x_2, x_3, \ldots, x_k$ were independent variables that were measured without error in an experiment. Hence $x_1, x_2, \ldots, x_k$ may be related and, indeed, may be functions of some other variables. The resulting model would still be regarded as linear *as long as these functions do not contain any unknown parameters*. For example, y might be the yield of chemical in a chemical plant. The independent variables measured to obtain a predictor of y might be

$x_1 =$ temperature of the chemical in a vat,

$x_2 =$ vat pressure,

$x_3 = x_1^2$ (the temperature squared),

$x_4 = x_1 x_2$,

$x_5 = e^{x_2}$,

$x_6 = \sin x_1$,

$x_7 =$ amount of catalyst,

and so on.

Note that we do not suggest this is a realistic model. The point we wish to make is that the independent variables may be nonlinear functions of other variables as long as they do not contain unknown parameters. The term "linear" as applied to our model simply refers to the linearity of y as a function of the unknown weights, $\beta_0, \beta_1, \beta_2, \ldots, \beta_k$. Hence the expected value of y,

$$E(y) = \beta_0 + \beta_1 x_1 + \beta_2 x_2 + \beta_3 x_3 + \cdots + \beta_k x_k,$$

may represent a curved surface in a $(k + 1)$-dimensional space. In brief, the general linear model is sufficiently general to provide a wide variety of models for physical phenomena. Experience has shown that it may be employed to develop predictors of y and to study the relationships of variables in the physical sciences, engineering, business, medicine, the biological sciences, and the social sciences. Indeed, it is a very powerful statistical tool.

3.5 Some Examples of Linear Models

One may construct many linear models to represent a response, y. Basically, the procedure is to express y as the sum of a number of terms where each term represents a particular type of contribution to the response and possesses a practical interpretation. The following are examples of linear models.

Example 3.1 The model of the relationship between y and a single independent variable, x, that results in a linear distribution of points was discussed in Sec. 3.2. The model

$$y = \beta_0 + \beta_1 x + \epsilon$$

was seen to express y as the *sum* of three components: β_0 represents the average response for y when $x = 0$, $\beta_1 x$ is the average amount that y would be expected to increase beyond β_0 for a given value of x, and ϵ is the unexplained random error.

Example 3.2 If a response, y, is related to an independent variable, x, as indicated in Fig. 3.5, an appropriate linear model might be

$$y = \beta_0 + \beta_1 x + \beta_2 x^2 + \epsilon,$$

where $E(\epsilon) = 0$ and $V(\epsilon) = \sigma^2$. Thus y is equal to the sum of four components: the first is the y-intercept, β_0; the second is the contribution of linear trend, $\beta_1 x$; the third is a component due to curvature, $\beta_2 x^2$; and the last represents the unexplained random error.

Example 3.3 In Chapter 1 we discussed methods of inference for a random variable with mean equal to μ and variance equal to σ^2. A linear model appropriate for this response is

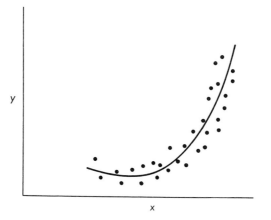

Figure 3.5

$$y = \mu + \epsilon,$$

where $E(\epsilon) = 0$ and $V(\epsilon) = \sigma^2$.

Thus y is equal to the sum of two components, its mean μ and a random component ϵ (that may be positive or negative).

As noted in Chapter 1, unbiased estimators of the model parameters, μ and σ^2, are $\bar{y}$ and

$$s^2 = \frac{\sum_{i=1}^{n} (y_i - \bar{y})^2}{n - 1},$$

respectively. Furthermore, when one assumes normality of the distribution of the random error, ϵ (and, hence, of y), methods of estimation and tests of hypotheses concerning μ are the familiar procedures based upon Student's t. (See Examples 1.5 and 1.8.)

Example 3.4

$$y = \beta_0 + \beta_1 x_1 + \beta_2 x_2 + \beta_3 x_1 x_2 + \beta_4 x_1^2 + \beta_5 x_2^2 + \epsilon$$

is a model for a response surface where y is a function of two independent variables, x_1 and x_2. The reader familiar with analytic geometry will note that the expected value of y,

$$E(y) = \beta_0 + \beta_1 x_1 + \beta_2 x_2 + \beta_3 x_1 x_2 + \beta_4 x_1^2 + \beta_5 x_2^2,$$

is the equation of a conic surface.

Examples 3.1, 3.2, and 3.4 present models for relationships which are quite familiar to the reader because x, x_1, and x_2 are *quantitative* variables.

However, for many experimental situations this interpretation is much too restrictive. For example, the independent variables may be *qualitative*, such as "type of catalyst" in a chemical experiment, "type of stimuli" in a psychological experiment, or "foremen" in a study of the variables affecting yield in a manufacturing production study.

Example 1.9 is a simple example of an experiment in which the independent variable, "type of diet," is qualitative. The object of the experiment is to compare the difference in the effect of two diets, A and B, on the gain in weight of rats. The model presented in Example 3.5 describes the gain in weight, y, as a function of diet.

Example 3.5 Let μ_A and μ_B equal the average gain in weight of rats fed on the two diets, A and B. Then we could represent the gain in weight, y, as

$$y = \mu_A + \beta x + \epsilon,$$

where $\beta = \mu_B - \mu_A$ is the difference in the mean gain in weight for the two diets and is the object of interest in the experiment. The *dummy variable*, x, is defined as

$x = 1$ if the response was made on a rat fed on diet B,

$x = 0$ if fed on diet A.

Thus, when we are predicting the gain in weight for rats fed on diet A, the dummy variable x would be set equal to zero, and the model would be

$$y = \mu_A + \epsilon.$$

For diet B, x would be set equal to one, and y would be

$$y = \mu_A + \beta + \epsilon \qquad \text{(where } \beta = \mu_B - \mu_A\text{).}$$

Substituting,

$$y = \mu_A + (\mu_B - \mu_A) + \epsilon$$

or

$$y = \mu_B + \epsilon.$$

The reader will observe that we have written a model for measurements generated by an experiment conducted to compare two population means. Appropriate assumptions regarding the random error, ϵ, lead to the familiar methods of inference discussed in Chapter 1.

A model for the comparison of three or more population means for a qualitative variable is easily handled using dummy variables. Example 3.6 illustrates the model for three different "treatments." The term "treatment" is used to refer to a specific experimental condition for a qualitative variable.

Example 3.6 Suppose that three treatments are randomly assigned to the experimental units employed in an experiment. For example, we might compare three different methods of case hardening steel bars. If twelve bars are to be used in the experiment, we could randomly assign the twelve bars to the treatments (methods of case hardening), assigning four bars to each method. If the mean responses (hardness measurements) for the three treatments are $\mu_A, \mu_B,$ and μ_C, respectively, then a model for the response, y, is

$$y = \mu_A + \beta_1 x_1 + \beta_2 x_2 + \epsilon.$$

The dummy independent variables, x_1 and x_2, would be defined as

$$x_1 = 1 \quad \text{if treatment B is applied,}$$
$$x_1 = 0 \quad \text{if not;}$$
$$x_2 = 1 \quad \text{if treatment C is applied,}$$
$$x_2 = 0 \quad \text{if not;}$$

and

$$\beta_1 = \mu_B - \mu_A,$$
$$\beta_2 = \mu_C - \mu_A.$$

Then when an observation has been made for an experimental unit receiving treatment A, $x_1 = 0$, $x_2 = 0$, and

$$y = \mu_A + \epsilon.$$

If treatment B is applied, $x_1 = 1$, $x_2 = 0$, and

$$y = \mu_A + \beta_1 + \epsilon = \mu_A + (\mu_B - \mu_A) + \epsilon$$

or

$$y = \mu_B + \epsilon.$$

If treatment C is applied, $x_1 = 0$, $x_2 = 1$, and

$$y = \mu_A + \beta_2 + \epsilon = \mu_A + (\mu_C - \mu_A)$$
$$= \mu_C + \epsilon.$$

Note that the dummy variables flip treatment differences (differences between treatment means) in and out of the model so that y is always equal to the appropriate treatment mean plus a random error. An extension to more than three treatments would obviously require more treatment differences introduced by dummy variables. Thus p treatments would require $(p - 1)$ terms associated with treatment differences. All of the β's in the model would represent comparisons of the treatment means with treatment A.

Example 3.7 As a final example, suppose that we wish to model the yield of chemical in a chemical plant as a function of the temperature of the vat, pressure, production shift (first, second, or third) and foremen (Jones,

Smith, and Adams). The response, y, might be

$$y = \beta_0 + \beta_1 x_1 + \beta_2 x_2 + \beta_3 x_1 x_2 + \beta_4 x_1^2 + \beta_5 x_2^2$$
$$+ \beta_6 x_3 + \beta_7 x_4 + \beta_8 x_5 + \beta_9 x_6 + \epsilon,$$

where

$x_1 =$ temperature;

$x_2 =$ pressure;

$x_3 = 1$ if response is measured on second shift,
    $= 0$ if not;

$x_4 = 1$ if response is measured on third shift,
    $= 0$ if not;

$x_5 = 1$ if Smith is foreman when the response is measured,
    $= 0$ if not;

$x_6 = 1$ if Adams is foreman when the response is measured,
    $= 0$ if not.

This particular model incorporates both quantitative and qualitative variables: x_1 and x_2 are quantitative variables while x_3, x_4, x_5, and x_6 are dummy variables associated with the two qualitative variables, "shifts" and "foremen." A second interesting point is that the model states that the average change in y for a one-unit change in temperature is $(\beta_1 + \beta_3 x_2 + 2\beta_4 x_1)$ and therefore is *dependent* on the pressure, x_2. The term involving $x_1 x_2$, called an *interaction* term, is included to account for the fact that temperature and pressure are not thought to affect y in an independent manner in this example. The additive component for interaction, $\beta_3 x_1 x_2$, will vary depending upon the specific temperature-pressure combination.

3.6 Summary

This chapter discusses mathematical models, their use, and, particularly, the distinction between deterministic and probabilistic mathematical models. Probabilistic mathematical models are constructed so that one may develop a theory that permits a bound to be placed upon the error of prediction when one attempts to predict y for fixed values of the independent variables. The same theory enables one to make inferences regarding the unknown parameters in the model (β_0, β_1, β_2, etc.) and to give a measure of goodness for these inferences.

The general linear model will be employed throughout this text to explain natural phenomena, to illustrate the functioning of some experimental designs, and to provide a basis for the analysis of data generated by experiments.

Examples were presented in Sec. 3.5 to illustrate the manner in which quantitative and qualitative variables may be incorporated in the linear model. The construction of the appropriate linear model for a specific experimental situation requires both experience and good judgment and is therefore not easily explained in a single chapter. We will attempt to develop some facility in this area as the design and analysis of experiments are discussed in succeeding chapters.

The procedure for fitting a linear model to a set of data will be discussed in Chapter 6.

Exercises $1-5$

1. Draw a graph for the following curves:
   (a) $y = 3x + 2$.
   (b) $y = x^2$.
   (c) $y = x^2 + 2x + 1$.
   (d) $y = x^2 - 2x + 1$.

2. Refer to Exercise 1, parts b, c and d. Recall that the presence of a linear term of the form cx in the equation of a parabola *translates* the vertex of the curve to the left (c) or right (d) of the origin. Graph the following parabolas and compare with those in Exercise 1 (b, c, d). Note the vertical *translation*.
   (a) $y = x^2 + 2$.
   (b) $y = x^2 + 2x + 3$.
   (c) $y = x^2 - 2x + 3$.
   (d) $y = x^2 - 2$.
   (e) $y = x^2 + 2x - 1$.
   (f) $y = x^2 - 2x - 1$.

3. Given a polynomial function of x,
$$y = \beta_0 + \beta_1 x + \beta_2 x^2 + \beta_3 x^3 + \cdots + \beta_k x^k.$$
   Let $k = 1$ and obtain the equation of a straight line. Find the values of β_0 and β_1 for the line that passes through the two points $(0, 1)$ $(2, 4)$.

4. Refer to Exercise 3; let $k = 2$ and obtain the equation of a parabola. Find the values of β_0, β_1 and β_2 for the parabola that passes through the three points $(0, 6)$, $(2, 2)$ and $(3, 3)$.

5. Refer to Exercise 3. In general, how many distinctly different points would be required to fit a polynomial of order k? How does this number compare with the number of unknown parameters in the model?

6. What is the difference between a deterministic and a probabilistic mathematical model?

7. What is the difference between quantitative and qualitative variables?

8. Write the probabilistic model relating y to two quantitative variables, x_1 and x_2. Assume that the response surface is a plane.

9. Consult a textbook on analytic geometry to find the equation and sketch of the surface for an *elliptic paraboloid*. Note that this would provide a good model for a response surface that was cup-shaped over the experimental region.

10. Write a probabilistic model relating y to two variables, one quantitative and one qualitative. Assume that each of the two variables was at two levels and that two experiments were conducted for all combinations (four) of the variables levels. Further, assume that x_1 and x_2 do not interact.

11. How many terms must be included in the model for a qualitative variable investigated at p levels in a sequence of experiments?

12. Give the maximum number of terms that may be included in the linear model for a quantitative variable investigated at p levels.

13. Write the general linear model and give the assumptions associated with the random variable ϵ.

14. In what respect is the general linear model "linear"?

15. An experimenter applied five different types of paint, say A, B, C, D, and E, to pieces of wood siding to test for resistance to mildew. Fifty test pieces of wood were randomly assigned, ten each, to the five types of paint. Write a probabilistic model for the response in this experiment.

References

Anderson, R. L., and T. A. Bancroft, *Statistical Theory in Research.* New York: McGraw-Hill Book Company, 1952. Chapter 13.

Graybill, F. A., *An Introduction to Linear Statistical Models*, Vol. I. New York: McGraw-Hill Book Company, 1961.

Some Noise-Reducing
Experimental Designs

4.1 Introduction

Consider an experiment concerned with the joint effect of temperature and pressure on the strength of an extruded plastic. Particular pressure-temperature combinations, commonly called *treatments*, would be selected for study and a specified number of pieces of plastic would be extruded at each pressure-temperature combination. A single piece of plastic that will be tested and yield a strength measurement is called an *experimental unit*. It is the object on which a measurement is made.

The term "experimental design" has been employed in a restricted sense to describe the manner in which the treatments are to be assigned to the experimental units. The example described in Sec. 2.4 of Chapter 2 presents two methods for assigning treatments to the experimental units for a simple comparative experiment. This paired or blocked design produced a sizable increase in information in comparison with the completely randomized design by reducing the noise (experimental error) affecting the estimation of the difference in the treatment means.

A second way to affect the quantity of information in an experiment is by the *selection of treatments*. Thus, if we wish to study the effect of pressure and temperature on the strength of plastic, we might produce two pieces of plastic at each of the following four pressure-temperature combinations: 100 psi, 300°F; 100 psi, 400°F; 150 psi, 300°F; and 150 psi, 400°F. Or, as an alternative procedure, we might choose eight different pressure-temperature combinations and produce only one piece per combination. Although both procedures utilize eight experimental units, the quantity of information pertinent to the objective of the study may vary greatly. An example that is trivial but illustrates our point would be to choose all pressure-temperature combinations in such a way that the temperature varies but pressure is held constant. Certainly this procedure will fail to provide any information concerning the effect of pressure changes on plastic strength.

In this text we will think of experimental design as including both the selection of treatments and the method for assigning treatments to the experimental units. The former procedure has the effect of shifting information in the experiment and, in this sense, increases the volume of the signal that the experimenter wishes to detect. The latter procedure generally has the effect of reducing the noise or experimental error.

Experimental designs may be classified in many different ways, the particular method being subject to the arbitrary choice of the author. Most authors subdivide a discussion of designs according to the type of investigation for which the design was constructed. This yields topics such as block designs, factorial experiments, sample survey designs, and response surface designs (just to mention a few). While adhering to this terminology and method of classification, we will place all designs in one of two classes according to their primary effect on the quantity of information in an experiment. Thus we will think of designs as being either "noise reducers" or "volume increasers." Knowing how a design works, and what its purpose is, will make the learning process easier for the student and help him understand how to design experiments. Furthermore, our approach illuminates the similarity between designs used in sample survey theory and those used in the traditional design of experiments, which is a way of bringing order to an often confusing topic.

As various types of designs are discussed in Chapters 4 and 5, the reader will note that most designs are multifunctional. That is, they tend to both reduce noise and increase the volume of the signal at the same time. Not withstanding this difficulty, we will find that specific designs tend to lean heavily toward one or the other objective. This makes our task of classification relatively easy.

We will make no attempt to catalogue the literally hundreds of experimental designs (and combinations thereof) that might be introduced. Rather, we will concentrate on some of the more important simple designs of the noise-reducing and volume-increasing types and explain how they work. References to extensive catalogues of these designs will be given at the end of this and succeeding chapters.

Block designs, in general, are examples of noise-reducing experimental designs. The two simplest, the randomized block design and the Latin square design, are presented in this chapter. Some comments on more complicated block designs appear in Sec. 4.10, and many other illustrations will appear in examples later in the text.

The factorial type of experiment is an example of a "volume shifter." The complete factorial experiment will be discussed in Chapter 5.

Finally, note that we are not attempting to dispose of the design of experiments in two chapters. Rather, we will introduce the topic and then postpone further discussion until we learn a unified method for analysis. The design and analysis of experiments will then be woven into the remaining discussion by means of numerous examples.

4.2 The Randomized Block Design

We have observed that the paired-difference experiment discussed in Sec. 2.4 is an example of a "noise-reducing" experiment and, in particular, that it is a simple example of a randomized block design. The quantity of information in the experiment was increased by making comparisons within the relatively homogeneous conditions of a piece of material. The only difference between that example and the general case is that the randomized block design may be applied to more than two treatments and, in theory, to as many as we please. (In practice, the number of treatments is kept to a minimum to maintain the within-block homogeneity in which a comparison of treatments is to be made. As the block size increases, the within-block variability tends to increase.)

For example, suppose that we wish to compare the effects of four different stain-resistant chemicals which vary substantially from one piece of material to another. We might select pieces of material from three bolts of fabric and compare all four chemicals within the relatively homogeneous conditions provided by each piece of material. Thus each piece of material would be cut into four pieces representing the experimental units. The treatments A, B, C, and D would be randomly assigned to the four units, and this would be repeated for each of the three pieces of material. The result would be a randomized block design consisting of three blocks and four treatments. A diagrammatic representation of this design is presented in Fig. 4.1.

Figure 4.1   A randomized block design with four treatments,
A, B, C and D, and three blocks

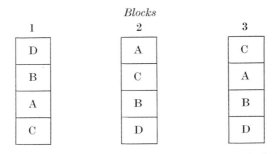

Experimental situations for which the randomized block design would be appropriate are numerous and are easily detected with a bit of practice. Many experienced researchers lacking knowledge of statistics block their experiments by attempting to maintain a constant experimental environment while looking at the variable of interest. This is the principle of blocking. The following examples illustrate the wide variation in character that the blocks may assume.

Suppose that we wish to compare the wearing quality of two types of automobile tires using a 20,000-mile road test as a basis for comparison. If only the rear wheels of each automobile are to be used and ten automobiles are to be employed in the experiment, two methods of design might be suggested. We could randomly assign ten tires each of type A and type B to the twenty wheels. This procedure, known as a *completely randomized design*, has the obvious disadvantage that the wear measurements would vary greatly from automobile to automobile depending upon the driver, his method of accelerating and decelerating, and the road surface to which the tires were exposed. A better method of design would be to block out the driver-automobile noise by making comparisons within each automobile. Thus the automobile would be a block containing two experimental units (the two rear wheels). One each of tire types A and B would be randomly assigned to the rear wheels of each automobile, yielding a randomized block design consisting of ten blocks and two treatments.

People may often be viewed as blocks. For example, suppose that we wish to compare the average length of time for four methods of assembling a device in a manufacturing plant. Should we assign a fixed number of people (say eight) to each method of assembly and record the length of time each takes to assemble the device? This would follow a completely randomized design. Most likely, we would recognize the variation in the physical dexterity of individuals and attempt to block this noise out of the experiment. To do this we would have each person assemble the device according to all four methods, A, B, C, and D, assigning the sequence of assembly in a random order. Thus each person would be a block, and comparisons of the assembly times for the four methods would be made within the relatively stable conditions provided by each person. As a final comment, we note that we are assuming that the assemblers do not become fatigued during the sequence of four assemblies and that their assembly time is not thereby increased as they move from the first to the last. If assembler fatigue did exist, we would wish to block in two directions, a topic that will be discussed in Sec. 4.6.

Pieces of test equipment often vary greatly in their characteristics. If a number of pieces of test equipment are to be used to test for differences in the average response of three different types of a device (A, B, and C), each piece of equipment should be assigned one each of A, B, and C, which would be tested in a random order. This procedure would block on pieces of test equipment and eliminate their variability in making a comparison between the average yields of A, B, and C.

As a final example, we might note that a very common source of variability in an experiment is time. Various uncontrolled variables seem to create variations in the response of interest during the time duration of the experiment. Suppose that we plan to compare five different treatments, A, B, C, D, and E, and wish to apply each to four experimental units. If the experiments must be run sequentially in time, we would divide time into four blocks, testing one each of A, B, C, D, and E in each of the four time blocks in a random order. Thus, we might be able to run only five tests per day. The day (or block) would be subdivided into five time periods which would randomly be assigned to A, B, C, D, and E. The entire experiment would require four blocks (days). Comparisons of the treatments would be made within each day, thereby eliminating any day-to-day variability.

4.3 The Model for a Randomized Block Design

Utilizing the discussion of linear models, Chapter 3, the reader will observe that the response y for a randomized block design is a function of two qualitative variables, "blocks" and "treatments." Let us first attempt to write a model for the specific case illustrated by Fig. 4.1, which consisted of four treatments randomly assigned within three blocks; then we shall proceed to the general case.

Recall that a qualitative variable investigated for p different levels (or treatments) necessitated the incorporation of $(p - 1)$ β's in the model representing the $(p - 1)$ independent differences between the levels. These β's, or level differences, were introduced by dummy variables. With this in mind we note that the three blocks require two β's representing block differences; likewise the four treatments require three β's representing treatment differences. These five parameters, along with the constant, β_0, would appear in the model as follows:

$$y = \beta_0 + \beta_1 x_1 + \beta_2 x_2 + \beta_3 x_3 + \beta_4 x_4 + \beta_5 x_5 + \epsilon,\dagger$$

where

$x_1 = 1$ if the measurement is made in block 2,
$x_1 = 0$ if not;
$x_2 = 1$ if the measurement is made in block 3,
$x_2 = 0$ if not;
$x_3 = 1$ if treatment B is applied,
$x_3 = 0$ if not;
$x_4 = 1$ if treatment C is applied,
$x_4 = 0$ if not;
$x_5 = 1$ if treatment D is applied,
$x_5 = 0$ if not.

We have mentioned earlier that our objective is to make inferences regarding the parameters of the model, $\beta_0, \beta_1, \beta_2, \beta_3, \beta_4$, and β_5. What is their practical interpretation? To answer this question, let us suppose that we are interested in predicting the average response for treatment A in block 1. For this observation

$$x_1 = x_2 = x_3 = x_4 = x_5 = 0$$

and

$$y = \beta_0 + \epsilon.$$

Therefore, β_0 must be the average response for treatment A in block 1.

What is β_1? Suppose that we continue to measure the response for an observation receiving treatment A but make the observation in block 2. Then $x_1 = 1$ and

$$x_2 = x_3 = x_4 = x_5 = 0$$

and

$$y = \beta_0 + \beta_1 + \epsilon.$$

Evidently we expect the response to jump upward or downward (depending upon whether β_1 is positive or negative) by the amount β_1 when we move from block 1 to block 2. Therefore β_1 must be the difference in the average response between block 2 and block 1.

When the observation is made on treatment A in block 3,

†The random error, ϵ, is assumed to possess the properties specified for the general linear model, Chapter 3. This will be true for all subsequent models discussed in this text unless otherwise specified.

$$x_1 = x_3 = x_4 = x_5 = 0$$

and

$$x_2 = 1.$$

Therefore, the response is

$$y = \beta_0 + \beta_2 + \epsilon,$$

and β_2 is certainly the difference between the average response of block 3 and block 1.

In brief, one level of a qualitative variable appears in the constant, β_0, and all other levels are compared with it.

A similar interpretation may be made for the treatment differences, $\beta_3, \beta_4,$ and β_5. For example, we have observed that the response for treatment A in block 2 is

$$y = \beta_0 + \beta_1 + \epsilon.$$

If an experimental unit receiving treatment B is measured in block 2, $x_3 = 1$, then

$$y = \beta_0 + \beta_1 + \beta_3 + \epsilon.$$

Comparing the two models, we note that the only difference is β_3. Therefore, β_3 must be the amount that we expect the response to increase (or decrease) on the average as we move from treatment A to treatment B. In other words, β_3 is the difference in the average response between treatments B and A. Similarly, β_4 and β_5 are the differences in the average response between treatments C and A, and D and A, respectively.

The resulting model enables the experimenter to model *each* response, y, measured in the experiment. For example, let us refer to Fig. 4.1 and model the observation on the experimental unit in the top left position of block 1. Note that this observation received treatment D. Then, adhering to our definition of the dummy variables, $x_1 = x_2 = 0$ (since the measurement was made in block 1), $x_3 = x_4 = 0$. and $x_5 = 1$ (since treatment D was applied to this experimental unit). Then the model for this response would be

$$y_{1D} = \beta_0 + \beta_5 + \epsilon_{1D}.$$

(The subscript on y and ϵ is an identifier indicating that this is the observation measured on the experimental unit receiving treatment D in block 1.)

Similarly, we could write the model for the response for the experimental unit receiving treatment B in block 3. Then $x_1 = 0$, $x_2 = 1$, $x_3 = 1$, $x_4 = 0$, $x_5 = 0$, and

$$y_{3B} = \beta_0 + \beta_2 + \beta_3 + \epsilon_{3B}.$$

Note that the twelve random errors associated with the twelve experimental units will likely all be different.

In general, the model for a randomized block experiment consisting of p

treatments laid out in b blocks will require a constant, β_0, that will equal the average response for one of the treatments in a particular block. The choice of the treatment-block combination is arbitrarily selected by the experimenter. We will in general use the combination of treatment A in block 1. In addition to β_0, we will require $(b - 1)$ β's representing the $(b - 1)$ comparisons of the remaining blocks with block 1. Likewise, $(p - 1)$ β's would be needed to represent the $(p - 1)$ comparisons of the remaining treatments with treatment A. As in the previous examples, each block and treatment difference would be brought into the model when required by means of a dummy variable, which would assume a value of 0 or 1. The model would be

$$y = \beta_0 + \underbrace{\beta_1 x_1 + \beta_2 x_2 + \cdots + \beta_{(b-1)} x_{(b-1)}}_{\text{The } (b-1) \text{ block differences}}$$

$$\underbrace{+ \; \beta_b x_b + \beta_{(b+1)} x_{(b+1)} + \cdots + \beta_{(b+p-2)} x_{(b+p-2)} + \epsilon}_{\text{The } (p-1) \text{ treatment differences}}$$

4.4 How the Randomized Block Design Reduces Noise

We have indicated how a randomized block design reduces noise for the paired-difference example, Sec. 2.4, and have given several examples of experimental situations in Sec. 4.2 for which the randomized block design is appropriate. What actually takes place can be more readily observed if we use our linear models.

Once again let us consider the randomized block design consisting of four treatments laid out in three blocks as illustrated in Fig. 4.1 and recall that the objective of the randomized block design is to compare the effect of a set of treatments on the average response for y. Selecting any pair of treatments, say A and B, how would one estimate the difference in the average response between B and A? We guess that the procedure would be to subtract the average of all observations receiving treatment A from the average of those receiving treatment B. Keeping in mind that A and B were each assigned to three experimental units (see Fig. 4.1) and that each observation can be expressed in terms of our model, we could obtain $\bar{y}_B$ and $\bar{y}_A$ by averaging their respective observations. The three observations receiving treatment B are

$$y_{1B} = \beta_0 + \beta_3 + \epsilon_{1B},$$

$$y_{2B} = \beta_0 + \beta_1 + \beta_3 + \epsilon_{2B},$$

$$y_{3B} = \beta_0 + \beta_2 + \beta_3 + \epsilon_{3B}.$$

Averaging,

$$\bar{y}_B = \frac{\sum\limits_{i=1}^{3} y_{iB}}{3} = \beta_0 + \frac{\beta_1 + \beta_2}{3} + \beta_3 + \bar{\epsilon}_B,$$

where $\bar{\epsilon}$ is the average of ϵ_{1B}, ϵ_{2B}, and ϵ_{3B}.
Similarly, the three observations receiving treatments A are

$$y_{1A} = \beta_0 + \epsilon_{1A},$$
$$y_{2A} = \beta_0 + \beta_1 + \epsilon_{2A},$$
$$y_{3A} = \beta_0 + \beta_2 + \epsilon_{3A}.$$

Averaging,

$$\bar{y}_A = \frac{\sum\limits_{i=1}^{3} y_{iA}}{3} = \beta_0 + \frac{\beta_1 + \beta_2}{3} + \bar{\epsilon}_A.$$

Finally, the estimate of the difference between treatments B and A is

$$\bar{y}_B - \bar{y}_A = \left(\beta_0 + \frac{\beta_1 + \beta_2}{3} + \beta_3 + \bar{\epsilon}_B \right) - \left(\beta_0 + \frac{\beta_1 + \beta_2}{3} + \bar{\epsilon}_A \right)$$
$$= \beta_3 + \underbrace{(\bar{\epsilon}_B - \bar{\epsilon}_A)}_{\substack{\text{Error of} \\ \text{estimation}}}.$$

And what is β_3? Returning to our discussion of the model in Sec. 4.3, we note that β_3 is indeed the actual difference in the average response between treatments B and A. The quantity $(\bar{\epsilon}_B - \bar{\epsilon}_A)$ is the error of estimation and is the noise that tends to obscure the true difference, β_3.

The point to note is that in obtaining the difference, $(\bar{y}_B - \bar{y}_A)$, β_0 and $[(\beta_1 + \beta_2)/3]$ cancel out leaving only β_3, the parameter that we wish to estimate, plus the error of estimation, $(\bar{\epsilon}_B - \bar{\epsilon}_A)$. What would happen if there were really a difference between the blocks (that is, if β_1 and β_2 differed from zero) and a *completely randomized* design were employed? Then the experimental units would be randomly assigned to the treatments, three units assigned to each, and it would be improbable that each block would now contain one each of the treatments A, B, C, and D. If the same treatments appear more than once in the same block, will the block effects cancel when one calculates $\bar{y}_B - \bar{y}_A$? The answer is no, for then

$$\bar{y}_B - \bar{y}_A = \beta_3 + \underbrace{\text{(block effects that do not cancel)} + (\bar{\epsilon}_B - \bar{\epsilon}_A)}_{\text{Error of estimation}}$$

Thus we see that for the completely randomized design, the error of estimation will be increased by an amount involving the block effects $(\beta_1$ and $\beta_2)$ that do not cancel. These effects, which inflate the error of estimation, cancel out for the randomized block design and thereby reduce the noise in the experiment.

The manner in which the block effects are removed from the error of estimation in estimating the difference between treatments B and A would apply in the comparison of any pair of treatments. For example, if β_3 and β_4 are the differences between the effects of treatments B and A and treatments C and A, respectively, it is easy to see that

$(\beta_4 - \beta_3)$ = difference in mean response between treatments C and B.

As an exercise, the student may verify that the difference $\bar{y}_C - \bar{y}_B$ is

$$\bar{y}_C - \bar{y}_B = (\beta_4 - \beta_3) + (\bar{\epsilon}_C - \bar{\epsilon}_B).$$

Although we shall defer discussion of the method of fitting linear models until Chapter 6, it is interesting to observe that we can easily obtain estimates of any pair of treatment differences once we have estimated β_3, β_4, and β_5!

Blocking not only enables the experimenter to reduce the noise when comparing a set of treatments, it also permits him to look at the effect of a second qualitative variable—blocks. For example, suppose that we wish to compare the effects of blocks 3 and 1. The four observations in block 3 are

$$y_{3C} = \beta_0 + \beta_2 + \beta_4 + \epsilon_{3C},$$

$$y_{3A} = \beta_0 + \beta_2 + \epsilon_{3A},$$

$$y_{3B} = \beta_0 + \beta_2 + \beta_3 + \epsilon_{3B},$$

$$y_{3D} = \beta_0 + \beta_2 + \beta_5 + \epsilon_{3D}.$$

The average of these four observations is

$$\bar{y}_3 = \frac{\sum_{i=1}^{D} y_{3i}}{4} = \beta_0 + \beta_2 + \frac{\beta_3 + \beta_4 + \beta_5}{4} + \bar{\epsilon}_3.$$

Similarly, the student may verify that the average of the four observations in block 1 is

$$\bar{y}_1 = \beta_0 + \frac{\beta_3 + \beta_4 + \beta_5}{4} + \bar{\epsilon}_1.$$

Subtracting,

$$\bar{y}_3 - \bar{y}_1 = \beta_2 + \underbrace{(\bar{\epsilon}_3 - \bar{\epsilon}_1)}_{\substack{\text{Error of} \\ \text{estimation}}}$$

Note that β_2 is the difference in the average response between blocks 3 and 1 and that $(\bar{\epsilon}_3 - \bar{\epsilon}_1)$ is the error of estimation. Blocking cancels out the treatment effects that would contribute to the error of estimation of the block differences just as it eliminated the block effects in the comparison of treatments. As a result, the experiment provides an opportunity to investigate the effects of two qualitative variables, blocks and treatments, and do both with a smaller error of estimation than that obtained for a completely randomized design.

4.5 The Degrees of Freedom Available for Estimating σ^2

The reader will recall that analysis of the paired-difference experiment, Sec. 2.4, indicated that blocking both increased and reduced the amount of information in an experiment. The reduction, caused by a loss in the number of degrees of freedom available for estimating σ^2, was negligible for that example in comparison with the increase in information obtained by the reduction of noise. Although this will often be the case, it may happen that there is no difference between blocks and hence that blocking causes a loss in information due to a loss in degrees of freedom. How serious will this loss be and how may it be evaluated?

Unfortunately we cannot answer these questions without previewing some of the results of fitting linear models (Chapter 6) and the methods for making inferences concerning the unknown parameters of the linear model. Let it suffice to say that confidence intervals for the unknown parameters will employ a Student's t that will possess the same number of degrees of freedom as s^2, the estimator of σ^2, where σ^2 is the variance of the random error, ϵ. Since the value of the t used to form the confidence interval increases as the degrees of freedom *decrease*, we must know how to calculate the *number* of degrees of freedom associated with our estimator of σ^2. We will then be able to calculate the number of degrees of freedom lost by blocking and hence determine whether the loss will cause a serious increase in the magnitude of the calculated confidence intervals.

A complete explanation of the number of degrees of freedom available for estimating σ^2 is linked to the probability distribution of the estimator of σ^2. A discussion of this topic, found in most introductory texts on the theory of statistics, will be omitted but will appear in references listed at the end of this chapter. As a substitute, we will attempt an explanation consisting of a statement of fact and an appeal to the reader's intuition.

Suppose that an experiment is conducted to study the relationship between two variables, y and x. Two experiments are conducted, yielding two points shown in Fig. 4.2.

If one asked how many straight lines one can fit through two points, the answer would be "One." In other words, two points are required to

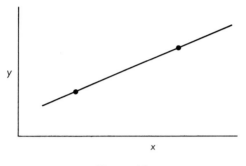

Figure 4.2

estimate the two unknown parameters, β_0 and β_1, appearing in the probabilistic model for the straight line,

$$y = \beta_0 + \beta_1 x + \epsilon.$$

As an extension of the previous example, suppose that we wish to fit a parabolic probabilistic model to a set of three points (Fig. 4.3). The probabilistic model for a parabola is

$$y = \beta_0 + \beta_1 x + \beta_2 x^2 + \epsilon.$$

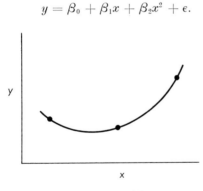

Figure 4.3

How many parabolas can one pass through three points? The answer is "One." In other words, it requires *three* points to estimate the *three* unknown parameters of the parabola.

The examples above lead us to a well-known principle. That is, it requires a minimum of k points to fit a model containing k parameters.

Now suppose that we are fitting a straight line through five points as indicated in Fig. 4.4. In this case the line does not pass through all of the points as it does in Fig. 4.2. Certainly the deviations of the points from the line provide information for estimating σ^2.

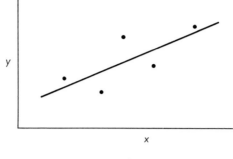

Figure 4.4

How will the information contained in the five points be divided between the estimation of the unknown parameters in the model and the estimation of σ^2? The reply to this question will be stated without proof.

The number of data points could be regarded as the total number of bits of information (or *degrees of freedom*) available for estimating the unknown parameters associated with the linear model. If we use the assumptions and procedure that we will encounter in Chapter 6, the number of degrees of freedom utilized in estimating the parameters in the linear model (that is, in fitting the model to the data points) will exactly equal the number of parameters in the model, and the remaining number of degrees of freedom will be available for estimating σ^2. This important principle will apply throughout the remainder of this text.

For example, a randomized block design consisting of $b = 3$ blocks and $p = 4$ treatments provides a total of $n = 12$ degrees of freedom. Six of these will be utilized for the estimation of the six unknown parameters in the linear model, leaving six for the estimation of σ^2. The model for a corresponding completely randomized design would not contain the two block parameters and would therefore provide eight degrees of freedom for the estimation of σ^2. Hence blocking in this situation would cause a loss of two degrees of freedom for estimating σ^2, a very small loss indeed considering the possible gain that might be acquired through a reduction in noise. Specifically, the value of t employed for a 95 per cent confidence interval would only increase from 2.306 to 2.447 for a reduction from 8 to 6 degrees of freedom. Obviously this slight reduction in degrees of freedom would not seriously affect the width of confidence intervals utilizing Student's t and would suggest that the experimenter should block and gamble on a reduction in noise if he has any reason at all to suspect a difference between the blocks. If he is wrong, the slight loss in degrees of freedom will cause only a small loss in the amount of information available. Note that this will not be true if the remaining number of degrees of freedom is very small. A decrease in the number of degrees of freedom causes a rather sizable increase in the tabulated value of t employed in a confidence interval when the number of degrees of freedom is small.

4.6 Blocking in Two Directions: The Latin Square Design

Suppose that we wish to conduct some experiments to compare the effect of five different chemicals on a material manufactured in a continuous process such as paper, textiles, or the like. Further suppose that the response of interest is the strength of the material and that the material is collected on a roll as it proceeds from the end of the production line.

Recognizing that the strength of the material could vary in time, we would be inclined to block on time, thus comparing the effect of the chemicals on material samples selected across the roll as indicated in Fig. 4.5. If the treatments were randomly assigned to the blocks of five experimental units as indicated in Fig. 4.5, the result would produce blocking in *one* direction and yield a randomized block design.

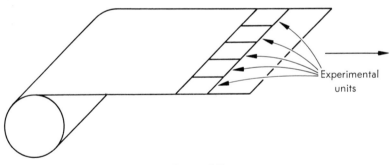

Figure 4.5

Now suppose, as often is the case, that the process produces a trend in strength from one side of the roll to the other. For example, the strength may be much greater on the outside edges than in the middle. If this situation exists, treatments assigned to the middle three experimental units would always read lower than those on the outside. The net effect would be a comparison of the treatments in the presence of a second element of noise that would have the effect of inflating the experimental error. Noise introduced along and across the roll can be reduced by using a design that blocks in two directions. The design, called a Latin square, requires a square layout of experimental units taking five strips of material across the roll, each of which would be divided into five experimental units. The layout would be as shown in Fig. 4.6. The columns represent the original blocks and the rows represent positions across the roll. Note that the Latin square arrangement places all five treatments in each row as well as in each column and does so with some degree of freedom. That is, there are a number of 5 × 5 arrangements that place all five treatments

Figure 4.6   A 5 × 5 Latin square design

Columns

(Lengthwise position on roll)

		1	2	3	4	5
	1	A	B	C	D	E
Rows	2	B	C	D	E	A
(position	3	C	D	E	A	B
across						
roll)	4	D	E	A	B	C
	5	E	A	B	C	D

in each row and column. Presumably, we select one at random so as to permit some random assignment of experimental errors to the treatments. This helps to satisfy our assumption that, in repeated sampling, the random errors, ϵ, are independent from one observation to another.

A 3 × 3 configuration would be required to compare three treatments, and, in general, a $p \times p$ arrangement to compare p treatments.

Examples of two-directional trends, for which a Latin square design would be desirable, are numerous. Davies (1960) gives an excellent example of a wear test where the objective is to compare the amount of wear of four different materials subjected to abrasion on a wear-test machine that possesses four test positions. Extraneous variability may be introduced into the data in two directions because the wear may vary from position to position (perhaps caused by unequal pressure of application of the abrasive material) and may vary from run to run in time because of erosion of the abrasive material. To block out these effects (if present) the experimenter would use a 4 × 4 Latin square design that requires four pieces for each type of material tested. Each material would be tested on each position of the machine and in each of the necessary four runs. Runs and positions would correspond to the columns and rows, respectively, of the Latin square.

If four different types of automobile tires were to be compared by means of a road test, we might block in one direction on automobiles, placing one each of tire types A, B, C, and D on each automobile. Suspecting that the wear would vary considerably from wheel to wheel, we could block on wheel positions. Thus four automobiles would provide a Latin square. Each tire type would appear on each automobile and also on each wheel position.

Consider the comparison of the four different methods of assembly, A, B, C and D, of an industrial device discussed in Sec. 4.2. For that example, people were blocks, and comparisons of the length of time to assemble were made within each person. Now suppose that each task produces a certain amount of fatigue so that, in general, the time for a person to assemble the device according to the last assigned method is longer than for the first, thus indicating a trend over the sequence of assignment. Noise contributed by both of these trends could be reduced by using a Latin square design where columns and rows would be "people" and "position in the assembly sequence," respectively.

Two-directional noise is often introduced by time. Suppose that some treatments are to be compared in an electronic experiment where the response is affected, to some extent, by the line voltage. If the entire set of tests cannot be completed within a single day, we might wish to block on days to eliminate the effect of varying line voltage as well as any other time variables that might affect the response. At the same time, we might suspect that the line voltage would vary within the day according to a definite pattern induced by the variation in the local demand for electricity. Two trends—days and time periods within days—produce a two-directional source of noise that may be reduced by a Latin square design. For example, if five treatments are to be compared, one would require five days and five test periods within each day. The resulting design would be a 5×5 Latin square.

4.7 The Model for a Latin Square Design

The comparison of treatments within a Latin square design implies the presence of three qualitative variables: rows, columns, and treatments. Since each of these qualitative variables will possess p levels for a $p \times p$ Latin square, each will require $(p - 1)$ parameters corresponding to the $(p - 1)$ independent differences between levels.

The model for a 3×3 Latin square will be given as an example. As in the case for the randomized block design, one level of each qualitative variable would be chosen as the level with which comparisons are to be made. Thus, we might define β_0 to be the average response for treatment A in row 1, column 1 (see Fig. 4.7).

Figure 4.7   A 3 × 3 Latin square

Columns

	1	2	3
	A	B	C
Rows	B	C	A
	C	A	B

Then

$$y = \beta_0 + \underbrace{\beta_1 x_1 + \beta_2 x_2}_{\substack{\text{Row} \\ \text{differences}}} + \underbrace{\beta_3 x_3 + \beta_4 x_4}_{\substack{\text{Column} \\ \text{differences}}} + \underbrace{\beta_5 x_5 + \beta_6 x_6}_{\substack{\text{Treatment} \\ \text{differences}}} + \epsilon,$$

where

β_1 = difference between rows 2 and 1,
β_2 = difference between rows 3 and 1,
β_3 = difference between columns 2 and 1,
β_4 = difference between columns 3 and 1,
β_5 = difference between treatments B and A,
β_6 = difference between treatments C and A.

As indicated previously, the dummy variables, $x_1, x_2, x_3, x_4, x_5,$ and x_6, take values equal to 1 or 0 depending upon whether the observation was recorded for the respective level of the qualitative variable. For example, the model for the observation in the second row, third column, would imply $x_1 = 1$, $x_2 = 0$, $x_3 = 0$, $x_4 = 1$, $x_5 = 0$, $x_6 = 0$. Similarly, we could write a model for all nine of the observations in Fig. 4.7.

The model for a $p \times p$ Latin square design would contain $[1 + 3(p - 1)]$ parameters corresponding to β_0 and the $(p - 1)$ parameters for each of the three qualitative variables.

4.8 How the Latin Square Blocks in Two Directions

The way in which the Latin square design blocks in two directions can be shown using the same procedure employed to illustrate the operation of the randomized block design. An abbreviated demonstration applicable to the 3 × 3 Latin square shown in Fig. 4.4 follows.

If we wish to compare any pair of treatments, for example, A and B, we would be inclined to subtract the average of the three treatments receiving treatment A from the average of those receiving treatment B. Hopefully, this should estimate β_5, which is the difference between the effects of treatments B and A.

Keeping in mind that we may write a model for each of the nine observations in the experiment, the reader may verify that the average of the
three observations receiving treatment B is

$$\bar{y}_B = \frac{\sum\limits_{i=1}^{3}\sum\limits_{j=1}^{3} y_{ijB}}{3} = \beta_0 + \frac{\beta_1 + \beta_2}{3} + \frac{\beta_3 + \beta_4}{3} + \beta_5 + \bar{\epsilon}_B.$$

Similarly,

$$\bar{y}_A = \frac{\sum\limits_{i=1}^{3}\sum\limits_{j=1}^{3} y_{ijA}}{3} = \beta_0 + \frac{\beta_1 + \beta_2}{3} + \frac{\beta_3 + \beta_4}{3} + \bar{\epsilon}_A.$$

Subtracting,

$$\bar{y}_B - \bar{y}_A = \beta_5 + \underbrace{\bar{\epsilon}_B - \bar{\epsilon}_A}_{\substack{\text{Error of} \\ \text{estimation}}}.$$

Note that both the row differences and column differences cancel, leaving
the parameter estimated, β_5, plus ($\bar{\epsilon}_B - \bar{\epsilon}_A$), the error of estimation.

What would have occurred if the experiment had been blocked in only
one direction, say rows? Since this would imply a random assignment of
the three treatments in the rows, it would be quite possible for one or more
of the columns to contain two or more experimental units receiving the same
treatment. If this were the case, the column effects would not cancel and the
difference, $\bar{y}_B - \bar{y}_A$, would equal

$$\bar{y}_B - \bar{y}_A = \beta_5 + \underbrace{\text{(column effects)} + \bar{\epsilon}_B - \bar{\epsilon}_A.}_{\text{Error of estimation}}$$

The error of estimation would then be inflated owing to the presence of
the column effects.

The Latin square design, like the randomized block, not only reduces
the magnitude of the error in estimating the differences between a pair of
treatments, it also permits the experimenter to investigate the effect of the
two remaining qualitative variables, rows and columns. Although the
experiment was not constructed primarily to investigate the effect of three
variables, we would like to know whether a difference does exist between
rows and between columns in order to evaluate the gain in information
obtained by the two-directional blocking. Secondly, if we find that rows
and columns do appear to affect the response, we may be led to the discovery
of important process variables.

The reader may verify that the difference between the averages of two
columns will equal the appropriate column parameter plus an error of
estimation involving only the random errors. The estimate of the difference
between a pair of rows may be calculated in a similar manner.

4.9 The Degrees of Freedom Available for Estimating σ^2 for the Latin Square Design

Recall that the number of degrees of freedom available for estimating σ^2 is equal to n, the number of observations in the experiment, less one degree of freedom for each parameter in the model. The $p \times p$ Latin square will require $n = p^2$ observations, and the number of parameters in the model will equal $[1 + 3(p - 1)]$. Therefore, the number of degrees of freedom available for estimating σ^2 will be

$$\text{d.f.} = p^2 - [1 + 3(p - 1)] = p^2 - 3p + 2$$
$$= (p - 1)(p - 2).$$

For the 3×3 Latin square, the number of degrees of freedom associated with the estimate of σ^2 is

$$\text{d.f.} = (2)(1) = 2,$$

a very small number. The loss in degrees of freedom incurred by using the Latin square design rather than a comparable randomized block design consisting of three blocks is 2 degrees of freedom, corresponding to the two column parameters added to the model. The reader will note that the t-values corresponding to 2 degrees of freedom are much larger than for 4, suggesting that a sizable reduction in noise would have to be obtained in order to compensate for the loss in degrees of freedom and still provide an increase in the amount of information in the experiment.

The effect of a loss in degrees of freedom for the Latin square design in comparison with a randomized block design containing the same number of total observations, n, is much less for a 4×4 Latin square or larger. A randomized block design constructed to compare four treatments in four blocks would leave 9 degrees of freedom for estimating σ^2 compared with 6 for the 4×4 Latin square. The increase in the tabulated t-values is not too serious as one moves from 9 to 6 degrees of freedom, indicating that the loss of information due to the increase in the number of parameters in the model is slight. Hence it will pay the experimenter to employ the Latin square design if he suspects a possible trend in two directions. This would not apply to a 3×3 (or 2×2) unless an estimate of σ^2 based on an adequate number of degrees of freedom were available from prior experimentation.

4.10 Other Block Designs

The randomized block design and the Latin square represent two of the simplest types of block designs. Actually, designs are available to remove trends in three or more directions. For example, a design known as a Latin cube will remove three-directional trends. Or suppose that the experimenter ran a 4 × 4 Latin Square and, after doing so, decided that he did not have sufficient information in the experiment. He then might wish to replicate the entire Latin square, thereby producing two 4 × 4 Latin squares conducted at different times. He could then regard each of the two time periods as large blocks containing the 16 observations of a 4 × 4 Latin square, thus producing blocking in three directions.

A further variation in blocking occurs when the block contains fewer experimental units than the number of treatments. By properly assigning the treatments to a specified number of blocks, one can still obtain an estimate of the difference between a pair of treatments free of block effects. These are known as *incomplete block designs*.

A catalogue of some incomplete block designs as well as other types of block designs may be found in the references listed at the end of this chapter.

4.11 Some Comments on Blocking

As the experimenter increases the number of treatments that he wishes to compare, the size of the block must correspondingly increase. And, as the block gets larger, the within-block variability generally increases, thus reducing the advantage of blocking. This difficulty can often be overcome by using an *incomplete* block design.

Another point to note concerns the assumptions implied by the model for the block designs. Note that we assume that the effect of any row or column of the Latin square remains the same, regardless of the combination of row, column, and treatment. In other words, if a trend exists within columns (caused by a difference between rows), we assume that this trend will be exactly the same for *all* columns, neglecting experimental error. Likewise, we assume that the trend within rows (caused by a difference between columns) is exactly the same for all rows. If the trend within a column varied from column to column, we would say that columns and rows were *interacting*.

The Latin square design is not constructed to detect row-column, column-treatment, or row-treatment interactions if they exist. Although we will have more to say on this point subsequently, let it suffice to state that blocking will fail to remove these interactions and hence will be ineffective in reducing the experimental error. The net effect will be a loss of information corresponding to the loss in degrees of freedom (due to blocking) available for estimating σ^2.

Finally, we would note that the models given in previous sections for the randomized block and Latin square designs are not unique. That is, when we vary the values that the dummy variables assume (from 0 and 1 to some other pair of values), the model parameters change in interpretation. We adhere to the "zero-one" coding of the dummy variables at this point to maintain consistency in our discussion as well as to simplify the interpretation of the model parameters. The effect of coding dummy and quantitative variables will be discussed in greater detail in Chapter 9.

4.12 The Importance of Randomization

A discussion of randomization is pertinent to this chapter and, at the same time, is premature because a proper understanding of its importance is tied to inference making, which will be discussed in succeeding chapters. We simply remind our reader that these procedures are based upon the assumption that the random error, ϵ, possesses a normal distribution in repeated sampling with expected value and variance equal to zero and σ^2, respectively, for fixed settings of the independent variables of the linear model. Further, we assume that the random errors associated with repeated observations are independent of each other in a probabilistic sense.

That the assumptions of the linear model are rarely satisfied in practice is quite obvious. The experimenter does not know all of the important variables in a process and does not know the true functional relationship. Hence, the function chosen to fit the true relation is only an approximation, and the variables included in the experiment form only a subset of the total. The random error, ϵ, is thus a composite of error caused by the failure to include all of the important process variables as well as the error in approximating the function.

Although many unmeasured and important independent variables affecting the response do not vary in a completely random manner during the conduct of a designed experiment, we hope their behavior is such that their cumulative effect varies in a random manner and satisfies the assumptions upon which our inferential procedures are based. The randomization of treatments to the experimental units in a randomized block design as well as the random selection of a Latin square configuration has the effect of randomly assigning these error effects (associated with experimental units) to the treatments and assists in satisfying the assumptions basic to our inferential procedures.

Exercises

1. How do block designs increase the quantity of information in an experiment?

2. Think of an experimental situation in some applied field for which

a randomized block design would be appropriate. Write the linear model for the experiment.

3. Write the linear model appropriate for a randomized block design consisting of two blocks and three treatments.

4. Refer to Figure 4.1. Write the model for each observation receiving treatment B and C, respectively, and then sum to obtain the two treatment averages, $\bar{y}_B$ and $\bar{y}_C$. Show that

$$(\bar{y}_C - \bar{y}_B) = (\beta_4 - \beta_3) + (\bar{\epsilon}_C - \bar{\epsilon}_B).$$

Satisfy yourself that $(\beta_4 - \beta_3)$ is the difference in the average response for treatments C and B by referring to the model as defined in Section 4.3.

5. Refer to Figure 4.1. Suppose that the experimental unit receiving treatment A in block 1 is destroyed so that y_{1A} is missing. Now find the two treatment averages, $\bar{y}_A$ and $\bar{y}_B$ and then the difference, $(\bar{y}_B - \bar{y}_A)$. How does this compare with the difference obtained in Section 4.4?

6. How many degrees of freedom will be available for estimating σ^2 for the design, Exercise 3?

7. Suppose that the experiment, Exercise 3, were not blocked and that the three treatments were randomly assigned, each to two of the six experimental units. How many degrees of freedom will be available for estimating σ^2? Find the t-value (for a fixed α) in both this design and that of Exercise 6, and compare. Will the loss in degrees of freedom due to blocking cause a sizable increase in the t-value that will be used in constructing confidence intervals for the model parameters?

8. Compare the number of degrees of freedom available for estimating σ^2 for a randomized block design consisting of six treatments in three blocks with a completely randomized design utilizing a corresponding 18 experimental units. Follow the instructions of Exercise 7.

9. Give the configuration for treatment assignment for a 4×4 Latin square.

10. Think of an experimental situation for which a Latin square design would be appropriate.

11. Refer to Figure 4.7. Obtain the difference between the two row averages, $(\bar{y}_{R2} - \bar{y}_{R1})$, and show that this is equal to β_1, the difference in the average response between row 2 and row 1 plus and minus the averages of some random errors. Note that treatment and column differences cancel.

12. Repeat the instructions of Exercise 11 for row 3 and row 2, Figure 4.7, and confirm that this estimates the true average difference between rows 3 and 2.

13. Refer to Figure 4.7. Find the difference between the averages of column

3 and 1, $(\bar{y}_{C3} - \bar{y}_{C1})$, to show that treatment and row effects cancel leaving β_4 plus and minus the averages of some random errors.

14. Suppose that a randomized block design is used for a situation where a trend exists in two directions. What effect will this have on the error of estimation of treatment differences?

15. Will one gain, lose, or retain the same amount of information if one uses a Latin square design when a trend exists in only one direction? Justify your answer.

16. Refer to Figure 4.6. Write the model appropriate for this 5 × 5 Latin square.

17. Refer to Figure 4.6. Find the difference between the averages for treatments B and C. Note that row and column effects cancel.

18. Refer to Figure 4.6. Suppose that the observation in the second row, second column is lost. Repeat the instructions of Exercise 17. What happens to the error of estimation?

19. How many degrees of freedom are available for estimating σ^2 for the 5 × 5 Latin square, Figure 4.6? How many would be available if one observation were lost as indicated in Exercise 18?

20. Suppose that the experiment, Figure 4.6, had not been blocked on columns and that the five treatments had been randomly assigned to the five observations in each row. How many degrees of freedom would be available for estimating σ^2? Will blocking on columns and the use of the Latin square design, Figure 4.6, produce a serious loss in information due to the reduction in degrees of freedom? (Compare t-values.)

21. Why does one randomly assign the treatments to the experimental units in each block of the randomized block design? Why randomly select the configuration for a Latin square design?

References

Cochran, W. G., and G. M. Cox, *Experimental Design*, 2nd ed. New York: John Wiley & Sons, Inc., 1957. Chapter 4.

Davies, O. L., *Design and Analysis of Industrial Experiments*, 2nd ed. London and Edinburgh: Oliver and Boyd; New York: Hafner Publishing Company, Inc., 1960. Chapter 5.

Finney, D. J., *An Introduction to the Theory of Experimental Design*. Chicago: University of Chicago Press, 1960.

5

An Example of a Volume-Increasing Design

5.1 Introduction

In this chapter we shall study the effect of a set of variables on a response of interest and, particularly, the choice of combinations of levels of the variables to be run in the experiment. As previously mentioned, we have included this aspect of planning the experiment within the scope of "design" because "level selection" is one way of shifting information in the experiment (and, hence, increasing the "volume") to focus on the parameters of interest.

Traditionally this type of problem has been regarded as a "method of experimentation" rather than a type of design. Hence, the designs that we now intend to discuss are generally known as "factorial-type experiments" rather than factorial designs. We will continue to use this descriptive term but will think of the factorial experiment as an example of a volume-shifting, and hence a volume-increasing, design.

5.2 The Factorial Experiment

Suppose we wish to investigate the effect of ten variables on the yield of a chemical, y, and that, particularly, we wish to determine which of the ten are most important in predicting the response. ("Important" means that they contribute information for the prediction of y.) The experimenter may then use his knowledge of the physical situation to determine whether the important variables are causative, or related to causative variables, so that he can presumably control the response and move toward a region of higher yield.

In order to limit the number of runs necessary to determine the effect of all ten variables, we would conduct a "screening experiment." Each variable would be investigated at only two levels (two settings of intensity) to observe whether y changes as the independent variable moves from one level to another. Since one can fit only a straight line through two points, we would be able to estimate only the linear effect of each variable with a two-level experiment. (As previously noted, we would require three levels to introduce a quadratic or curvature term to permit a parabolic fit for a particular variable.)

Why should we not use more than two levels for each variable in a screening experiment? The answer, of course, is that it would require too many runs and hence be too expensive. Even if the change in y were curvilinear as x_1 changes from a to b as shown in Fig. 5.1, the linear approximation would imply an increasing slope and hence indicate that x_1 is an important variable in predicting y. Once the screening experiment has

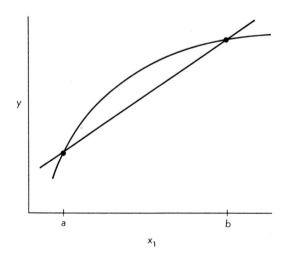

Figure 5.1

located important variables, these can be investigated in future experimentation to determine whether the response is a curvilinear function, if this information is desired.

The selection of the two levels to be used for each variable is very important, as indicated in Fig. 5.2. If the levels are too close, say a and b, the change in y may be so small that it will be undetected in the experiment.

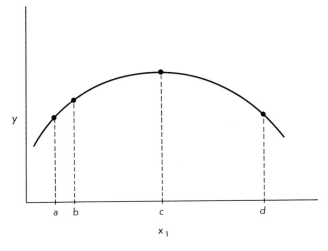

Figure 5.2

If too large, say from a to d, the estimated change in y may be negligible because the levels are located on either side of a maximum or minimum. The desirable situation is to neither effect a very small change nor "straddle a mountain." We would prefer a level selection as suggested by the change from a to c. Our luck in selecting levels corresponding to a and c for each variable will depend upon our knowledge of the physical situation and good judgment.

Suppose that we accept the desirability of a two-level experiment, that our level selection has been accomplished, and that we now face the problem of choosing the combinations of levels that will be applied to the experimental units. Since it is difficult to illustrate graphically in more than two dimensions, we will continue our discussion using only two of the ten independent variables, say temperature and pressure, keeping in mind that in reality we have a total of ten.

We have decided that we will investigate pressure at 50 and 80 pounds per square inch and temperature at 100 and 200 degrees Fahrenheit as indicated in Fig. 5.3 and that pressure-temperature combinations to be included in the experiment will be indicated by points in this graph.

One method of selecting the pressure-temperature levels to be assigned

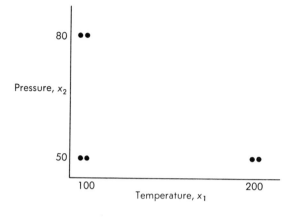

Figure 5.3

to the experimental units would be to use the familiar "one-at-a-time" approach. According to this procedure, nine of the variables, $x_1, x_2, \ldots, x_9$, are held constant and x_{10} is varied. Then the first eight variables, $x_1, x_2, \ldots, x_8$, and x_{10}, are held constant and x_9 is varied. The process described is repeated for each of the remaining eight variables with the result that the experimenter obtains an estimate of the effect of each of the variables on the response while all the others are held constant. This procedure would *appear* to be extremely logical and consistent with our concept of blocking —that is, making comparisons within relatively homogeneous conditions —but this is not the case, as we will demonstrate.

The "one-at-a-time" approach is illustrated in Fig. 5.3 for the two variables, temperature and pressure. We would hold pressure constant at 50 psi (pounds per square inch) and observe the response y at 100°F and 200°F, thus yielding one pair of y-values to estimate the average change in response due to temperature. Then we would hold temperature constant at 100°F and conduct a run at 80 psi. This observation, along with the one at the starting point (50 psi, 100°F) would produce one difference to estimate the average change in y as pressure changes from 50 to 80 psi. The three runs just described are indicated as points on the pressure-temperature plane, Fig. 5.3.

As noted, the three runs indicated in Fig. 5.3 produce one difference to estimate the average change in response due to temperature and one difference to estimate the average change in response due to pressure. The standard deviation of the estimator of these changes will be inversely proportional to the square root of the number of differences employed in the estimate. Hence we may wish to replicate the experiment so as to obtain two differences to estimate each of the changes. This would require six runs, two each

at 50 psi, 100°F; 50 psi, 200°F; and 80 psi, 100°F. The two runs are indicated
with two dots at each of these pressure-temperature levels.

A second method of selecting the level combinations would be to choose
the same three runs as implied by the "one-at-a-time" approach and then
to choose the fourth at 80 psi, 200°F as indicated in Fig. 5.4. In other words,

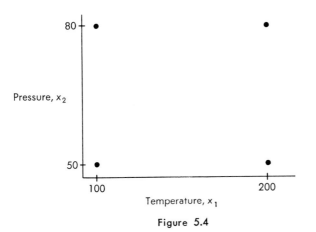

Figure 5.4

we have varied *both* variables at the same time and, surprisingly, we would
say that these four runs provide more information concerning our experimental objective than the six runs of the "one-at-a-time" method. The
argument would proceed as follows:

Suppose that the experimenter tested the response at each of the four
pressure-temperature combinations shown in Fig. 5.4 and that the resulting
four response measurements produced the graph shown in Fig. 5.5.

When the pressure was held at 50 psi, the response increased as the tem-

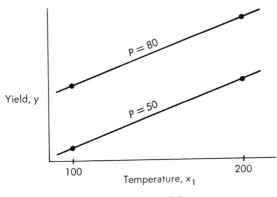

Figure 5.5

perature changed from 100 to 200°F. A similar change occurred when the pressure was equal to 80 psi. Hence *each* line (corresponding to a pressure level) yields one difference 'to estimate the average change in response due to temperature; the four runs yield *two* differences to estimate the average change in response due to temperature, the same as for the *six* runs of the "one-at-a-time" approach. Similarly, we may use the two y-values corresponding to 50 psi, 100°F and 80 psi, 100°F to obtain one difference to estimate the average change in response due to a change in pressure. A second difference may be obtained using the responses at 50 psi, 200°F and 80 psi, 200°F. Consequently, if the response behaves in the manner indicated in Fig. 5.5, we obtain two differences to estimate the average change in response due to temperature and two to estimate the average change in response due to pressure. Furthermore, this is accomplished with only $n = 4$ runs in comparison with the $n = 6$ runs of the "one-at-a-time" approach.

A natural reaction to this discussion is to point out that our argument is predicated on the assumption that the response behaves in the manner indicated in Fig. 5.5. Suppose, on the other hand, that the response increases as temperature increases when the pressure is equal to 50 psi and decreases when the pressure is equal to 80 psi, as indicated in Fig. 5.6.

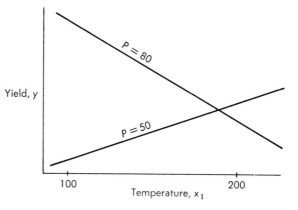

Figure 5.6

Now we observe that our earlier argument is invalid because the change in response, corresponding to a temperature change from 100°F to 200°F, increases when $x_2 = 50$ psi and decreases when $x_2 = 80$ psi. The differences would tend to cancel one another, giving a very small estimate of the average change in response due to temperature.

At first glance, the above difficulty would appear to destroy the utility of our second method of design. This is not the case. Indeed, when the response behaves as in Fig. 5.6, the *"average change in response due to temperature" is no longer meaningful from a practical point of view* and hence we no longer wish to estimate this quantity. The differing slopes of the response lines of Fig. 5.6 reveal a far more important relation concerning the effect of pressure and temperature on the yield of chemical. Pressure and temperature *interact,* or "react" with each other, so that the yield of chemical will depend upon the particular pressure-temperature combination employed.

The failure to detect factor *interactions*, which is often the consequence of a "one-at-a-time" investigation, can lead the experimenter to very erroneous conclusions. Thus if interaction exists, as shown in Fig. 5.6, the investigator using the "one-at-a-time" method would obtain points on the $P = 50$ psi line and conclude that the response rises as temperature increases. Similarly, a graph of the response at the points 50 psi, 100°F and 80 psi, 100°F would suggest that the response rises as pressure increases. If the experimenter attempts to develop a production process based on this information, he will likely design the process to operate at the high temperature and pressure levels, 80 psi, 200°F, thus hoping to achieve a high yield of chemical. If so, he will receive an unpleasant surprise, because this combination of pressure and temperature, owing to interaction, produces a very low yield!

Interactions between the variables in an experiment are extremely important. If present, they tell us that we *cannot* study the effect of one variable on the response independent of the other. Furthermore, main effects (linear effects) are meaningless and the response must be investigated at each pressure-temperature combination.

The four runs indicated in Fig. 5.4 are called a *factorial experiment*. A *factor* is a "variable." These terms are used interchangeably by statisticians. Thus the experiment implied by Fig. 5.4 involves two variables or two "factors."

Suppose that the experimenter has decided on the levels to be investigated for each factor involved in his study. *Then a complete factorial experiment is one that includes all combinations of the levels of the factors, taking one level from each factor.* The factorial experiment, Fig. 5.4, involves two factors each at two levels. The complete experiment would then require $(2)(2) = 4$ runs. If ten variables were studied at each of two levels, the complete factorial experiment would require $(2)(2)(2) \ldots (2) = 2^{10}$ runs.

A two-factor experiment with pressure at two levels and temperature at three levels, called a 2×3 factorial, would require the $(2)(3) = 6$ runs indicated in Fig. 5.7.

The combinations of levels for a 2^3 factorial (three factors each at two

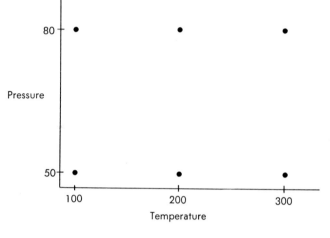

Figure 5.7

levels) is shown in Fig. 5.8, where the factors are indicated as temperature, pressure, and the amount of catalyst. The points indicating the pressure-temperature-catalyst levels are located at the corners of a cube. Four of the points will be run at the high level and four at the low level of each factor, thus yielding four differences to estimate the average change in

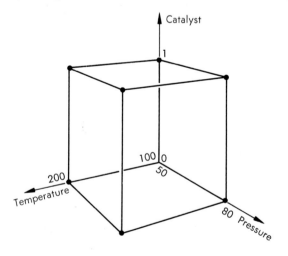

Figure 5.8

response due to each variable *if no interactions exist*. The corresponding "one-at-a-time" approach would require four observations at the origin and four on each axis in order to acquire the same number of differences.

Therefore, assuming no interactions, the "one-at-a-time" method would require *twice* as many observations to obtain the same number of differences.

By far the most important feature of the factorial experiment is its ability to make inferences concerning factor interactions. Thus, factor level selection that varies all factors at the same time shifts information to focus on interactions. In contrast, the "one-at-a-time" method *provides no information* on factor interactions. Furthermore, the factorial experiment will result in the same number of differences to estimate main effects of the factors if no interactions exist and will do so with fewer runs than required by the "one-at-a-time" method.

Examples of factorial experiments will be given in Sec. 5.3 and will also appear in later chapters, where the design and analysis of a number of experiments will be discussed in detail.

Before terminating this section, we would ask the reader what happened to the information purchased by the experimenter in the two-factor experiment, Fig. 5.3. Did he really buy less information with six runs than that acquired with the four runs of the 2×2 factorial, Fig. 5.4? In fact the six runs provide more total information, but it is not focused on the interaction and main-effect parameters that are the object of the investigation. Rather, the six runs provide more accurate information on the response at each of the three pressure-temperature combinations shown in Fig. 5.3. Two runs were made at each point in comparison to only one for the factorial experiment. Information concerning the average response at the three points may prove of interest, but it fails to investigate the presence of factor interactions.

5.3 The Linear Model for a Factorial Experiment

We will introduce our discussion of the linear model for the factorial experiment by giving a few examples and then will generalize. The most elementary example is the model for the 2×2 factorial experiment discussed in the preceding section,

$$y = \beta_0 + \beta_1 x_1 + \beta_2 x_2 + \beta_3 x_1 x_2 + \epsilon,$$

where x_1 = temperature, x_2 = pressure. If the term $\beta_3 x_1 x_2$ is deleted, the factorial model is the equation of a plane in a three-dimensional space where *the slopes, β_1 and β_2, represent the average change in response for a one-unit change in temperature and pressure, respectively*. If interaction is present (that is, β_3 differs from zero), the average change in y for a one-unit change in temperature is equal to $(\beta_1 + \beta_3 x_2)$ and is therefore dependent upon the level of pressure. The quantity $\beta_3 x_1 x_2$ is the pressure-temperature interaction term.

The model for a 2 × 3 factorial (two factors, one at two levels, one at three levels) as indicated in Fig. 5.7 is

$$y = \beta_0 + \underbrace{\beta_1 x_1 + \beta_2 x_2 + \beta_3 x_2^2}_{\text{Main effects}} + \underbrace{\beta_4 x_1 x_2 + \beta_5 x_1 x_2^2}_{\text{Interactions}} + \epsilon.$$

Recall that two levels for a factor would imply only a linear fit to the data, three levels, a quadratic, and so on. As a consequence, the model will contain a linear term for pressure, $\beta_1 x_1$, and both linear and quadratic terms, $\beta_2 x_2$ and $\beta_3 x_2^2$, for temperature since pressure and temperature were held at two and three levels, respectively. Terms involving cross products, such as $\beta_4 x_1 x_2$ and $\beta_5 x_1 x_2^2$, are called *interaction terms*. The remaining terms, excepting the constant, β_0, are called *main effects*.

The calculus is not necessary to our discussion but it does shed light on the rationale for writing the factorial model. A theorem in mathematics, known as Taylor's theorem, states that when certain rather general conditions are satisfied, a function, y, of $x_1, x_2, \ldots, x_k$, may be expanded into a power series—that is, a polynomial in the variables $x_1, x_2, \ldots, x_k$. The theorem states further that the remainder (the difference between the actual value of the function and the Taylor series approximation) will decrease as the number of terms of the series increases. This is true if Taylor's series is written in terms of increasing power. The idea, of course, is to *approximate* the function (in our case, a response surface) by using a few of the first terms of the Taylor series. The reader will observe that the factorial model involves the terms of lower order for a polynomial approximation to our response surface.

Another way to explain the factorial model is to consider the response, y, as the ordinate of a response surface as mentioned in Chapter 3. If the experimental region is very small the response surface will be fairly flat over the region, and a plane will provide an excellent approximation to the response. In reality, the response surface likely possesses curvature so that the model must add quadratic $(x_1^2, x_2^2, \ldots, x_k^2)$ and cubic $(x_1^3, x_2^3, \ldots, x_k^2)$ as well as interaction terms (cross products) as the experimental region is expanded.

The model for a 2³ factorial (three factors each at two levels) is

$$y = \beta_0 + \underbrace{\beta_1 x_1 + \beta_2 x_2 + \beta_3 x_3}_{\text{Main effects}}$$

$$+ \underbrace{\beta_4 x_1 x_2 + \beta_5 x_1 x_3 + \beta_6 x_2 x_3}_{\substack{\text{Two-way} \\ \text{interactions}}} + \underbrace{\beta_7 x_1 x_2 x_3}_{\substack{\text{Three-way} \\ \text{interaction}}} + \epsilon.$$

Since each factor occurs at only *two* levels, we can include only linear terms in the main effects. The terms $\beta_4 x_1 x_2$, $\beta_5 x_1 x_3$, and $\beta_6 x_2 x_3$ give a measure of the interactions of the variables taken in pairs. The term $\beta_7 x_1 x_2 x_3$ is a three-way interaction that provides an adjustment to the two-way interactions and which should be, in accordance with Taylor's theorem, of smaller magnitude than the two-way interactions and the main effects.

The model for a $2 \times 2 \times 3$ factorial is

$$y = \beta_0 + \underbrace{\beta_1 x_1 + \beta_2 x_2 + \beta_3 x_3 + \beta_4 x_3^2}_{\text{Main effects}}$$

$$+ \underbrace{\beta_5 x_1 x_2 + \beta_6 x_1 x_3 + \beta_7 x_1 x_3^2 + \beta_8 x_2 x_3 + \beta_9 x_2 x_3^2}_{\text{Two-way interactions}}$$

$$+ \underbrace{\beta_{10} x_1 x_2 x_3 + \beta_{11} x_1 x_2 x_3^2}_{\text{Three way interactions}} + \epsilon.$$

The main-effect terms for x_1 and x_2 include only linear terms, since each of these factors was held at two levels. The third variable, x_3, was investigated at three levels and hence permitted both the linear and quadratic (x_3 and x_3^2) terms to appear in the model. The two-way and three-way interaction terms (familiar to the student acquainted with Taylor's series) are indicated above.

The preceding examples indicate the principle employed in writing the model for a complete factorial experiment, *a principle that holds regardless of whether the variables are quantitative, qualitative, or mixed.* First write the constant, β_0, and then all main-effect terms. If a factor is quantitative, main-effect terms are those involving powers of the variable equal to one less than the number of levels. (Thus, if x_2 possesses four levels, the main-effect terms for x_2 would include $x_2, x_2^2,$ and x_2^3.) If the factor is qualitative, include β's, introduced by dummy variables, equal in number to one less than the number of levels.

In addition to main-effect terms, the complete factorial model for a k-factor experiment will contain two-way, three-way, ..., and k-way interaction terms. The two-way interaction terms are obtained by multiplying the variables associated with a pair of main effects obtained from *different* factors. Consider two factors, the first quantitative at three levels and the second qualitative at four levels. If x_1 and x_1^2 are the variable portions of main-effect terms for the quantitative factor and $x_2, x_3,$ and x_4 are the dummy variables associated with the qualitative factor, then there are $(2)(3) = 6$ two-way interaction terms. These are $x_1 x_2, x_1 x_3, x_1 x_4, x_1^2 x_2, x_1^2 x_3,$ and $x_1^2 x_4$. Three-way interaction terms are formed by the product of the variable portions of three main-effect terms from three different factors. In general, a k-way interaction term is the product of the variable portions of the main-effect terms from k different factors. The number of p-way, $p = 2, 3, \ldots, k$, interaction terms associated with a specific group of p factors will be determined by the number of distinctly different combinations of p main-effect terms, taking one from each factor. We will illustrate this principle with examples.

Example 5.1 Write the model for a $3 \times 2 \times 3$ factorial experiment where the first factor is qualitative and the last two are quantitative.

Solution:

$$y = \beta_0 + \underbrace{\beta_1 x_1 + \beta_2 x_2 + \beta_3 x_3 + \beta_4 x_4 + \beta_5 x_4^2}_{\text{Main effects}}$$

$$+ \beta_6 x_1 x_3 + \beta_7 x_1 x_4 + \beta_8 x_1 x_4^2 + \beta_9 x_2 x_3 + \beta_{10} x_2 x_4^2$$

$$+ \underbrace{\beta_{11} x_2 x_4^2 + \beta_{12} x_3 x_4 + \beta_{13} x_3 x_4^2}_{\text{Two-way interactions}}$$

$$+ \underbrace{\beta_{14} x_1 x_3 x_4 + \beta_{15} x_1 x_3 x_4^2 + \beta_{16} x_2 x_3 x_4 + \beta_{17} x_2 x_3 x_4^2}_{\text{Three-way interactions}}$$

$$+ \epsilon.$$

Note that two-way interactions include all products of the main effects from different factors taken in pairs. Three-way interaction terms are products of the variable portions of three main-effect terms from three different factors.

Example 5.2 Write the model for a $3 \times 2 \times 2 \times 2$ factorial.

Solution: Designate the four variables as $x_1, x_2, x_3,$ and x_4, respectively. Then

$$y = \beta_0 + \underbrace{\beta_1 x_1 + \beta_2 x_1^2 + \beta_3 x_2 + \beta_4 x_3 + \beta_5 x_4}_{\text{Main effects}}$$

$$+ \beta_6 x_1 x_2 + \beta_7 x_1 x_3 + \beta_8 x_1 x_4 + \beta_9 x_1^2 x_2 + \beta_{10} x_1^2 x_3$$

$$+ \underbrace{\beta_{11} x_1^2 x_4 + \beta_{12} x_2 x_3 + \beta_{13} x_2 x_4 + \beta_{14} x_3 x_4}_{\text{Two-way interactions}}$$

$$+ \beta_{15} x_1 x_2 x_3 + \beta_{16} x_1 x_2 x_4 + \beta_{17} x_1 x_3 x_4 + \beta_{18} x_1^2 x_2 x_3$$

$$+ \underbrace{\beta_{19} x_1^2 x_2 x_4 + \beta_{20} x_1^2 x_3 x_4 + \beta_{21} x_2 x_3 x_4}_{\text{Three-way interactions}}$$

$$+ \underbrace{\beta_{22} x_1 x_2 x_3 x_4 + \beta_{23} x_1^2 x_2 x_3 x_4}_{\text{Four-way interactions}} + \epsilon.$$

As in Example 5.1, two-way interactions involve cross products of the five main-effect terms taken in pairs from different factors. Likewise, the three-way and four-way interaction terms are constructed by taking the product of the main-effect variables in threes and fours, respectively, from different factors.

5.4 Estimating σ^2 for the Factorial Experiment

The reader will observe an interesting point regarding the preceding factorial models. That is, they contain the *same* number of terms as the number of runs in the factorial experiment and hence leave no degrees of freedom for the estimation of σ^2. This result is not surprising, since we would suspect that n runs would permit the estimation of n parameters. This being the case, where will we obtain the necessary degrees of freedom to estimate σ^2?

The preceding question suggests three answers. If we have an estimate of σ^2 available from a prior experiment, this estimate may be employed in making inferences regarding the parameters of the model. When no prior experimental results are available, we *might drop high-order terms in the model and use these degrees of freedom to estimate* σ^2. When this is done, we do not conclude that these terms are nonexistent; rather we hope that, consistent with Taylor's theorem, high-order terms will be small in relation to low-order terms and hence be negligible for practical purposes in approximating the response surface. Or, if we feel that the high-order terms are important, we could replicate the experiment, increase n, and hence acquire degrees of freedom for estimating σ^2. All three of these procedures will be illustrated in the analysis of examples in forthcoming chapters.

5.5 Overcoming Some Disadvantages of the Factorial Experiment

A disturbing problem facing the beginner is the large number of runs required for the complete factorial experiment. For example, a screening experiment involving the study of ten variables on a response would require 2^{10} or 1024 runs if each variable were investigated at two levels. One solution for this apparent difficulty is intuitively appealing. Since it requires n runs to estimate the n parameters of a complete factorial experiment, and since we do not really need the high-order terms to approximate the response function, we might suspect that we could conduct a subset of the n runs required for the complete factorial experiment, discarding the information needed to estimate high-order terms and retaining that required for the low-order terms in the model.

Something of this nature can be accomplished (but not as simply as described above) by the use of *fractional factorial experiments.* Fractional factorial experiments require, as the name implies, only a fraction of the number of runs specified for the complete factorial experiment, and they permit the estimation of the coefficient parameters of low-order terms.

Unfortunately, the estimators of certain high-order terms in the linear model will be identically the same as for some low-order terms, thus confounding the results of the experiment. However, if the experimental region is not so large as to induce a great deal of curvature, the high-order terms will be negligible and hence will not unduly distort the estimation of main effects or low-order interactions.

Fractional factorial experiments will be discussed in detail in Chapter 11.

5.6 Some Comments on Factorial Experiments

We have stated earlier that most designs are multifunctional—that is, they tend to be both "volume-increasers" and "noise-reducers" to some extent. Although the factorial experiment is primarily a volume-increasing experiment constructed to focus information on factor interactions and main effects, it also reduces noise.

Noise in experimentation is a composite of the effect of all of the variables affecting the response that have not been measured in the experiment and are not included in the linear model. Many of these variables are unknown; many others each contribute a negligible amount to the error but the cumulative effect may be sizable. Hence the selection of the most important variables contributing information for the prediction of y as the factors in the factorial experiment will reduce the variance, σ^2, of the random error, ϵ. Conversely, the failure to include one or more important variables in the experiment will inflate this quantity which we call a random error.

Stressing the value of the factorial experiment in investigating factor interactions also explains why the block designs, Chapter 4, are not useful for this purpose. It is not unknown for the novice in experimental design to extoll the virtues of the 2×2 Latin square as a design which permits one to investigate the effect of three variables (rows, columns, and treatments) with only four observations. This design would be appropriate *only* if no factor interactions exist. The number of degrees of freedom available in the experiment is insufficient to estimate the constant, β_0, the three parameters associated with linear terms, and also those associated with the three two-way and the one three-way interaction terms. Although the Latin square configuration does change the variables at the same time, it provides only a fraction of the runs required for a complete factorial experiment.

Other fractional factorial experiments will usually provide a much better and more economical method of reducing the number of required runs (if the physical situation justifies their use) than the selection provided by a Latin square or other block designs. The point we stress is that block designs should be employed as noise-reducing designs and not to investigate the effect of a number of variables on the response when interactions are present.

In practice, the experimenter will attempt to employ *both* principles of design to increase the quantity of information in the experiment. That is, he will block to reduce noise and will employ factorial experiments to shift information to focus on interactions and main effects. The factor combinations of the factorial experiment are the "treatments" of the randomized block and the Latin square designs. For example, a 2 × 3 factorial would require six factor combinations that would be regarded as six experimental treatments, and a single replication of the experiment would involve a random assignment of the six treatments in some relatively homogeneous block. Each replication (repetition of the entire experiment) would form a block, the number of blocks being determined by the precision desired in the experiment. Additional discussion of this point will be deferred until examples are presented in subsequent chapters.

Exercises

1. What is the meaning of the term "factor"?
2. What is meant by the "level of a factor"?
3. What is a factorial experiment?
4. What is the objective of a factorial experiment?
5. In what sense does a factorial experiment increase the quantity of information in an experiment?
6. Why is it important to locate factor interactions?
7. Write the linear model for a 2 × 2 factorial experiment. Give the average change in y for a one-unit change in x_1. (Assume that the two independent variables are x_1 and x_2.)
8. Write the linear model for a 2^3 factorial experiment when the three independent variables are x_1, x_2, and x_3. Give the average change in y for a one-unit change in x_1.
9. Give the maximum number of parameters to be included in the linear model to represent the main effects for a factor investigated at four levels.

10. Write the linear model for a $2 \times 3 \times 3$ factorial. Assume that all three variables are quantitative. How many main-effect terms will the model contain? Two-way interactions? Three-way interactions?

11. Repeat Exercise 10 and assume that one of the factors at three levels is qualitative and that the other two are quantitative.

12. Write the model for a 3×3 factorial. Assume that both variables are quantitative.

13. Repeat Exercise 12. Assume that both variables are qualitative.

14. Repeat Exercise 11. Assume that one variable is qualitative and that one is quantitative.

15. Give the number of main-effect terms for a 2^6 factorial. How many two-way interactions will the model contain? Three-way interactions? Four-way interactions? Five-way interactions? Six-way interactions?

16. Refer to Exercise 15. If the complete factorial model is used, how many degrees of freedom will be available for estimating σ^2? If four, five, and six-way interaction terms are deleted from the model, how many degrees of freedom will be available for estimating σ^2?

17. What justification might one have for deleting high-order interaction terms in order to gain degrees of freedom for estimating σ^2?

18. Refer to Exercise 17. In what other way can one obtain degrees of freedom for estimating σ^2?

19. Can one investigate factor interactions with a Latin square design? Justify your answer.

20. The four factor combinations of a 2×2 factorial experiment may be viewed as the treatments of a randomized block design. For example, if only four experimental units can be tested per day, we might randomly assign the four factor combinations to the experimental units. If the experimenter performed three replications of this 2×2 factorial (i.e., the 2×2 factorial experiment was run on three successive days), write the linear model for the experiment. (Let x_1 and x_2 represent the two factors of the factorial experiment.)

21. Refer to Exercise 20. How many degrees of freedom will be available for estimating σ^2?

22. Refer to Exercise 20. Suppose that there is a trend in the response *within* a day and that this trend is, for all practical purposes, the same from day to day. What design might be appropriate for a replicated factorial type of experiment?

23. A common experimental problem involves a comparison of rates—for example the rates of two chemical reactions or the rates of growth for

two different types of bacteria. Suppose that the growth (for example, the number per cubic millimeter) is recorded for two different types of bacteria, say A and B, at five different points in time. Further, assume that it is *known* that the growth curves for both types of bacteria are approximately straight lines over the time period involved. These curves might appear as shown in Figure 5.9.

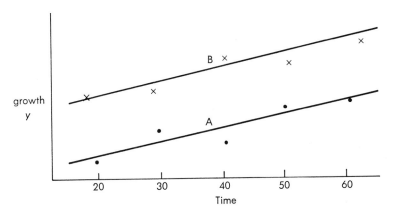

Figure 5.9

(a) Identify the variables in the experiment and state whether they are qualitative or quantitative.

(b) What type of factorial experiment does this represent?

(c) Write a simple linear model to represent the ten responses of Figure 5.9. Assume that the average growth is really linear for both types of bacteria *and that the lines are parallel* but have different y intercepts.

(d) What parameter of the model measures the rates of growth for the two types of bacteria?

(e) If the model, (c), were employed, how many degrees of freedom would be available for estimating σ^2?

24. Refer to Exercise 23. Add *one* term to the model that will permit the slopes of the two lines to be unequal. (Note that in a comparison of growth rates, this would be the term of interest. If the parameter associated with the term were equal to zero, it would imply equal growth rates. A value differing from zero would imply differing growth rates and would give the amount of the difference.) How many degrees of freedom will be available for estimating σ^2?

25. Extend the model of Exercise 24 to include a comparison of the growth

rates for *three* different types of bacteria, each evaluated at five points of time as indicated in Figure 5.9.

(a) Identify the variables in the experiment and state whether they are qualitative or quantitative.

(b) What type of factorial experiment will this represent?

(c) Write the linear model for the experiment and identify the *two* terms that permit a comparison of the three growth rates.

(d) If this model is employed, how many degrees of freedom will be available for estimating σ^2?

26. Refer to Exercise 22. Suppose that the experimental conditions are as described and that the 2×2 factorial experiment is replicated four times in a Latin square configuration treating days as "columns" and time periods within a day as "rows."

(a) Write the linear model for the experiment.

(b) How many responses (values of y) will be recorded for the experiment?

(c) How many degrees of freedom will be available for estimating σ^2?

27. Suppose that an experimenter plans to conduct a 2^3 factorial experiment to investigate the effect of three independent variables on a response. If he thinks that he requires two replications of the experiment (requiring $n = 16$ runs), why might it be more desirable to include a fourth variable and run a 2^4 factorial, which would also require $n = 16$ runs?

28. Why is the randomized block design a poor design to use to investigate the effect of two qualitative variables on a response? Likewise, why is the Latin square design inappropriate for use in studying the effect of three variables on a response?

References

Cochran, W. G., and G. M. Cox, *Experimental Design*, 2nd ed. New York: John Wiley & Sons, Inc., 1957. Chapter 5.

Davies, O. L., *Design and Analysis of Industrial Experiments*, 2nd ed. London and Edinburgh: Oliver and Boyd; New York: Hafner Publishing Company, Inc., 1960. Chapter 7.

Finney, D. H., *An Introduction to the Theory of Experimental Design*. Chicago: University of Chicago Press, 1960.

National Bureau of Standards, *Fractional Factorial Designs for Factors at Two Levels*. Washington, D.C.: U.S. Government Printing Office, 1957.

———, *Fractional Factorial Experiment Designs for Factors at Three Levels*. Washington, D.C.: U.S. Government Printing Office, 1959.

6

Fitting the General
Linear Model

6.1 Introduction

Fitting the general linear model to a set of data means that one desires to estimate the unknown model parameters, $\beta_0, \beta_1, \ldots, \beta_k$, so as to obtain the best possible fit, however "best" may be defined. In this chapter we will consider the problem of estimation of the unknown β's and the consequent acquisition of a prediction equation for predicting y for given values of the quantitative or dummy variables, $x_1, x_2, \ldots, x_k$. A measure of goodness of these estimates, tests of hypotheses concerning the β's, and other interesting inferential problems associated with the linear model will be discussed in Chapter 7 and succeeding chapters.

The method that will be employed for fitting a linear model to a set of data points is the familiar method of least squares. Although most readers have been exposed to the theory of least squares in a discussion of simple linear regression and correlation, we will briefly review the basic concepts.

The logic employed in fitting a straight line through a set of points by eye bears a marked resemblance to that which is basic to the method of least squares. A straight edge is shifted back and forth through a set of points (see Fig. 6.1) so as to minimize, in a subjective manner, the distance between the straight edge and the points. In the method of least squares, deviations from points to the fitted line are measured in a direction parallel with the y-axis, and the "best-fitting" line is defined to be the one that minimizes the sum of squares of deviations. This is called the *least-squares criterion* of goodness of fit.

The importance of the least-squares criterion is that it provides an objective procedure that can be applied to a model containing any number of independent variables. In effect, it provides us with multidimensional graph paper and ruler, enabling us to slip the ruler through the points in a multidimensional space just as we would fit a straight line through a set of points by eye. In this sense, the method of least squares is intuitively appealing and powerful. Finally, we would stress that statisticians do not really know that the method of least squares is the "best" method for fitting linear models, however "best" might be defined. We do know that it provides minimum-variance unbiased linear estimates of the unknown model parameters when the assumptions regarding the model (primarily those concerning the random error ϵ) are satisfied—and this is reassuring. Perhaps the most important point in its favor is that it has been employed effectively to fit response surfaces in real life.

6.2 Method of Least Squares: Fitting a Straight Line

In this section we will develop the least-squares estimators of the two parameters of the model for a straight line, a topic included in most introductory courses in statistics. Although most introductory courses focus attention on the method and the formulas for the resulting estimators of the model parameters, we will be concerned primarily with the *type* of solution obtained for this simple model. Examination of this special case will provide insight and lead us to a better understanding of the form of the solution for the general linear model.

Suppose that we have a sample of n paired observations on two variables, x and y, where each (x, y) pair defines a point on a graph as indicated in Fig. 6.1. Further assume that the coordinates of a particular point will be numbered by subscripts, (x_1, y_1), (x_2, y_2), . . . , and that in general any point, say the ith point, will possess coordinates (x_i, y_i).

The statistical linear model to be fitted to the n data points is

$$y = \beta_0 + \beta_1 x + \epsilon,$$

where the expected value of y is the equation of a straight line—that is,

$$E(y) = \beta_0 + \beta_1 x.$$

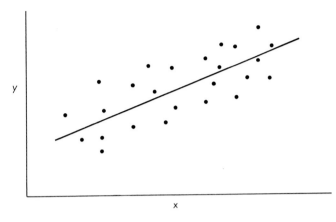

Figure 6.1

We will indicate the prediction equation obtained by fitting a line through n points as

$$\hat{y} = \hat{\beta}_0 + \hat{\beta}_1 x.$$

The quantities $\hat{\beta}_0$ and $\hat{\beta}_1$ are estimates of β_0 and β_1, respectively, and $\hat{y}$ is both an estimate of the expected value of y as well as a particular value of y for a given value of x. That is, we would predict either the expected value of y or a particular value of y by substituting the appropriate value of x in the prediction equation.

As previously mentioned, the least-squares criterion chooses as the best-fitting line the one that minimizes the sum of squares of deviations of the points. Denoting (x_i, y_i) as the coordinates of the ith point and observing that the predicted value of y_i is

$$\hat{y}_i = \hat{\beta}_0 + \hat{\beta}_1 x_i,$$

we obtain the deviation of y_i from predicted as the quantity

$$y_i - \hat{y}_i = y_i - (\hat{\beta}_0 + \hat{\beta}_1 x_i).$$

The sum of squares of the n deviations, often called "sum of squares for error," is

$$\text{SSE} = \sum_{i=1}^{n} (y_i - \hat{y}_i)^2$$

$$= \sum_{i=1}^{n} [y_i - (\hat{\beta}_0 + \hat{\beta}_1 x_i)]^2.$$

It is this quantity that we wish to minimize.

The simplest method for finding the values of $\hat{\beta}_0$ and $\hat{\beta}_1$ that minimize SSE makes use of the calculus, a procedure that we will illustrate for the benefit of the reader acquainted with that subject. Those unfamiliar with the calculus will lose little by skipping over this portion of material to the solution for $\hat{\beta}_0$ and $\hat{\beta}_1$ and the attending comments.

The calculus tells us that the minimization of a function of two variables, $\hat{\beta}_0$ and $\hat{\beta}_1$, can be obtained by finding the two partial derivatives,

$$\frac{\partial\,\text{SSE}}{\partial\hat{\beta}_0} \quad \text{and} \quad \frac{\partial\,\text{SSE}}{\partial\hat{\beta}_1},$$

and setting each equal to zero. Solving simultaneously for $\hat{\beta}_0$ and $\hat{\beta}_1$, we will obtain a pair of values representing a maximum, minimum, or saddle point on the SSE surface. We state without proof that the least-squares solution will imply a minimum for SSE.

Noting that SSE is a sum of a number of terms (each representing a quantity to the second power) and recalling that the derivative of a sum is equal to the sum of the derivatives of each term, we obtain

$$\frac{\partial\,\text{SSE}}{\partial\hat{\beta}_0} = \frac{\partial\left\{\sum_{i=1}^{n}[y_i - (\hat{\beta}_0 + \hat{\beta}_1 x_i)]^2\right\}}{\partial\hat{\beta}_0}$$

$$= \sum_{i=1}^{n} 2[y_i - (\hat{\beta}_0 + \hat{\beta}_1 x_i)](-1).$$

Similarly,

$$\frac{\partial\,\text{SSE}}{\partial\hat{\beta}_1} = \sum_{i=1}^{n} 2[y_i - (\hat{\beta}_0 + \hat{\beta}_1 x_i)](-x_i).$$

Setting these partial derivatives equal to zero,

$$-2\sum_{i=1}^{n}[y_i - (\hat{\beta}_0 + \hat{\beta}_1 x_i)] = 0,$$

$$-2\sum_{i=1}^{n}[y_i - (\hat{\beta}_0 + \hat{\beta}_1 x_i)]\,x_i = 0,$$

and solving simultaneously, we obtain the least-squares solutions for $\hat{\beta}_0$ and $\hat{\beta}_1$ and, consequently, obtain the least-squares line.

We shall not complete the solution of the two least-squares equations shown above for this simple linear model. Rather, we point to the nature of the two equations and note that both are linear in $\hat{\beta}_0$ and $\hat{\beta}_1$. Thus the acquisition of the least-squares estimates for the straight line requires the solution of a pair of simultaneous linear equations, a familiar problem in high school algebra.

6.3 Minimizing *SSE* for the General Linear Model

Let us now extend our discussion to the general linear model containing k variables,

$$y = \beta_0 + \beta_1 x_1 + \beta_2 x_2 + \beta_3 x_3 + \ldots + \beta_k x_k + \epsilon,$$

where

$$E(y) = \beta_0 + \beta_1 x_1 + \beta_2 x_2 + \beta_3 x_3 + \ldots + \beta_k x_k$$

and the prediction equation that we wish to obtain is

$$\hat{y} = \hat{\beta}_0 + \hat{\beta}_1 x_1 + \hat{\beta}_2 x_2 + \hat{\beta}_3 x_3 + \ldots + \hat{\beta}_k x_k.$$

Note that the variables $x_1, x_2, x_3, \ldots, x_k$ may be quantitative or they may be dummy variables associated with some qualitative variables.

We assume that the data points represent a sample of n joint measurements on $(y, x_1, x_2, x_3, \ldots, x_k)$, where each joint measurement establishes a point in a $(k + 1)$-dimensional space. Once again, we wish to choose the unknown model parameters so as to minimize the sum of squares of deviations of the points from the prediction equation, where

$$\text{SSE} = \sum_{i=1}^{n} (y_i - \hat{y}_i)^2$$

$$= \sum_{i=1}^{n} [y_i - (\hat{\beta}_0 + \hat{\beta}_1 x_{1i} + \hat{\beta}_2 x_{2i} + \cdots + \hat{\beta}_k x_{ki})]^2.$$

As before, the solution that minimizes SSE will be obtained as the solution of the set of simultaneous *least-squares equations*.

$$\frac{\partial \text{SSE}}{\partial \hat{\beta}_0} = 0, \quad \frac{\partial \text{SSE}}{\partial \hat{\beta}_1} = 0, \quad \ldots, \quad \frac{\partial \text{SSE}}{\partial \hat{\beta}_k} = 0.$$

Without actually performing the differentiations, the student familiar with the calculus will note that each partial derivative involves the derivative of a *sum of squares* and, as in the fitting of the straight line, each reduces to a linear equation in $\hat{\beta}_0, \hat{\beta}_1, \hat{\beta}_2, \ldots, \hat{\beta}_k$ when the partial derivative is equated to zero. Thus the fitting of a general linear model containing $(k + 1)$ parameters requires the solution of $(k + 1)$ linear equations in $(k + 1)$ unknowns.

It is not necessary to take partial derivatives to obtain the least-squares equations for each linear model of interest, because the equations follow a familiar pattern. It only remains for us to present them to the reader. To do this, we will introduce a new topic, matrices, and some of the simple operations of matrix algebra. The least-squares equations will then be written as a simple expression involving matrices.

The use of simple matrix operations greatly simplifies the presentation of the least-squares equations over a comparable discussion using ordinary algebra and, in addition, we will find that this technique produces the equations in a form in which they may be readily solved on an electronic computer. Finally, and most important, as a consequence of the least-squares solution our approach will produce all of the variances of the estimators of the model parameters, $\hat{\beta}_0, \hat{\beta}_1, \hat{\beta}_2, \ldots, \hat{\beta}_k$.

6.4 Matrices and Matrix Algebra

The following represents a very elementary and condensed discussion of matrices and matrix operations. The reader seeking a more comprehensive introduction to the subject may consult references indicated at the end of this chapter.

We will define a *matrix*† as a rectangular array (arrangement) of real numbers as indicated in Fig. 6.2 and will indicate specific matrices symbolic-

Figure 6.2   A 2 × 3 Matrix

$$\underset{2 \times 3}{A} = \begin{bmatrix} 6 & 0 & -1 \\ 4 & 2 & 7 \end{bmatrix}$$

ally with capital letters. The numbers in the matrix, *elements*, appear in specific row-column positions, all of which are filled. The number of rows and columns may vary from one matrix to another, so we conveniently describe the size of a matrix by giving its *dimensions*—that is, the number of its rows and columns. Thus matrix A, Fig. 6.2, possesses dimensions 2 × 3 because it contains two rows and three columns. Similarly, for

$$\underset{4 \times 1}{B} = \begin{bmatrix} 1 \\ -3 \\ 0 \\ 7 \end{bmatrix}, \quad \underset{2 \times 2}{C} = \begin{bmatrix} 2 & 0 \\ -1 & 4 \end{bmatrix},$$

the dimensions of B and C are 4 × 1 and 2 × 2, respectively. Note that the row dimension always appears first and that the dimensions may be written below the identifying symbol of the matrix as indicated for matrices A, B, and C.

As in ordinary algebra, an element of a matrix may be indicated by a symbol, a, b, . . . , and its row-column position identified by means of a double subscript. Thus a_{21} would be the element in the second row, first column. Rows are numbered in order from top to bottom and columns from left to right. Thus in Fig. 6.2, $a_{21} = 4$, $a_{13} = -1$, and so on.

Elements in a particular row are identified by their column subscript and hence are numbered from left to right. Thus the first element in a row is on the left. Likewise, elements in a particular column are identified by their row subscript and therefore are identified from the top element in the column to the bottom. For example, the first element in column 2 of matrix A, Fig. 6.2, is 0, the second is 2. Likewise, the first, second, and third elements of row 1 are 6, 0, and -1, respectively.

The term "matrix algebra" involves, as the name implies, an algebra

†For a more general definition of a matrix, see Halmos (1958).

dealing with matrices much as the ordinary algebra deals with real numbers or symbols representing real numbers. Hence we will wish to state rules for the addition and multiplication of matrices as well as to define other elements of an algebra. In so doing, we will point out the similarities as well as the dissimilarities between matrix and ordinary algebra. Finally, we will use our matrix operations to state and solve a very simple *matrix equation*. This, as the reader may suspect, will be the solution for the least-squares equations that we desire.

6.5 Addition of Matrices

Two matrices, say A and B, can be added *only* if they are of the same dimensions. The sum of the two matrices will be a matrix obtained by adding *corresponding* elements of matrices A and B—that is, elements in corresponding positions. This being the case, the resulting sum will be a matrix of the same dimensions as A and B.

Example 6.1   Find the indicated sum of the matrices A and B, shown below:

$$\underset{2\times3}{A} = \begin{bmatrix} 2 & 1 & 4 \\ -1 & 6 & 0 \end{bmatrix}, \quad \underset{2\times3}{B} = \begin{bmatrix} 0 & -1 & 1 \\ 6 & -3 & 2 \end{bmatrix}.$$

Solution:

$$\begin{aligned} A + B &= \begin{bmatrix} 2 & 1 & 4 \\ -1 & 6 & 0 \end{bmatrix} + \begin{bmatrix} 0 & -1 & 1 \\ 6 & -3 & 2 \end{bmatrix} \\ &= \begin{bmatrix} (2+0) & (1-1) & (4+1) \\ (-1+6) & (6-3) & (0+2) \end{bmatrix} = \begin{bmatrix} 2 & 0 & 5 \\ 5 & 3 & 2 \end{bmatrix}. \end{aligned}$$

Example 6.2   Find the sum of the matrices

$$\underset{3\times3}{A} = \begin{bmatrix} 1 & 0 & 3 \\ 1 & -1 & 4 \\ 2 & -1 & 0 \end{bmatrix}, \quad \underset{3\times3}{B} = \begin{bmatrix} 4 & 2 & -1 \\ 1 & 0 & 6 \\ 3 & 1 & 4 \end{bmatrix}.$$

Solution:

$$A + B = \begin{bmatrix} 5 & 2 & 2 \\ 2 & -1 & 10 \\ 5 & 0 & 4 \end{bmatrix}.$$

Note that $(A + B) = (B + A)$, as in ordinary algebra, and remember that we never add matrices of unlike dimensions.

6.6 Multiplication of a Matrix by a Real Number

We desire a rule for multiplying a matrix by a real number, for example $3A$, where

$$A = \begin{bmatrix} 2 & 1 \\ 4 & 6 \\ -1 & 0 \end{bmatrix}.$$

Certainly, we would want $3A$ to equal $(A + A + A)$ to conform with the addition rule. Hence $3A$ would mean that each element in the A matrix must by multiplied by the multiplier, 3, and

$$3A = \begin{bmatrix} 3(2) & 3(1) \\ 3(4) & 3(6) \\ 3(-1) & 3(0) \end{bmatrix} = \begin{bmatrix} 6 & 3 \\ 12 & 18 \\ -3 & 0 \end{bmatrix}.$$

In general, given a real number c and a matrix A with elements a_{ij}, the product cA will be a matrix whose elements are equal to ca_{ij}.

6.7 Matrix Multiplication

The rule for matrix multiplication requires "row-column multiplication," which we will define subsequently. The procedure may seem a bit complicated to the novice but should not prove too difficult after practice. We will illustrate with an example. Let A and B be

$$A = \begin{bmatrix} 2 & 0 \\ 1 & 4 \end{bmatrix}, \qquad B = \begin{bmatrix} 5 & 2 \\ -1 & 3 \end{bmatrix}.$$

An element in the *ith row* and *jth column* of the product, AB, is obtained by multiplying the *ith row of A* by the *jth column of B*. Thus the element in the first row, first column of AB is obtained by multiplying the first row of A by the first column of B. Likewise, the element in the first row, second column would be the product of the first row of A and the second column of B. Notice that we always use the rows of A and the columns of B, where A is the matrix to the left of B in the product, AB.

Row-column multiplication is relatively easy. Obtain the products, first row element by first column element, second row element by second column element, third by third, and so on, and then sum. Remember that row and column elements are numbered from left to right and top to bottom, respectively.

Applying these rules to our example,

$$\underset{2\times2\ 2\times2}{A\,B} = \begin{bmatrix} 2 & 0 \\ 1 & 4 \end{bmatrix} \begin{bmatrix} 5 & 2 \\ -1 & 3 \end{bmatrix} = \begin{bmatrix} \boxed{10} & 4 \\ 1 & 14 \end{bmatrix}.$$

The first row-first column product would be $(2)(5) + (0)(-1) = 10$, which is located (and circled) in the first row-first column of AB. Likewise, the element in the first row, second column is equal to the product of the first row of A and the second column of B or $(2)(2) + (0)(3) = 4$. The second row-first column product is $(1)(5) + (4)(-1) = 1$ and is located in the second row-first column of AB. Finally, the second row-second column product is $(1)(2) + (4)(3) = 14$.

Example 6.3   Find the products AB and BA, where

$$A = \begin{bmatrix} 2 & 1 \\ 1 & -1 \\ 0 & 4 \end{bmatrix} \quad \text{and} \quad B = \begin{bmatrix} 4 & -1 & -1 \\ 2 & 0 & 2 \end{bmatrix}.$$

Solution:

$$\underset{3\times 2\;2\times 3}{AB} = \begin{bmatrix} 2 & 1 \\ 1 & -1 \\ 0 & 4 \end{bmatrix}\begin{bmatrix} 4 & -1 & -1 \\ 2 & 0 & 2 \end{bmatrix} = \begin{bmatrix} 10 & -2 & 0 \\ 2 & -1 & -3 \\ 8 & 0 & 8 \end{bmatrix},$$

$$\underset{2\times 3\;3\times 2}{BA} = \begin{bmatrix} 4 & -1 & -1 \\ 2 & 0 & 2 \end{bmatrix}\begin{bmatrix} 2 & 1 \\ 1 & -1 \\ 0 & 4 \end{bmatrix} = \begin{bmatrix} 7 & 1 \\ 4 & 10 \end{bmatrix}.$$

Note that in matrix algebra, unlike ordinary algebra, AB does not equal BA. Since A contains three rows and B contains three columns, we can form $(3)(3) = 9$ row-column combinations and hence nine elements for AB. In contrast, B contains only two rows, A two columns, and hence the product BA will possess only $(2)(2)$ elements corresponding to the four different row-column combinations.

Furthermore, we observe that row-column multiplication is predicated on the assumption that the rows of the matrix on the left contain the same number of elements as the columns of the matrix on the right so that "corresponding elements" will exist for the row-column multiplication. What do we do when this condition is not satisfied? We agree never to multiply two matrices, say AB, where the rows of A and the columns of B contain an unequal number of elements.

An examination of the dimensions of the matrices will tell whether they can be multiplied as well as give the dimensions of the product. Writing the dimensions underneath the two matrices,

$$\underset{m\times p \quad p\times q}{A \; B}$$

Dimensions
of AB

we observe that the inner two numbers, giving the number of elements in a row of A and column of B, respectively, must be equal. The outer two numbers, indicating the number of rows of A and columns of B, give the dimensions of the product matrix. The reader may verify the operation of this rule for Example 6.3.

Example 6.4 Obtain the product AB:

$$\underset{1\times 3 \; 3\times 2}{A \; B} = [2 \quad 1 \quad 0]\begin{bmatrix} 2 & 0 \\ 0 & 3 \\ -1 & 0 \end{bmatrix} = [4 \quad 3].$$

Note that product AB is (1×2) and that BA is undefined because of the respective dimensions of A and B.

Example 6.5 Find the product AB, where

$$A = [1 \quad 2 \quad 3 \quad 4], \qquad B = \begin{bmatrix} 1 \\ 2 \\ 3 \\ 4 \end{bmatrix}.$$

Solution:

$$\underset{1\times 4 \; 4\times 1}{A \; B} = [1 \quad 2 \quad 3 \quad 4]\begin{bmatrix} 1 \\ 2 \\ 3 \\ 4 \end{bmatrix} = [30].$$

Note that this example produces a different method for writing a sum of squares.

6.8 Identity Elements

The identity elements for addition and multiplication in the ordinary algebra are 0 and 1, respectively. Thus, in addition, 0 plus any other element, say a, is identically equal to a — that is,

$$0 + 2 = 2, \qquad 0 + (-9) = -9.$$

Similarly, the multiplication of the identity element, 1, by any other element, say a, is equal to a — that is,

$$(1)(5) = 5, \qquad (1)(-4) = -4.$$

In matrix algebra, two matrices are said to be equal when all corresponding elements are equal. With this in mind we will define the identity matrices in a manner similar to that employed in the ordinary algebra. Hence, if A is any matrix, a matrix B will be an identity matrix for addition if

$$A + B = A \quad \text{and} \quad B + A = A.$$

It can easily be seen that the identity matrix for addition is one in which every element is equal to zero. This matrix is of interest but of no practical importance in our work.

Similarly, if A is any matrix, the identity matrix for multiplication is a matrix I which satisfies the relation

$$AI = A \quad \text{and} \quad IA = A.$$

This matrix, called "*the identity matrix*," is the *square* matrix shown in Fig. 6.3. That is, all elements in the *main diagonal* of the matrix, running

Figure 6.3   The identity matrix

$$
I_{n \times n} =
\begin{bmatrix}
1 & 0 & 0 & \cdot & \cdots & \cdot \\
0 & 1 & 0 & \cdot & \cdots & \cdot \\
0 & 0 & 1 & \cdot & \cdots & \cdot \\
0 & 0 & 0 & 1 & \cdots & \cdot \\
\cdot & \cdot & \cdot & & & \\
\cdot & \cdot & \cdot & & & \\
0 & 0 & 0 & \cdot & \cdots & 1
\end{bmatrix}
$$

from top left to bottom right, are equal to one; all other elements equal zero. Note that the identity matrix is always indicated by the symbol I.

Unlike the ordinary algebra, which contains only one identity element for multiplication, matrix algebra must contain an infinitely large number of identity matrices. Thus we must have matrices with dimensions 1×1, 2×2, 3×3, 4×4, and so on, so as to provide an identity of the correct dimensions to permit multiplication. All will be of the pattern indicated in Fig. 6.3.

That the I matrix satisfies the relation

$$IA = AI = A$$

can be easily shown by an example.

Example 6.6   Let

$$A = \begin{bmatrix} 2 & 1 & 0 \\ -1 & 6 & 3 \end{bmatrix}.$$

Show that $IA = A$ and $AI = A$.

Solution:

$$I_{2\times2}\,A_{2\times3} = \begin{bmatrix} 1 & 0 \\ 0 & 1 \end{bmatrix} \begin{bmatrix} 2 & 1 & 0 \\ -1 & 6 & 3 \end{bmatrix} = \begin{bmatrix} 2 & 1 & 0 \\ -1 & 6 & 3 \end{bmatrix} = A,$$

$$A_{2\times3}\,I_{3\times3} = \begin{bmatrix} 2 & 1 & 0 \\ -1 & 6 & 3 \end{bmatrix} \begin{bmatrix} 1 & 0 & 0 \\ 0 & 1 & 0 \\ 0 & 0 & 1 \end{bmatrix} = \begin{bmatrix} 2 & 1 & 0 \\ -1 & 6 & 3 \end{bmatrix} = A.$$

6.9 The Inverse of a Matrix

In order that matrix algebra be useful, we must be able to construct and solve matrix equations for a matrix of unknowns in a manner similar to that employed in ordinary algebra. This, in turn, requires a method of performing "division."

For example, we would solve the simple equation in ordinary algebra,

$$2x = 6,$$

by "dividing" both sides of the equation by 2 and obtaining $x = 3$. Another way to view this operation is to define the reciprocal of each element in an algebraic system and to think of "division" as multiplication by the reciprocal of an element. Thus, we could solve the equation

$$2x = 6$$

by multiplying both sides of the equation by the reciprocal of 2. Since every element in the real number system possesses a reciprocal with the exception of 0, the multiplication operation eliminates the need for division.

The reciprocal of a number, c, in ordinary algebra is a number, b, that satisfies the relation

$$cb = 1,$$

that is, the product of a number by its reciprocal must equal the identity element for multiplication. For example, the reciprocal of 2 is $\frac{1}{2}$ and $2(\frac{1}{2}) = 1$.

A reciprocal in matrix algebra is called the *inverse* of a matrix and is defined as follows:

Definition 6.1   *Let $\underset{n\times n}{A}$ be a square matrix. Then if a matrix A^{-1} can be found such that*

$$AA^{-1} = I \qquad and \qquad A^{-1}A = I,$$

then A^{-1} is called the inverse of A.

Note that the requirement for an inverse in matrix algebra is the same as in ordinary algebra—that is, the product of A by its inverse must equal the identity matrix for multiplication. Furthermore, the inverse is undefined for nonsquare matrices, and hence many matrices in matrix algebra do not have inverses (recall that 0 was the only element in the real number system without an inverse). Finally, we state without proof that many square matrices do not possess inverses. Those which do will be identified in Sec. 6.12, and a method will be given for finding the inverse of a matrix.

6.10 The Transpose of a Matrix

We have just discussed a relationship between a matrix and its inverse. A second useful matrix relationship defines the *transpose* of a matrix.

Definition 6.2   *Let A be a matrix of dimensions $p \times q$. Then A', called the transpose of A, is defined to be a matrix obtained by interchanging corresponding rows and columns of A— that is, first with first, second with second, and so on.*

For example, let

$$A_{3 \times 2} = \begin{bmatrix} 2 & 0 \\ 1 & 1 \\ 4 & 3 \end{bmatrix}.$$

Then

$$A'_{2 \times 3} = \begin{bmatrix} 2 & 1 & 4 \\ 0 & 1 & 3 \end{bmatrix}.$$

Note that the first and second rows of A' are identical with the first and second columns, respectively, of A.

As a second example, let

$$Y = \begin{bmatrix} y_1 \\ y_2 \\ y_3 \end{bmatrix}.$$

Then $Y' = [y_1 \quad y_2 \quad y_3]$. As a point of interest, we observe that

$$Y'Y = \sum_{i=1}^{3} y_i^2.$$

Finally, if

$$A = \begin{bmatrix} 2 & 1 & 4 \\ 0 & 2 & 3 \\ 1 & 6 & 9 \end{bmatrix},$$

then

$$A' = \begin{bmatrix} 2 & 0 & 1 \\ 1 & 2 & 6 \\ 4 & 3 & 9 \end{bmatrix}.$$

6.11 A Matrix Expression for a System of Simultaneous Linear Equations

We will now introduce the reader to one of the very simple and important applications of matrix algebra.

Let

$$2v_1 + v_2 = 5,$$
$$v_1 - v_2 = 1$$

be a pair of simultaneous linear equations in the two variables, v_1 and v_2. We will then define three matrices:

$$\underset{2\times 2}{A} = \begin{bmatrix} 2 & 1 \\ 1 & -1 \end{bmatrix}, \qquad \underset{2\times 1}{V} = \begin{bmatrix} v_1 \\ v_2 \end{bmatrix}, \qquad \underset{2\times 1}{G} = \begin{bmatrix} 5 \\ 1 \end{bmatrix}.$$

Note that A is the matrix of coefficients of the unknowns when the equations are each written with the variables appearing in the same order, reading left to right, and with the constants on the right-hand side of the equality sign. The V matrix gives the unknowns in a column and in the same order as they appear in the equations. Finally, the G matrix contains the constants in a column exactly as they occur in the set of equations.

The simultaneous system of two linear equations may now be written in matrix algebra as

$$AV = G,$$

a statement that can easily be verified by multiplying A and V and then comparing with G.

$$AV = \begin{bmatrix} 2 & 1 \\ 1 & -1 \end{bmatrix} \begin{bmatrix} v_1 \\ v_2 \end{bmatrix} = \begin{bmatrix} (2v_1 + v_2) \\ (v_1 - v_2) \end{bmatrix} = \begin{bmatrix} 5 \\ 1 \end{bmatrix} = G.$$

The reader will observe that corresponding elements in AV and G are equal — that is, $2v_1 + v_2 = 5$ and $v_1 - v_2 = 1$. Therefore, $AV = G$.

The method for writing a pair of linear equations in two unknowns as a matrix equation can easily be extended to a system of r equations in r unknowns.

For example, if the equations are:

$$a_{11}v_1 + a_{12}v_2 + a_{13}v_3 + \ldots + a_{1r}v_r = g_1$$
$$a_{21}v_1 + a_{22}v_2 + a_{23}v_3 + \ldots + a_{2r}v_r = g_2$$
$$a_{31}v_1 + a_{32}v_2 + a_{33}v_3 + \ldots + a_{3r}v_r = g_3$$
$$\begin{matrix} \cdot & \cdot & \cdot & & \cdot & \cdot \\ \cdot & \cdot & \cdot & & \cdot & \cdot \\ \cdot & \cdot & \cdot & & \cdot & \cdot \end{matrix}$$
$$a_{r1}v_1 + a_{r2}v_2 + a_{r3}v_3 + \ldots + a_{rr}v_r = g_r$$

define:

$$A = \begin{bmatrix} a_{11} & a_{12} & a_{13} & \cdots & a_{1r} \\ a_{21} & a_{22} & a_{23} & \cdots & a_{2r} \\ a_{31} & a_{32} & a_{33} & \cdots & a_{3r} \\ \cdot & \cdot & \cdot & & \cdot \\ \cdot & \cdot & \cdot & & \cdot \\ \cdot & \cdot & \cdot & & \cdot \\ a_{r1} & a_{r2} & a_{r3} & & a_{rr} \end{bmatrix}, \quad V = \begin{bmatrix} v_1 \\ v_2 \\ v_3 \\ \cdot \\ \cdot \\ \cdot \\ v_r \end{bmatrix}, \quad G = \begin{bmatrix} g_1 \\ g_2 \\ g_3 \\ \cdot \\ \cdot \\ \cdot \\ g_r \end{bmatrix}.$$

Observe that A is, once again, a square matrix of variable coefficients, while V and G are column matrices containing the variables and constants, respectively. Then $AV = G$.

Thus, regardless of how large the system of equations, if we possess n linear equations, in n unknowns, the system may be written as the simple matrix equation, $AV = G$.

The reader will observe that the matrix V contains all of the unknowns, while A and G are "constant" matrices.

Our objective, of course, is to solve for the matrix of unknowns, V, where the equation $AV = G$ is similar to the equation

$$2v = 6$$

in ordinary algebra. This being true, we would not be too surprised to find that the methods of solution are the same. In ordinary albegra both sides of the equation are multiplied by the reciprocal of 2; in matrix algebra both sides of the equation are multiplied by A^{-1}.

Then

$$A^{-1}(AV) = A^{-1}G$$

or

$$A^{-1}AV = A^{-1}G.$$

But, $A^{-1}A = I$ and $IV = V$. Therefore, $V = A^{-1}G$. In other words, the solution to the system of simultaneous linear equations can be obtained by finding A^{-1} and then obtaining the product, $A^{-1}G$. The solution values of $v_1, v_2, v_3, \ldots, v_r$ will appear in sequence in the column matrix, $V = A^{-1}G$.

6.12 Inverting a Matrix

We have indicated in Sec. 6.11 that the key to the solution of a system of simultaneous linear equations by the method of matrix algebra rests on the acquisition of the inverse of the A matrix. Many methods exist for inverting matrices [see National Bureau of Standards (1954) and Dwyer (1951).] The method that we present is not the best from a computational point of view, but it works very well for the matrices associated with most experimental designs and it is one of the easiest to present to the novice. It will depend upon a theorem in matrix algebra and the use of *row operations*.

Before defining row operations on matrices, one must state what is meant by the "addition" of two rows of a matrix and the multiplication of a row by a constant. We will illustrate with the A matrix for the system of two simultaneous linear equations,

$$A = \begin{bmatrix} 2 & 1 \\ 1 & -1 \end{bmatrix}.$$

Two rows of a matrix may be added by adding corresponding elements. Thus if the two rows of the A matrix are added, one obtains a new row with elements $[(2 + 1)(1 - 1)] = [3 \quad 0]$. Multiplication of a row by a constant means that each element in the row is multiplied by the constant. Twice the first row of the A matrix would generate the row $[4 \quad 2]$. With these ideas in mind, we will define three ways to operate on a row in a matrix.

(1) A row may be multiplied by a constant.
(2) A row may be multiplied by a constant and added to or subtracted from another row (which is identified as the one upon which the operation is performed).
(3) Two rows may be interchanged.

Given matrix A, it is quite easy to see that one might perform a series of row operations that would yield some new matrix B. In this connection, we state without proof a surprising and interesting theorem from the matrix algebra; namely, there exists some matrix C such that

$$CA = B.$$

In other words, a series of row operations on a matrix A is equivalent to multiplying A by some matrix C. We will use this principle to invert a matrix.

Place the matrix A, which is to be inverted, alongside an identity matrix of the same dimensions:

$$A = \begin{bmatrix} 2 & 1 \\ 1 & -1 \end{bmatrix}, \qquad I = \begin{bmatrix} 1 & 0 \\ 0 & 1 \end{bmatrix}.$$

Then perform identically the same row operations on A and I in such a way that A changes to an identity matrix. In doing so, we must have multiplied A by a matrix C so that $CA = I$. Therefore, C must be the inverse of A! The problem, of course, is to find the unknown matrix C and, fortunately, this proves to be of little difficulty. Since we performed identically the same row operations on A and I, the identity matrix must have changed to $CI = C = A^{-1}$. See Fig. 6.4.

Figure 6.4 Symbolic representation of matrix inversion

$$A = \begin{bmatrix} 2 & 1 \\ 1 & -1 \end{bmatrix}, \qquad I = \begin{bmatrix} 1 & 0 \\ 0 & 1 \end{bmatrix}.$$

$$\Big\downarrow \text{(same row operations)} \Big\downarrow$$

$$CA = I \qquad\qquad CI = C = A^{-1}$$

We will illustrate with the following example.

Example 6.7 Invert the matrix

$$A = \begin{bmatrix} 2 & 1 \\ 1 & -1 \end{bmatrix}.$$

Solution:

$$A = \begin{bmatrix} 2 & 1 \\ 1 & -1 \end{bmatrix}, \quad I = \begin{bmatrix} 1 & 0 \\ 0 & 1 \end{bmatrix}.$$

Step 1: Operate on row 1 by multiplying row 1 by $\frac{1}{2}$. (Note: it is helpful to the beginner to identify the row upon which he is operating *since all other rows will remain unchanged, even though they may be used in the operation.* We will star the row upon which the operation is being performed.)

$$\begin{matrix} * \\ \end{matrix}\begin{bmatrix} 1 & \frac{1}{2} \\ 1 & -1 \end{bmatrix} \qquad \begin{bmatrix} \frac{1}{2} & 0 \\ 0 & 1 \end{bmatrix}$$

Step 2: *Operate on row 2* by subtracting row 1 from row 2.

$$\begin{matrix} \\ * \end{matrix}\begin{bmatrix} 1 & \frac{1}{2} \\ 0 & -\frac{3}{2} \end{bmatrix} \qquad \begin{bmatrix} \frac{1}{2} & 0 \\ -\frac{1}{2} & 1 \end{bmatrix}$$

(Note: even though row 1 was used to operate on row 2, row 1 remains unchanged.)

Step 3: Multiply row 2 by $(-\frac{2}{3})$.

$$\begin{matrix} \\ * \end{matrix}\begin{bmatrix} 1 & \frac{1}{2} \\ 0 & 1 \end{bmatrix} \qquad \begin{bmatrix} \frac{1}{2} & 0 \\ \frac{1}{3} & -\frac{2}{3} \end{bmatrix}$$

Step 4: Operate on row 1 by multiplying row 2 by $\frac{1}{2}$ and subtracting from row 1.

$$\begin{matrix} * \\ \end{matrix}\begin{bmatrix} 1 & 0 \\ 0 & 1 \end{bmatrix} \qquad \begin{bmatrix} \frac{1}{3} & \frac{1}{3} \\ \frac{1}{3} & -\frac{2}{3} \end{bmatrix}$$

(Note that row 2 is simply used to operate on row 1 and hence remains unchanged.) Hence the inverse of A must be

$$A^{-1} = \begin{bmatrix} \frac{1}{3} & \frac{1}{3} \\ \frac{1}{3} & -\frac{2}{3} \end{bmatrix}.$$

A ready check on the calculations for the inversion procedure is available because $A^{-1}A$ must equal the identity matrix, I. Thus

$$A^{-1}A = \begin{bmatrix} \frac{1}{3} & \frac{1}{3} \\ \frac{1}{3} & -\frac{2}{3} \end{bmatrix} \begin{bmatrix} 2 & 1 \\ 1 & -1 \end{bmatrix} = \begin{bmatrix} 1 & 0 \\ 0 & 1 \end{bmatrix}.$$

Example 6.8 Invert the matrix

$$A = \begin{bmatrix} 2 & 0 & 1 \\ 1 & -1 & 2 \\ 1 & 0 & 0 \end{bmatrix}$$

and check the results.

Solution:

$$A = \begin{bmatrix} 2 & 0 & 1 \\ 1 & -1 & 2 \\ 1 & 0 & 0 \end{bmatrix}, \qquad I = \begin{bmatrix} 1 & 0 & 0 \\ 0 & 1 & 0 \\ 0 & 0 & 1 \end{bmatrix}.$$

Step 1: Multiply row 1 by $\frac{1}{2}$.

$$*\begin{bmatrix} 1 & 0 & \frac{1}{2} \\ 1 & -1 & 2 \\ 1 & 0 & 0 \end{bmatrix} \qquad \begin{bmatrix} \frac{1}{2} & 0 & 0 \\ 0 & 1 & 0 \\ 0 & 0 & 1 \end{bmatrix}$$

Step 2: Operate on row 2 by subtracting row 1 from row 2.

$$*\begin{bmatrix} 1 & 0 & \frac{1}{2} \\ 0 & -1 & \frac{3}{2} \\ 1 & 0 & 0 \end{bmatrix} \qquad \begin{bmatrix} \frac{1}{2} & 0 & 0 \\ -\frac{1}{2} & 1 & 0 \\ 0 & 0 & 1 \end{bmatrix}$$

Step 3: Operate on row 3 by subtracting row 1 from row 3.

$$\begin{bmatrix} 1 & 0 & \frac{1}{2} \\ 0 & -1 & \frac{3}{2} \\ 0 & 0 & -\frac{1}{2} \end{bmatrix} \qquad \begin{bmatrix} \frac{1}{2} & 0 & 0 \\ -\frac{1}{2} & 1 & 0 \\ -\frac{1}{2} & 0 & 1 \end{bmatrix}$$

Step 4: Operate on row 2 by multiplying row 3 by 3 and adding to row 2.

$$*\begin{bmatrix} 1 & 0 & \frac{1}{2} \\ 0 & -1 & 0 \\ 0 & 0 & -\frac{1}{2} \end{bmatrix} \qquad \begin{bmatrix} \frac{1}{2} & 0 & 0 \\ -2 & 1 & 3 \\ -\frac{1}{2} & 0 & 1 \end{bmatrix}$$

Step 5: Multiply row 2 by (-1).

$$* \begin{bmatrix} 1 & 0 & \frac{1}{2} \\ 0 & 1 & 0 \\ 0 & 0 & -\frac{1}{2} \end{bmatrix} \quad \begin{bmatrix} \frac{1}{2} & 0 & 0 \\ 2 & -1 & -3 \\ -\frac{1}{2} & 0 & 1 \end{bmatrix}$$

Step 6: Operate on row 1 by adding row 3 to row 1.

$$* \begin{bmatrix} 1 & 0 & 0 \\ 0 & 1 & 0 \\ 0 & 0 & -\frac{1}{2} \end{bmatrix} \quad \begin{bmatrix} 0 & 0 & 1 \\ 2 & -1 & -3 \\ -\frac{1}{2} & 0 & 1 \end{bmatrix}$$

Step 7: Multiply row 3 by (-2).

$$\begin{bmatrix} 1 & 0 & 0 \\ 0 & 1 & 0 \\ * & 0 & 1 \end{bmatrix} \quad \begin{bmatrix} 0 & 0 & 1 \\ 2 & -1 & -3 \\ 1 & 0 & -2 \end{bmatrix} = A^{-1}$$

The seven row operations have changed the A matrix to the identity matrix and, barring errors of calculation, have changed the identity to A^{-1}. Checking,

$$A^{-1}A = \begin{bmatrix} 0 & 0 & 1 \\ 2 & -1 & -3 \\ 1 & 0 & -2 \end{bmatrix} \begin{bmatrix} 2 & 0 & 1 \\ 1 & -1 & 2 \\ 1 & 0 & 0 \end{bmatrix} = \begin{bmatrix} 1 & 0 & 0 \\ 0 & 1 & 0 \\ 0 & 0 & 1 \end{bmatrix}.$$

We see that $A^{-1}A = I$ and hence that the calculations are correct.

Note that the sequence of row operations required to convert A to I is not unique. One person might achieve the inverse by using five row operations while another might require ten, and the end result will be the same. However, in the interests of efficiency it is desirable to employ a system.

The reader will observe that the inversion process utilizes row operations to change off-diagonal elements in the A matrix to zeros and the main diagonal elements to ones. One systematic procedure is as follows: change the top left element into a one and then perform row operations to change all other elements in the *first* column to zero. Then move to the diagonal element in the second row, second column, change it into a one, and eliminate all elements in the *second* column *below* the main diagonal. This process is repeated, moving down the main diagonal from top left to bottom right until all elements below the main diagonal have been changed to zeros. To eliminate nonzero elements above the main diagonal, operate on all elements in the last column, changing each to zero; then move to the next to last column and repeat the process. Continue this procedure until you arrive at the first element in the first column, which was the starting point. This procedure is indicated diagrammatically in Fig. 6.5.

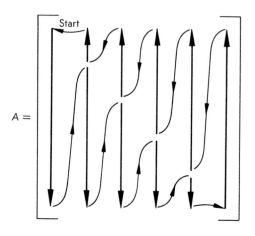

$A =$

Figure 6.5

Matrix inversion is a tedious process, at best, and requires every bit as much labor as the solution of a system of simultaneous equations by elimination or substitution. The reader will be pleased to learn that we do not expect him to develop a facility for matrix inversion. Fortunately, most matrices associated with designed experiments follow patterns and are easily inverted.

It will be beneficial to the reader to invert a few of the 2×2 and 3×3 matrices given as exercises at the end of this chapter. In practice, matrices lacking pattern and particularly large matrices may be inverted most efficiently and economically using an electronic computer. (Programs for matrix inversion have been developed for most electronic computers.)

We emphasize that obtaining the solution for the least-squares equations by matrix inversion has distinct advantages that may or may not be apparent. Not the least of these is the fact that the inversion procedure is systematic and hence is particularly suitable for electronic computation. However, the major advantage is that the inversion procedure will automatically produce the variances of the estimators of all parameters in the linear model.

Before leaving the topic of matrix inversion, we ask how one may identify a matrix that has an inverse. Reference to a discussion of linear equations in ordinary algebra should reveal the answer.

Clearly, a unique solution for a system of simultaneous linear equations cannot be obtained unless the equations are independent. Thus, if one of the equations is a linear combination of the others, the equations are dependent. Coefficient matrices associated with dependent systems of linear equations do not possess an inverse. Furthermore, we state without proof that a matrix, A, can be inverted if and only if the determinant for A is nonzero.

6.13 Solving a System of Simultaneous Linear Equations

We have finally obtained all of the ingredients necessary for solving the system of simultaneous linear equations,

$$2v_1 + v_2 = 5,$$

$$v_1 - v_2 = 1,$$

presented in Sec. 6.10. Recalling that the matrix solution to the system of equations, $AV = G$ is $V = A^{-1}G$, we obtain

$$V = A^{-1}G = \begin{bmatrix} \frac{1}{3} & \frac{1}{3} \\ \frac{1}{3} & -\frac{2}{3} \end{bmatrix} \begin{bmatrix} 5 \\ 1 \end{bmatrix} = \begin{bmatrix} 2 \\ 1 \end{bmatrix}.$$

Hence the solution is

$$V = \begin{bmatrix} v_1 \\ v_2 \end{bmatrix} = \begin{bmatrix} 2 \\ 1 \end{bmatrix}$$

—that is, $v_1 = 2$ and $v_2 = 1$, a fact that may be verified by substitution of these values in the original linear equations.

Example 6.9 Solve the system of simultaneous linear equations.

$$2v_1 + v_3 = 4,$$

$$v_1 - v_2 + 2v_3 = 2,$$

$$v_1 = 1.$$

Solution: The coefficient matrix for these equations,

$$A = \begin{bmatrix} 2 & 0 & 1 \\ 1 & -1 & 2 \\ 1 & 0 & 0 \end{bmatrix},$$

appeared in Example 6.8. In that example, we found that

$$A^{-1} = \begin{bmatrix} 0 & 0 & 1 \\ 2 & -1 & -3 \\ 1 & 0 & 0 \end{bmatrix}.$$

Solving,

$$V = A^{-1}G = \begin{bmatrix} 0 & 0 & 1 \\ 2 & -1 & -3 \\ 1 & 0 & -2 \end{bmatrix} \begin{bmatrix} 4 \\ 2 \\ 1 \end{bmatrix} = \begin{bmatrix} 1 \\ 3 \\ 2 \end{bmatrix}.$$

Thus $v_1 = 1$, $v_2 = 3$, and $v_3 = 2$ give the solution to the set of three simultaneous linear equations.

6.14 The Least-Squares Equations and the Solution for the General Linear Model

At the point of interruption of our discussion in Sec. 6.3 we had stated that the estimation of the $(k + 1)$ parameters of the general linear model requires the solution of a system of simultaneous linear equations. We now return to the discussion of Sec. 6.3 and express the least-squares equations in matrix notation.

We will modify the general linear model by introducing a new variable, x_0, which will appear as the coefficient of the constant, β_0. This will be a *dummy variable* which will be defined always to equal one—that is, $x_0 = 1$. Then the general linear model will be

$$y = \beta_0 x_0 + \beta_1 x_1 + \beta_2 x_2 + \ldots + \beta_k x_k + \epsilon.$$

The n joint observations on $(y, x_1, x_2, \ldots, x_k)$ resulting from n "experiments" will be presented in two data matrices.

$$
Y = \begin{bmatrix} y_1 \\ y_2 \\ y_3 \\ y_4 \\ \cdot \\ \cdot \\ \cdot \\ y_n \end{bmatrix},
\qquad
X = \begin{matrix} \begin{matrix} x_0 & x_1 & x_2 & x_3 & \cdots & x_k \end{matrix} \\ \begin{bmatrix} 1 & x_{11} & x_{21} & x_{31} & \cdots & x_{k1} \\ 1 & x_{12} & x_{22} & x_{32} & \cdots & x_{k2} \\ 1 & x_{13} & x_{23} & x_{33} & \cdots & x_{k3} \\ 1 & x_{14} & x_{24} & x_{34} & \cdots & x_{k4} \\ \cdot & \cdot & \cdot & \cdot & & \cdot \\ \cdot & \cdot & \cdot & \cdot & & \cdot \\ \cdot & \cdot & \cdot & \cdot & & \cdot \\ 1 & x_{1n} & x_{2n} & x_{3n} & & x_{kn} \end{bmatrix} \end{matrix}.
$$

The symbols $x_0, x_1, x_2, x_3, \ldots, x_k$ have been written above the columns of the X matrix to indicate that the measurements in a particular column pertain to one specific independent variable. Thus the first column contains the n values of $x_0 = 1$, the second column contains the n measurements made on x_1, the third column, x_2, and so on. The *first* rows of both the Y and X matrices give the measurements made on $(y, x_0, x_1, x_2, x_3, \ldots, x_k)$ obtained from the *first* experiment. Measurements in the second, third, and jth rows correspond, respectively, to the measurements made during the second, third, and, in general, the jth experiments. For example, if the first experiment produced $y = 86$ and $x_1 = 2$, $x_2 = -1$, $x_3 = 70, \ldots,$ and $x_k = 1$, then the first rows of the Y and X matrices would equal

$$
\underset{n \times 1}{Y} = \begin{bmatrix} 86 \\ \cdot \\ \cdot \\ \cdot \\ \cdot \end{bmatrix},
\qquad
\underset{n \times (k+1)}{X} = \begin{bmatrix} 1 & 2 & -1 & 70 & \cdots & 1 \\ \cdot & \cdot & \cdot & \cdot & & \cdot \\ \cdot & \cdot & \cdot & \cdot & & \cdot \\ \cdot & \cdot & \cdot & \cdot & & \cdot \end{bmatrix}.
$$

Having defined the Y and X matrices, we now define the $\hat{\beta}$ matrix which contains all of the estimates of the model parameters,

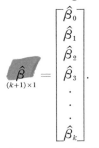

$$\hat{\beta}_{(k+1)\times 1} = \begin{bmatrix} \hat{\beta}_0 \\ \hat{\beta}_1 \\ \hat{\beta}_2 \\ \hat{\beta}_3 \\ \cdot \\ \cdot \\ \cdot \\ \hat{\beta}_k \end{bmatrix}.$$

Note that the estimates take the same order in the column as they appear in the linear model as one moves from left to right.

Although proof is omitted, it is interesting to note that SSE can be written as a matrix expression involving $\hat{\beta}$, Y, and X. Rules can then be given for the simultaneous partial differentiation of SSE with respect to the $\hat{\beta}$ matrix so as to give, in one step, all of the partial derivatives of SSE with respect to $\hat{\beta}_0, \hat{\beta}_1, \hat{\beta}_2, \ldots, \hat{\beta}_k$ in a simple matrix expression. Setting this matrix of partial derivatives equal to zero, we obtain the matrix equation,

$$(X'X)\hat{\beta} - X'Y = 0.$$

Transposing $X'Y$ to the right of the equality sign, we acquire the least-squares equation,

$$(X'X)\hat{\beta} = X'Y.$$

The matrix of unknowns, $\hat{\beta}$, corresponds to the V matrix in Sec. 6.10, the $(X'X)$ matrix to the coefficient matrix, A, and $X'Y$ to the G matrix. (Recall that the X' matrix is the transpose of the X matrix.)

The solution of the least-squares equation easily follows from the results of Sec. 6.10. Multiplying both sides of the equation by $(X'X)^{-1}$, we obtain

$$\hat{\beta} = (X'X)^{-1}X'Y.$$

Thus all of the parameter estimates can be obtained by calculating $X'X$, $X'Y$, obtaining the inverse of $(X'X)$, and then performing the final multiplication, $(X'X)^{-1}X'Y$. We will illustrate the procedure with several very simple examples.

Example 6.10   Fit a straight line to the data.

y	x
0	-2
0	-1
1	0
1	1
3	2

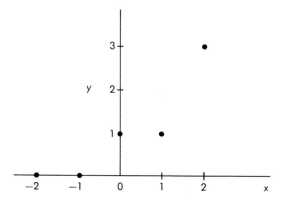

Figure 6.6

Solution: A plot of the data is given in Fig. 6.6. The linear model and the Y and X matrices would equal

$$y = \beta_0 + \beta_1 x + \epsilon,$$

$$Y = \begin{bmatrix} 0 \\ 0 \\ 1 \\ 1 \\ 3 \end{bmatrix}, \qquad X = \begin{bmatrix} 1 & -2 \\ 1 & -1 \\ 1 & 0 \\ 1 & 1 \\ 1 & 2 \end{bmatrix}.$$

Note that the X matrix contains two columns corresponding to the dummy variable, x_0, and the variable, x.

The next step is to obtain the matrix products, $X'X$ and $X'Y$:

$$X'X = \begin{bmatrix} 1 & 1 & 1 & 1 & 1 \\ -2 & -1 & 0 & 1 & 2 \end{bmatrix} \begin{bmatrix} 1 & -2 \\ 1 & -1 \\ 1 & 0 \\ 1 & 1 \\ 1 & 2 \end{bmatrix} = \begin{bmatrix} 5 & 0 \\ 0 & 10 \end{bmatrix},$$

$$X'Y = \begin{bmatrix} 1 & 1 & 1 & 1 & 1 \\ -2 & -1 & 0 & 1 & 2 \end{bmatrix} \begin{bmatrix} 0 \\ 0 \\ 1 \\ 1 \\ 3 \end{bmatrix} = \begin{bmatrix} 5 \\ 7 \end{bmatrix}.$$

The inverse of the $(X'X)$ matrix is obtained by performing identical row operations on $(X'X)$ and I so as to change $(X'X)$ to I.

$$(X'X) = \begin{bmatrix} 5 & 0 \\ 0 & 10 \end{bmatrix}, \qquad I = \begin{bmatrix} 1 & 0 \\ 0 & 1 \end{bmatrix}.$$

This can be accomplished with two simple row operations, namely by multiplying the first row by $\frac{1}{5}$ and the second row by $\frac{1}{10}$.

$$\begin{bmatrix} 1 & 0 \\ 0 & 1 \end{bmatrix}\begin{bmatrix} \frac{1}{5} & 0 \\ 0 & \frac{1}{10} \end{bmatrix} = (X'X)^{-1}.$$

Finally we have

$$\hat{\beta} = (X'X)^{-1}X'Y.$$

Substituting,

$$\hat{\beta} = \begin{bmatrix} \frac{1}{5} & 0 \\ 0 & \frac{1}{10} \end{bmatrix}\begin{bmatrix} 5 \\ 7 \end{bmatrix} = \begin{bmatrix} 1 \\ .7 \end{bmatrix}$$

Since

$$\hat{\beta} = \begin{bmatrix} \hat{\beta}_0 \\ \hat{\beta}_1 \end{bmatrix},$$

it is clear that $\hat{\beta}_0 = 1$, $\hat{\beta}_1 = .7$, and the prediction equation is

$$\hat{y} = \hat{\beta}_0 + \hat{\beta}_1 x$$

or

$$\hat{y} = 1 + .7x.$$

A sketch of this prediction line on Fig. 6.6 indicates a good fit to the data points and provides a rough check on the calculations.

Example 6.11   Fit a parabola to the data of Fig. 6.6 using the model,

$$y = \beta_0 + \beta_1 x + \beta_2 x^2 + \epsilon.$$

Solution: The X matrix for this example will differ from that of Example 6.10 only by the addition of a third column corresponding to x^2. (Note that $x_1 = x$ and $x_2 = x^2$ and $k = 2$ in the notation of the general linear model.) Thus

$$Y = \begin{bmatrix} 0 \\ 0 \\ 1 \\ 1 \\ 3 \end{bmatrix}, \qquad X = \begin{matrix} \begin{matrix} x_0 & x & x^2 \end{matrix} \\ \begin{bmatrix} 1 & -2 & 4 \\ 1 & -1 & 1 \\ 1 & 0 & 0 \\ 1 & 1 & 1 \\ 1 & 2 & 4 \end{bmatrix} \end{matrix}.$$

The three variables x_0, x, and x^2 are shown above their respective columns in the X matrix. Thus for the first measurement, $y = 0$, $x_0 = 1$, $x = -2$, and $x^2 = 4$. For the second measurement, $y = 0$, $x_0 = 1$, $x = -1$, and $x^2 = 1$. Succeeding rows of the Y and X matrices are obtained in a similar manner.

The matrix products, $X'X$ and $X'Y$, are

$$(X'X) = \begin{bmatrix} 1 & 1 & 1 & 1 & 1 \\ -2 & -1 & 0 & 1 & 2 \\ 4 & 1 & 0 & 1 & 4 \end{bmatrix} \begin{bmatrix} 1 & -2 & 4 \\ 1 & -1 & 1 \\ 1 & 0 & 0 \\ 1 & 1 & 1 \\ 1 & 2 & 4 \end{bmatrix} = \begin{bmatrix} 5 & 0 & 10 \\ 0 & 10 & 0 \\ 10 & 0 & 34 \end{bmatrix},$$

$$(X'Y) = \begin{bmatrix} 1 & 1 & 1 & 1 & 1 \\ -2 & -1 & 0 & 1 & 2 \\ 4 & 1 & 0 & 1 & 4 \end{bmatrix} \begin{bmatrix} 0 \\ 0 \\ 1 \\ 1 \\ 3 \end{bmatrix} = \begin{bmatrix} 5 \\ 7 \\ 13 \end{bmatrix}.$$

We omit the process of inverting $(X'X)$ and simply state that it is equal to

$$(X'X)^{-1} = \begin{bmatrix} \frac{17}{35} & 0 & -\frac{1}{7} \\ 0 & \frac{1}{10} & 0 \\ -\frac{1}{7} & 0 & \frac{1}{14} \end{bmatrix}$$

The reader may verify that $(X'X)^{-1}(X'X) = I$.

Finally,

$$\hat{\beta} = (X'X)^{-1} X'Y$$

$$= \begin{bmatrix} \frac{17}{35} & 0 & -\frac{1}{7} \\ 0 & \frac{1}{10} & 0 \\ -\frac{1}{7} & 0 & \frac{1}{14} \end{bmatrix} \begin{bmatrix} 5 \\ 7 \\ 13 \end{bmatrix} = \begin{bmatrix} \frac{4}{7} \\ \frac{7}{10} \\ \frac{3}{14} \end{bmatrix} \approx \begin{bmatrix} .57 \\ .7 \\ .214 \end{bmatrix}.$$

Hence, $\hat{\beta}_0 = .57$, $\hat{\beta}_1 = .7$, and $\hat{\beta}_2 = .214$, and the prediction equation is

$$\hat{y} = .57 + .7x + .214x^2.$$

A graph of this parabola on Fig. 6.6 will indicate a good fit to the data points.

We will conclude this section by fitting a linear model to the six data points generated by a (2×3) factorial experiment. Although fictitious, we will imagine that these six runs represent a first replication of the experiment in a sequence to be composed of several replications.

Example 6.12 A (2×3) factorial experiment was conducted to determine the effect of pressure and temperature on the yield of a chemical. Pressure and temperature levels employed in the experiment were:

Pressure (psi)	Temperature (°F)
50	100
80	200
	300

Assume that it is known that the pressure and temperature variables cannot interact. Fit the (2×3) factorial model to the data after first deleting interaction terms.

The data are indicated below:

Response Y	Pressure Actual	Pressure Coded	Temperature Actual	Temperature Coded
21	50	−1	100	−1
23	50	−1	200	0
26	50	−1	300	1
22	80	1	100	−1
23	80	1	200	0
28	80	1	300	1

Solution: A study of Examples 6.10 and 6.11 will reveal that equal spacing of the independent variables about zero simplifies the $(X'X)$ matrix and reduces the labor involved in inversion. With this in mind, as well as a desire to reduce the magnitude of the measurements on the independent variables, we will code pressure and temperature as follows:

Pressure P	x_1	Temperature T	x_2
50	−1	100	−1
80	1	200	0
		300	1

Coding has the effect of shifting the origin to a new point and changing the units of measurements. To illustrate, observe that the coded pressure, x_1, is equal to −1 when $P = 50$ and 1 when $P = 80$. This would make $x_1 = 0$ correspond to $P = 65$, the new origin. Secondly, it is clear that a one-unit-change in x_1 is equivalent to a 15-unit change in P. Therefore

$$x_1 = \frac{P - 65}{15}.$$

The reader may verify this relationship by substituting the two values of P in the equation and noting the resulting values of x_1.

Similarly, the temperature may be coded using a variable, x_2, where

$$x_2 = \frac{T - 200}{100}.$$

Note that the origin is shifted to $T = 200$ and that the measurements are in units of $100°F$.

The linear model for the (2×3) factorial, deleting the two interaction terms, is

$$y = \beta_0 + \beta_1 x_1 + \beta_2 x_2 + \beta_3 x_2^2 + \epsilon.$$

The Y and X matrices for the data are

$$Y = \begin{bmatrix} 21 \\ 23 \\ 26 \\ 22 \\ 23 \\ 28 \end{bmatrix}, \quad X = \begin{array}{cccc} x_0 & x_1 & x_2 & x_2^2 \\ \begin{bmatrix} 1 & -1 & -1 & 1 \\ 1 & -1 & 0 & 0 \\ 1 & -1 & 1 & 1 \\ 1 & 1 & -1 & 1 \\ 1 & 1 & 0 & 0 \\ 1 & 1 & 1 & 1 \end{bmatrix} \end{array}.$$

The reader may verify that

$$X'X = \begin{bmatrix} 6 & 0 & 0 & 4 \\ 0 & 6 & 0 & 0 \\ 0 & 0 & 4 & 0 \\ 4 & 0 & 0 & 4 \end{bmatrix},$$

$$(X'X)^{-1} = \begin{bmatrix} \frac{1}{2} & 0 & 0 & -\frac{1}{2} \\ 0 & \frac{1}{6} & 0 & 0 \\ 0 & 0 & \frac{1}{4} & 0 \\ -\frac{1}{2} & 0 & 0 & \frac{3}{4} \end{bmatrix},$$

$$X'Y = \begin{bmatrix} 143 \\ 3 \\ 11 \\ 97 \end{bmatrix},$$

and

$$\hat{\beta} = (X'X)^{-1} X'Y = \begin{bmatrix} \frac{1}{2} & 0 & 0 & -\frac{1}{2} \\ 0 & \frac{1}{6} & 0 & 0 \\ 0 & 0 & \frac{1}{4} & 0 \\ -\frac{1}{2} & 0 & 0 & \frac{3}{4} \end{bmatrix} \begin{bmatrix} 143 \\ 3 \\ 11 \\ 97 \end{bmatrix} = \begin{bmatrix} 23 \\ .5 \\ 2.75 \\ 1.25 \end{bmatrix}.$$

Hence the resulting prediction equation is

$$\hat{y} = 23 + .5x_1 + 2.75x_2 + 1.25x_2^2.$$

We may easily check the fit of the prediction equation by substituting the experimental values of x_1 and x_2 into the prediction equation and computing $\hat{y}$ for the six points. The predicted values of y along with the observed values are given in Table 6.1. It is interesting to note that the deviations between y and $\hat{y}$ are small for all six points.

Table 6.1 Comparison of $\hat{y}$ and y for Example 6.12

x_1	x_2	y	$\hat{y}$	$y - \hat{y}$
-1	-1	21	21.0	0
-1	0	23	22.5	.5
-1	1	26	26.5	$-.5$
1	-1	22	22.0	0
1	0	23	23.5	$-.5$
1	1	28	27.5	.5

Before leaving this example, we should observe that coding did simplify the $(X'X)$ matrix with no serious loss in interpretation. Coded values of temperature and pressure may be substituted as easily as uncoded values in the prediction equation.

6.15 Summary

Chapter 6 has been concerned with fitting the general linear model to a set of data points by the method of least squares. It was shown in Sec. 6.3 that the estimates of the model parameters required the solution of a system of simultaneous linear equations. A diversion to study some of the elementary aspects of matrix algebra permitted the expression of these equations in Sec. 6.14 in matrix notation and rendered the solution,

$$\hat{\beta} = (X'X)^{-1}X'Y.$$

It is clear that this solution estimates the model parameters but gives no measure of their goodness. This topic will be discussed in detail in Chapter 7 and, to some extent, in succeeding chapters.

The examples of fitting linear models presented in Chapter 6 were primarily intended to illustrate the procedure and were not intended to be realistic. A deeper understanding of the consequences of fitting linear models to sets of data will emerge as we proceed through the remaining chapters of the text.

Exercises

1. Fit the linear model $y = \beta_0 + \epsilon$ to the data of Example 1.8, Chapter 1. Note that $\hat{\beta}_0 = \bar{y}$ and that

$$\text{SSE} = \sum_{i=1}^{4} (y_i - \bar{y})^2.$$

2. Fit a straight line through the following five data points. Give the estimates of β_0 and β_1.

y	3	2	1	1	.5
x	-2	-1	0	1	2

Plot the points and sketch the fitted line as a check on the calculations.

3. Fit a straight line to the following data.

y	4	2	3.5	.5	0
x	0	1	2	3	4

Plot the points and sketch the fitted line as a check on the calculations.

4. Fit a straight line to the following data, plot the points, and then sketch the fitted line as a check on the calculations.

y	3	2	1	1	.5
x	-1	0	1	2	3

Note that the data points are the same as for Example 2 except that they are translated two units in the positive direction along the x-axis. What effect does symmetric spacing of the x-values about $x = 0$ have on the form of the $(X'X)$ matrix and the resulting calculations?

5. Fit a parabola through the following seven data points by estimating the model parameters, β_0, β_1 and β_2.

y	1	0	0	-1	-1	0	0
x	-3	-2	-1	0	1	2	3

Plot the points and sketch the fitted parabola as a check on the calculations.

6. Fit the cubic probabilistic model,

$$y = \beta_0 + \beta_1 x + \beta_2 x^2 + \beta_3 x^3 + \epsilon,$$

to the following data.

y	1	0	0	1	2	3	3
x	-3	-2	-1	0	1	2	3

(a) Plot the points and graph the fitted curve.
(b) Predict y when $x = 1$.

7. A response, y, is a function of three independent variables, x_1, x_2, and x_3, that are related as follows,

$$y = \beta_0 + \beta_1 x_1 + \beta_2 x_2 + \beta_3 x_3 + \epsilon.$$

(a) Fit this model to the following $n = 7$ data points.

y	1	0	0	1	2	3	3
x_1	-3	-2	-1	0	1	2	3
x_2	5	0	-3	-4	-3	0	5
x_3	-1	1	1	0	-1	-1	1

(b) Predict y when $x_1 = 1$, $x_2 = -3$, $x_3 = -1$. Compare with the observed response in the original data. Why are these two not equal?

8. The main diagonal of a square matrix is the diagonal formed by the elements moving from top left to bottom right. An $(X'X)$ matrix with non-zero main diagonal elements, c_{ii}, and all off-diagonal elements, $c_{ij} = 0$ ($i \neq j$) is called a diagonal matrix. Show that the inverse of a diagonal $(X'X)$ matrix, D, is a diagonal matrix whose diagonal elements are $D_{ii} = 1/c_{ii}$.

9. Show that $(X'X)$ is a symmetric matrix. A symmetric matrix is one whose elements, c_{ij}, satisfy the relationship $c_{ij} = c_{ji}$ for all i and j, where $i \neq j$.

10. Suppose that a $k \times k$ $(X'X)$ is partitioned into four submatrices,

$$\underset{k \times k}{X'X} = \left[\begin{array}{c|c} C_{11} & C_{12} \\ \hline C_{21} & C_{22} \end{array}\right],$$

where C_{11} and C_{22} are square matrices of dimensions $a \times a$ and $(k - a) \times (k - a)$, respectively. Further, suppose that $C_{12} = C_{21} = 0$. (Note that $C_{12} = C_{21}$ because $X'X$ is symmetric.) If C_{11}^{-1} and C_{22}^{-1} exist, show that

$$(X'X)^{-1} = \left[\begin{array}{c|c} C_{11}^{-1} & 0 \\ \hline 0 & C_{22}^{-1} \end{array}\right].$$

11. Repeat the instructions of Exercise 10 where $(X'X)$ is partitioned so that it contains j square submatrices $C_{11}, C_{22}, \ldots C_{jj}$ as shown below. Further,

$$(X'X) = \left[\begin{array}{c|c|c|c} C_{11} & C_{12} & \cdots & C_{1j} \\ \hline C_{21} & C_{22} & \cdots & C_{2j} \\ \hline \vdots & \vdots & \ddots & \vdots \\ \hline C_{j1} & C_{j2} & \cdots & C_{jj} \end{array}\right].$$

Suppose that $C_{11}, C_{22}, C_{33}, \ldots, C_{jj}$ all possess inverses and that the elements of all other sub-matrices in $(X'X)$, $C_{ij}(i \neq j)$, equal zero. Then show that

$$(X'X)^{-1} = \begin{bmatrix} C_{11}^{-1} & 0 & \cdots & 0 \\ 0 & C_{22}^{-1} & \cdots & 0 \\ \vdots & \vdots & \ddots & \vdots \\ 0 & 0 & \cdots & C_{jj}^{-1} \end{bmatrix}.$$

12. Refer to Exercise 28, Chapter 1.
   (a) Give an appropriate linear model for this experiment.
   (b) Fit the linear model to the data of Exercise 28 to estimate the difference in the population means.
   (c) Note that SSE will equal the pooled sum of squares of deviations,

   $$\text{SSE} = \sum_{j=1} (y_{1j} - \bar{y}_1)^2 + \sum_{j=1} (y_{2j} - \bar{y}_2)^2.$$

13. Refer to the paired difference experiment, Section 2.4.
   (a) Write a linear model for this experiment. (Recall that the paired-difference experiment is a simple example of a randomized block design.)
   (b) Fit the linear model to the data of Table 2.1 to estimate the difference in the average response between Methods B and A.
   (c) Note that SSE will equal

   $$\text{SSE} = \sum_{i=1}^{9} (d_i - \bar{d})^2.$$

14. A 2^4 factorial experiment was conducted to investigate the effect of four factors: temperature, T_1; pressure, p; catalyst, C; and temperature, T_2, on the yield of a chemical.
   (a) The levels of the four factors are shown below. If each of the four factors is coded to produce the four variables, x_1, x_2, x_3 and x_4, respectively, give the linear equation relating each coded variable to its corresponding original.

T_1	x_1	P	x_2	C	x_3	T_2	x_4
50	-1	10	-1	1	-1	100	-1
70	1	20	1	2	1	200	1

   (b) Suppose that the variables *do not* interact. Write the appropriate linear model for the experiment.
   (c) Fit the linear model (b) to the experimental data given below:

				x_4			
				+1		−1	
				x_3		x_3	
				−1	1	−1	1
x_1	−1	x_2	−1	22.2	24.5	24.4	25.9
			1	19.4	24.1	25.2	18.4
	+1	x_2	−1	22.1	19.6	23.5	16.5
			1	14.2	12.7	19.3	16.0

(d) Predict y when $T_1 = 50$, $P = 20$, $C = 1$, and $T_2 = 200$.

15. Refer to Exercise 14. Suppose that the experimenter suspects that main effects and two-way interactions may exist but that all higher-order interactions are negligible.

(a) Write the appropriate linear model for the experiment.

(b) Fit the linear model (a) to the data.

(c) Predict y when $T_1 = 50$, $P = 20$, $C = 1$ and $T_2 = 200$. Compare with the results of Exercise 14(d).

16. Suppose that an independent variable, T, takes values 20, 35, 50, 65, and 80 during an experiment. Find a coded variable, x, that is linearly related to T so that the values of x will be equally spaced about their origin, and assume values such that $|x| \leq 2$. (Give the relationship between x and T.)

17. Repeat Exercise 16 if T takes values 120, 145, 170, and 195 and if $|x| \leq 3$.

18. What is the advantage of selecting equally spaced levels of independent variables?

19. If independent variables are equally spaced as noted in Exercise 17, what is the advantage of coding to new variables that represent symmetric spacing about the origin?

20. What is the advantage of scaling coded variables (changing units) so that they may assume values that fall approximately in the range $x \leq 10$?

21. Why would one wish to code the values of an independent variable, x, even if the levels selected were not equally spaced?

22. The sales of a product in a sales territory are known to be a function of the population, P, and advertising expenditure per person, E. The sales for $n = 8$ sales areas, along with their population (in millions) and advertising expenditures (dollars per person) are given below.

Sales y	Population x_1	Advertising x_2
3.6	2.4	.16
2.5	1.3	.21
4.2	5.1	.12
4.1	4.9	.14
4.0	3.2	.26
5.1	6.7	.10
4.3	3.6	.41
1.5	.7	.11

(a) Fit the linear model,

$$y = \beta_0 + \beta_1 x_1 + \beta_2 x_2 + \epsilon$$

to the data.

(b) Predict y when $x_1 = 3.2$, $x_2 = .26$, and compare with the observed value of y.

23. Refer to Exercise 23, Chapter 5, and the comparison of the growth rates for bacteria types, A and B. The growth, y, recorded at five equally spaced (and coded) points of time, is recorded below.

Bacteria type	Time				
	-2	-1	0	1	2
A	8.0	9.0	9.1	10.2	10.4
B	10.0	10.3	12.2	12.6	13.9

(a) Fit the linear model,

$$y = \beta_0 + \beta_1 x_1 + \beta_2 x_2 + \beta_3 x_1 x_2 + \epsilon$$

to the $n = 10$ data points. Let $x_1 = 1$ if the point refers to bacteria type B and $x_1 = 0$ if the point refers to type A. Let $x_2 = $ (coded time).

(b) Plot the data points and graph the two growth lines. Note that β_3 is the difference between the slopes of the two lines and represents slope-bacteria-type interaction.

(c) Predict the growth of bacteria type A at time $x_2 = 0$ and compare with the graph. Repeat the process for bacteria type B.

24. A chemist wished to determine the effect of developer strength, temperature, and development time on the light density of photographic film. A 2^3 factorial experiment, replicated in three blocks (time) was employed, thus yielding a randomized block design. The eight factor combinations represent the treatments which were randomly assigned in time. The data for the experiment are shown below (the three independent variables are presented in coded form).

Developer strength x_1	Temperature x_2	Time x_3	Response		
			Block I	Block II	Block III
-1	-1	-1	0	1	0
-1	-1	1	3	4	4
-1	1	-1	0	0	0
-1	1	1	2	3	2
1	-1	-1	3	2	2
1	-1	1	8	8	10
1	1	-1	1	2	0
1	1	1	7	8	8

(a) Write the linear model for the experiment, including all terms for the complete 2^3 factorial as well as those representing block differences.

(b) Fit the linear model to the data.

(c) Predict the response in Block II when $x_1 = -1$, $x_2 = 1$ and $x_3 = 1$.

References

Aitken, A. C., *Determinants and Matrices*, 9th ed. New York: Interscience Publishers, Inc., 1958.

Dwyer, P. S., *Linear Computations*. New York: John Wiley & Sons, Inc., 1951.

Halmos, P. R., *Finite-Dimensional Vector Spaces*, 2nd ed. New York: D. Van Nostrand Company, Inc., 1958.

MacDuffie, C. C., *The Theory of Matrices*. New York: Chelsea Publishing Company, 1956.

National Bureau of Standards, *Basic Theorems in Matrix Theory*. Washington, D. C.: U.S. Government Printing Office, 1960.

————, *Contributions to the Solution of Systems of Linear Equations and the Determination of Eigenvalues*. Washington, D. C.: U.S. Government Printing Office, 1954.

Perlis S., *Theory of Matrices*. Reading, Mass.: Addison-Wesley Publishing Company, Inc., 1952.

7

Inference Making

7.1 Introduction

Estimation of the parameters of the general linear model was discussed in Chapter 6 but no measure of goodness was provided for the estimators. In this chapter we will consider the problem of placing bounds on the error of estimation for any one of the parameters, such as β_i. Specifically, we will give a confidence interval for β_i and will also present a statistical procedure to test an hypothesis concerning its value.

A second important inferential problem concerns the estimation and statistical tests of hypotheses for linear functions of $\beta_0, \beta_1, \beta_2, \ldots, \beta_k$. For example, if y is the yield of chemical in a manufacturing plant and $x_1, x_2, x_3, \ldots, x_k$ are production variables such as the temperature of the process, the pressure, and so on, we might wish to estimate the mean value of y (the expected yield) for given settings of $x_1, x_2, x_3, \ldots, x_k$. Thus, the expected value of y, given $x_1, x_2, x_3, \ldots, x_k$,

$$E(y) = \beta_0 + \beta_1 x_1 + \beta_2 x_2 + \cdots + \beta_k x_k,$$

is a linear function of the model parameters.

Finally, we may wish to predict a particular value of y for given settings of $x_1, x_2, x_3, \ldots, x_k$, such as the yield of chemical for one single day. Although y is not a parameter, we can employ $\hat{y}$ as the prediction equation and give bounds for the error of prediction.

If one were to repeatedly sample, using n data points, and each time fit a particular linear model, he would find that the estimates of $\beta_0, \beta_1, \beta_2, \ldots,$ β_k would vary from sample to sample. This variability is caused by the random behavior of y, which, in turn, varies because of ϵ, the only random component in the linear model. With this in mind, it is quite apparent that the variances and covariances of $\hat{\beta}_0, \hat{\beta}_1, \hat{\beta}_2, \ldots, \hat{\beta}_k$ (which are computed from the observed values of y) will depend upon the variances and covariances of the random errors $\epsilon_1, \epsilon_2, \epsilon_3, \ldots, \epsilon_n$ associated with the observations on y.

It is worthwhile to reiterate that one is at liberty to select any set of assumptions regarding the behavior of the random error, ϵ. These assumptions then lead to a particular method of estimation, a theoretical distribution of the estimators of the model parameters in repeated sampling, and, consequently, a means of evaluating the goodness of the estimation procedure.

The adequacy of the resulting inferential procedures, which may be investigated theoretically as well as empirically, will depend upon how well the procedures work in practice.

7.2 Variances and Covariances of the Parameter Estimators

As noted in Chapter 3, we will assume that the random errors $\epsilon_1, \epsilon_2, \epsilon_3,$ $\ldots, \epsilon_n$ are mutually independent and that the expected value and variance of ϵ for a given set of values $x_1, x_2, \ldots, x_k$ are equal to zero and σ^2, respectively. Based on these assumptions, it can be shown that the variance of any one of the estimators, say $\hat{\beta}_i$, is

$$V(\hat{\beta}_i) = c_{ii}\sigma^2$$

and the covariance of any pair of estimators, say $\hat{\beta}_i$ and $\hat{\beta}_j$, is

$$\text{Cov}(\hat{\beta}_i, \hat{\beta}_j) = c_{ij}\sigma^2.$$

The quantities c_{ii} and c_{ij} are elements of the $(X'X)^{-1}$ matrix.

The element c_{ij} appears in the ith row and the jth column of $(X'X)^{-1}$. (Keep in mind that there are a zeroth row and column corresponding to x_0.) Thus

$$(X'X)^{-1} = \begin{bmatrix} c_{00} & c_{01} & c_{02} & \cdots & c_{0k} \\ c_{10} & c_{11} & c_{12} \cdot & & \\ c_{20} & c_{21} & c_{22} & & \\ \vdots & \vdots & \vdots & & \\ c_{k0} & c_{k1} & c_{k2} & \cdots & c_{kk} \end{bmatrix}$$

To illustrate, the variances of $\hat{\beta}_0$ and $\hat{\beta}_1$ for Example 6.10 are

$$V(\hat{\beta}_0) = c_{00}\sigma^2 = (\tfrac{1}{5})\sigma^2,$$

$$V(\hat{\beta}_1) = c_{11}\sigma^2 = (\tfrac{1}{10})\sigma^2,$$

where $c_{00} = \tfrac{1}{5}$ and $c_{11} = \tfrac{1}{10}$ are the diagonal elements of $(X'X)^{-1}$. Similarly, the covariance of $\hat{\beta}_0$ and $\hat{\beta}_1$ is $c_{01}\sigma^2$, where $c_{01} = c_{10} = 0$.
The variances of $\hat{\beta}_0$, $\hat{\beta}_1$, $\hat{\beta}_2$, and $\hat{\beta}_3$, Example 6.12, are

$$V(\hat{\beta}_0) = c_{00}\sigma^2 = \tfrac{1}{2}\sigma^2,$$

$$V(\hat{\beta}_1) = c_{11}\sigma^2 = \tfrac{1}{6}\sigma^2,$$

$$V(\hat{\beta}_2) = c_{22}\sigma^2 = \tfrac{1}{4}\sigma^2,$$

$$V(\hat{\beta}_3) = c_{33}\sigma^2 = \tfrac{3}{4}\sigma^2.$$

The covariances of all pairs of estimators are equal to zero with the exception of $\hat{\beta}_0$ and $\hat{\beta}_3$, whose covariance is

$$\text{Cov}\,(\hat{\beta}_0, \hat{\beta}_3) = c_{03}\sigma^2 = -\tfrac{1}{2}\sigma^2.$$

The importance of the variances of the model parameters is quite apparent. Regardless of the distribution of an estimator, say $\hat{\beta}_i$, it is likely to be mound-shaped, thus permitting one to use the empirical rule to place a

$$\pm 2\sigma_{\hat{\beta}_i} = \pm 2\sigma\sqrt{c_{ii}}$$

bound on the error of estimation. The probability that the error of estimation is less than $2\sigma\sqrt{c_{ii}}$ will be approximately equal to .95.

The covariance of a pair of estimators, say $\hat{\beta}_i$ and $\hat{\beta}_j$, assumes importance when we are seeking the variance of a linear function of the parameter estimators. This topic will be explained in Sec. 7.7.

7.3 Estimating σ^2

Since σ^2 is rarely known, it must be estimated as a prelude to estimation or tests of hypotheses concerning the parameters of the linear model.

Intuitively, we would suspect that the sum of squares of deviations of the observations about their predicted values would be used in calculating an estimate of σ^2 and, indeed, this is true. Given a linear model containing $(k + 1)$ parameters (as was the case for the general linear model), the quantity

$$s^2 = \frac{\text{SSE}}{n - (k + 1)}$$

is an unbiased estimator of σ^2. Furthermore, if we assume that the random errors, $\epsilon_1, \epsilon_2, \ldots, \epsilon_n$ are normally distributed, the quantity

$$[n - (k + 1)]\frac{s^2}{\sigma^2}$$

can be shown to possess a chi-square distribution in repeated sampling (with $[n - (k + 1)]$ degrees of freedom).

The divisor of SSE, $[n - (k + 1)]$, called "the number of degrees of freedom" available for estimating σ^2, *will always equal n, the number of data points, less one degree of freedom for each parameter in the model.* The reader is referred to the discussion of the concept of degrees of freedom and its relation to the quantity of information available for estimating σ^2 presented in Sec. 4.5.

Several simple examples illustrating our procedure for estimating σ^2 are well known to the reader.

Given a random sample of n measurements, $y_1, y_2, y_3, \ldots, y_n$, from a population with mean μ and variance σ^2, we recall the estimator of σ^2 is

$$s^2 = \frac{\sum_{i=1}^{n} (y_i - \bar{y})^2}{n - 1}.$$

Since the model for this response,

$$y = \mu + \epsilon$$

(see Example 3.3), contains one parameter, it is clear that the number of degrees of freedom available for estimating σ^2 is $(n - 1)$. The reader may verify that

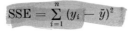
$$\text{SSE} = \sum_{i=1}^{n} (y_i - \bar{y})^2$$

and that our estimator of σ^2 is, indeed, the familiar quantity,

$$s^2 = \frac{\text{SSE}}{n - 1} = \frac{\sum_{i=1}^{n} (y_i - \bar{y})^2}{n - 1}.$$

Similarly, we considered the problem of comparing means associated with two populations possessing equal variances (see Sec. 1.9). The model for the response, y, given in Example 3.5,

$$y = \mu_A + \beta x + \epsilon,$$

contains two parameters. It would follow that the number of degrees of freedom available for estimating σ^2 is equal to $(n_1 + n_2 - 2)$. The reader may verify that the SSE obtained in fitting the model to the set of $(n_1 + n_2)$ data points is the pooled sum of squares,

$$\sum_{i=1}^{n_1} (y_{1i} - \bar{y}_1)^2 + \sum_{i=1}^{n_2} (y_{2i} - \bar{y}_2)^2,$$

and, hence, that the estimator of σ^2 is the familiar pooled estimator of the variance,

$$s^2 = \frac{\text{SSE}}{n - (k+1)} = \frac{\sum\limits_{i=1}^{n_1}(y_{1i} - \bar{y})^2 + \sum\limits_{i=1}^{n_2}(y_{2i} - \bar{y})^2}{(n_1 + n_2) - 2}.$$

Example 7.1 Estimate σ^2 for Example 6.10.

Solution: The prediction equation, Example 6.10,

$$\hat{y} = 1 + .7x,$$

can be employed to calculate the predicted value of y for each value of x as indicated in Table 7.1. The squares of each of the five deviations are given in column 5, and SSE, the total, is equal to 1.10.

Table 7.1 Calculation of SSE for Example 6.10

x	y_i	$\hat{y}_i$	$(y_i - \hat{y}_i)$	$(y_i - \hat{y}_i)^2$
-2	0	$-.4$	.4	.16
-1	0	.3	$-.3$	.09
0	1	1	0	0
1	1	1.7	$-.7$	.49
2	3	2.4	.6	.36
				1.10

$$\text{SSE} = \sum_{i=1}^{5}(y_i - \hat{y}_i)^2 = 1.10$$

Then

$$s^2 = \frac{\text{SSE}}{n-2} = \frac{1.10}{3} = .367.$$

The acquisition of SSE by calculating each predicted value of y and, consequently, the square of each deviation is exceedingly tedious. Fortunately most of this labor can be avoided since it can be proven that

$$\text{SSE} = Y'Y - \hat{\beta}'X'Y.$$

The matrices, $\hat{\beta}$ and $(X'Y)$, were calculated in fitting the linear model and

$$Y'Y = [y_1, y_2, y_3, \ldots, y_n]\begin{bmatrix} y_1 \\ y_2 \\ \vdots \\ y_n \end{bmatrix} = \sum_{i=1}^{n} y_i^2$$

is simply the sum of squares of the y-values. Thus, for the Example 7.1,

$$\mathrm{SSE} = Y'Y - \hat{\beta}'X'Y$$
$$= 11 - [1 \quad .7]\begin{bmatrix} 5 \\ 7 \end{bmatrix} = 11 - 9.9$$

or

$$\mathrm{SSE} = 1.1.$$

The reader will note that this is equal to the value for SSE obtained from Table 7.1.

7.4 A Test of an Hypothesis Concerning β_i

To be able to establish a test of an hypothesis and confidence intervals for a model parameter, say β_i, one must make an assumption regarding the probability distribution for the random error, ϵ. We will assume that this error is normally distributed for fixed values of $x_1, x_2, x_3, \ldots, x_n$. Based on this assumption, it can be shown that estimates of a particular parameter, say β_i, are normally distributed in repeated sampling with $E(\hat{\beta}_i) = \beta_i$ and, as mentioned in Sec. 7.2, $\sigma_{\hat{\beta}_i} = \sigma\sqrt{c_{ii}}$. Using this information, we may then construct a large-sample normal-deviate test with test statistic

$$z = \frac{\hat{\beta}_i - \beta_i}{\sigma\sqrt{c_{ii}}}$$

to test the hypothesis

$$H_0: \beta_i = \beta_{i0}.$$

The rejection region for a two-tailed test would be

$$|z| \geq z_{\alpha/2}.$$

As in the case of the simple normal-deviate tests studied in an elementary course, one must either know σ or possess a good estimate based upon an adequate number of degrees of freedom. (What would be adequate is a debatable point. We suggest that the estimate be based upon 30 or more degrees of freedom.) When this estimate is unavailable (which is usually the case), an estimate of σ may be calculated from the experimental data (in accordance with the procedure of Sec. 7.3) and substituted for σ in the z-statistic. The resulting quantity,

$$t = \frac{\hat{\beta}_i - \beta_i}{s\sqrt{c_{ii}}},$$

can be shown to possess a Student's t distribution with $[n - (k + 1)]$ degrees of freedom. Thus a test of an hypothesis concerning a parameter, β_i, reverts to the familiar t-test of elementary statistics.

Example 7.2 Do the data, Example 6.11, present sufficient evidence to indicate curvature in the response function?

Solution: The verbal question stated above assumes that the probabilistic model is a realistic description of the true response and implies a test of the hypothesis, $\beta_2 = 0$, in the linear model, $y = \beta_0 + \beta_1 x + \beta_2 x^2 + \epsilon$. (If $\beta_2 = 0$, the quadratic term will not appear and the expected value of y will represent a straight-line function of x.) The first step in the solution is the calculation of SSE and s^2.

$$\text{SSE} = Y'Y - \hat{\beta}'X'Y$$
$$= 11 - \begin{bmatrix} \frac{4}{7} & \frac{7}{10} & \frac{3}{14} \end{bmatrix} \begin{bmatrix} 5 \\ 7 \\ 13 \end{bmatrix} = .457.$$

Then

$$s^2 = \frac{\text{SSE}}{n-3} = \frac{.457}{2} = .229 \qquad \text{and} \qquad s = .48.$$

(Note: the model contains three parameters and hence SSE is based upon $(n - 3) = 2$ degrees of freedom.)

The estimate of β_2 obtained from Example 6.11 was $\hat{\beta}_2 = \frac{3}{14} \approx .214$. Then

$$t = \frac{\hat{\beta}_2 - 0}{s\sqrt{c_{22}}} = \frac{.214}{.48\sqrt{\frac{1}{14}}} = 1.67.$$

If we take $\alpha = .05$, the value of $t_{\alpha/2} = t_{.025}$ for 2 degrees of freedom is 4.303, and the rejection region would be

Reject if $|t| \geq 4.303$.

Since the calculated value of t is less than 4.303, we cannot reject the null hypothesis that $\beta_2 = 0$. Note that we *do not* accept $H_0 : \beta_2 = 0$. We would have to know the probability of making a type II error—that is, the probability of falsely accepting H_0 for some specified alternative value of β_2, before we would accept. Or, as indicated in Chapter 1, we could look at the width of the confidence interval for β_2 to see whether it is sufficiently small to detect a departure from zero that would be of practical significance. We will show that the confidence interval for β_2 is quite large, suggesting that the experimenter collect more data before reaching a decision.

7.5 A Confidence Interval for β_i

It can be shown that a $(1 - \alpha)$ confidence interval for β_i is

$$\hat{\beta}_i \pm t_{\alpha/2} s\sqrt{c_{ii}}.$$

In other words, the confidence interval is equal to $\hat{\beta}_i$ plus and minus t times the *estimated* standard deviation of $\hat{\beta}_i$. The confidence intervals for the mean of a normal population, and the difference between the means of two normal populations (Sec. 1.9) are two examples of this result.

Example 7.3   Calculate a 95 per cent confidence interval for the parameter β_2 of Example 7.2.

Solution: The tabulated value for $t_{.025}$, based upon 2 degrees of freedom, is 4.303.

Then the 95 per cent confidence interval for β_2 is

$$\hat{\beta}_2 \pm t_{.025} s \sqrt{c_{22}}.$$

Substituting, we get

$$.214 \pm (4.303)(.48)\sqrt{\tfrac{1}{14}} \quad \text{or} \quad .214 \pm .552.$$

Thus, for example, if we wish to estimate β_2 correct to within .15 units, it is obvious that the confidence interval is too wide and that the sample size must be increased.

7.6 Choosing the Sample Size

The determination of the appropriate sample size to acquire a fixed amount of information was studied in Chapter 3 for the simplest type of sampling— that is, simple random sampling. We will now extend this procedure to the more complicated sampling methods implied by a designed experiment. In doing so, we will be pleased to note the simplicity and the similarity of our method to that employed in determining the sample size for simple random sampling.

Two distinct differences exist between the inferential problems associated with the designed experiment and those of the simple random sampling of Chapter 1. Most of the estimation and test procedures of Chapter 1 implied experimentation to investigate a single population parameter or a single difference between a pair of population parameters. In contrast, the designed experiments of Chapters 4 and 5 suggest an interest in a number of population parameters, all of which appear in the linear model for the experiment. A second difference was created by the restriction placed on the random sampling—that is, blocking. This also has the effect of increasing the number of parameters in the linear model.

The reader will observe that *the quantity of information contained in a designed experiment will vary from parameter to parameter as indicated by the variation in the diagonal elements of* $(X'X)^{-1}$ *and hence in the variances of the parameter estimators.* For example, note the difference in the variances of the parameter estimators for Example 6.12. Furthermore, the addition of new data points will add varying amounts of information for the estimation of the model parameters, depending upon the conditions under which each data point is obtained. The points will have the effect of increasing the number of rows of the X matrix, changing some or all of the elements in $X'X$ and, consequently, $(X'X)^{-1}$. Furthermore, since the variance of the estimator of a parameter, say β_i, is

$$V(\hat{\beta}_i) = c_{ii}\sigma^2,$$

it is clear that an increase in the quantity of information pertinent to β_i will be reflected in a reduction in c_{ii}.

For our purposes, we will assume that the experimenter has decided upon the design to be employed, that he possesses an approximate value for σ^2 and, from a number of model parameters of interest, has identified one which is of primary importance. He will then specify a bound on the error of estimation for the primary parameter, and the number of data points will be selected to achieve that bound. In effect, we will select the number of data points so that the variance of the estimator of the primary parameter, and its confidence interval, will be less than or equal to some specified value. The primary parameter, of which we speak, need not be a single model parameter. It could be any linear function of the model parameters, such as the expected value of y for a given setting of the independent variables.

The data points could be added to the design one at a time, but it would be simpler to consider *replications*—that is, complete repetitions—of the experiment. This would imply the addition of whole blocks, each a replication, to the randomized block design, while a replication of a 4×4 Latin square would require running a second 4×4 Latin square. Hence, in deciding on the size of the experiment, we will be selecting the number of replications required to reduce the variance of a specified estimator to some desired value. To do this we must investigate the effect of replication on the elements of $(X'X)^{-1}$ and consequently on the variance of the estimator of the primary parameter.

To illustrate the procedure, consider the following example.

Example 7.4 Suppose that we were to replicate the five points of Example 6.11 a total of k times. (This would provide a total of $5k$ points.) Approximately how large must k be in order to estimate β_2 with an error of less than .15 with probability equal to .95?

Solution: The X matrix for this replicated experiment will contain $5k$ rows and, as before, three columns corresponding to the variables x_0, x, and x^2. If the first five rows represent the first replication, the second five represent the second replication, and so on, the X matrix will appear as shown below.

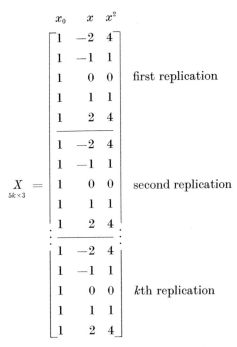

$$
\underset{5k \times 3}{X} = \begin{array}{ccc} x_0 & x & x^2 \end{array}
$$

Now imagine the multiplication of $X'X$. The reader may confirm that $(X'X)$ will be a (3×3) matrix and that each of its elements will be k times as large as the corresponding element for the single replication.

Therefore, since the $(X'X)$ matrix for the single replication (five points) was

$$
\begin{bmatrix} 5 & 0 & 10 \\ 0 & 10 & 0 \\ 10 & 0 & 34 \end{bmatrix},
$$

the $(X'X)$ matrix for k replications would be

$$
k \begin{bmatrix} 5 & 0 & 10 \\ 0 & 10 & 0 \\ 10 & 0 & 34 \end{bmatrix}.
$$

Finally, it is clear that the inverse of a constant, k, times a matrix, A, is

$$
\frac{1}{k} A^{-1},
$$

since

$$
\left(\frac{1}{k} A^{-1}\right)(kA) = I.
$$

Hence the inverse of the $(X'X)$ matrix for the k replications is

$$\frac{1}{k} \begin{bmatrix} \frac{17}{35} & 0 & -\frac{1}{7} \\ 0 & \frac{1}{10} & 0 \\ -\frac{1}{7} & 0 & \frac{1}{14} \end{bmatrix}$$

and the variance of $\hat{\beta}_2$ is $(1/14k)\sigma^2$.

We have previously stated that we wished to estimate β_2 with an error of less than .15 units. Since the confidence interval for β_2 is

$$\hat{\beta}_2 \pm ts\sqrt{c_{22}},$$

we wish the quantity $ts\sqrt{c_{22}}$ to be approximately less than .15.

Since one cannot vouch for the value of s when additional data are collected, our best guess of its value would be the estimate obtained from the first replication. The t-value selected will depend upon the number of degrees of freedom available for estimating σ^2, and this will depend upon k. As a first guess, we might choose $t = 2$. Then

$$ts\sqrt{c_{22}} \leq .15$$

or

$$2(.48)\sqrt{\frac{1}{14k}} \leq .15.$$

Solving, we obtain $k = 2.93$. Thus it would require approximately $k = 3$ replications of the five points to obtain an estimate of β_2 with a bound on the error of estimation less than or equal to .15. A more accurate estimate of σ would reduce the uncertainty associated with this statement.

The $(X'X)$ matrix for k replications of an experiment will equal k times the $(X'X)$ matrix for a single replication *if the replication does not require the addition of new parameters to the linear model.* If new block parameters are added to correspond to the replication, some, but not all, of the elements will be multiplied by k. We prefer not to delve further into this subject but leave each example to the reader, who can easily perform the multiplication, $X'X$, and analyze the result. The effect of replication on $(X'X)^{-1}$, which is our objective, may or may not be obvious.

Subsequent sections will give other examples illustrating the procedure for selecting the number of replications required to generate a specified quantity of information.

7.7 Estimation and Tests Concerning a Linear Function of the Model Parameters

A linear function of the model parameters is very often the primary object of interest to the experimenter. For example, suppose that in a particular model β_1 and β_2 represent the differences between treatments B and A, and C and A, respectively. If the experimenter were interested in the difference between the effects of treatments C and B, he would wish to make inferences concerning the *linear function*, $\beta_2 - \beta_1$. And, as previously noted, we are often interested in making inferences about the expected value of y which is also a linear function of the model parameters. In order to do this, we must obtain an estimator of the linear function and investigate its behavior in repeated sampling.

Suppose that we wish to make an inference about some linear function of the model parameters, say

$$a_0\beta_0 + a_1\beta_1 + a_2\beta_2 + \cdots + a_k\beta_k,$$

where $a_0, a_1, a_2, \ldots, a_k$ are constants (some of which may equal zero). Then it is easy to see that the same linear function of the parameter estimators,

$$l = a_0\hat{\beta}_0 + a_1\hat{\beta}_1 + a_2\hat{\beta}_2 + \cdots + a_k\hat{\beta}_k,$$

possesses an expected value (by Theorem 1.4)

$$E(l) = a_0 E(\hat{\beta}_0) + a_1 E(\hat{\beta}_1) + \cdots + a_k E(\hat{\beta}_k)$$
$$= a_0\beta_0 + a_1\beta_1 + a_2\beta_2 + \cdots + a_k\beta_k$$

and is therefore an unbiased estimator of

$$a_0\beta_0 + a_1\beta_1 + a_2\beta_2 + \cdots + a_k\beta_k.$$

Applying the same theorem, we find the variance of l,

$$V(l) = a_0^2 V(\hat{\beta}_0) + a_1^2 V(\hat{\beta}_1) + a_2^2 V(\hat{\beta}_2) + \cdots + a_k^2 V(\hat{\beta}_k)$$
$$+ 2a_0 a_1 \text{Cov}(\hat{\beta}_0, \hat{\beta}_1) + 2a_0 a_2 \text{Cov}(\hat{\beta}_0, \hat{\beta}_2) + \cdots + 2a_1 a_2 \text{Cov}(\hat{\beta}_1, \hat{\beta}_2)$$
$$+ \cdots + 2a_{k-1} a_k \text{Cov}(\hat{\beta}_{k-1}, \hat{\beta}_k),$$

where $V(\hat{\beta}_i) = c_{ii}\sigma^2$ and $\text{Cov}(\hat{\beta}_i, \hat{\beta}_j) = c_{ij}\sigma^2$. Defining the $(k+1) \times 1$ matrix,

$$a = \begin{bmatrix} a_0 \\ a_1 \\ a_2 \\ \vdots \\ a_k \end{bmatrix},$$

the reader may verify that $V(l)$ is equal to

$$V(l) = [a'(X'X)^{-1}a]\sigma^2.$$

Finally, when we note that $\hat{\beta}_0, \hat{\beta}_1, \hat{\beta}_2, \ldots, \hat{\beta}_k$ will be normally distributed in repeated sampling (Sec. 7.4), it is clear that l is a linear function of normally distributed random variables and hence, by Theorem 1.3, will itself be normally distributed in repeated sampling.

Knowing that l is normally distributed with mean and variance,

$$E(l) = \beta_0 + \beta_1 x_1 + \beta_2 x_2 + \cdots + \beta_k x_k$$

and $V(l) = [a'(X'X)^{-1}a]\sigma^2$, we conclude that

$$z = \frac{l - E(l)}{\sqrt{V(l)}} = \frac{l - E(l)}{\sigma\sqrt{a'(X'X)^{-1}a}}$$

is a standard normal deviate that could be employed to test an hypothesis,

$$H_0: E(l) = E_0(l),$$

when $E_0(l)$ is some specified value. Likewise, a large-sample $(1 - \alpha)$ confidence interval for $E(l)$ would be

$$l \pm z_{\alpha/2}\sigma\sqrt{a'(X'X)^{-1}a}.$$

Furthermore, as we might suspect, if one substitutes s for σ, the quantity

$$t = \frac{l - E(l)}{s\sqrt{a'(X'X)^{-1}a}}$$

possesses a Student's t distribution in repeated sampling with $[n - (k + 1)]$ degrees of freedom and hence provides a test statistic to test the hypothesis

$$H_0: E(l) = E_0(l).$$

For a two-tailed test and a given α, the null hypothesis would be rejected if $|t| \geq t_{\alpha/2}$.

The corresponding $(1 - \alpha)$ confidence interval for $E(l)$ is

$$l \pm t_{\alpha/2}s\sqrt{a'(X'X)^{-1}a},$$

where the tabulated value of t, $t_{\alpha/2}$, is based upon $[n - (k + 1)]$ degrees of freedom.

We will illustrate the use of this test and confidence interval in Sec. 7.8.

7.8 Estimation and a Test for the Expected Value of y

As noted in Sec. 7.1, we very often are interested in estimating or testing an hypothesis concerning the expected value of y for a *given setting of the independent variables*. As such, the independent variables will be constant. The expected value of y will be a linear function of $\beta_0, \beta_1, \beta_2, \ldots, \beta_k$ and hence will represent a special case of the problem presented in Sec. 7.7.

Since the predictor of the expected value of y is

$$\hat{y} = \hat{\beta}_0 + \hat{\beta}_1 x_1 + \hat{\beta}_2 x_2 + \cdots + \hat{\beta}_k x_k,$$

it follows that $a_0 = 1$, $a_1 = x_1$, $a_2 = x_2, \ldots, a_k = x_k$, and that

$$a = \begin{bmatrix} 1 \\ x_1 \\ x_2 \\ x_3 \\ \vdots \\ x_k \end{bmatrix}.$$

We will illustrate with an example.

Example 7.5 Suppose that the 2×3 factorial experiment, Example 6.12, was replicated, thus providing two complete replicates of the original six runs. Further, suppose that the calculated prediction equation was

$$\hat{y} = 22.8 + .6x_1 + 2.6x_2 + 1.1x_2^2$$

and that SSE was calculated to be equal to 2.1. Use this information to find a 95 per cent confidence interval for the average yield of chemical when the pressure and temperature settings are 50 psi and 300°F, respectively.

Solution: Using the results of Sec. 7.6, the reader may verify that the $(X'X)^{-1}$ matrix for the two replications of the (2×3) factorial is equal' to $\frac{1}{2}$ times the $(X'X)^{-1}$ matrix for the single replication, or

$$(X'X)^{-1} = \frac{1}{2} \begin{bmatrix} \frac{1}{2} & 0 & 0 & -\frac{1}{2} \\ 0 & \frac{1}{6} & 0 & 0 \\ 0 & 0 & \frac{1}{4} & 0 \\ -\frac{1}{2} & 0 & 0 & \frac{3}{4} \end{bmatrix} = \begin{bmatrix} \frac{1}{4} & 0 & 0 & -\frac{1}{4} \\ 0 & \frac{1}{12} & 0 & 0 \\ 0 & 0 & \frac{1}{8} & 0 \\ -\frac{1}{4} & 0 & 0 & \frac{3}{8} \end{bmatrix}.$$

2 reps

From Example 6.12, where the pressure and temperature equal 50 psi and 300°F, $x_1 = -1$ and $x_2 = 1$. Then

$$\hat{y} = \hat{\beta}_0 + \hat{\beta}_1 x_1 + \hat{\beta}_2 x_2 + \hat{\beta}_3 x_2^2$$

and

$$a = \begin{bmatrix} x_0 \\ x_1 \\ x_2 \\ x_2^2 \end{bmatrix} = \begin{bmatrix} 1 \\ -1 \\ 1 \\ 1 \end{bmatrix}.$$

The quantity $a'(X'X)^{-1}a$ that appears in $V(l)$ is

$$a'(X'X)^{-1}a = \begin{bmatrix} 1 & -1 & 1 & 1 \end{bmatrix} \begin{bmatrix} \frac{1}{4} & 0 & 0 & -\frac{1}{4} \\ 0 & \frac{1}{12} & 0 & 0 \\ 0 & 0 & \frac{1}{8} & 0 \\ -\frac{1}{4} & 0 & 0 & \frac{3}{8} \end{bmatrix} \begin{bmatrix} 1 \\ -1 \\ 1 \\ 1 \end{bmatrix}$$

$$= \frac{1}{3}.$$

The estimator of σ^2, based on 8 degrees of freedom, is

$$s^2 = \frac{\text{SSE}}{n - (k + 1)} = \frac{1}{12 - 4} = \frac{2.1}{8} = .263$$

and $s = .512$.

Finally, we require the value of $\hat{y}$ when $x_1 = -1$ and $x_2 = 1$. It was given that

$$\hat{y} = 22.8 + .6x_1 + 2.6x_2 + 1.1x_2^2.$$

Substituting $x_1 = -1$ and $x_2 = 1$, we obtain $\hat{y} = 25.9$.

Then the 95 per cent confidence interval for the expected value of y for $x_1 = -1$ and $x_2 = 1$ is

$$\hat{y} \pm t_{\alpha/2}s\sqrt{a'(X'X)^{-1}a}$$

or

$$25.9 \pm (2.306)(.512)\sqrt{\tfrac{1}{3}} \qquad \text{or} \qquad 25.9 \pm .68.$$

7.9 Predicting a Particular Value of y

Suppose that instead of the *expected* yield of chemical for a given pressure-temperature combination, as discussed in Example 7.5, we wish to predict the actual yield of chemical for a particular day. In other words, we wish to predict a particular value of y for some run to be made in the future.

Note that y is a random variable, not a parameter, and predicting its value therefore presents a departure from the stated objective of making inferences concerning population parameters. Yet, if the distribution of a random variable, y, is known and a single value of y is selected at random from the population, what would you predict for the observed value? We contend that one would select a value of y near the *center* of the distribution, in particular, the expected value of y. Thus, we would employ $\hat{y}$ as a predictor of a particular value of y as well as of $E(y)$.

The error of predicting a particular value of y, using $\hat{y}$ as the predictor, will be the difference between the observed value of $\hat{y}$ and the predicted:

$$\text{Error} = y - \hat{y}.$$

Let us now investigate the properties of this error in repeated sampling.

First note that both y and $\hat{y}$ are random variables and that the error is a linear function of y and $\hat{y}$. Then, applying Theorem 1.3, we conclude that the error is normally distributed because it is a linear function of normally distributed random variables.

Applying Theorem 1.4, which gives the formulas for the expected value and variance of a linear function of random variables, we obtain

$$E(\text{error}) = E(y - \hat{y}) = E(y) - E(\hat{y}),$$

and since $E(\hat{y}) = E(y)$,

$$E(\text{error}) = 0.$$

Likewise,
$$V(\text{error}) = V(y - \hat{y}) = V(y) + V(\hat{y}) - 2\,\text{Cov}\,(y, \hat{y}).$$
Since we assume that the predicted value of y was not employed in the calculation of $\hat{y}$ and that, in fact, it was randomly selected and hence is independent of $\hat{y}$, it follows that the covariance of y and $\hat{y}$ is equal to zero. Then
$$\begin{aligned} V(\text{error}) &= V(y) + V(\hat{y}) \\ &= \sigma^2 + [a'(X'X)^{-1}a]\sigma^2 \\ &= \sigma^2[1 + a'(X'X)^{-1}a]. \end{aligned}$$

We have now shown that the error of predicting a particular value of y is normally distributed with mean and variance equal to zero and $\sigma^2[1 + a'(X'X)^{-1}a]$, respectively. It follows that
$$z = \frac{\text{error}}{\sigma\sqrt{1 + a'(X'X)^{-1}a}} = \frac{y - \hat{y}}{\sigma\sqrt{1 + a'(X'X)^{-1}a}}$$
follows a standard normal distribution. Furthermore, substituting s for σ, it can be shown that
$$t = \frac{y - \hat{y}}{s\sqrt{1 + a'(X'X)^{-1}a}}$$
follows a Student's t distribution with $[n - (k + 1)]$ degrees of freedom. We will use this result to place a bound on the error of prediction and, in doing so, will construct a prediction interval for the random variable, y. The procedure employed will be similar to that used to construct all of the confidence intervals presented in the preceding chapters.

We commence by placing a $(1 - \alpha)$ probability statement on t:
$$P[-t_{\alpha/2} < t < t_{\alpha/2}] = (1 - \alpha).$$
Substituting for t,
$$P\left[-t_{\alpha/2} < \frac{y - \hat{y}}{s\sqrt{1 + a'(X'X)^{-1}a}} < t_{\alpha/2}\right] = 1 - \alpha.$$

In other words, in repeated sampling, the inequality within the brackets will hold with probability equal to $(1 - \alpha)$. Furthermore, the inequality will continue to hold with the same probability if each term is multiplied by the same factor or if the same quantity is added to each term of the inequality. Hence multiply each term by $s\sqrt{1 + a'(X'X)^{-1}a}$ and then add $\hat{y}$ to each. The result,
$$P[\hat{y} - t_{\alpha/2}s\sqrt{1 + a'(X'X)^{-1}a} < y < \hat{y} + t_{\alpha/2}s\sqrt{1 + a'(X'X)^{-1}a}]$$
$$= 1 - \alpha$$
places an interval about y that will hold with probability $1 - \alpha$. The result is a $(1 - \alpha)$ prediction interval for y,
$$\hat{y} \pm t_{\alpha/2}s\sqrt{1 + a'(X'X)^{-1}a}.$$
Or, thinking in terms of a bound on the error of predicting y, we would expect

the error to be less in absolute value than

$$t_{\alpha/2}s\sqrt{1 + a'(X'X)^{-1}a}$$

with probability equal to $(1 - \alpha)$. We will illustrate with an example.

Example 7.6 Predict the yield of chemical for a single day, using the results of Example 7.5, and place a bound on the error of prediction. Assume that the pressure and temperature will be set at 50 psi and 300°F, respectively.

Solution: The predicted value of y will be the same as that obtained for $E(y)$ in Example 7.5, or $\hat{y} = 25.9$. Borrowing from the results of Example 7.5, the error of prediction will be less than

$$t_{.025}s\sqrt{1 + a'(X'X)^{-1}a} = (2.306)(.512)\sqrt{1 + \tfrac{1}{3}}$$
$$= 1.36$$

with probability equal to .95.

7.10 Some Examples

Example 7.7 *The analysis of a replicated* 2×2 *factorial experiment* A 2×2 factorial experiment was conducted to determine the effect of oil viscosity and temperature on the cylinder wear of a diesel engine. The four factorial combinations of the factorial experiment were assigned in random order for running on each of two engines (which would be regarded as blocks). The resulting randomized block design produced the data shown in the table. Fit the linear model and draw appropriate conclusions from the analysis.

Engine (block)	Oil viscosity Actual	Coded x_1	Temperatures Actual	Coded x_2	Wear
1	5	-1	10	-1	3
	5	-1	20	1	5
	10	1	10	-1	7
	10	1	20	1	4
2	5	-1	10	-1	5
	5	-1	20	1	8
	10	1	10	-1	9
	10	1	20	1	5

Solution: In order to simplify the $(X'X)$ matrix, we will code as in Example 6.12. Thus

$$x_1 = \frac{\text{viscosity} - 7.5}{2.5},$$

$$x_2 = \frac{\text{temperature} - 15}{5}.$$

The linear model appropriate for the experiment is

$$y = \beta_0 + \underbrace{\beta_1 x_1 + \beta_2 x_2 + \beta_3 x_1 x_2}_{\text{Treatment effects}} + \underbrace{\beta_4 x_3}_{\substack{\text{Block} \\ \text{difference}}} + \epsilon.$$

As noted in Chapter 4, we could let β_0 be the mean response when $(x_1 = 0, x_2 = 0)$ in *block* 1 and let $x_3 = 0$ if in block 1 and $x_3 = 1$ if in block 2. Then β_4 would be the difference in the mean response between blocks 2 and 1.

However, since the design contains *only two blocks*, a simpler method of coding is available. That is, we will let $x_3 = -1$ in block 1 and $x_3 = 1$ in block 2. *Then the slope β_4 will represent only one-half the difference between blocks 2 and 1.* (Remember, the slope is the average change in y for a one-unit change in x_3. Since $x_3 = -1$ for block 1 and $x_3 = 1$ for block 2, the difference between the blocks represents a two-unit change in x_3 and hence the average difference between blocks equals $2\beta_4$.)

The Y and X matrices are

$$Y = \begin{bmatrix} 3 \\ 5 \\ 7 \\ 4 \\ 5 \\ 8 \\ 9 \\ 5 \end{bmatrix}, \quad X = \begin{bmatrix} 1 & -1 & -1 & 1 & -1 \\ 1 & -1 & 1 & -1 & -1 \\ 1 & 1 & -1 & -1 & -1 \\ 1 & 1 & 1 & 1 & -1 \\ 1 & -1 & -1 & 1 & 1 \\ 1 & -1 & 1 & -1 & 1 \\ 1 & 1 & -1 & -1 & 1 \\ 1 & 1 & 1 & 1 & 1 \end{bmatrix}.$$

The $X'Y$, $(X'X)$, and $(X'X)^{-1}$ are

$$X'Y = \begin{bmatrix} 46 \\ 4 \\ -2 \\ -12 \\ 8 \end{bmatrix}, \quad X'X = \begin{bmatrix} 8 & 0 & 0 & 0 & 0 \\ 0 & 8 & 0 & 0 & 0 \\ 0 & 0 & 8 & 0 & 0 \\ 0 & 0 & 0 & 8 & 0 \\ 0 & 0 & 0 & 0 & 8 \end{bmatrix},$$

$$(X'X)^{-1} = \begin{bmatrix} \frac{1}{8} & 0 & 0 & 0 & 0 \\ 0 & \frac{1}{8} & 0 & 0 & 0 \\ 0 & 0 & \frac{1}{8} & 0 & 0 \\ 0 & 0 & 0 & \frac{1}{8} & 0 \\ 0 & 0 & 0 & 0 & \frac{1}{8} \end{bmatrix},$$

and

$$\hat{\beta} = (X'X)^{-1}X'Y = \begin{bmatrix} \frac{1}{8} & 0 & 0 & 0 & 0 \\ 0 & \frac{1}{8} & 0 & 0 & 0 \\ 0 & 0 & \frac{1}{8} & 0 & 0 \\ 0 & 0 & 0 & \frac{1}{8} & 0 \\ 0 & 0 & 0 & 0 & \frac{1}{8} \end{bmatrix} \begin{bmatrix} 46 \\ 4 \\ -2 \\ -12 \\ 8 \end{bmatrix} = \begin{bmatrix} 5.75 \\ .50 \\ -.25 \\ -1.50 \\ 1.00 \end{bmatrix}.$$

Then the prediction equation is

$$\hat{y} = 5.75 + .5x_1 - .25x_2 - 1.5x_1x_2 + x_3.$$

Note that the plus-minus coding made $(X'X)$ a diagonal matrix and, consequently, the inversion of $(X'X)$ a simple operation.

Calculating,

$$\text{SSE} = Y'Y - \hat{\beta}'X'Y$$
$$= 294 - 293 = 1,$$

$$s^2 = \frac{\text{SSE}}{n - (k + 1)} = \frac{1}{3},$$

$$s = .557.$$

In order to interpret the results of the experiment we might test an hypothesis concerning the parameters of the linear model or we could obtain a confidence interval for each. Since each parameter estimator possesses the same variance, $c_{ii}\sigma^2 = \frac{1}{8}\sigma^2$, the confidence interval will be

$$\hat{\beta}_i \pm t_{\alpha/2}s\sqrt{\tfrac{1}{8}},$$

where t is based upon 3 degrees of freedom.

Substituting, we get

$$\hat{\beta}_i \pm (3.182)(.577)\sqrt{\tfrac{1}{8}}$$

or

$$\hat{\beta}_i \pm .649.$$

Or, viewed from the standpoint of a statistical test of an hypothesis that $\beta_i = 0$, the test statistic will be

$$t = \frac{\hat{\beta}_i}{s\sqrt{\tfrac{1}{8}}} = \frac{\hat{\beta}_i}{(.577)\sqrt{\tfrac{1}{8}}} = \frac{\hat{\beta}_i}{.204}.$$

The null hypothesis will be rejected if $|t| \geq 3.182$ for $\alpha = .05$.

Do viscosity and temperature affect the wear of a diesel engine? To answer this, we would commence by conducting a test concerning the interaction term, β_3. Thus

$$t = \frac{\hat{\beta}_3}{.204} = \frac{-1.5}{.204} = -7.35.$$

Since t falls in the rejection region, it is quite apparent that evidence is present to indicate a viscosity-temperature interaction; therefore both of these variables appear to affect the wear of the diesel engine. Corresponding tests on β_1 and β_2 would not present sufficient evidence to indicate that they differ from zero, but this is of little consequence when interaction is present. Additional data would provide more accurate estimates of the parameters of the response surface, β_1, β_2, and β_3.

Do the data present sufficient evidence to indicate a difference in mean response between engines (blocks)? The reader may verify that the t-statistic calculated to test the hypothesis that $\beta_4 = 0$ (if $\beta_4 = 0$, then $2\beta_4$, the actual difference between blocks, will equal zero) falls in the rejection region. Hence, the data provide sufficient evidence to indicate a difference in the wear between the two engines.

A study of the prediction equation,

$$\hat{y} = 5.75 + .5x - .25x_2 - 1.5x_1x_2 + x_3,$$

will suggest the combination of viscosity and temperature in the experimental region that will imply minimum engine wear. In this connection, it should be noted that the prediction equation gives an approximation to the true response surface over the region of experimentation and may provide a very poor fit to the surface elsewhere. The actual minimum average wear may occur outside of the experimental region. Further experimentation will tend to locate this point with greater precision.

Example 7.8 *The analysis of a randomized block design* An experiment was conducted to compare the effect of four different chemicals, A, B, C, and D, in producing water resistance in textiles. A strip of material, randomly selected from a bolt, was cut into four pieces and the pieces were randomly assigned to receive one of the four chemicals, A, B, C, or D. This process was replicated three times, thus producing a randomized block design. The design, with moisture-resistance measurements, is shown below (low readings indicate low moisture penetration). Analyze the results of the experiment.

Blocks (bolt samples)

1	2	3
C 9.9	D 13.4	B 12.7
A 10.1	B 12.9	D 12.9
B 11.4	A 12.2	C 11.4
D 12.1	C 12.3	A 11.9

Solution: The data with averages and totals are summarized in the accompanying table.

Treatment	A	B	C	D	Totals	Averages†
1	10.1	11.4	9.9	12.1	43.5	10.875
Blocks 2	12.2	12.9	12.3	13.4	50.8	12.700
3	11.9	12.7	11.4	12.9	48.9	12.225
Totals	34.2	37.0	33.6	38.4	143.2	
Averages†	11.400	12.333	11.200	12.800		

†Averages were rounded to the nearest thousandth.

The model for the randomized block design with three blocks and four treatments is

$$y = \beta_0 + \beta_1 x_1 + \beta_2 x_2 + \beta_3 x_3 + \beta_4 x_4 + \beta_5 x_5 + \epsilon$$

as defined in Sec. 4.3. Then β_0 is defined as the mean response for treatment A in block 1; β_1 and β_2 are the mean differences between blocks 2 and 1 and 3 and 1, respectively; β_3, β_4, and β_5 are the mean differences between treatments B and A, C and A, and D and A, respectively. The dummy variables, x_1, x_2, x_3, x_4, and x_5, are assigned values of 1 or 0, as discussed in Sec. 4.3.

The Y, X, $X'X$, and $X'Y$ matrices are

$$Y = \begin{bmatrix} 10.1 \\ 12.2 \\ 11.9 \\ 11.4 \\ 12.9 \\ 12.7 \\ 9.9 \\ 12.3 \\ 11.4 \\ 12.1 \\ 13.4 \\ 12.9 \end{bmatrix}, \quad X = \begin{bmatrix} 1 & 0 & 0 & 0 & 0 & 0 \\ 1 & 1 & 0 & 0 & 0 & 0 \\ 1 & 0 & 1 & 0 & 0 & 0 \\ 1 & 0 & 0 & 1 & 0 & 0 \\ 1 & 1 & 0 & 1 & 0 & 0 \\ 1 & 0 & 1 & 1 & 0 & 0 \\ 1 & 0 & 0 & 0 & 1 & 0 \\ 1 & 1 & 0 & 0 & 1 & 0 \\ 1 & 0 & 1 & 0 & 1 & 0 \\ 1 & 0 & 0 & 0 & 0 & 1 \\ 1 & 1 & 0 & 0 & 0 & 1 \\ 1 & 0 & 1 & 0 & 0 & 1 \end{bmatrix},$$

$$X'X = \begin{bmatrix} 12 & 4 & 4 & 3 & 3 & 3 \\ 4 & 4 & 0 & 1 & 1 & 1 \\ 4 & 0 & 4 & 1 & 1 & 1 \\ 3 & 1 & 1 & 3 & 0 & 0 \\ 3 & 1 & 1 & 0 & 3 & 0 \\ 3 & 1 & 1 & 0 & 0 & 3 \end{bmatrix}, \quad X'Y = \begin{bmatrix} 143.2 \\ 50.8 \\ 48.9 \\ 37.0 \\ 33.6 \\ 38.4 \end{bmatrix}.$$

(Note that the $(X'X)$ and $X'Y$ matrices for the randomized block design follow a definite pattern and can be acquired without matrix multiplication.) The next step, the inversion of $X'X$, is not unreasonably difficult but it is certainly tedious for the beginner. We will give the inverse (which the reader may verify),

$$(X'X)^{-1} = \begin{bmatrix} \frac{1}{2} & -\frac{1}{4} & -\frac{1}{4} & -\frac{1}{3} & -\frac{1}{3} & -\frac{1}{3} \\ -\frac{1}{4} & \frac{1}{2} & \frac{1}{4} & 0 & 0 & 0 \\ -\frac{1}{4} & \frac{1}{4} & \frac{1}{2} & 0 & 0 & 0 \\ -\frac{1}{3} & 0 & 0 & \frac{2}{3} & \frac{1}{3} & \frac{1}{3} \\ -\frac{1}{3} & 0 & 0 & \frac{1}{3} & \frac{2}{3} & \frac{1}{3} \\ -\frac{1}{3} & 0 & 0 & \frac{1}{3} & \frac{1}{3} & \frac{2}{3} \end{bmatrix},$$

and then will suggest a short-cut that will circumvent the inversion process. (The $(X'X)^{-1}$ matrix possesses a very specific pattern for an experimental design. Knowledge of the $(X'X)^{-1}$ pattern for a design is another way to reduce the labor in analyzing a designed experiment.)

It will be recalled that we needed $(X'X)^{-1}$ for two reasons: to solve the least-squares equations and to provide the c_{ii} and c_{ij} needed to obtain the variances and covariances of the estimators. *We will now acquire both the least-squares solution and the necessary elements of $(X'X)^{-1}$ without inverting the matrix.*

As noted in Chapter 6, the least-squares equations were

$$(X'X)\hat{\beta} = X'Y.$$

(Solving, we obtained $\hat{\beta} = (X'X)^{-1}X'Y$.) Hence $(X'X)$ is the coefficient matrix of the least-squares equations and $X'Y$ is the matrix of constants on the right-hand side of the equality signs. Then the least-squares equations are

$$12\hat{\beta}_0 + 4\hat{\beta}_1 + 4\hat{\beta}_2 + 3\hat{\beta}_3 + 3\hat{\beta}_4 + 3\hat{\beta}_5 = 143.2$$
$$4\hat{\beta}_0 + 4\hat{\beta}_1 \qquad + \hat{\beta}_3 + \hat{\beta}_4 + \hat{\beta}_5 = 50.8$$
$$4\hat{\beta}_0 \qquad + 4\hat{\beta}_2 + \hat{\beta}_3 + \hat{\beta}_4 + \hat{\beta}_5 = 48.9$$
$$3\hat{\beta}_0 + \hat{\beta}_1 + \hat{\beta}_2 + 3\hat{\beta}_3 \qquad = 37.0$$
$$3\hat{\beta}_0 + \hat{\beta}_1 + \hat{\beta}_2 \qquad + 3\hat{\beta}_4 \qquad = 33.6$$
$$3\hat{\beta}_0 + \hat{\beta}_1 + \hat{\beta}_2 \qquad + 3\hat{\beta}_5 = 38.4$$

To solve these equations we will guess the values of $\hat{\beta}_1$, $\hat{\beta}_2$, $\hat{\beta}_3$, $\hat{\beta}_4$, and $\hat{\beta}_5$ and then solve for the one remaining estimate, $\hat{\beta}_0$. The guessed values can be tested by substitution in the least-squares equations.

Recalling that $\hat{\beta}_1$ is the difference in the mean response between blocks 2 and 1, we would suspect that $\hat{\beta}_1$ is equal to the difference in the averages of the four observations in blocks 2 and 1, or

$$\hat{\beta}_1 = \bar{B}_2 - \bar{B}_1$$
$$= 12.700 - 10.875$$
$$= 1.825,$$

where $\bar{B}_1$ is the average of the observations in block 1. Likewise, β_2, the difference in the average response between blocks 3 and 1, would be estimated as

$$\hat{\beta}_2 = \bar{B}_3 - \bar{B}_1$$
$$= 12.225 - 10.875$$
$$= 1.350.$$

Similarly, since β_3, β_4, and β_5 are the differences between treatments B and A, C and A, and D and A, respectively, we would guess that

$$\hat{\beta}_3 = \bar{T}_B - \bar{T}_A = .933,$$
$$\hat{\beta}_4 = \bar{T}_C - \bar{T}_A = -.200,$$
$$\hat{\beta}_5 = \bar{T}_D - \bar{T}_A = 1.400,$$

where $\bar{T}_A$, $\bar{T}_B$, $\bar{T}_C$, and $\bar{T}_D$ are the four treatment averages.

Having guessed all of the least-squares estimates except one, we may now choose any one of the least-squares equations and solve for $\hat{\beta}_0$. We will use the last equation:

$$3\hat{\beta}_0 + \hat{\beta}_1 + \hat{\beta}_2 + 3\hat{\beta}_5 = 38.4.$$

Substituting,

$$3\hat{\beta}_0 + 1.825 + 1.350 + 4.200 = 38.4.$$

Solving,

$$\hat{\beta}_0 = 10.341667.$$

The lengthy description of the preceding procedure is not indicative of the length of time required to obtain the least-squares solution. The calculations can be made very rapidly as soon as the block and treatment averages have been obtained. *One note of caution: the estimates of β_1, β_2, β_3, β_4, and β_5 should be calculated correct to at least six significant figures so as to obtain an accurate value for $\hat{\beta}_0$. Slight rounding errors in these estimates can cause large errors in the calculation of SSE.*

With experience, the reader will find it easy to guess the least-squares estimates for many experimental designs. Estimates of the parameters of a Latin square design easily can be obtained using the same method that we have employed for the randomized block design. Likewise, some (but not all) of the estimates of the parameters of a factorial-type experiment may be guessed. Note that guessed values of the solution should be checked to make certain that they satisfy the least-squares equations.

Once the estimates have been acquired, the solution proceeds as usual.

That is, we construct the $\hat{\beta}$ matrix,

$$\hat{\beta} = \begin{bmatrix} 10.341667 \\ 1.825000 \\ 1.350000 \\ .933333 \\ -.200000 \\ 1.400000 \end{bmatrix}.$$

Then

$$\text{SSE} = Y'Y - \hat{\beta}'X'Y$$
$$= 1721.76 - 1721.2250$$
$$= .535$$

and

$$s^2 = \frac{\text{SSE}}{n - (k + 1)} = \frac{.535}{6} = .0892,$$

$$s = .299.$$

Although we do not possess the c_{ii} (since $(X'X)$ was not inverted), they easily can be obtained using our knowledge of elementary statistics. We note that each of the estimates, $\hat{\beta}_1$, $\hat{\beta}_2$, $\hat{\beta}_3$, $\hat{\beta}_4$, and $\hat{\beta}_5$, was obtained by taking the difference between a pair of independent sample means. Referring to Chapter 1, we recall that

$$\sigma_{(\bar{y}_1 - \bar{y}_2)} = \sigma\sqrt{\frac{1}{n_1} + \frac{1}{n_2}}.$$

Since $\hat{\beta}_1$ and $\hat{\beta}_2$ represent the difference between two sample averages each containing four measurements, it is clear that

$$\sigma_{\hat{\beta}_1} = \sigma\sqrt{c_{11}} = \sigma\sqrt{\frac{1}{n_1} + \frac{1}{n_2}}$$

and that

$$c_{11} = c_{22} = \frac{1}{n_1} + \frac{1}{n_2},$$

where

$$n_1 = n_2 = 4.$$

Therefore,

$$c_{11} = c_{22} = \frac{1}{4} + \frac{1}{4} = .5.$$

Likewise, $\hat{\beta}_3$, $\hat{\beta}_4$, and $\hat{\beta}_5$ represent the differences between independent sample averages each containing $n_1 = n_2 = 3$ observations. Then

$$c_{33} = c_{44} = c_{55} = \frac{1}{n_1} + \frac{1}{n_2} = \frac{1}{3} + \frac{1}{3} = \frac{2}{3}.$$

Then a 95 per cent confidence interval for the block differences, β_1 and β_2, will be $\hat{\beta}_i \pm t_{.025}s\sqrt{.5}$, $i = 1, 2$, where $t_{\alpha/2} = 2.447$ is based upon 6 degrees of freedom. These confidence intervals are

$$\beta_1: \quad 1.825 \pm .517,$$
$$\beta_2: \quad 1.350 \pm .517.$$

Similarly, the 95 per cent confidence intervals for the treatment differences, β_3, β_4, and β_5, are $\hat{\beta}_i(i = 3, 4 \text{ or } 5) \pm t_{.025}s\sqrt{\frac{2}{3}}$ or

$$\beta_3: \quad .933 \pm .597,$$
$$\beta_4: \quad -.200 \pm .597,$$
$$\beta_5: \quad 1.400 \pm .597.$$

Do the data present sufficient evidence to indicate a difference in moisture resistance for the four chemicals? Although we will consider a more general statistical test to answer this question when the analysis of variance is discussed in Chapter 8, it is quite apparent from the confidence intervals that a difference does exist. Chemicals C and A appear to give the least penetration, and both differ significantly from chemicals B and D.

The 95 per cent confidence intervals for the individual treatment means,

$$\left. \begin{array}{c} \bar{T}_i \pm t_{.025}\dfrac{s}{\sqrt{3}} \\[2ex] \text{or} \quad \bar{T}_i \pm (2.447)\dfrac{.299}{\sqrt{3}} \end{array} \right\} \quad i = \text{A, B, C, and D,}$$

are given below:

$$\text{A:} \quad 11.400 \pm .422,$$
$$\text{B:} \quad 12.333 \pm .422,$$
$$\text{C:} \quad 11.200 \pm .422,$$
$$\text{D:} \quad 12.800 \pm .422.$$

Note that one does not look at the data and then decide on the comparisons to be made between treatments, because the expected value of the difference between the largest and smallest treatment responses will be larger than for a pair of treatments selected at random. In order to validate probability statements, treatment comparisons of interest should be chosen independently of the data. Conveniently, the confidence intervals will be the same for the comparison of any pair of treatments.

Example 7.9 *A* 3 × 5 *factorial experiment* Refer to Exercise 25, Chapter

5, for a comparison of the growth rates of three types of bacteria where growth is measured at five equally spaced points in time. The data for the experiment are given in the accompanying table.

Bacteria type	Time				
	1	*2*	*3*	*4*	*5*
A	5.2	5.9	7.7	7.9	9.4
B	8.2	9.0	9.1	10.5	10.5
C	10.0	10.3	12.1	12.7	13.6

Do the data present sufficient evidence to indicate a difference in the growth rates for the three types of bacteria?

Solution: The model for the experiment is

$$y = \beta_0 + \beta_1 x_1 + \beta_2 x_2 + \beta_3 x_3 + \beta_4 x_1 x_3 + \beta_5 x_2 x_3 + \epsilon$$

where

$x_1 = 1$ if point is associated with bacteria type B,

$x_1 = 0$ if not;

$x_2 = 1$ if point is associated with bacteria type C,

$x_2 = 0$ if not;

$x_3 =$ time (coded $x_3 =$ time $- 3$),

$\beta_0 =$ mean growth for bacteria type A at zero time ($x_3 = 0$) (that is, the y-intercept for the growth line for type A),

$\beta_1 =$ difference between the mean growth for types B and A at zero time ($x_3 = 0$) (that is, difference between B and A y-intercepts),

$\beta_2 =$ difference in the mean growth between types C and A at zero time ($x_3 = 0$) (that is, difference between the C and A y-intercepts),

$\beta_3 =$ mean rate of growth per unit time for bacteria type A (slope of growth line for type A),

$\beta_4 =$ difference between the mean rate of growth for types B and A (this is a slope-bacteria type interaction term),

$\beta_5 =$ difference between the mean rate of growth for types C and A (like β_4, this is a slope-bacteria type interaction term).

Since we are interested in the difference between the mean rates of growth, we will wish to make inferences concerning β_4 and β_5.

The $Y, X, (X'X), (X'Y)$, and $(X'X)^{-1}$ matrices are as shown below:

$$
Y = \begin{bmatrix} 5.2 \\ 5.9 \\ 7.7 \\ 7.9 \\ 9.4 \\ 8.2 \\ 9.0 \\ 9.1 \\ 10.5 \\ 10.5 \\ 10.0 \\ 10.3 \\ 12.1 \\ 12.7 \\ 13.6 \end{bmatrix}, \quad X = \begin{bmatrix} 1 & 0 & 0 & -2 & 0 & 0 \\ 1 & 0 & 0 & -1 & 0 & 0 \\ 1 & 0 & 0 & 0 & 0 & 0 \\ 1 & 0 & 0 & 1 & 0 & 0 \\ 1 & 0 & 0 & 2 & 0 & 0 \\ 1 & 1 & 0 & -2 & -2 & 0 \\ 1 & 1 & 0 & -1 & -1 & 0 \\ 1 & 1 & 0 & 0 & 0 & 0 \\ 1 & 1 & 0 & 1 & 1 & 0 \\ 1 & 1 & 0 & 2 & 2 & 0 \\ 1 & 0 & 1 & -2 & 0 & -2 \\ 1 & 0 & 1 & -1 & 0 & -1 \\ 1 & 0 & 1 & 0 & 0 & 0 \\ 1 & 0 & 1 & 1 & 0 & 1 \\ 1 & 0 & 1 & 2 & 0 & 2 \end{bmatrix},
$$

$$
X'X = \begin{bmatrix} 15 & 5 & 5 & 0 & 0 & 0 \\ 5 & 5 & 0 & 0 & 0 & 0 \\ 5 & 0 & 5 & 0 & 0 & 0 \\ 0 & 0 & 0 & 30 & 10 & 10 \\ 0 & 0 & 0 & 10 & 10 & 0 \\ 0 & 0 & 0 & 10 & 0 & 10 \end{bmatrix}, \quad X'Y = \begin{bmatrix} 142.1 \\ 47.3 \\ 58.7 \\ 26.1 \\ 6.1 \\ 9.6 \end{bmatrix},
$$

$$
(X'X)^{-1} = \begin{bmatrix} \frac{1}{5} & -\frac{1}{5} & -\frac{1}{5} & 0 & 0 & 0 \\ -\frac{1}{5} & \frac{2}{5} & \frac{1}{5} & 0 & 0 & 0 \\ -\frac{1}{5} & \frac{1}{5} & \frac{2}{5} & 0 & 0 & 0 \\ 0 & 0 & 0 & \frac{1}{10} & -\frac{1}{10} & -\frac{1}{10} \\ 0 & 0 & 0 & -\frac{1}{10} & \frac{1}{5} & \frac{1}{10} \\ 0 & 0 & 0 & -\frac{1}{10} & \frac{1}{10} & \frac{1}{5} \end{bmatrix}.
$$

Then,

$$
\hat{\beta} = (X'X)^{-1}X'Y = \begin{bmatrix} \frac{1}{5} & -\frac{1}{5} & -\frac{1}{5} & 0 & 0 & 0 \\ -\frac{1}{5} & \frac{2}{5} & \frac{1}{5} & 0 & 0 & 0 \\ -\frac{1}{5} & \frac{1}{5} & \frac{2}{5} & 0 & 0 & 0 \\ 0 & 0 & 0 & \frac{1}{10} & -\frac{1}{10} & -\frac{1}{10} \\ 0 & 0 & 0 & -\frac{1}{10} & \frac{1}{5} & \frac{1}{10} \\ 0 & 0 & 0 & -\frac{1}{10} & \frac{1}{10} & \frac{1}{5} \end{bmatrix} \begin{bmatrix} 142.1 \\ 47.3 \\ 58.7 \\ 26.1 \\ 6.1 \\ 9.6 \end{bmatrix} = \begin{bmatrix} 7.22 \\ 2.24 \\ 4.52 \\ 1.04 \\ -.43 \\ -.08 \end{bmatrix}
$$

and
$$\hat{y} = 7.22 + 2.24x_1 + 4.52x_2 + 1.04x_3 - .43x_1x_3 - .08x_2x_3,$$
$$\text{SSE} = Y'Y - \hat{\beta}'X'Y = 1422.21 - 1420.8910$$
$$= 1.2190,$$
and
$$s^2 = \frac{\text{SSE}}{n - (k + 1)} = \frac{1.2190}{(15 - 6)} = .1354,$$
$$s = .368.$$

From the $(X'X)^{-1}$ matrix we obtain $c_{44} = c_{55} = \frac{1}{5}$. Then the test statistics to test the hypotheses
$$H_0: \beta_4 = 0 \quad \text{and} \quad H_0: \beta_5 = 0$$
are, respectively,
$$t = \frac{\hat{\beta}_4}{s\sqrt{\frac{1}{5}}} \quad \text{and} \quad t = \frac{\hat{\beta}_5}{s\sqrt{\frac{1}{5}}}.$$

For $\alpha = .05$, the tabulated t-value based upon 9 degrees of freedom is $t_{.025} = 2.262$, and the rejection region for both tests would be
$$|t| \geq 2.262.$$
Substituting into the two test statistics, we obtain
$$t = \frac{\hat{\beta}_4}{s\sqrt{\frac{1}{5}}} = \frac{-.43}{(.368)(.472)} = -2.48$$
and
$$t = \frac{\hat{\beta}_5}{s\sqrt{\frac{1}{5}}} = \frac{-.08}{(.368)(.472)} = -.46.$$

Hence we would reject the hypothesis that $\beta_4 = 0$, but there is not sufficient evidence to indicate that β_5 differs from zero. In other words, the data present sufficient evidence to indicate a difference in the rates of growth for bacteria types B and A but not between C and A. A 95 per cent confidence interval for the estimate of the difference in the rate of growth would be
$$\hat{\beta}_i \pm t_{.025}s\sqrt{\frac{1}{5}}, \quad i = 4, 5,$$
or
$$\hat{\beta}_i \pm .393.$$

The width of the confidence interval provides an indication of the quantity of information in the experiment that may be focused on the differing growth rates.

7.11 Summary and Comments

The preceding chapter has presented the methodology necessary for making inferences concerning any of the model parameters $\beta_0, \beta_1, \beta_2, \beta_3,$ $\ldots, \beta_k$ or any linear function of these parameters. The prediction equation,

$\hat{y}$, an important linear function of the parameter estimators, was employed to predict both the expected value and a particular value of y. Although these procedures provide the experimenter with powerful tools, the difficult problem of forming a practical interpretation of the results remains.

Consider an experimental situation where the simple model

$$\hat{y} = \beta_0 + \beta_1 x_1 + \beta_2 x_2 + \beta_3 x_3 + \epsilon$$

is employed. What can one conclude if a test of the hypothesis $\beta_1 = 0$ is rejected? If the experiment were designed and the change in y actually occurred when x_1 was changed, we would likely infer that x_1 is a causative variable in the process. However, if the data are collected in an uncontrolled situation, say production or economic data, the conclusion is less clearly defined. Rejection of the hypothesis simply indicates evidence that β_1 differs from zero. An interpretation of this result is that x_1 contributes information for the prediction of y when the model specified above is used. There is no implication that x_1 caused y to change. Indeed, x_1 could be highly correlated with some variable that does not even appear in the model and which is one of the causative variables in the process.

Consider the four treatments of the randomized block design, Example 7.8. Should one test the three hypotheses, $\beta_3 = 0$, $\beta_4 = 0$, and $\beta_5 = 0$ with individual t-tests to decide whether a real difference exists between the chemicals? Let us suppose that there is no difference in the moisture resistance for the four chemicals. Then the probability of falsely rejecting H_0 for *each* of the three tests will be $\alpha = .05$ if one tests at a 5 per cent level of significance. However, the chance of falsely rejecting *at least one of the three hypotheses* in three tests will be greater than the probability of falsely rejecting exactly one in one test. Indeed, if these tests were independent of one another, this probability would equal $1 - P(\text{accepting on all three tests}) = 1 - (.95)^3 = .14$. Or, if one were to conduct ten *independent* t-tests, each at the $\alpha = .05$ level of significance, the probability of falsely rejecting in *at least one test* would be $[1 - (.95)^{10}] = .401$. Hence, while the probability of falsely rejecting on an individual test may be $\alpha = .05$, the probability of falsely rejecting on repeated tests will be much larger.

It should be quite clear that one does not conduct statistically independent t-tests in practice. Each t-statistic will employ the same estimate of σ, s, which if underestimated may cause all of the test statistics to fall in the rejection region. The discussion above simply notes that the increase in the probability of falsely rejecting at least one of the null hypotheses in repeated tests increases if the tests are statistically independent. We would expect the same to occur if the tests were dependent. It does not negate the value of the individual t-tests but indicates that conclusions drawn should be evaluated with proper caution. Certainly if one were to reject all or most of the β's associated with treatment differences in a randomized block design, he would expect a real difference to exist between treatments. Nevertheless, it would be desirable to test a multiparameter hypothesis that all treatment β's equal zero (implying that no difference exists between treatments) and to do so at a fixed level of α.

A multiparameter statistical test of the hypothesis that no difference exists between treatments (or between the levels of some factor) is of limited value. As the number of parameters involved in the hypothesis increases, the power of the test—that is, its ability to detect departures from the null hypothesis—diminishes. In this sense the test behaves like a beam of light from a fixed power source. The more concentrated the beam, the greater the intensity at a fixed point. As the beam is expanded to cover a broader area, the intensity per square inch diminishes. As a consequence the multiparameter test may fail to detect treatment differences (owing to lack of power) that may be revealed by the individual t-tests.

The value of the multiparameter test is that if the test statistic falls in the rejection region, the experimenter can feel fairly certain that a difference does exist between treatments; thus he eliminates the higher risk of incorrectly drawing this conclusion based upon multiple t-tests. However, once a difference is apparent, he will then wish to consider either a ranking of the treatment yields or single-degree-of-freedom tests (or confidence intervals) for comparisons of special interest. If the multiparameter test statistic does not fall in the rejection region, we will still wish to look at the single-degree-of-freedom t-tests for comparisons of interest because of the greater power of these tests in contrast to the multiparameter test. In other words, one usually reverts to the single-degree-of-freedom t-tests (or confidence intervals) discussed in this chapter even if a test of a multi-parameter hypothesis is conducted.

Multiparameter tests of hypotheses concerning the model parameters will be discussed in Chapter 8 along with a measure of goodness of fit of the linear model. Additional comments on the practical implications of the t-tests (discussed in this chapter), the multiparameter tests, and other aspects of the interpretation of the experimental results will be presented in succeeding chapters.

Although desk calculation of designed experiments is not terribly laborious, modern data analysis is most often performed by electronic computers. Computer programs have been written for the calculations described in this text.

Exercises

1. Calculate SSE for Example 6.11, Chapter 6:
   (a) Directly by constructing a table similar to Table 7.1.
   (b) Using the formula SSE $= Y'Y - \hat{\beta}'X'Y$.
   (c) Calculate s^2.
   (d) How many degrees of freedom are associated with s^2?

2. Calculate SSE for Example 6.12, Chapter 6:
   (a) Directly by constructing a table similar to Table 7.1.
   (b) Using the formula SSE $= Y'Y - \hat{\beta}'X'Y$.
   (c) Calculate s^2.
   (d) How many degrees of freedom are associated with s^2?

3. Calculate SSE and s^2 for the data of Exercise 2, Chapter 6. How many degrees of freedom are associated with s^2?

4. Do the data, Exercise 2, Chapter 6, present sufficient evidence to indicate that the slope β_1 differs from zero? (Test the null hypothesis, $\beta_1 = 0$ using $\alpha = .05$.)

5. Find a 95 per cent confidence interval for the slope β_1, Exercise 4.

6. Do the data, Exercise 5, Chapter 6, present sufficient evidence to indicate a lack of linearity in the relation between y and x? (Test the hypothesis that the quadratic coefficient, β_2, equals zero using $\alpha = .10$.)

7. Find a 90 per cent confidence interval for β_2, Exercise 6.

8. Refer to Exercise 7, Chapter 6. Do the data present sufficient evidence to indicate that x_3 contributes information for the prediction of y? (Test the hypothesis $\beta_3 = 0$, using $\alpha = .05$.)

9. Refer to Exercise 4. Approximately how many complete replications of the five points would be required to estimate β_1 correct to within .4 units with probability equal to .95?

10. Refer to Exercise 8. How many complete replications of this experiment would be required to estimate β_3 correct to within .5 with probability equal to .95?

11. Refer to Exercise 4. Find a 95 per cent confidence interval for the expected value of y, given $x = 1$.

12. Refer to Exercise 4. Find a 95 per cent prediction interval for y, given $x = 1$.

13. Refer to Exercise 8. Find a 95 per cent confidence interval for the expected value of y, given $x_1 = 1$, $x_2 = -3$, $x_3 = -1$.

14. Refer to Exercise 8. Find a 95 per cent prediction interval for y given $x_1 = 1$, $x_2 = -3$, and $x_3 = -1$.

15. Refer to Exercise 14, Chapter 6. Do the data present sufficient evidence to indicate that T_1 contributes information for the prediction of y? P? C? T_2? (Test hypotheses, respectively, that $\beta_1 = 0$, $\beta_2 = 0$, $\beta_3 = 0$, and $\beta_4 = 0$, using an $\alpha = .05$.)

16. Refer to Exercise 14, Chapter 6. Find a 95 per cent confidence interval for β_1, the coefficient of the coded temperature variable, x_1.

17. Refer to Exercise 14, Chapter 6. Approximately how many complete replications of the 2^4 factorial would be required to estimate β_1 correct within 1.0, with probability equal to .95?

18. Refer to Exercise 14, Chapter 6. Find a 90 per cent confidence interval for the expected value of y, given $T_1 = 50$, $P = 20$, $C = 1$, and $T_2 = 200$.

19. Refer to Exercise 14, Chapter 6. Find a 90 per cent prediction interval for y, given $T_1 = 50$, $P = 20$, $C = 1$, and $T_2 = 200$.

20. Refer to Exercise 14, Chapter 6. Suppose that we question the experimenter's claim that no interactions, particularly two-way interactions, exist between T_1, P, C, and T_2. Refit a linear model that includes all of the terms of the linear model given in Exercise 14, Chapter 6, and also include all two-way interaction terms. Conduct individual t-tests to determine whether sufficient evidence exists to indicate the presence of particular two-way interactions. Use $\alpha = .05$. State your conclusions.

21. Refer to Exercise 20. If the six t-tests for interactions were statistically independent (they are not independent but would be approximately independent in this experiment if s^2 were based on a large number of degrees of freedom) and if none of the interactions were actually present, what is the probability of falsely rejecting at least one of the null hypotheses and concluding that one or more of the interactions actually exist?

22. Refer to Exercise 22, Chapter 6. Find a 95 per cent prediction interval for y, given $x_1 = 3.2$ and $x_2 = .26$.

23. Refer to Exercise 23, Chapter 6. Do the data present sufficient evidence to indicate a difference in the rates of growth for the two types of bacteria?

24. Refer to Exercise 23, Chapter 6. Obtain a 95 per cent confidence interval for the difference in the two rates of growth.

25. Refer to Exercise 23, Chapter 6. Find a 90 per cent confidence interval for the expected growth for bacteria type B at time $x_2 = 1$.

26. Refer to Exercise 23, Chapter 6. Find a 90 per cent prediction interval for the growth y of bacteria type B at time $x_2 = 1$.

27. Refer to Exercise 23, Chapter 6. Approximately how many replications

of the experiment would be required if one wished to reduce the half-width of the 90 per cent confidence interval for $E(y)$, given bacteria B and $x_2 = 1$, to approximately .2?

28. Refer to Exercise 24, Chapter 6.
   (a) Do the data present sufficient evidence to indicate that time interacts with either developer strength or temperature? Test hypotheses concerning each of the two appropriate parameters, using an $\alpha = .05$.
   (b) Is the linear effect due to time statistically significant? Test using $\alpha = .05$.

29. Refer to Exercise 24, Chapter 6. Find a 95 per cent confidence interval for each of the seven parameters of the 2^3 factorial model (excluding β_0). (Note that these intervals are of equal width for a 2^k factorial experiment.)

30. Refer to Exercise 24, Chapter 6. Approximately how many replications (blocks) of the 2^3 factorial experiment would be required to estimate the coefficient of x_1 correct to within .2 units, with probability equal to .95?

31. Refer to Exercise 24, Chapter 6. Place 95 per cent confidence intervals about the two parameters representing block differences. Do these intervals suggest a real difference between blocks?

32. *A simple analysis of covariance.* The absorption (or uptake) of a chemical in an organism of a rat for two different diets, A and B, was known to be affected by the weight (or size) of the rat. A completely randomized design utilizing four rats for each treatment was employed in the experiment, and the initial weight of each rat was recorded so that a comparison of diets could be made after adjusting for treatments. The initial weight is called a *covariate*, and the resulting comparison of treatments, adjusted for the covariate, is called an *analysis of covariance*. The data for the experiment is given below:

x_1: weight	12	10	13	16	15	11	14	13
Diet	A	A	A	A	B	B	B	B
Response	14.1	12.5	14.1	17.3	14.8	10.0	15.1	13.4

   (a) Write the linear model for the experiment.
   (b) Fit the linear model to the data.
   (c) Estimate the difference in mean response between the two diets using a 95 per cent confidence interval.

33. Refer to Exercise 32. Do the data present sufficient evidence to indicate that the covariate, rat's weight, affects the response? (Test the hypothesis that $\beta_1 = 0$.)

34. Refer to Exercise 32. If the covariate had been ignored in this experi-

ment, would the data present sufficient evidence to indicate a difference between the mean response for treatments? Analyze ignoring the covariate.

35. Refer to Exercise 32. Approximately how many observations per diet would be required to estimate the difference between mean response for diets correct to within .3?

36. Refer to Exercise 32. Find a 90 per cent confidence interval for the expected value of the uptake for rats weighing 12 ounces on diet B.

37. Refer to Exercise 32. Find a 90 per cent prediction interval for the uptake of a 12-ounce rat on diet B.

38. The rates of reaction for three different chemicals were compared by recording the response (reaction) for each chemical at five points in time. If the response for each chemical were linear over the experimental time period, a comparison of rates of reaction would be equivalent to a comparison of the slopes of the three lines. The data for the experiment is given below:

Time

Chemical	−2	−1	0	1	2
A	5.7	6.0	7.6	7.8	9.2
B	8.0	9.0	9.1	10.2	10.4
C	10.0	10.8	12.2	12.6	13.9

(a) Graph the response lines for the three treatments.
(b) Write the linear model for the experiment.
(c) How many degrees of freedom will be available for estimating σ^2?
(d) Fit the linear model to the data.
(e) Calculate SSE.
(f) Obtain 95 per cent confidence intervals for each of the two parameters associated with the difference between treatment-time slopes. *test whether there are diff between the slopes*
(g) Do the results of (f) suggest a difference between the rates of reaction for the three chemicals?

39. An experiment was conducted to relate yield in a chemical plant to temperature and pressure. A 2 × 3 factorial design was used for the experiment. The experiment was replicated to provide additional degrees of freedom for estimating σ^2.

Pressure Levels		Temperature Levels	
Actual	Coded x_1	Actual	Coded x_2
50	−1	100	−1
80	1	200	0
		300	1

$$x_1 = \frac{\text{Pressure} - 65}{15} \qquad x_2 = \frac{\text{Temperature} - 200}{100}$$

Response Y	Pressure		Temperature	
	Actual	Coded	Actual	Coded
21	50	-1	100	-1
23	50	-1	200	0
26	50	-1	300	1
22	80	1	100	-1
23	80	1	200	0
28	80	1	300	1
22	50	-1	100	-1
23	50	-1	200	0
27	50	-1	300	1
21	80	1	100	-1
23	80	1	200	0
27	80	1	300	1

(a) Fit the model $y = \beta_0 + \beta_1 x_1 + \beta_2 x_2 + \beta_3 x_1 x_2 + \beta_4 x_2^2 + \epsilon$.

(b) Calculate SSE.

(c) Do the data present sufficient evidence to indicate an interaction between x_1 and x_2?

(d) Is the quadratic temperature term important in predicting yield?

40. Refer to Exercise 39. Find a 90 per cent confidence interval for the expected yield for $P = 80$, $T = 300$.

41. Refer to Exercise 39. Find a 90 per cent prediction interval for the yield for $P = 80$, $T = 300$.

42. Refer to Exercise 39. Approximately how many replications would be required to estimate the linear pressure coefficient correct to within .2 with probability equal to .90?

43. Suppose that a linear model $y = \beta_0 + \beta_1 x_1 + \beta_2 x_2 + \beta_3 x_3 + \beta_4 x_4 + \epsilon$ is fitted to a set of data, resulting in

$$X'X = \begin{bmatrix} 9 & 3 & 3 & 3 & 3 \\ 3 & 3 & 0 & 1 & 1 \\ 3 & 0 & 3 & 1 & 1 \\ 3 & 1 & 1 & 3 & 0 \\ 3 & 1 & 1 & 0 & 3 \end{bmatrix} \quad \text{and} \quad X'X^{-1} = \begin{bmatrix} \frac{5}{9} & -\frac{1}{3} & -\frac{1}{3} & -\frac{1}{3} & -\frac{1}{3} \\ -\frac{1}{3} & \frac{2}{3} & \frac{1}{3} & 0 & 0 \\ -\frac{1}{3} & \frac{1}{3} & \frac{2}{3} & 0 & 0 \\ -\frac{1}{3} & 0 & 0 & \frac{2}{3} & \frac{1}{3} \\ -\frac{1}{3} & 0 & 0 & \frac{1}{3} & \frac{2}{3} \end{bmatrix}.$$

(a) Derive the variance of $(\hat{\beta}_1 - \hat{\beta}_2)$.

(b) If $s^2 = 1$ and $\hat{\beta}_1 - \hat{\beta}_2 = 1$, find a 95 per cent confidence interval for $\beta_1 - \beta_2$.

References

Graybill, F. A., *An Introduction to Linear Statistical Models*, Vol. I. New York: McGraw-Hill Book Company, 1961.

Kempthorne, O., *The Design and Analysis of Experiments*. New York: John Wiley & Sons, Inc., 1952.

Rao, C. R., *Linear Statistical Inference and Its Applications*. John Wiley & Sons, Inc., 1965.

8

Multiparameter Hypotheses: The Analysis of Variance

8.1 Introduction

Exploratory studies of the effect of a number of variables on a response are often conducted using two-level complete (or fractional) factorial experiments (see Example 7.7). The resulting analysis leads either to the estimation (using confidence intervals) of the individual parameters associated with main effects and interactions or individual t-tests of hypotheses that the parameters equal zero. If one rejects the hypothesis that a particular parameter, such as a two-way interaction between two variables (say temperature and pressure), is equal to zero, we conclude that temperature and pressure jointly affect the response and that the effect is dependent upon the pressure-temperature combination. This then poses an interesting question. What is the probability that our inference-making procedures would lead us to this conclusion when, actually, the null hypothesis is true and the parameter associated with the two-way interaction actually equals zero?

Flip a coin and the probability of observing a head on a single toss is equal to $\frac{1}{2}$. Flip the coin five times and the probability of observing *at least* one head is equal to $\{1 - p[\text{observing no heads}]\}$ or $1 - (\frac{1}{2})^5 = \frac{31}{32}$. This experiment essentially outlines the problem arising from repeated single-degree-of-freedom t-tests as discussed in Sec. 7.11. The experimenter may protect himself against the risk of making a type I error on a single t-test with selected probability, α. However, if he conducts k independent t-tests, each with the same α, the probability of falsely rejecting *at least* one of the k null hypotheses, assuming all are true, is $\{1 - p[\text{not rejecting on all } k \text{ tests}]\}$ or $\{1 - (1 - \alpha)^k\}$. If $\alpha = .05$ and $k = 2$, the probability of falsely rejecting at least one of two null hypotheses (assuming both true) is $\{1 - (.95)^2\}$ or .0975, a value almost double the selected $\alpha = .05$. For a larger k the risk of falsely rejecting at least one of the null hypotheses increases and becomes uncomfortably large. And, although we recognize that the t-tests for hypotheses associated with the general linear model are not truly independent, the dependence varying greatly in many cases from one pair of tests to another, the argument presented above indicates the increased risk of making a type I error when conducting repeated t-tests and implies that one should exercise caution in drawing practical conclusions under these circumstances.

The probability of "falsely rejecting" and concluding that some model parameter differs from zero is further increased by many experimenters because they utilize the data to decide the comparisons to be made rather than choosing these beforehand. For example, in deciding whether a difference exists between treatments in a randomized block experiment, it is tempting to compare the treatments possessing the largest and smallest sample means. If five treatments are involved in the experiment, all of which possess identically the same population means, the sample means for a given experiment will order themselves at random. Certainly the expected value of the difference between the largest and smallest sample means will be larger than for any pair selected at random.

The probabilities associated with the type I and type II errors, α and β, for the t-test of Sec. 7.4 are evaluated over a set of comparisons that, in a sense, have been selected at random. That is, we decide, before looking at the data, which treatments are to be compared, and the resulting individual t-tests will be conducted with measures of risk, α and β, that have been indicated in earlier discussion. If one insists on comparing the largest and smallest sample means, the evidence of a real difference between their respective population means will be obtained by consulting the probability distribution of the difference between the largest and smallest sample means (for a set of p treatments) and this will vary with the number of treatments, p. The t-tests described in Sec. 7.4 would be invalid for this comparison.

The reader should keep in mind that the difficulties discussed in the preceding paragraphs do not in any way invalidate the Student's t-test. We simply note certain limitations to the use of such tests and indicate that conclusions should be reached with some degree of caution.

A number of statistical techniques are available for protecting against making a type I error in repeated t-tests. The first of these is based upon a procedure known as the *analysis of variance* and essentially involves a simultaneous test of an hypothesis concerning a set of the parameters of the linear model. The other techniques are primarily ranking procedures which proceed in complexity from a simple comparison of the largest and smallest treatment means in a set to methods for ranking the treatment means in subgroups. All of these multiparameter procedures possess advantages and disadvantages from a practical point of view and vary in their appeal depending upon the inclination of the experimenter. The major disadvantage is that as one attempts to broaden the statements made concerning a set of parameters, the discriminatory power of the procedure diminishes. Thus, as in elementary statistical tests, as one attempts to reduce the probability α for a fixed sample size, the probability of failing to reject when the null hypothesis is false, β, increases. As noted in Sec. 7.11, we would likely solve this problem by first employing a multiparameter procedure to see whether evidence exists to imply a difference between treatments; then we would use the more powerful and discriminating single-degree-of-freedom t-tests (or confidence intervals) presented in Sec. 7.4 and 7.5.

This chapter is primarily concerned with the use of the analysis of variance in multiparameter tests. A brief discussion of ranking procedures will be presented in Sec. 8.10.

8.2 A Test Statistic to Test H_0: $\beta_{g+1} = \beta_{g+2} = \cdots = \beta_k = 0$

In seeking an intuitively appealing test statistic to test an hypothesis concerning a set of parameters of the linear model, we are led to a consideration of the sum of squares of deviations, SSE. Suppose, for example, we were to fit a model,

Model 1: $y = \beta_0 + \beta_1 x_1 + \beta_2 x_2 + \cdots + \beta_g x_g + \epsilon$, where $g < k$,

to the data and then calculate the sum of squares of deviations of the observed values of y, $\underline{SSE}_1$. Having done this, we then fit the linear model,

Model 2: $y = \beta_0 + \beta_1 x_1 + \beta_2 x_2 + \cdots + \beta_g x_g + \beta_{g+1} x_{g+1} + \cdots + \beta_k x_k + \epsilon$,

which contains all of the terms of Model 1 plus the terms involving x_{g+1}, $x_{g+2}, \ldots, x_k$. Then we calculate the sum of squares of deviations for this model, $\underline{SSE}_2$. Finally, let us suppose that $x_{g+1}, x_{g+2}, \ldots, x_k$ really contribute a substantial quantity of information for the prediction of y not contained in the variables, $x_1, x_2, \ldots, x_g$ (that is, at least one of the parameters β_{g+1}, $\beta_{g+2}, \ldots, \beta_{g+k}$ actually differs from zero); what would be the relation between SSE_1 and SSE_2? Intuitively, we see that if $x_{g+1}, x_{g+2}, \ldots, x_k$ are important information-contributing variables, Model 2, which contains all of the variables of Model 1 plus the additions $x_{g+1}, x_{g+2}, \ldots, x_k$, should predict with a *smaller* error of prediction than Model 1 and hence SSE_2 should be less than SSE_1. The greater the difference, $(\mathrm{SSE}_1 - \mathrm{SSE}_2)$, the stronger the evidence to support the alternative hypothesis that $x_{g+1}, x_{g+2}, \ldots, x_k$ contribute information for the prediction of y and to reject the null hypothesis,

$$H_0\colon \beta_{g+1} = \beta_{g+2} = \cdots = \beta_k = 0.$$

Models 1 and 2 are known as the *reduced* and *complete* models, respectively, for a test of the null hypothesis indicated above. The drop in the sum of squares of deviations, $(\mathrm{SSE}_1 - \mathrm{SSE}_2)$, is called the *sum of squares associated with the variables* $x_{g+1}, x_{g+2}, \ldots, x_k$, *adjusted for the variables* $x_1, x_2, x_3, \ldots, x_g$.

How large is "large"? Although the drop in SSE measures the weight of evidence favoring a rejection of the hypothesis,

$$H_0\colon \beta_{g+1} = \beta_{g+2} = \cdots = \beta_k = 0,$$

we must now use it to acquire a suitable test statistic whose probability distribution, when the null hypothesis is true, is known. Then we will know whether the observed drop is large enough (and sufficiently improbable) to support the rejection of H_0.

To acquire this test statistic, let us *assume* that the null hypothesis is true and then examine the quantities that we have calculated. Particularly, note that

$$\mathrm{SSE}_1 = \mathrm{SSE}_2 + (\mathrm{SSE}_1 - \mathrm{SSE}_2).$$

In other words, we have partitioned SSE_1 into two parts, SSE_2 and the drop $(\mathrm{SSE}_1 - \mathrm{SSE}_2)$, as indicated in Fig. 8.1. Further, assuming H_0 true $(\beta_{g+1} = \beta_{g+2} = \cdots = \beta_k = 0)$, it follows that

$$s_1^2 = \frac{\mathrm{SSE}_1}{n - (g + 1)} \quad \leftarrow reduced\ model$$

is an unbiased estimator of σ^2, the variance of the random error ϵ. Keeping

Figure 8.1

in mind that we are primarily concerned with the drop ($SSE_1 - SSE_2$), we now wonder whether the two components of SSE_1, namely SSE_2 and ($SSE_1 - SSE_2$), might also provide unbiased estimators of σ^2 when divided by appropriate divisors. And, indeed, this can be shown to be true. Both

complete
model

$$s_2^2 = \frac{SSE_2}{n - (k + 1)} \quad \text{and} \quad s_3^2 = \frac{(SSE_1 - SSE_2)}{k - g}$$

are unbiased estimators of σ^2 and, furthermore, can be shown to be statistically independent.

Hence a good decision-maker for testing the hypothesis

$$H_0: \beta_{g+1} = \beta_{g+2} = \cdots = \beta_k = 0$$

would be the ratio

$$F = \frac{s_3^2}{s_2^2}.$$

If H_0 is true, both s_3^2 and s_2^2 will provide independent unbiased estimates of σ^2 and will be of relatively the same magnitude and F, the ratio, will assume a value near 1. (It can be proven that the expected value of F *is not* equal to 1.) On the contrary, when H_0 is false, s_2^2 will still provide an unbiased estimator of σ^2 but s_3^2, calculated from the drop ($SSE_1 - SSE_2$), will be inflated and possess an expected value equal to σ^2 plus a positive quantity involving the sums of squares of the parameters, $\beta_{g+1}, \beta_{g+2}, \ldots, \beta_k$. The larger the drop, the greater will be the amount of evidence favoring a rejection of H_0 and the more inflated s_3^2 will be in relation to s_2^2. *Then large values of the F-statistic will favor a rejection of H_0.*

The derivation of the probability distribution of the F-statistic, assuming H_0 true, is a familiar exercise encountered in an introductory course in statistical theory. While we omit the proof, it can be shown (assuming H_0 true) that

$$\chi_3^2 = \frac{[n - (g + 1)]s_1^2}{\sigma^2} = \frac{SSE_1}{\sigma^2},$$

$$\chi_2^2 = \frac{[n - (k + 1)]s_2^2}{\sigma^2} = \frac{SSE_2}{\sigma^2},$$

and

$$\chi_1^2 = \frac{(k - g)s_3^2}{\sigma^2} = \frac{SSE_1 - SSE_2}{\sigma^2}$$

possess chi-square probability distributions in repeated sampling with $[n - (g + 1)]$, $[n - (k + 1)]$, and $(k - g)$ degrees of freedom, respectively. Further, it can be shown that χ_2^2 and χ_1^2 are statistically independent. The resulting ratio,

$$F_{\nu_1, \nu_2} = \frac{s_3^2}{s_2^2} = \frac{\chi_1^2}{\chi_2^2} \frac{[n - (k + 1)]}{(k - g)},$$

possesses the well-known F distribution with $\nu_1 = (k - g)$ and $\nu_2 = [n - (k + 1)]$ degrees of freedom.

The density function for the F distribution depends upon the two parameters, $\nu_1 = (k - g)$ and $\nu_2 = [n - (k + 1)]$, which represent the degrees of freedom, associated with the numerator and denominator sums of squares of deviations, $(SSE_1 - SSE_2)$ and SSE_2, respectively. A graph of the distribution for F with $\nu_1 = 2$ and $\nu_2 = 8$ degrees of freedom is shown in Fig. 8.2. To locate the rejection region for the F-test, we seek a point, F_α, such that

$$P[F > F_\alpha] = \alpha.$$

Note that the F-test always utilizes a single-tailed rejection region.

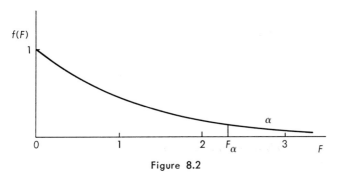

Figure 8.2

Although the formula for the density function of the F-statistic is omitted, it is sufficient to state that the area under the curve cannot simply be obtained and hence must be tabulated. The values of F_α for $\alpha = .10, .05,$ and $.01$ for specific values of ν_1 and ν_2 are presented in Tables 3, 4, and 5 respectively, of Appendix III. Thus, for $\alpha = .05$, $F_{.05}$ with $\nu_1 = 2$ and $\nu_2 = 8$ is equal to 4.46, as shown in Table 4.

8.3 An Example

Let us reconsider the randomized block design of Example 7.8 and test the hypothesis that all parameters associated with treatment differences simultaneously equal zero and hence that no difference exists between treatments. Specifically, let

$$H_0: \beta_3 = \beta_4 = \beta_5 = 0.$$

H_0: $\beta_3 = \beta_4 = \beta_5 = 0$

Since we have already fitted the complete model and acquired the necessary $SSE_2 = .535$, we need only fit the reduced model to obtain SSE_1. This model, obtained by dropping x_3, x_4, and x_5 from the complete model, is

$$\text{Model 1:} \quad y = \beta_0 + \beta_1 x_1 + \beta_2 x_2 + \epsilon,$$

where β_1 and β_2 represent the block differences as before. The Y matrix will be unchanged, and the new X matrix can be obtained from the old by deleting the columns associated with x_3, x_4, and x_5. Thus

$$Y = \begin{bmatrix} 10.1 \\ 12.2 \\ 11.9 \\ 11.4 \\ 12.9 \\ 12.7 \\ 9.9 \\ 12.3 \\ 11.4 \\ 12.1 \\ 13.4 \\ 12.9 \end{bmatrix} \quad \text{and} \quad X = \begin{bmatrix} 1 & 0 & 0 \\ 1 & 1 & 0 \\ 1 & 0 & 1 \\ 1 & 0 & 0 \\ 1 & 1 & 0 \\ 1 & 0 & 1 \\ 1 & 0 & 0 \\ 1 & 1 & 0 \\ 1 & 0 & 1 \\ 1 & 0 & 0 \\ 1 & 1 & 0 \\ 1 & 0 & 1 \end{bmatrix}.$$

A further simplification, which the reader may verify, reveals that the $(X'X)$ and $X'Y$ matrices may be obtained from the $X'X$ and $X'Y$ matrices for the complete model by deleting all rows and columns corresponding to x_3, x_4, and x_5. Thus

$$(X'X) = \begin{bmatrix} 12 & 4 & 4 \\ 4 & 4 & 0 \\ 4 & 0 & 4 \end{bmatrix} \quad \text{and} \quad X'Y = \begin{bmatrix} 143.2 \\ 50.8 \\ 48.9 \end{bmatrix}.$$

We may now find $(X'X)^{-1}$ or guess the estimates of the block differences, β_1 and β_2, as illustrated in Example 7.7. We will choose the latter procedure and guess

$$\hat{\beta}_1 = \bar{B}_2 - \bar{B}_1 = 1.825$$

and

$$\hat{\beta}_2 = \bar{B}_3 - \bar{B}_1 = 1.350,$$

which are identically the same as the estimates obtained for the complete model! Only $\hat{\beta}_0$ will change.

Substituting into the last least-squares equation to solve for $\hat{\beta}_0$, we obtain

$$4\hat{\beta}_0 + 4\hat{\beta}_2 = 48.9 \quad \text{or} \quad \hat{\beta}_0 = 10.875.$$

Then the $\hat{\beta}$ matrix for the reduced model is

$$\hat{\beta} = \begin{bmatrix} \hat{\beta}_0 \\ \hat{\beta}_1 \\ \hat{\beta}_2 \end{bmatrix} = \begin{bmatrix} 10.875 \\ 1.825 \\ 1.350 \end{bmatrix}$$

and

$$\mathrm{SSE}_1 = Y'Y - \hat{\beta}'X'Y$$
$$= 1721.76 - 1716.0250$$
$$= 5.735.$$

same as before

Substituting, we find the drop in SSE to be

$$\mathrm{SSE}_1 - \mathrm{SSE}_2 = 5.735 - .535 \quad \text{SSE from before}$$
$$= 5.200.$$

The two estimates of σ^2 are

$$s_2^2 = \frac{\mathrm{SSE}_2}{n - (k+1)} = .0891,$$
$$12 - (5+1)$$

$\beta_6 \ldots \beta_k$
$k = 5$

as indicated in Example 7.8, and

$$s_3^2 = \frac{\mathrm{SSE}_1 - \mathrm{SSE}_2}{k - g} = \frac{5.2}{3} = 1.733.$$
$$5 - 2$$

Finally, we calculate the variance ratio,

$$F = \frac{s_3^2}{s_2^2} = \frac{1.733}{.0892} = 19.4.$$

Comparing with the tabulated value (Table III.4) for $\alpha = .05$ and $\nu_1 = 3$, $\nu_2 = 6$, degrees of freedom, we observe that the calculated value, $F = 19.4$, is greater than the tabulated value of $F_{.05} = 4.76$ and hence falls in the rejection region. We therefore conclude that the data present sufficient evidence to indicate a difference between treatments. With this conclusion, we would then look at the individual comparisons of treatments as described in Example 7.8.

Similarly, we could test the hypothesis that "there is no difference between blocks" or equivalently

$$H_0: \beta_1 = \beta_2 = 0.$$

Model 1 for this hypothesis would be obtained from the complete model by eliminating x_1 and x_2, or

Model 1: $\quad y = \beta_0 + \beta_3 x_3 + \beta_4 x_4 + \beta_5 x_5 + \epsilon.$

We would then fit Model 1 to the data, calculate SSE, calculate the drop, $(\mathrm{SSE}_1 - \mathrm{SSE}_2)$, and then the F-statistic. We leave this as an exercise for the reader.

8.4 The Analysis of Variance for Orthogonal Designs

A multifactor design is said to be *orthogonal* if the estimators of the parameters associated with any one factor are uncorrelated with those of another.[†]

It can be shown that if each level of one factor appears the same number of times with the levels of a second factor, and this is true for all pairs of factors in the experiment, then the design will be orthogonal.

For example, if one factor, or qualitative variable, is "blocks," of which there are four, and the second factor is "treatments," of which there are three, then all three treatments must appear in each block in order that the design be orthogonal. If the observation associated with treatment C in block 1 is destroyed, the design becomes nonorthogonal.

Factorial experiments, by definition, are orthogonal, and the Latin square design which places all treatments in each row and column would, likewise, be orthogonal. As a matter of fact, most experimental designs encountered in introductory texts on the design of experiments are orthogonal.

Orthogonal designs possess patterns and hence readily permit the development of formulas representing the drop in the sums of squares of deviations associated with interesting sets of parameters. These formulas, which can be developed by fitting complete and reduced models, exist for all of the common orthogonal designs as well as for many that possess specific nonorthogonal patterns. They conveniently eliminate the necessity of repeated fittings of linear models in analyzing data and thus reduce the computational work involved in analyzing designed experiments. Thus, the reader may verify that the formula for the drop in SSE associated with treatments in a randomized block design containing b blocks and p treatments, called *the sum of squares for treatments* is

$$\mathrm{SST} = \frac{\sum_{i=1}^{p} T_i^2}{b} - \mathrm{CM}$$

where CM, *called the correction for the mean*, is the familiar quantity,

$$\mathrm{CM} = \frac{\left(\sum_{i=1}^{n} y_i \right)^2}{n},$$

T_i is the total of all observations receiving treatment i, and b is the number of blocks (number of observations in a treatment total).

For Example 7.8, described in Sec. 8.3,

[†]See O. Kempthorne, *The Design and Analysis of Experiments* (New York: John Wiley & Sons, Inc., 1952), p. 49.

$\left(\Sigma \, T_i\right)^2$

$$\text{SST} = \frac{\sum\limits_{i=1}^{4} T_i^2}{3} - \text{CM}$$

$$= \frac{(34.2)^2 + (37.0)^2 + (33.6)^2 + (38.4)^2}{3} - \frac{(143.2)^2}{12}$$

$$= 1714.05 - 1708.85$$

$$= 5.2.$$

The reader may verify that this is exactly the same quantity as obtained by fitting the complete and the reduced models in Sec. 8.3.

Similarly, we may obtain the drop in SSE associated with the block parameters of a randomized block design, called *sum of squares for blocks*, using a formula similar to that employed to obtain SST, namely,

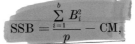

$$\text{SSB} = \frac{\sum\limits_{i=1}^{b} B_i^2}{p} - \text{CM},$$

where B_i is the total of all observations in block i, CM is the correction for the mean, and p is the number of treatments (or observations in a block total).

For Example 7.8

$$\text{SSB} = \frac{\sum\limits_{i=1}^{3} B_i^2}{4} - \text{CM},$$

$$= \frac{(43.5)^2 + (50.8)^2 + (48.9)^2}{4} - \frac{(143.2)^2}{12}$$

$$= 1716.025 - 1708.853$$

$$= 7.172$$

The estimates of σ^2 obtained from the drops in SSE associated with blocks and treatments are called *mean squares* in the parlance of the analysis of variance and designated by the symbols MSB and MST, respectively. The mean squares are calculated by dividing the sums of squares by the appropriate number of degrees of freedom, which will always equal the number of parameters, $(k - g)$, involved in the respective null hypotheses. Thus, in the randomized block design, blocks and treatments will possess $(b - 1)$ and $(p - 1)$ degrees of freedom, respectively, and

$$\text{MSB} = \frac{\text{SSB}}{b - 1} = \frac{7.172}{2} = 3.586,$$

$$\text{MST} = \frac{\text{SST}}{p - 1} = \frac{5.2}{3} = 1.733.$$

The substituted numerical values are those for Example 7.8.

The sum of squares for error for the complete model, denoted as SSE_2 in Sec. 8.3, is the sum of squares for error, SSE, that we calculated in Chapter 7. With this in mind, we will drop the subscript and designate the quantity as SSE. Similarly, we will drop the subscript on s_2^2, the estimator of σ^2 obtained from the complete model, and employ the symbol s^2 used in Chapter 7. We might note that s^2 is often called the *mean square for error* and is denoted by the symbol MSE in some texts.

A most important property of orthogonal designs is that the total sum of squares of deviations of the observations about their mean,

$$\sum_{i=1}^{n} (y_i - \bar{y})^2 = \sum_{i=1}^{n} y_i^2 - CM,$$

can be partitioned into the important sums of squares plus SSE. Hence, for the randomized block design, it can be shown that the following represents an identity:

$$\sum_{i=1}^{n} (y_i - \bar{y})^2 = SSB + SST + SSE.$$

This unique property of orthogonal designs provides a very simple computational procedure for calculating SSE. The total sum of squares of deviations and the sums of squares for blocks and treatments can easily be obtained using an electric desk calculator. Then SSE can be obtained by subtraction. Thus, for Example 7.8,

$$\begin{aligned} SSE &= \sum_{i=1}^{n} (y_i - \bar{y})^2 - SSB - SST \\ &= 12.907 - 7.172 - 5.200 \\ &= .535. \end{aligned}$$

This procedure probably produces a slight reduction in computational labor over the use of the formula

$$SSE = Y'Y - \hat{\beta}'X'Y$$

presented in Chapter 7. That the two formulas are equivalent, and essentially involve the same squaring and computational procedure, can easily be seen by comparison. However, the computation of SSE by subtraction is less prone to rounding errors because all division operations *follow* multiplication operations, thus eliminating computational errors arising from the multiplication of rounded numbers.

The computed results of the multiparameter analysis of the data are presented in an analysis of variance (ANOVA) table. The ANOVA table for a randomized block design containing p treatments in b blocks is shown in Table 8.1.

Table 8.1   ANOVA table for a randomized block design containing b blocks and p treatments

Source	d.f.	SS	MS	F
Blocks	$b - 1$	SSB	MSB	MSB$/s^2$
Treatments	$p - 1$	SST	MST	MST$/s^2$
Error	$bp - b - p + 1$	SSE	s^2	
Total	$n - 1 = bp - 1$	$\sum_{i=1}^{bp} (y_i - \bar{y})^2$		

The first column of Table 8.1 gives the source of the sum of squares of deviations, the second column, the degrees of freedom associated with each, and the respective sum of squares and mean squares appear in the third and fourth columns. The computed F-values appear in column 5. Note that the degrees of freedom for blocks, treatment, and error sum to the total number of degrees of freedom, $(n - 1) = (bp - 1)$, associated with the total sum of squares of deviations of the observations taken about their mean,

$$\sum_{i=1}^{bp} (y_i - \bar{y})^2.$$

Similarly, the sums of squares add to the total.

The ANOVA table for Example 7.8 would appear as shown in Table 8.2.

Table 8.2   ANOVA table for example 7.8

Source	d.f.	SS	MS	F
Blocks	2	7.172	3.586	40.2
Treatments	3	5.200	1.733	19.4
Error	6	.535	.0892	
Total	11	12.907 = $y'y - CM$		

The reader may verify that the tabulated value of F to test an hypothesis of "no difference between blocks" based on an $\alpha = .05$ and $\nu_1 = 2$ and $\nu_2 = 6$ degrees of freedom is $F_{.05} = 5.14$. It is clear that the computed value of F exceeds the tabulated value and hence falls in the rejection region. We therefore reject the null hypothesis and conclude that a sizable difference exists between blocks (materials) in their resistance to moisture penetration. A similar conclusion was reached concerning the difference between treatments (chemicals) earlier in Sec. 8.3. These conclusions support the analysis of the data presented in Example 7.8.

To conclude, we might note that the term *"analysis of variance"* applied to the analysis of data by partitioning the total sum of squares of deviations to obtain the drops in SSE associated with sets of parameters is quite descriptive of the procedure. Since these sums of squares are employed to obtain independent estimates of the variance, σ^2, assuming the null hypothesis to be true, the analysis is, indeed, an "analysis of variance."

8.5 Expected Mean Squares

In Sec. 8.3 we stated that the expected value of the mean square for treatments, MST, was equal to σ^2 plus a positive function of the squares of the treatment parameters when the null hypothesis is false. Likewise, it can be shown that the expected value of MSB, when H_0 is false (block differences do not equal zero), is equal to σ^2 plus a positive function of the block parameters. *Proof of these statements is not necessary for the present discussion and may be omitted without detracting from the succeeding material.* However, we will illustrate for the inquisitive reader the procedure for deriving the expected values of MST and MSB for a randomized block design containing b blocks and p treatments. The derivation is tedious, and we suggest that the reader fill in the omitted algebraic steps as he follows the proof. Expected mean squares for other designs may be derived in a similar manner.

The model for the randomized block design containing b blocks and p treatments is given in Sec. 4.3. In order not to confuse the block and treatment parameters in the model, let $\beta_1, \beta_2, \ldots, \beta_{b-1}$ represent the $(b-1)$ block differences and let $\tau_1, \tau_2, \tau_3, \ldots, \tau_{p-1}$ represent the $(p-1)$ treatment differences. In addition, we recall that

$$E(\epsilon_i) = 0, \qquad i = 1, 2, \ldots, n,$$

$$V(\epsilon_i) = \sigma^2,$$

and

$$\text{Cov}\,(\epsilon_i, \epsilon_j) = 0,$$

since the random errors are assumed to be independent.

With a few algebraic manipulations, the reader may verify that

$$\text{SST} = \frac{\sum\limits_{i=1}^{p} T_i^2}{b} - \text{CM}$$

$$= b \sum\limits_{i=1}^{p} (\bar{T}_i - \bar{y})^2,$$

where $\bar{T}_i$ is the average of the observations receiving treatment i and $\bar{y}$ is the average of all $n = bp$ observations.

Then by adding and subtracting $E(\bar{y})$ and $E(\bar{T}_i)$ within the parentheses, we obtain

$$\text{SST} = b \sum\limits_{i=1}^{p} (\bar{T}_i - \bar{y})^2$$

$$= b \sum\limits_{i=1}^{p} \{[\bar{T}_i - E(\bar{T}_i)] - [\bar{y} - E(\bar{y})] - [E(\bar{y}) - E(\bar{T}_i)]\}^2.$$

Squaring the multinomial expression within the brackets and summing, several of the terms combine, leaving

$$\text{SST} = b\left\{\sum_{i=1}^{p} [\bar{T}_i - E(\bar{T}_i)]^2 - 2\sum_{i=1}^{p} [\bar{T}_i - E(\bar{T}_i)][E(\bar{y}) - E(\bar{T}_i)]\right.$$
$$\left. - p[\bar{y} - E(\bar{y})]^2 + \sum_{i=1}^{p} [E(\bar{y}) - E(\bar{T}_i)]^2\right\}.$$

Before taking the expected value of SST, we remind the reader that if u is a random variable, then the variance of u is defined to be

$$V(u) = E\{[u - E(u)]^2\}.$$

Therefore, $E\{[\bar{T}_i - E(\bar{T}_i)]^2\} = V(\bar{T}_i)$, and so on.

Also, note that $\bar{T}_i$, the average of the observations receiving treatment i, would equal

$$\bar{T}_i = \beta_0 + \frac{\sum_{j=1}^{b-1} \beta_j}{b} + \tau_{i-1} + \bar{\epsilon}_i,$$

where τ_{i-1} is the "difference between treatment i and treatment A" and $\bar{\epsilon}_i$ is the average of the b independent random errors associated with the b observations in $\bar{T}_i$. (See Sec. 4.4.) Further note that the only random quantity in $\bar{T}_i$ is $\bar{\epsilon}_i$. Since the b random errors in $\bar{\epsilon}_i$ are independent with the same mean and variance,

$$V(\bar{T}_i) = V(\bar{\epsilon}) = \frac{\sigma^2}{b}.$$

Similarly, the only random component of $\bar{y}$ is $\bar{\epsilon}$, which is the average of the $n = bp$ independent random errors associated with the $n = bp$ observed values of y. Then

$$V(\bar{y}) = V(\bar{\epsilon}) = \frac{\sigma^2}{n} = \frac{\sigma^2}{bp}.$$

Finally note that the expected value of the second term of SST is equal to zero, since

$$E\left\{-2\sum_{i=1}^{p} [\bar{T}_i - E(\bar{T}_i)][E(\bar{y}) - E(\bar{T}_i)]\right\} = -2\sum_{i=1}^{p} E[\bar{T}_i - E(\bar{T}_i)][E(\bar{y}) - E(\bar{T}_i)]$$
$$= 0$$

since $E[\bar{T}_i - E(\bar{T}_i)] = E(\bar{T}_i) - E(\bar{T}_i) = 0$.

With these facts in mind and recalling that the expected value of a sum of random variables is equal to the sum of the expected values,

$$E(\text{SST}) = b\left[\sum_{i=1}^{p} E\{[\bar{T}_i - E(\bar{T}_i)]^2\}\right.$$
$$\left. - pE\{[\bar{y} - E(\bar{y})]^2\} + E\sum_{i=1}^{p} \{[E(\bar{y}) - E(\bar{T}_i)]\}^2\right]$$
$$= b\sum_{i=1}^{p} V(\bar{T}_i) - bpV(\bar{y}) + b\sum_{i=1}^{p} [E(\bar{y}) - E(\bar{T}_i)]^2,$$

(note that the last term in SST is a constant)

$$E(\text{SST}) = b\left(p\frac{\sigma^2}{b}\right) - bp\left(\frac{\sigma^2}{bp}\right) + b\sum_{i=1}^{p}[E(\bar{y}) - E(\bar{T}_i)]^2$$

$$= (p-1)\sigma^2 + b\sum_{i=1}^{p}[E(\bar{y}) - E(\bar{T}_i)]^2.$$

Finally, since MST = SST/$(p-1)$,

$$E(\text{MST}) = \frac{1}{p-1}E(\text{SST})$$

$$= \sigma^2 + b\sum_{i=1}^{p}\frac{[E(\bar{y}) - E(\bar{T}_i)]^2}{p-1}$$

$$= \sigma^2 + \theta_\tau$$

where

$$\theta_\tau = b\sum_{i=1}^{p}\frac{[E(\bar{y}) - E(\bar{T}_i)]^2}{p-1}.$$

The reader may verify that the constant β_0 and the block parameters in $\bar{y}$ and $\bar{T}_i$ cancel in the quantity $(\bar{y} - \bar{T}_i)$, leaving only treatment parameters and the quantities $\bar{\epsilon}$ and $\bar{\epsilon}_i$. This expression simplifies:

$$E(\bar{\epsilon}) = E(\bar{\epsilon}_i) = 0.$$

Then if we define $\tau_A = \tau_0 = 0$,

$$\theta_\tau = \frac{b\sum_{i=1}^{p}\left[\frac{\sum_{i=1}^{p-1}\tau_j}{p} - \tau_{i-1}\right]^2}{p-1}.$$

Then

$$\frac{\sum_{i=1}^{p-1}\tau_i}{p}$$

is the average of the "treatment effects," and θ_τ is equal to $b/(p-1)$ times the sum of squares of deviations of the τ_i about their mean. *This sum of squares of deviations* (and hence θ_τ) could be equal to zero only if

$$\tau_1 = \tau_2 = \cdots = \tau_{p-1} = \tau_A = 0$$

and H_0 is true. If H_0 is false,

$$E(\text{MST}) = \sigma^2 + \theta_\tau,$$

where θ_τ is a function only of the treatment differences and $\theta_\tau > 0$. Thus, as explained in Sec. 8.3, when H_0 is false, $E(\text{MST}) > \sigma^2$, which, in probability, makes F assume larger values than when H_0 is true.

Owing to the similarity of the formulas for SST and SSB, it is clear that an interchange of block and treatment symbols would yield

$$E(\text{MSB}) = \sigma^2 + p\sum_{i=1}^{b}\frac{[E(\bar{y}) - E(\bar{B}_i)]^2}{b-1}$$

$$= \sigma^2 + \theta_B.$$

θ_B is equal to the product of $p/(b-1)$ and the sum of squares of deviations of the block parameters about their mean. When H_0 is true, $\theta_B = 0$ and $E(\text{MSB}) = \sigma^2$. When false, $E(\text{MSB}) = \sigma^2 + \theta_B$ where $\theta_B > 0$.

8.6 The Analysis of Variance For a Latin Square Design

The linear model for a $p \times p$ Latin square design contains $(p-1)$ parameters representing treatment differences, $(p-1)$ for row differences, and $(p-1)$ for column differences. (See Sec. 4.7.) While the primary analysis-of-variance test is a test of the hypothesis that there is "no difference between treatments," we can also test an hypothesis that the row parameters are identically equal to zero and also the hypothesis that the column parameters equal zero. Thus it is necessary to calculate the sums of squares (drops in SSE obtained by fitting complete and reduced models) for treatments, rows, and columns.

Let SST, SSR, and SSC represent the sums of squares for treatments, rows, and columns, respectively and let

T_i = total of the p observations receiving treatment i,
R_i = total of the p observations in row i,
C_i = total of the p observations in column i,

and

$$\text{CM} = \frac{\left(\sum\limits_{i=1}^{n} y_i\right)^2}{n} \qquad (\text{where } n = p^2).$$

Then it can be shown that

$$\sum_{i=1}^{n} (y_i - \bar{y})^2 = \text{SSE} + \text{SSR} + \text{SSC} + \text{SST},$$

where SSR, SSC, and SST are the sums of squares for rows, columns, and treatments, respectively, and

$$\text{SSR} = \frac{\sum\limits_{i=1}^{p} R_i^2}{p} - \text{CM},$$

$$\text{SSC} = \frac{\sum\limits_{i=1}^{p} C_i^2}{p} - \text{CM},$$

$$\text{SST} = \frac{\sum\limits_{i=1}^{p} T_i^2}{p} - \text{CM}.$$

The ANOVA table for the Latin square design is as shown in Table 8.3.

Table 8.3   ANOVA table for a $p \times p$ Latin square design

Source	d.f.	SS	MS	F
Rows	$p-1$	SSR	$\text{MSR} = \text{SSR}/(p-1)$	MSR/s^2
Columns	$p-1$	SSC	$\text{MSC} = \text{SSC}/(p-1)$	MSC/s^2
Treatments	$p-1$	SST	$\text{MST} = \text{SST}/(p-1)$	MST/s^2
Error	p^2-3p+2	SSE	s^2	
Total	p^2-1	$\sum\limits_{i=1}^{n} (y_i - \bar{y})^2$		

We will illustrate the analysis of variance for the Latin square with an example.

Example 8.1   A 4×4 Latin square design was employed to investigate the gasoline consumption at a fixed horsepower for four different gasolines, A, B, C, and D. Four engines were employed in the experiment and each gasoline was tested in each of the engines. The accompanying tabulation shows the results. Do the data present sufficient evidence to indicate a difference between treatments? Engines? Test times?

Columns (engines)

	1	2	3	4
1	D 19.5	B 16.8	A 19.8	C 19.2
2	B 18.0	A 17.9	C 17.9	D 17.7
3	A 18.1	C 21.0	D 17.5	B 17.2
4	C 20.1	D 19.2	B 17.0	A 18.5

Solution:

$$\text{CM} = \frac{\left(\sum\limits_{i=1}^{16} y_i\right)^2}{16} = \frac{87{,}261.16}{16} = 5453.8225,$$

$$\text{SSR} = \frac{\sum\limits_{i=1}^{4} R_i^2}{4} - \text{CM}$$

$$= \frac{(75.3)^2 + (71.5)^2 + (73.8)^2 + (74.8)^2}{4} - \text{CM} = 2.133,$$

$$SSC = \frac{\sum\limits_{i=1}^{4} C_i^2}{4} - CM$$

$$= \frac{(75.7)^2 + (74.9)^2 + (72.2)^2 + (72.6)^2}{4} - CM = 2.203,$$

$$SST = \frac{\sum\limits_{i=1}^{4} T_i^2}{4} - CM$$

$$= \frac{(74.3)^2 + (69.0)^2 + (78.2)^2 + (73.9)^2}{4} - CM = 10.663.$$

Total $SS = \sum\limits_{i=1}^{16} (y_i - \bar{y})^2 = \sum\limits_{i=1}^{16} y_i^2 - CM = 22.058.$

Finally,

$$Y'Y - CM$$

$$SSE = \sum\limits_{i=1}^{16} (y_i - \bar{y})^2 - SSR - SSC - SST$$

$$= 7.059.$$

The sum of squares, degrees of freedom, and mean squares for the analysis are presented in Table 8.4.

Table 8.4   ANOVA table for a 4×4 Latin square

Source	d.f.	SS	MS	F
Rows	3	2.133	.711	.60
Columns	3	2.203	.734	.62
Treatments	3	10.663	3.554	3.02
Error	6	7.059	1.177	
Total	15	22.058		

It is clear that the calculated F-values for rows and columns do not fall in the rejection region and hence there is no evidence to indicate a difference between engines or between test time periods. The tabulated critical values for F based on $\nu_1 = 3$ and $\nu_2 = 6$ degrees of freedom are $F_{.05} = 4.76$ and $F_{.10} = 3.29$. Thus the computed $F = 3.02$ for treatments is not statistically significant at either the $\alpha = .05$ or the .10 levels.

The failure of the F-statistic to indicate a difference between treatments could be caused by insufficient replication in the experiment or the fact that the differences are truly negligible. This will depend upon the magnitude of treatment difference that the experimenter considers to be of practical importance. The information pertinent to treatment differences is indicated by the half-width of the confidence interval for the difference in a pair of treatment means, $t_{a/2}s\sqrt{2/p}$ or $(2.447)(1.08)\sqrt{2/4} = 1.868$ for $\alpha = .05$.

The data would seem to suggest that little is to be gained by blocking on engines and time. If one were fairly certain that interactions between fuels, engines, and test periods were negligible and wished to employ the design to investigate the difference between engines and test time periods as well as gasolines, replication of the two-directional blocking would depend upon the magnitude of the difference in mean fuel consumption between engines and test periods that one wished to detect. If we were fairly certain that these effects were negligible for practical purposes, we would likely discontinue blocking on engines. However, since extraneous factors might enter in time, it would seem desirable to continue blocking on time with a random assignment of the fuels to the engines. The experiment would be replicated so as to reduce the confidence interval for an estimate of the difference in mean fuel consumption to some desired degree of accuracy. We will reserve this problem as an exercise for the student.

8.7 The Analysis of Variance for a *k*-way Classification

A *k*-way classification of data originates from an experiment involving *k* independent variables or "factors" which may be either quantitative or qualitative. If a response is measured for all combinations of levels of the variables exactly the same number of times, the experiment is one which produces a *k*-way classification of the data with an equal number of observations per cell. (In referring to a "*k*-way classification" in the subsequent discussion, we will imply the special type that yields an equal number of observations per cell.) Thus a *k*-way classification is a special type of orthogonal design and resembles a factorial experiment. For example, the randomized block design is a $k = 2$ way classification since it involves two variables, blocks and treatments, and the data may be displayed in a row-column table with one observation in each cell.

In contrast, the Latin square design does not produce a *k*-way classification because all treatments do not appear with a particular row and column combination. Thus if treatment A appears in row 1, column 1, we know that the position is occupied and that no other treatments could possibly appear with that row-column combination.

A *k*-factor factorial experiment, by definition, produces a *k*-way classification of the data, and it is the analysis of variance for the factorial experiment that is of primary interest to us in this section. The same analysis-of-variance formulas will apply, however, if some of the qualitative variables represent directions of blocking, as long as the data satisfy the requirement of the k-way classification.

Suppose that the factors in the experiment are denoted by the symbols $A, B, C, D, \ldots, G$ and

$$A_i = \text{sum of all responses receiving the } i\text{th level of factor } A,$$

$$(AB)_{ij} = \text{sum of all responses receiving the } i\text{th level of } A \text{ and, at the same time, the } j\text{th level of } B,$$

and, in general,

$$(ABCD\ldots)_{ijkm\ldots} = \text{sum of all responses receiving the } i\text{th level of } A, \text{ the } j\text{th level of } B, \text{ the } k\text{th level of } C, \text{ the } m\text{th level of } D, \text{ and so on.}$$

Let SSA denote the sum of squares, and hence the drop in SSE, associated with the main-effect parameters of factor A. Similarly, define the main-effect sum of squares for B, C, D, and G as SSB, SSC, SSD, and SSG, respectively. The sum of squares, and hence the drop in SSE, for parameters implying a two-way interaction between factors A and B will be denoted as SS(AB). Other two-way interaction sums of squares will be denoted in the same manner. The sum of squares associated with the parameters for three-way interaction, four-way interaction, $\ldots$, and the k-way interaction will be denoted by the symbol SS followed by the appropriate three factors, four factors, $\ldots$, or k factors, respectively, shown in parentheses.

Finally, let $n_{ABC}\ldots$ be the number of observations in an $(ABC \cdots)_{ijk}\ldots$ total. (Note that this will be the same for all combinations of levels of $A, B, C, \ldots$, because of the k-way classification.) Thus, n_A and n_{AB} will equal the number of observations in the treatment total, A_i, and the total $(AB)_{ij}$, respectively.

The formulas for the appropriate sums of squares for the analysis of variance will be given below for main effects and interactions using the symbols A, AB, ABC, and so on with the understanding that the formulas for the sums of squares for other main effects and interactions are identical and simply imply an interchange in symbols. The number of degrees of freedom attached to a particular sum of squares will equal the number of parameters contained in the linear model associated with the analysis-of-variance null hypothesis.

Main effects:

$$\mathrm{SS}A = \frac{\sum_i A_i^2}{n_A} - \mathrm{CM}.$$

Two-way interaction:

$$SS(AB) = \frac{\sum\limits_{i,j} (AB)^2_{ij}}{n_{AB}} - SSA - SSB - CM.$$

Three-way interaction:

$$SS(ABC) = \frac{\sum\limits_{i,j,k} (ABC)^2_{ijk}}{n_{ABC}} - SS(AB) - SS(AC) - SS(BC)$$
$$- SSA - SSB - SSC - CM.$$

In general, the sum of squares for the interaction of $ABCD \ldots$ is equal to

$$SS(ABCD\cdots) = \frac{\sum\limits_{i,j,k,l} (ABCD\cdots)^2_{ijkl\cdots}}{n_{ABCD\cdots}}$$
$$- \text{[the sums of squares of all possible}$$
$$\text{subcombinations of } A, B, C, D, \ldots]$$
$$- CM.$$

Example 8.2 Write the analysis of variance for a replicated $2 \times 3 \times 4$ factorial experiment.

Solution: The analysis of variance for two replications of a $2 \times 3 \times 4$ factorial experiment, when the factors are A, B, and C, is shown in Table 8.5.

Table 8.5   ANOVA for a $2 \times 3 \times 4$ factorial

Source	d.f.	SS	MS
A	1	SSA	SSA
B	2	SSB	SSB/2
C	3	SSC	SSC/3
AB	2	SS(AB)	SS(AB)/2
AC	3	SS(AC)	SS(AC)/3
BC	6	SS(BC)	SS(BC)/6
ABC	6	SS(ABC)	SS(ABC)/6
Replications	1	SSR	SSR
Error	23	SSE	SSE/23
Total	47	$\sum\limits_{i=1}^{48} (y_i - \bar{y})^2$	

This assumes that, essentially, the experiment was blocked in time, thus producing four "variables" or factors, A, B, C, and blocks. The breakdown of the sums of squares by source would include the main effects, A, B, and C, and all two-way and three-way interactions. Only the "main-effect" source is included for replications because the ($2 \times 3 \times 4$) factorial combinations of the basic experiment are assumed to be randomly assigned within each replication. *The interaction of replication with the other sources does not appear because this constitutes the sums of squares for error, SSE.*

As a matter of fact, it is interesting to note that in viewing a randomized block design as a two-way classification, the SSE obtained in the experiment is actually the block-treatment interaction. A bit of thought will reveal the rationality of this point of view, for certainly the failure of a specific treatment difference to be the same from block to block is a measure of the experimental error. At the same time we note that this is, indeed, block-treatment interaction.

In conclusion, note that the number of degrees of freedom associated with each source of variability (excluding SSE) is exactly equal to the number of parameters that would represent the source in the linear model.

Example 8.3   A study to investigate the effect of teaching machines and length of study time on student achievement utilized four teaching machines and three lengths of study time, 30, 60, and 90 hours. The objective of the study was to determine whether the effectiveness of the teaching machines varied depending upon the study time, and particularly whether the optimal teaching machine was dependent upon the length of study time. Thus we wish to determine whether there is evidence of a machine-time interaction. Twenty-four students were selected at random from the fifth grade in a particular school and two were assigned to each of the twelve machine-time combinations. Achievement test scores recorded at the end of the study period are shown in the appropriate cells of the accompanying table. Do the data present sufficient evidence to indicate a machine-time interaction?

		Teaching machine				
		A_1	A_2	A_3	A_4	Totals
	B_1, 30	61	72	54	59	476
		49	65	53	63	
Study	B_2, 60	77	84	69	96	595
time		61	72	53	83	
	B_3, 90	90	109	78	110	747
		86	100	79	95	
	Totals	424	502	386	506	1818

Solution: The experiment described above is a 3×4 factorial experiment with two observations per cell. Therefore, the sources of variation with their respective degrees of freedom will be:

Source	d.f.
Between machines, A	3
Between times, B	2
$A \times B$	6
Error	12
Total	23

Utilizing the formulas of Sec. 8.7 appropriate for a k-way classification of data,

$$\text{CM} = \frac{\left(\sum_{i=1}^{24} y_i\right)^2}{24} = \frac{(1818)^2}{24} = 137{,}713.5,$$

$$\text{SS}A = \frac{\sum_{i=1}^{4} A_i^2}{6} - \text{CM} = \frac{(424)^2 + (502)^2 + (386)^2 + (506)^2}{6} - \text{CM}$$
$$= 1755.2$$

$$\text{SS}B = \frac{\sum_{i=1}^{3} B_i^2}{8} - \text{CM} = \frac{(476)^2 + (595)^2 + (747)^2}{8} - \text{CM} = 4612.8,$$

$$\text{SS}(AB) = \frac{\sum_{i,j} (AB)_{ij}^2}{2} - \text{SS}A - \text{SS}B - \text{CM}$$
$$= \frac{(110)^2 + (138)^2 + (176)^2 + \cdots + (205)^2}{2}$$
$$- 1755.2 - 4612.8 - \text{CM}$$
$$= 337.6$$

$$\text{Total SS} = \sum_{i=1}^{24} y_i^2 - \text{CM} = 145{,}098 - \text{CM} = 7384.5.$$

Finally,

$$\text{SSE} = \text{Total (SS)} - \text{SS}A - \text{SS}B - \text{SS}(AB)$$
$$= 7384.5 - 1755.2 - 4612.8 - 337.6$$
$$= 678.9.$$

The analysis-of-variance table is given below.

Source	d.f.	SS	MS
Between machines, A	3	1755.2	585.1
Between times, B	2	4612.8	2306.4
$A \times B$	6	337.6	56.3
Error	12	678.9	56.6
Total	23	7384.5	

The test of the hypothesis that the (AB) interaction parameters simultaneously equal zero would employ the test statistic,

$$F = \frac{\text{MS}(AB)}{s^2} = \frac{56.3}{56.6} = .99$$

based upon $\nu_1 = 6$ and $\nu_2 = 12$ degrees of freedom, respectively. Since the corresponding critical value of F, for $\alpha = .05$, is $F_{.05} = 3.00$, there is no evidence to indicate that A and B interact.

To test an hypothesis of "no difference between machines" one would use the test statistic,

$$F = \frac{\text{MS}A}{s^2} = \frac{585.1}{56.6} = 10.3$$

Since the computed value of F exceeds the corresponding critical value of F based upon $\nu_1 = 3$ and $\nu_2 = 12$ degrees of freedom, $F_{.05} = 3.49$, we reject the null hypothesis and conclude that the machines differ in the average student achievement that they produce. The experimenter is now faced with the problem of selecting the "best" based upon some practical criterion.

Example 8.4 Refer to Example 8.3. Suppose that the upper and lower numbers in each cell, respectively, denote students randomly selected from each of two fifth grades, say C_1 and C_2.

(a) Find the sum of squares for grades.
(b) Give the analysis of variance.
(c) Test to see whether there is sufficient evidence to indicate a machine-time interaction.
(d) Find the confidence interval for the difference between a pair of cell means.

Solution: The addition of "classes" (replications) to the experimental situation simply adds one more direction in the k-way classification (now $k = 3$). The only modification that one might note is that the interaction of "classes" with the other sources of variability is the sum of squares for error, SSE.

Then, (a) the sum of squares for classes is

$$\text{SSR} = \frac{\sum\limits_{i=1}^{2} C_i^2}{12} - \text{CM} = \frac{(959)^2 + (859)^2}{12} - \text{CM} = 416.7.$$

(b) The analysis of variance will be:

Source	d.f.	SS	MS
Between machines, A	3	1755.2	585.1
Between times, B	2	4612.8	2306.4
$A \times B$	6	337.6	56.3
Between replicates, R	1	416.7	416.7
Error	11	262.2	23.8
Total	23	7384.5	

(c) To test the null hypothesis that the AB interaction parameters are simultaneously equal to zero, we calculate

$$F = \frac{\text{MS}(AB)}{s^2} = \frac{56.3}{23.8} = 2.37.$$

Since the computed value of F, based on $\nu_1 = 6$ and $\nu_2 = 11$ degrees of freedom, is less than the tabulated value, $F_{.05} = 3.09$, there is not sufficient evidence to indicate the presence of machine-time interaction. There is, however, an apparent difference in the mean response between the two fifth-grade classes. ($F = 416.7/23.8 = 17.5$ exceeds the tabulated $F_{.05} = 4.84$ based upon $\nu_1 = 1$ and $\nu_2 = 11$ degrees of freedom.)

(d) Since a comparison of cell means will utilize two observations per cell and

$$\sigma_{\bar{y}_1 - \bar{y}_2} = \sqrt{\frac{\sigma_1^2}{n_1} + \frac{\sigma_2^2}{n_2}},$$

then, since $\sigma_1^2 = \sigma_2^2 = \sigma^2$ and $n_1 = n_2 = 2$,

$$\sigma_{\bar{y}_1 - \bar{y}_2} = \sigma\sqrt{\frac{1}{2} + \frac{1}{2}} = \sigma.$$

The 95 per cent confidence interval, based upon $\nu = 11$ degrees of freedom, is

$$(\bar{y}_1 - \bar{y}_2) \pm t_{.025} s$$

Substituting, the interval estimate is

$$(\bar{y}_1 - \bar{y}_2) \pm (2.201)\sqrt{23.8} \qquad \text{or} \qquad (\bar{y}_1 - \bar{y}_2) \pm 10.7.$$

8.8 The Coefficient of Determination

A useful measure of the goodness of fit of the linear model can be obtained by comparing the sums of squares of deviations for the complete model,

$$(1) \quad y = \beta_0 + \beta_1 x_1 + \beta_2 x_2 + \beta_3 x_3 + \cdots + \beta_k x_k + \epsilon,$$

and the model

$$(2) \quad y = \beta_0 + \epsilon.$$

In other words, we compare the general linear model with the simplest possible model in which none of the independent variables appear. We are therefore questioning the importance of the entire set of independent variables, $x_1, x_2, x_3, \ldots, x_k$, as information contributors; this, we might note, is a special case of the general problem of investigating the importance of a set of variables (as information contributors) discussed in Sec. 8.2.

It is clear that the sum of squares of deviations for model 2 is the total sum of squares of the analysis of variance (see also Exercise 1, Chap. 6),

$$\sum_{i=1}^{n} (y_i - \bar{y})^2.$$

Then if the sum of squares of deviations for the complete model is designated as SSE, the drop in the sum of squares of deviations, from model 2 to model 1, is

$$\sum_{i=1}^{n} (y_i - \bar{y})^2 - SSE.$$

Expressed as a fraction of the total, we have the *coefficient of determination*,

$$r^2 = \frac{\sum_{i=1}^{n} (y_i - \bar{y})^2 - SSE}{\sum_{i=1}^{n} (y_i - \bar{y})^2} = 1 - \frac{SSE}{\sum_{i=1}^{n} (y_i - \bar{y})^2}.$$

Thus if $r^2 = .7$ for a particular example, it means that 70 per cent of the sum of squares of deviations of the y_i about their mean, $\bar{y}$, can be explained by the variables $x_1, x_2, \ldots, x_k$. Obviously the coefficient of determination is bounded,

$$0 \leq r^2 \leq 1.$$

An $r^2 = 1$ implies that $SSE = 0$ and the least-squares predictor passes through all of the experimental points. If $r^2 = 0$,

$$SSE = \sum_{i=1}^{n} (y_i - \bar{y})^2,$$

and no information is contributed by $x_1, x_2, x_3, \ldots, x_k$.

Example 8.5   Find the coefficient of determination for Example 7.8.

Solution: The sums of squares of deviations for the complete model and the total sums of squares were found to be equal to $SSE = .535$ (Example 7.8) and 12.907 (Sec. 8.4). Then the coefficient of determination is

$$r^2 = 1 - \frac{.535}{12.907} = .959.$$

While we are primarily concerned with the coefficient of determination, r^2, it is worth noting that the quantity r is the coefficient of multiple correlation which assumes importance in some statistical analyses. Particularly, if $k = 1$, r is the simple coefficient of linear correlation that the student encounters in most introductory courses in statistics.

8.9 A Test of Goodness of Fit of the Linear Model

The term "experimental error" applies to the error or variation in the response, y, for fixed or controlled experimental conditions. It is caused by the nonhomogeneity of the experimental material as well as error of measurement.

We have noted earlier that the random error, ϵ, for many experimental situations is a composite of the experimental error and an error due to lack of fit of the linear model. Thus it is not likely that we would manage to include all of the important variables in the linear model and, even if they were included, that we would select the exact function to model the response. If the measurements are taken so that the omitted variables assume values in a random manner, they contribute to the "experimental error." This effect cannot be separated from the true experimental error unless the omitted variables have been measured. However, given a set of independent variables and a corresponding linear model, it is possible to conduct a statistical test to determine whether sufficient evidence exists to indicate an incorrect functional relation in the linear model—or what is known as "lack of fit."

The procedure is to partition the sum of squares for "error" into two parts, one due to the experimental error and one due to "lack of fit."

A measure of the experimental error can only be obtained by fixing all of the independent variables and replicating the experiment. The attendant variability would be a measure of the experimental error. Thus the experiment must be replicated for *one or more* combinations of the independent variables.

Regard each setting of the independent variables as a treatment. For example, if the independent variables are set in two combinations, say A and B, and n_A and n_B replications, respectively, are obtained for each treatment, then it is well known that SSE is the pooled sum of squares,

$$\text{SSE} = \sum_{i=1}^{n_A} (y_{iA} - \bar{y}_A)^2 + \sum_{i=1}^{n_B} (y_{iB} - \bar{y}_B)^2.$$

The degrees of freedom associated with this sum of squares will be $(n_A + n_B - 2)$. (See Sec. 1.9.)

For replications of n_A, n_B, and n_C measurements for three treatments, it can also be shown that the sum of squares of deviations is the equal to the pooled sum of squares,

$$\text{SSE} = \sum_{i=1}^{n_A} (y_{iA} - \bar{y}_A)^2 + \sum_{i=1}^{n_B} (y_{iB} - \bar{y}_B)^2 + \sum_{i=1}^{n_C} (y_{iC} - \bar{y}_C)^2$$

with $n_A + n_B + n_C - 3$ degrees of freedom.

In general, for k distinctly different settings of the independent variables (k treatments) with n_A, n_B, ..., n_k replications per treatment, respectively, it can be shown that SSE is the pooled quantity,

$$\text{SSE} = \sum_{i=1}^{n_A} (y_{iA} - \bar{y}_A)^2 + \sum_{i=1}^{n_B} (y_{iB} - \bar{y}_B)^2 + \cdots + \sum_{i=1}^{n_k} (y_{ik} - \bar{y}_k)^2,$$

and that it is based upon $(n_A + n_B + \cdots + n_k - k)$ degrees of freedom. Thus one could partition a "sum of squares for error" possessing r degrees of freedom $(r > [n_A + n_B + \cdots + n_k - k])$ into a sum of squares for experimental error based upon $(n_A + n_B + \cdots + n_k - k)$ degrees of freedom and a sum of squares associated with "lack of fit" based upon $[r - (n_A + n_B + \cdots + n_k - k)]$ degrees of freedom. Under the null hypothesis that the assumed linear model is correct, these two quantities divided by their respective degrees of freedom would provide independent estimates of σ^2. If the model does not accurately describe the response, the estimate of σ^2 based upon replications for fixed values of the independent variables (the experimental error) will be less than that acquired from the remainder or mean square due to "lack of fit." Thus one could employ the F-statistic,

$$F = \frac{\text{mean square "lack of fit"}}{\text{mean square error}}, \quad s^2$$

to test an hypothesis that the model is appropriate for the response.

Example 8.6 An experiment was conducted to investigate the effect of machine insulation and machine speed on noise level (measured in decibels). A 2×3 factorial experiment was conducted with three replications for each of the six factor combinations (thus utilizing $n = 18$ machines). The data are shown below.

Insulation	Machine speed		
	-1	0	1
A	5.2	5.8	7.6
	4.8	6.2	7.9
	4.7	6.1	7.8
B	3.8	4.6	6.0
	4.2	4.9	6.2
	3.9	4.8	6.0

The experimenter has assumed that the increase in noise level is linear over the range of machine speed but that an insulation-speed interaction may be present.

(a) Write the linear model for the experiment.
(b) Fit the linear model (a) to the data and calculate SSE. To simplify calculations, use a $(+1, -1)$ coding for the qualitative variables, "insulations."
(c) Calculate the sum of squares of deviations associated with the experimental error by calculating the pooled sum of squares of deviations for the six treatment combinations.
(d) Partition the "sum of squares for error" obtained in (b) into a new SSE associated with experimental error and a sum of squares associated with "lack of fit."
(e) Test to see whether the data give sufficient evidence to indicate "lack of fit."

Solution: (a) The linear model is

$$y = \beta_0 + \beta_1 x_1 + \beta_2 x_2 + \beta_3 x_1 x_2 + \epsilon,$$

where

$$x_1 = \text{machine speed (coded)},$$

$$x_2 = \begin{cases} 1 & \text{if insulation } B \text{ is applied}, \\ -1 & \text{if insulation A is applied}. \end{cases}$$

Note that if no interaction exists (that is, $\beta_3 = 0$), the coding of x_2 would imply that the difference between the effect of insulations B and A is $2\beta_2$.

(b) The reader may verify that

$$(X'X) = \begin{bmatrix} 18 & 0 & 0 & 0 \\ 0 & 12 & 0 & 0 \\ 0 & 0 & 18 & 0 \\ 0 & 0 & 0 & 12 \end{bmatrix}, \quad (X'X)^{-1} = \begin{bmatrix} \frac{1}{18} & 0 & 0 & 0 \\ 0 & \frac{1}{12} & 0 & 0 \\ 0 & 0 & \frac{1}{18} & 0 \\ 0 & 0 & 0 & \frac{1}{12} \end{bmatrix},$$

$$X'Y = \begin{bmatrix} 100.5 \\ 14.9 \\ -11.7 \\ -2.3 \end{bmatrix}, \quad \hat{\beta} = \begin{bmatrix} 5.583 \\ 1.242 \\ -.650 \\ -.192 \end{bmatrix},$$

and SSE $= Y'Y - \hat{\beta}'X'Y = .738$.

(c) The sum of squares of deviations for experimental error is the pooled sum of squares over the six cells. For example, the sum of squares of deviations associated with insulation A and the first speed is

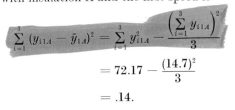

$$= 72.17 - \frac{(14.7)^2}{3}$$

$$= .14.$$

Computing the sums of squares for the other five cells in like manner, we obtain

$$\text{SS (experimental error)} = .433.$$

(d) The sum of squares of deviations from (b) based on $[n - (k + 1)]$ $= 18 - 4 = 14$ degrees of freedom can be partitioned into the sum of squares of deviations for experimental error (part c) based upon $(n_1 + n_2 + \cdots + n_6 - 6) = 18 - 6 = 12$ degrees of freedom and a sum of squares of deviations for "lack of fit" based upon $(14 - 12) = 2$ degrees of freedom. The analysis of variance is shown in Table 8.6. The single-degree-of-freedom sums of squares have been omitted because the t-tests for testing hypotheses, $\beta_i = 0$ $(i = 1, 2, \text{ or } 3)$, are *equivalent* to the corresponding F-tests of the analysis of variance. Thus it can be shown that an F with 1 and v degrees of freedom is related to a Student's t with v degrees of freedom: $F_{1,v} = t_v^2.$

Table 8.6 ANOVA table for Example 8.6

Source	d.f.	SS	MS
Treatments†	1		
Speed (linear)†	1		
(Linear speed) (treat)†	1		
Lack of fit	2⎰ 14	.305	.153
Experimental error	12⎱	.433	.036
Total	17		

(handwritten annotations: "6 groups · 2 df. for each group"; "$\frac{.305}{2}$"; "$\Sigma(y_i - \bar y)^2$")

†These sums of squares were not needed in this analysis and were therefore omitted.

(e) The test statistic to test for lack of fit is

$$F_{2, 12} = \frac{\text{MS (lack of fit)}}{s^2} = \frac{.153}{.036} = 4.25.$$

Since the computed F-value exceeds the critical value of $F_{.05}$ based upon $v_1 = 2$ and $v_2 = 12$ degrees of freedom, the test statistic falls in the rejection region and there is evidence to indicate lack of fit of the linear model. We therefore conclude that noise level is not linearly related to speed.

8.10 Some Other Multiparameter Inference-Making Procedures

Many experiments are exploratory, so that the experimenter has difficulty specifying meaningful treatment comparisons before he observes the data. If he waits until the data are collected and compares the largest versus the smallest treatment mean, the Student's t-test will be invalid and the probability of falsely rejecting the null hypothesis will greatly exceed the α associated with the tabulated critical value of t. On the other hand, if he selects a large number of comparisons to be investigated before he observes the data, the probability of rejecting the null hypothesis (when it is true) on *at least* one of the tests will be quite large.

The difficulty, of course, is that in an exploratory experiment little is known about the relative magnitude of the treatment means, and one is therefore faced with a large number of decisions to achieve a ranking. And, regardless of the inference-making procedure employed, it is intuitively clear that the more one attempts to say about the expected values of the treatment means, the greater the chance of making at least one incorrect decision. Thus some inference-making procedures, constructed so that the probability of making at least one type I error in the analysis is small, are conservative and operate with a relatively high probability of failing to detect treatment differences when they exist. Other methods operate with a much higher probability of committing at least one type I error but with an attendant increase in the power of the tests to detect real treatment differences.

We have suggested conducting an analysis-of-variance F-test to test the hypothesis of "no difference between treatments" and then making a limited number of treatment comparisons selected in advance with the use of tests or estimators utilizing Student's t. Other techniques to supplement or supplant this procedure are available and discussed in detail in Federer (1955). Of the many research publications on the ranking of treatment means, we mention a few. Newman (1939) provides critical values of the studentized range,

$$\frac{\bar{y}_{\max} - \bar{y}_{\min}}{s/\sqrt{n}}$$

where $\bar{y}_{\max}$ and $\bar{y}_{\min}$ are the treatment means with maximum and minimum responses, respectively, s^2 is the least-squares estimator of σ^2, and n is the number of observations in each treatment total (note that we here assume equal sample size). This critical value is employed in procedures suggested by Duncan (1955), Keuls (1952), and Tukey (13) for ranking the treatment means. Methods comparing several treatments with a control have been developed by Dunnett (1955), Paulson (1952), and Gupta and Sobel (1958).

Tukey's method would seem particularly appropriate because it provides for the comparison of any or all pairs of treatment means after observation of the data with a probability of falsely rejecting the hypothesis of equality on at least one comparison equal to a probability α. *Thus the α is a measure of risk of making a type I error expressed on an experiment-wise basis rather than applicable to a single comparison.* Tukey's procedure requires the calculation of the quantity,

$$\omega = q(p, \nu)\frac{s}{\sqrt{n_t}},$$

where p equals the number of treatments, each of which is based upon n_t observations, ν is equal to the number of degrees of freedom associated with s^2, and $q_\alpha(p, \nu)$ is tabulated in Table 6 for $\alpha = .05$ and $\alpha = .01$. If any pair of means differ by an amount equal to or greater than ω, the associated population means are concluded to be different. That is, one would reject the null hypothesis of equality.

Example 8.7   Use Tukey's ω test to compare the means of the randomized block design, Example 7.8.

Solution: For this experiment, $p = 4$, $\nu = 6$, $s = .30$, $n_t = 3$, and $q_{.05}(4, 6) = 4.90$. Then

$$\omega = q_{.05}(4, 6)\frac{s}{\sqrt{n_t}} = (4.90)\frac{(.30)}{\sqrt{3}} = .85$$

Ordering the treatment sample means, we obtain

$\bar{T}_C$	$\bar{T}_A$	$\bar{T}_B$	$\bar{T}_D$
11.2	11.4	12.3	12.8

Using the ω-test, it is clear that there is no evidence of a difference between the mean responses for treatments C and A, and B and D. This fact is indicated by lines linking these pairs in the ordering of the sample means shown above. On the other hand, we would reject the hypothesis of "no difference in mean response" for the pairs C and B, C and D, A and D, and A and B. The probability of falsely rejecting the null hypothesis of "no difference" on at least one of these tests is $\alpha = .05$ using Tukey's procedure. Note that Tukey's procedure requires that the treatment means be uncorrelated and have equal variances (and hence equal sample size). As described above, the method applies only to treatment differences.

Scheffe (1953) has proposed a procedure that applies to linear functions of the parameters of the general linear model. No requirements are placed on the variances and covariances of the parameter estimators. A good discussion of both Tukey's and Scheffe's procedures may be found in Scheffe (1959).

8.11 Transformations to Achieve Uniform Variance

As noted earlier, the experimenter rarely, if ever, knows whether the assumptions underlying the methodology of Chapters 7 and 8 are satisfied. Does he have the correct probabilistic model to fit the response in question? Is $E(y)$ equal to the true mean response and are the assumptions relative to the random error, ϵ, satisfied? From a philosophical point of view the answer is probably always "no," but the departures from the assumptions are often so slight that the statistical test and estimation procedures are unaffected.

Failure to select the appropriate model form for $E(y)$ can seriously bias the estimates of $E(y)$ as well as other parameters, but this bias should not be large if good judgment is used in the construction of the linear model. Unmeasured and unincluded variables in $E(y)$ will often oscillate sufficiently in repeated sampling and produce a random variation that simply magnifies the random error.

Randomization of the treatments to the experimental units in a design is an attempt to insure against correlation of the random errors. However, economic variables, such as measures of business activity, yield, profit, or measures of product quality in a manufacturing operation, are likely to yield correlated observations over time. If one is fortunate enough to measure some of the subsidiary independent variables which cause the correlation, these variables may be entered in the linear model and thereby reduce the correlation of adjacent observations. Autocorrelated models which relate the response at one point in time to the response at some preceding time, models which include transcendental terms, or other more sophisticated models may be required to characterize some responses measured over time.

One of the more common and detectable departures from assumptions is the failure of the variance of the response, y, to be constant from one set of values of the independent variables to another. This condition is often known in advance from knowledge of the probability distribution of the response. For example, if the response, y, is a count that follows a Poisson probability distribution, the variance of y will be proportional to $E(y)$. Similarly, one may wish to study the behavior of the sample variance, s^2, as a function of various conditions in an industrial process where the variance of the response, s^2, is proportional to the square of its mean—that is,

$$E(s_i^2) = \sigma_i^2 \qquad \text{and} \qquad V(s_i^2) = \frac{2\sigma_i^4}{n-1}.$$

Percentage response measurements generated by data from binomial populations will possess variances which are a function of the binomial parameters and the binomial sample sizes. Thus if a given percentage is based on a sample of n_i trials from a binomial population with parameters p_i, the variance of the percentage will be proportional to $p_i(1 - p_i)/n_i$.

The variance of the response, y, can often be stabilized by transforming the response measurements, particularly when $V(y)$ is a function of the mean, $E(y)$. For example, the square root of Poisson count data yields a response that will possess approximately a constant variance independent of its mean. Thus we would fit a linear model to $y^* = \sqrt{y}$, where y is the original Poisson response.

The appropriate response transformation to achieve approximate uniformity of variance can be derived when $V(y)$ is a function of $E(y)$. Letting y^* and y denote the transformed and the original response, respectively, let $y^* = g(y)$ and, for the sake of simplicity, let $E(y) = m$. Suppose that the transformation function, $g(y)$, is such that it may be expanded into a converging Taylor's series,

$$g(y) = g(m) + g'(m)(y - m) + g''(m)\frac{(y - m)^2}{2!} + \ldots,$$

giving a first-order approximation to $g(y)$,

$$y^* = g(y) = g(m) + g'(m)(y - m).$$

Then, letting $V(y^*) = C$, a constant, we have

$$V(y^*) = [g'(m)]^2 \, V(y) = C.$$

Now suppose that the relation between $V(y)$ and $E(y)$ is $V(y) = \phi(m)$. Substituting $\phi(m)$ into the expression for $V(y)$,

$$[g'(m)]^2 \, \phi(m) = C,$$

or the transformation function to achieve approximate uniform variance for y^* is

$$g(m) = \int \sqrt{\frac{c}{\phi(m)}} \, dm + k,$$

where k is the constant of integration. Actually, we may use the transformation,

$$y^* = g(y) = \int \frac{1}{\sqrt{\phi(y)}} \, dy,$$

since k does not affect $V(y^*)$ and we may let $C = 1$.

Example Suppose that $V(y) = m$, where $m = E(y)$. Find a transformation that will achieve approximate uniformity of variance of the response.

Solution: Letting y^* be the transformed response and $g(y)$ be the transformation, we obtain

$$g(m) = \int \frac{1}{\sqrt{m}} \, dm = 2\sqrt{m}.$$

The coefficient, 2, can be ignored; hence the transformation is

$$y^* = \sqrt{y}$$

as mentioned earlier in this section.

The reader can apply the method above to acquire the transformations given in Table 8.7. A more extensive list of transformations is given by Bartlett (1947). Bartlett also notes that $y^* = \sqrt{y + \frac{1}{2}}$ is an improvement on $y^* = \sqrt{y}$ for Poisson data if y, the count, tends to be small.

Table 8.7

$\phi(m)$	$y^* = g(y)$	$Approximate\ V(y^*)$
m	$\sqrt{y}$	0.25
m^2	$\ln y$	1
$\dfrac{m(1-m)}{n}$	$\sin^{-1} \sqrt{y}$ radians	$0.25/n$

For the very special case where the variance of each response is known—that is, $V(y_i) = \sigma_i^2$, the transformation

$$y_i^* = \frac{y_i}{\sigma_i}$$

will stabilize $V(y^*)$. This transformation will produce nearly uniform variance for y^* if σ_i is unknown but a good approximation is available.

Note that transforming the data has the disadvantage of changing the interpretation of the response and for this reason may be unacceptable to the experimenter.

8.12 Concluding Comments

The analysis of variance provides a test of an hypothesis concerning a set of parameters in the linear model and is particularly useful to test the hypothesis that no difference exists between the levels of some factor, such as treatments. For orthogonal designs, the computing formulas for the analysis of variance produce a substantial savings in labor over fitting of complete and reduced linear models and provide a better computational procedure by reducing rounding errors. And for those unimpressed with the utility of the analysis-of-variance F-tests, the computing formulas for orthogonal designs provide a very simple method for the computation of SSE which may be obtained by subtracting the appropriate sums of squares from

$$\sum_{i=1}^{n} (y_i - \bar{y})^2.$$

Finally, we will discover that the analysis of variance plays an important role in the analysis of experiments where the linear model contains more than one component of variability.

Fitting the linear model to a set of data or calculating various sums of squares of deviations in the analysis of variance are procedures that are unaffected by the validity of the assumptions concerning the random error, ϵ. However, these assumptions must hold in order that the statistical estimation and testing procedures discussed in Chapters 7 and 8 function as described. Fortunately, departures from normality in the distribution of the y_i for fixed values of the independent variables will not seriously affect stated confidence coefficients in interval estimation or α and β for statistical tests as long as the departure is not excessive. And randomization procedures will be helpful in protecting against correlation of the observations. Failure to satisfy the assumption of a constant variance, σ^2, for the random error, ϵ, and hence y, for fixed values of the independent variables will more seriously disturb the measures of goodness for the described estimation and test procedures. Conveniently, one may often transform the response measurements, y_i, to achieve uniform variance using the procedure discussed in Sec. 8.11.

Perhaps the important thing to note is that one would not expect the assumptions basic to a statistical procedure to hold exactly for a given practical situation. We recognize, however, that conclusions based upon the procedure rest upon these assumptions and therefore hope either that they are satisfied to a fair degree or that the existing aberrations will have little effect on the inferential procedures employed. The experimenter should be cognizant of the assumptions underlying statistical methods and be aware of the effect of the failure of these assumptions on statistical estimation and test procedures. Generally speaking, investigations have shown the analysis-of-variance procedures to be relatively insensitive to moderate departures from the underlying assumptions.

The procedure employed in comparing a set of treatment means may vary from one experimenter to another. The cautious will conduct an analysis-of-variance F-test (or utilize some equivalent multiparameter procedure) to determine whether sufficient evidence exists to indicate a difference between treatment means and, if the evidence is inadequate, will conclude their analysis. In doing so, they protect themselves against making a type I error but greatly increase the risk of failing to detect an important treatment difference when it exists. Individual degree-of-freedom t-tests selected in advance of observation of the data should be conducted; each will be valid with known α. If the number of tests is large, the probability of falsely rejecting on at least one test may be sizable, but for exploratory investigations the opportunity of unearthing important aspects of the experiment should not be ignored. In recognition of the high overall α for the experiment, one would wish to recheck in future experimentation those effects which appear to be statistically significant.

Many would argue that the multiparameter hypotheses of analysis of variance are impractical in many experimental situations because the experimenter does not really believe that there is "no difference in the mean response between treatments." Actually he expects the means to differ, even if by a very small amount, and he wishes to estimate the difference or to achieve a ranking in order that he may identify the "best," however' "best" may be defined. The ranking procedures of Sec. 8.10 are very helpful in this situation. Indeed, it would seem likely that estimation of treatment differences, estimation of $E(y)$ for fixed values of $x_1, x_2, \ldots, x_k$, or other properties of a response surface would be of greater practical value in many investigations than the inferences implied by the analysis-of-variance tests. This, of course, is a philosophical question that will evoke controversial opinions from professional statisticians. The reader will observe that the mathematical theory of statistics is exact but the assumptions underlying the theory are rarely verifiable in practice. Hence the application of the theory to the solution of practical problems is an art and subject to debate. A similar observation could be made with regard to most other professions.

As a final comment, one should recognize the importance and the basic role of linear models in the analysis of variance. The traditional computing formulas for sums of squares are worthless in the face of an undesigned experiment or one in which a large number of observations have been destroyed. Then the procedure for fitting the complete and reduced models to obtain the drop in sums of squares for error, while computationally tedious, will provide the *only* practical method for calculating the sums of squares necessary for a statistical test of an hypothesis concerning a set of model parameters. Thus it is a powerful procedure that underlies the analysis of both designed and undesigned experiments.

Exercises

1. Calculate the sum of squares for blocks for the randomized block design, Example 7.8, by fitting the reduced model and acquiring the drop in the sum of squares of deviations, $(\text{SSE}_1 - \text{SSE}_2)$.

2. A study was conducted to compare the effect of three levels of digitalis on the level of calcium in the heart muscle of dogs. A description of the actual experimental procedure is omitted, but it is sufficient to note

that the general level of calcium uptake varies from one animal to another so that comparison of digitalis levels (treatments) had to be blocked on heart muscles. That is, the tissue for a heart muscle was regarded as a block and comparisons of the three treatments were made within a given muscle. The calcium uptakes for the three levels of digitalis, A, B, C, were compared using the heart muscle of four dogs. The results are shown below:

Dogs

1	2	3	4
A 1342	C 1698	B 1296	A 1150
B 1608	B 1387	A 1029	C 1579
C 1881	A 1140	C 1549	B 1319

(a) Calculate the sums of squares for this experiment and construct an analysis-of-variance table.

(b) How many degrees of freedom are associated with SSE?

(c) Do the data present sufficient evidence to indicate a difference in the mean uptake of calcium for the three levels of digitalis?

(d) Do the data indicate a difference in the mean uptake in calcium for the four heart muscles?

(e) Give the standard deviation of the difference between the mean calcium uptake for two levels of digitalis.

(f) Find a 95 per cent confidence interval for the difference in mean response between treatments A and B.

3. Refer to Exercise 2. Approximately how many replications would be required for each treatment in order that the error of estimating the difference in mean response for a pair of treatments be less than 20 (with probability equal to .95)? Assume that additional observations would be made within a randomized block design.

4. The voltage within an electronic system was to be investigated for four different conditions, A, B, C, D but unfortunately the voltage measurements were affected by the line voltage within the laboratory. Since the line voltage assumed the same pattern within each day due to the usage patterns of various industrial firms in the area and since the general level of line voltage varied from day to day, a Latin square design was employed. The data are shown in the next page:

		Days			
		1	2	3	4
Time period within a day	1	A 116	B 108	C 126	D 112
	2	C 111	D 124	A 122	B 121
	3	B 120	C 115	D 126	A 109
	4	D 118	A 125	B 116	C 127

(a) Calculate the sums of squares for treatments, SST, by fitting complete and reduced models. Then calculate SST using the formula of Section 8.6.

(b) Calculate the sums of squares and construct an analysis of variance table for this experiment.

(c) How many degrees of freedom are associated with SSE?

(d) Give the values of MST, MS(days), and MS(time periods).

(e) Do the data present sufficient evidence to indicate a difference between treatments.

5. The yields of wheat in bushels per acre were compared for five different varieties, A, B, C, D, and E, at six different locations. Each variety was randomly assigned to a plot at each location. The results of the experiment are shown below:

Varieties	Location 1	2	3	4	5	6
A	35.3	31.0	32.7	36.8	37.2	33.1
B	30.7	32.2	31.4	31.7	35.0	32.7
C	38.2	33.4	33.6	37.1	37.3	38.2
D	34.9	36.1	35.2	38.3	40.2	36.0
E	32.4	28.9	29.2	30.7	33.9	32.1

(a) Construct an analysis-of-variance table for this experiment.

(b) Do the data present sufficient evidence to indicate a difference between varieties?

(c) Do the data present sufficient evidence to indicate a difference between locations?

(d) Find the 90 per cent confidence interval for the mean yield of variety B at location 1.

(e) Find a 95 per cent confidence interval for the difference in mean yields for varieties C and E.

6. Approximately how many replications of the 4×4 Latin square (Example 8.1) would be required in order to estimate the difference in mean response between a pair of fuels with an error of estimation less than 1.0 gallons with probability .95. (Assume that response measurements are given in gallons per unit time.)

7. Refer to Exercise 15, Chapter 6.
   (a) Test the hypothesis that no two-way interactions exist between T_1, P, C and T_2 using $\alpha = .05$.
   (Assume that higher-order interactions are negligible and that their respective degrees of freedom may be employed to estimate σ.
   (b) Give the complete model for this experiment.
   (c) Give the reduced model necessary for obtaining the drop in SSE associated with two-way interactions.
   (d) Calculate the sum of squares associated with two-way interactions by fitting the two models given in (a) and (b) and obtaining the drop in SSE.
   (e) Calculate the sums of squares for each of the six two-way interactions using the formulas of Section 8.7. Show that the sum of these six sums of squares of deviations is equal to the sum of squares for two-way interactions given in (c).
   (f) Use the mean squares of (d) to test an hypothesis that no two-way interactions exist.
   (g) How do the results of (f) compare with the conclusion of Exercise 20, Chapter 7?

8. Conduct an analysis of variance for the data, Exercise 15, Chapter 2.
   (a) Find SSE.
   (b) How many degrees of freedom are associated with SSE?
   (c) Do the data present sufficient evidence to indicate a difference between treated and untreated concrete?

9. Conduct an analysis of variance for the data in Exercise 18, Chapter 2.
   (a) Find SSE.
   (b) How many degrees of freedom are associated with SSE?
   (c) Do the data present sufficient evidence to indicate a difference in the mean response between stimuli?
   (d) Between subjects?

10. Refer to Exercise 39, Chapter 7.
   (a) Write the linear model for the complete 2×3 factorial experiment, assuming that all interactions may be present.
   (b) Regard the six factorial combinations as treatments and calculate SST, the total sum of squares of deviations, and SSE.

(c) Refer to (b). Do the data present sufficient evidence to indicate a difference between treatments?

(d) Find SS(Pressure), SS(Temperature) and SS(Pressure $\times$ Temperature), and give the complete analysis of variance table for the experiment.

(e) Do the data indicate a pressure-temperature interaction?

(f) A difference in the mean response for the two levels of pressure?

(g) The three levels of temperature?

11. Conduct an analysis of variance for the replicated 2×2 factorial experiment, Example 7.7.

(a) Find the sums of squares for oil viscosity, temperature, engines and the oil viscosity-temperature interaction.

(b) Find the total sum of squares of deviations and obtain SSE by subtraction. Check SSE with the answer, Example 7.7.

(c) Do the data present sufficient evidence to indicate an oil viscosity-temperature interaction? Use an F-test.

(d) Show that the F calculated in (c) is equal to the square of the value of the t-statistic used to test this interaction in Example 7.7, that the critical value of F is equal to $(t_{\alpha/2})^2$, and hence that the two tests are equivalent.

12. Why are the computing formulas for analyzing a k-way classification of little use in analyzing the data of Example 7.9?

13. Two methods for extracting metal from an ore, say A and B, were compared by taking ore samples from four locations in an ore field. Each of the four ore samples was then randomly divided and assigned to the two methods of extraction, one half to each. The measurements on the extracted metal (in pounds) are shown below:

A	B
27.2	26.1
24.3	23.6
29.7	29.4
32.9	32.3

(a) Write a linear model for this experiment. Define each symbol appearing in the model and give assumptions regarding any random components.

(b) Do the data present sufficient evidence to indicate a difference in the true average amount of metal removed from the ore by the two refining methods?

(c) Roughly, how much information is gained by making comparisons within ore cores in contrast to a random assignment of ore samples to the two refining methods? Explain.

(d) Approximately how many paired observations would be required to estimate the difference in mean yield correct to within .15 pounds?

14. Perform an analysis of variance for the data given in the randomized block design shown below:

Blocks

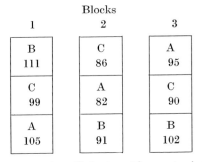

	1	2	3
	B	C	A
	111	86	95
	C	A	C
	99	82	90
	A	B	B
	105	91	102

(a) Do the data present sufficient evidence to indicate a difference between treatments?

(b) Blocks?

15. A replicated 2^3 factorial experiment, coded $(-1, +1)$ for each variable, yielded the prediction equation

$$\hat{y} = 2 + 3x_1 + .3x_2 + 4.1x_3 + .3x_1x_2 + 2.3x_2x_3 + x_1x_3 + .5x_4,$$

where x_1, x_2 and x_3 represent the levels of the three factors. The three-way interaction term was omitted from the linear model, and $x_4 = 1$ if the response was from replication 2 and $x_4 = -1$ if replication 1.

(a) How many degrees of freedom are available for estimation of σ^2?

(b) If $s^2 = 1$, do the data present sufficient evidence to indicate an x_1x_2 interaction? Show all work.

(c) Approximately how many replications of the 2^3 factorial would be required to estimate β_2, the coefficient of x_2, correct to within plus or minus .2?

16. What is an orthogonal design?

17. Fit the linear model

$$y = \beta_0 + \beta_1 x + \epsilon$$

to the following $n = 9$ data points, and test for lack of fit of the model.

x	-1	0	1
y	0, 1, 1	4, 5, 4.5	5.5, 6, 7

18. Explain why r^2 is a measure of goodness of fit of a linear model.

19. Refer to Exercise 14 and find r^2.

20. Find r^2 for the Latin square design, Exercise 4.

21. Refer to Exercise 11 and find r^2.

22. (a) Give the assumptions and describe Tukey's procedure for a multiple comparison of a set of means.

    (b) Given a set of five treatment means based on four observations each, $\bar{T}_1 = 3$, $\bar{T}_2 = 1$, $\bar{T}_3 = 1.7$, $\bar{T}_4 = 3.7$, $\bar{T}_5 = 2.3$, and $s^2 = 1$ based on $\nu = 10$ degrees of freedom, rank the treatment means using Tukey's procedure.

23. A chemist wishes to determine the effect on light density of photographic film for developer strength, temperature, and development time. A 2^3 factorial is replicated in 3 blocks, with the following results. Levels of developer strength, temperature, and time are coded with low level (-1) and high level (1). (This data appeared in Exercise 24, Chapter 6.)

x_1 Developer strength	x_2 Temperature	x_3 Time	Response Block I	Block II	Block III
-1	-1	-1	0	1	0
-1	-1	1	3	4	4
-1	1	-1	0	0	0
-1	1	1	2	3	2
1	-1	-1	3	2	2
1	-1	1	8	8	10
1	1	-1	1	2	0
1	1	1	7	8	8

    (a) Regard the 2^3 factorial combinations of the experiment as treatments, and analyze as a randomized block design. Find the sum of squares for treatments (SST), the sum of squares for blocks (SSB), and SSE.

    (b) Refer to (a). Do the data present sufficient evidence to indicate a difference between treatments?

    (c) Analyze, using the formulas for a k-way classification giving the sums of squares for all factor main effects, two- and three-way interactions.

24. Refer to Exercise 23. Do the data present sufficient evidence to indicate an interaction between developer strength and temperature?

25. Fit a linear model to the data of Exercise 23. Include all of the terms of the 2^3 factorial experiment as well as those associated with block differences.

26. Calculate r^2 for the fitted model, Exercise 25.

27. Refer to Exercise 25. Use t-tests to determine whether significant interactions exist between the factors x_1, x_2, and x_3. Note that these tests

yield the same results as F-tests based on the mean squares computed in Exercise 23, part (c).

28. Use Tukey's multiple comparison procedure to compare the variety means for Exercise 5.

29. Use Tukey's multiple comparison procedure to compare the treatment means for the Latin square design, Exercise 4.

30. Suppose that the variance of a response, y, is proportional to $E(y)$. Find a transformation that will stabilize the variance of the response measurements.

31. If a response, y, is a percentage based on data collected from a binomial population, $V(y)$ will vary depending on p. Find a transformation on y that will stabilize the variance of the response.

32. An experiment is conducted to study the effect of a number of process variables on the variability of a product quality characteristic. A random sample of $n = 10$ quality response measurements was taken for each setting of the independent variables, and s^2 was calculated. Thus s^2 is to be used as the response, y, for fitting a linear model.

    (a) Suppose that the initial quality measurements are normally distributed. Find the expected value and variance of s^2. (Note: You may use the result that the expected value and variance of a χ^2 random variable with v degrees of freedom are $E(\chi^2) = v$ and $V(\chi^2) = 2v$, respectively.

    (b) Let the variance of a response, y, be proportional to the square of its mean. Find a transformation that will approximately stabilize its variance.

33. A 2×2 factorial experiment was conducted to investigate the effect of pressure and temperature on yield of chemical in a manufacturing process. In addition to the four response measurements of the 2×2 factorial, four additional observations were made in the center of the experimental region. With the independent variables x_1 and x_2 coded $(-1, +1)$ the data appear as follows:

x_1
Temperature

	x_1 / x_2	-1	0	1
x_2 Pressure	-1	74		63
	0		87,84 88,81	
	1	80		82

(a) Fit a complete 2×2 linear model to the data.

(b) Do the data present evidence to indicate lack of fit of the model?

(c) Calculate r^2 for the model.

34. An experiment was conducted to compare the growth of fungus on house siding for three different types of house paints (P_1, P_2, and P_3), two exposures (E_1, E_2) and at three locations (L_1, L_2, and L_3) in the state of Florida. Four experimental surfaces were prepared for each paint-exposure-location and the fungus accumulation was measured on each over a one-year period.

	E_1			E_2		
	P_1	P_2	P_3	P_1	P_2	P_3
L_1	8	6	5	14	12	9
	7	6	8	12	11	5
	9	7	7	14	11	8
	8	8	7	15	11	7
L_2	6	5	1	14	10	7
	7	7	2	15	10	6
	7	7	2	13	10	7
	8	6	1	12	9	8
L_3	10	10	7	23	20	10
	11	10	5	22	21	8
	13	12	4	20	21	9
	11	11	4	21	19	8

(a) Analyze the data and draw conclusions regarding the effect of paint, exposure, and location on fungus growth.

(b) Give the standard deviation of the estimator of the difference in mean fungus growth for two paint-location combinations.

(c) Calculate the coefficient of determination.

35. Consider the following one-way classification consisting of three treatments, A, B, and C, where the number of observations per treatment varies from treatment to treatment.

A	B	C
24.2	24.5	26.0
27.5	22.7	
25.9		
24.7		

(a) Derive the formula for SST.

(b) Do the data present sufficient evidence to indicate a difference between treatments?

(c) Do the data present sufficient evidence to indicate a difference between treatments B and A?

(d) Use part (a) to deduce the general formula for SST for a one-way classification with unequal numbers of observations per treatment.

(e) Calculate the coefficient of determination for the data given above.

36. (a) Find the least-squares line for the following data.

(b) Find the SSE for (a).

(c) Find the pooled sum of squares within the $k = 6$ groups.

(d) Do the data present sufficient evidence to indicate that a straight line is an inadequate representation of $E(y)$?

(e) Find the least-squares line where the $k = 6$ response means $\bar{y}_i$, $i = 1, 2, \ldots, 6$, are employed as the response measurements. Compare with (a).

(f) Find the sum of squares of deviations of the $\bar{y}$ about the fitted least-squares line, part (e). How is this related to the sums of squares computed in (b) and (c)?

x	1.3	2.1	3.5	3.9	5.2	5.9
y	4.6	6.0	7.4	7.2	8.5	8.8
	5.5	5.5	7.7	8.5	8.0	9.2
	4.3	5.8	6.9	8.0	8.9	10.0
	5.0	6.3	6.6	7.9	9.2	9.8
	4.2	6.6	7.5	7.5	8.6	9.6

37. Refer to the analysis of the data, Exercise 23, and rank the eight factor combinations using Tukey's method of multiple comparison.

38. The following 2×2 Latin square design was employed to investigate the effect of two treatments, A and B, on a response, y, where prior experimentation has indicated that $V(y) = 1.0$.

(a) Complete an analysis-of-variance table for this design.

(b) Give two test statistics that might be employed to test an hypothesis of no difference between treatments.

(c) Do the data present sufficient evidence to indicate a difference in mean response between treatments? Rows? Columns?

	C_1	C_2
R_1	A 3	B 3
R_2	B 2	A 6

References

Bartlett, M. S. "The Use of Transformations," *Biometrics*, **3**, 39–52 (1947).

Cochran, W. G. and Cox, G. M., *Experimental Designs*, 2nd ed. New York: John Wiley & Sons, Inc., 1957.

Davies, O. L., *Design and Analysis of Industrial Experiments*. New York: Hafner Publishing Company, Inc., 1960.

Duncan, D. B., "Multiple Range and Multiple *F*-tests," *Biometrics*, **11**, 1–42 (1955).

Dunnett, C. W., "A Multiple Comparison Procedure for Comparing Several Treatments with a Control," *Journal of the American Statistical Association*, **50**, 1096–1121 (1955).

Federer, W. T., *Experimental Design*. New York: The Macmillan Company, 1955.

Gupta, S. S., and M. Sobel, "On Selecting a Subset Which Contains All Populations Better Than a Standard," *Annals of Mathematical Statistics*, **29**, 235–244 (1958).

Keuls, M., "The Use of the 'Studentized Range' in Connection with an Analysis of Variance," *Euphytica*, **1**, 112–122 (1952).

Newman, D., "The Distribution of the Range in Samples from a Normal Population Expressed in Terms of an Independent Estimate of Standard Deviation," *Biometrika*, **31**, 20–30 (1939).

Paulson, E., "On the Comparison of Several Experimental Categories with a Control," *Annals of Mathematical Statistics*, **23**, 239–246 (1952).

Scheffe, H., "A Method for Judging All Contrasts in the Analysis of Variance," *Biometrika*, **40**, 87–104 (1953).

———, *The Analysis of Variance*. New York: John Wiley & Sons, Inc., 1959. Chapter 3.

Steel, R. G. D., and J. H. Torrie, *Principles and Procedures of Statistics*. New York: McGraw-Hill Book Company, 1960. Chapter 7.

9

The Effect of Coding
on the Analysis

9.1 An Example

The following represents a 2^3 factorial experiment with the eight factor combinations (treatments) randomly assigned in two blocks. The response is the yield of a chemical, and the factors are pressure, amount of catalyst, and temperature. The data are displayed in Table 9.1.

The purpose of the following analyses is to illustrate the effect of coding on the analysis and conclusions as well as to point to some obvious difficulties that may develop. To simplify our discussion, suppose that we are particularly interested in determining whether the data present sufficient evidence to indicate a pressure-temperature interaction.

We have noted in examples and exercises that it is desirable to code equally spaced quantitative independent variables so that the values of the independent variables are equally spaced about the origin. For qualitative variables at two levels we may code either $(0, 1)$ or, preferably, $(-1, 1)$. The result is often a simplification of the $(X'X)$ matrix and a reduction in the computational effort in obtaining $(X'X)^{-1}$. We will give analyses of the

Table 9.1 Data for a replicated 2^3 factorial experiment

Block	Temperature	Pressure	Catalyst	y
	30	20	5	67
	80	20	5	83
	30	40	5	95
1	80	40	5	89
	30	20	7	71
	80	20	7	85
	30	40	7	98
	80	40	7	92
	30	20	5	77
	80	20	5	89
	30	40	5	79
2	80	40	5	78
	30	20	7	77
	80	20	7	92
	30	40	7	87
	80	40	7	85

data for two methods of coding and compare the results. The linear model will be

$$y = \beta_0 + \beta_1 x_1 + \beta_2 x_2 + \beta_3 x_3 + \beta_4 x_4 + \beta_5 x_1 x_2$$
$$+ \beta_6 x_1 x_3 + \beta_7 x_2 x_3 + \beta_8 x_1 x_2 x_3 + \epsilon,$$

where

$x_1 = $ coded temperature,
$x_2 = $ coded pressure,
$x_3 = $ coded catalyst,
$x_4 = $ dummy block variable.

Coding Method 1

Let

$$x_1 = \frac{T - 55}{25} \quad \text{or} \quad (-1, 1),$$

$$x_2 = \frac{P - 30}{10} \quad \text{or} \quad (-1, 1),$$

$$x_3 = C - 6 \quad \text{or} \quad (-1, 1),$$

$$x_4 = -1 \quad \text{if block 1,}$$
$$= +1 \quad \text{if block 2.}$$

Then

$$X'Y = \begin{bmatrix} 1344 \\ 42 \\ 62 \\ 30 \\ -16 \\ -72 \\ 0 \\ 12 \\ -2 \end{bmatrix}, \quad X'X = \begin{bmatrix} 16 & 0 & 0 & 0 & 0 & 0 & 0 & 0 & 0 \\ 0 & 16 & 0 & 0 & 0 & 0 & 0 & 0 & 0 \\ 0 & 0 & 16 & 0 & 0 & 0 & 0 & 0 & 0 \\ 0 & 0 & 0 & 16 & 0 & 0 & 0 & 0 & 0 \\ 0 & 0 & 0 & 0 & 16 & 0 & 0 & 0 & 0 \\ 0 & 0 & 0 & 0 & 0 & 16 & 0 & 0 & 0 \\ 0 & 0 & 0 & 0 & 0 & 0 & 16 & 0 & 0 \\ 0 & 0 & 0 & 0 & 0 & 0 & 0 & 16 & 0 \\ 0 & 0 & 0 & 0 & 0 & 0 & 0 & 0 & 16 \end{bmatrix},$$

or $(X'X) = 16I$ and $(X'X)^{-1} = \frac{1}{16}I$,

$$\hat{\beta} = \begin{bmatrix} 84 \\ 2.625 \\ 3.875 \\ 1.875 \\ -1.0 \\ -4.5 \\ 0 \\ 0.75 \\ -0.125 \end{bmatrix}, \quad$$

$$\text{SSE} = Y'Y - \hat{\beta}'X'Y = 368,$$

$$s^2 = \frac{SSE}{n - (k+1)} = \frac{368}{7} = 52.57$$

$$s = 7.25$$

Testing the hypothesis that $\beta_5 = 0$, the coefficient of the coded pressure-temperature interaction term, $x_1 x_2$, we calculate

$$t = \frac{\hat{\beta}_5}{s\sqrt{c_{55}}} = \frac{-4.5}{7.25\sqrt{\frac{1}{16}}} = -2.48.$$

Since the calculated value of the test statistic possesses an absolute value that exceeds the critical value of $t_{.05} = 2.365$, based upon $v = 7$ degrees of freedom, we reject the hypothesis that $\beta_5 = 0$ and conclude that there is sufficient evidence to indicate that β_5 differs from zero.

Coding Method 2

In contrast to coding method 1, suppose that we were immune to the computational hardships caused by a departure from the $(-1, +1)$ coding and decided to code

$$x_1 = \frac{T - 55}{25} \qquad (-1, 1),$$

$$x_2 = \frac{P - 30}{10} \qquad (-1, 1),$$

$$x_3 = \frac{C - 5}{2} \qquad (0, 1),$$

$$x_4 = 0 \qquad \text{if block 1,}$$
$$= 1 \qquad \text{if block 2.}$$

Then

$$X'Y = \begin{bmatrix} 1344 \\ 42 \\ 62 \\ 687 \\ 664 \\ -72 \\ 21 \\ 37 \\ -37 \end{bmatrix}, \qquad X'X = \begin{bmatrix} 16 & 0 & 0 & 8 & 8 & 0 & 0 & 0 & 0 \\ 0 & 16 & 0 & 0 & 0 & 0 & 8 & 0 & 0 \\ 0 & 0 & 16 & 0 & 0 & 0 & 0 & 8 & 0 \\ 8 & 0 & 0 & 8 & 4 & 0 & 0 & 0 & 0 \\ 8 & 0 & 0 & 4 & 8 & 0 & 0 & 0 & 0 \\ 0 & 0 & 0 & 0 & 0 & 16 & 0 & 0 & 8 \\ 0 & 8 & 0 & 0 & 0 & 0 & 8 & 0 & 0 \\ 0 & 0 & 8 & 0 & 0 & 0 & 0 & 8 & 0 \\ 0 & 0 & 0 & 0 & 0 & 8 & 0 & 0 & 8 \end{bmatrix},$$

$$(X'X)^{-1} = \begin{bmatrix} \frac{3}{16} & 0 & 0 & -\frac{1}{8} & -\frac{1}{8} & 0 & 0 & 0 & 0 \\ 0 & \frac{1}{8} & 0 & 0 & 0 & 0 & -\frac{1}{8} & 0 & 0 \\ 0 & 0 & \frac{1}{8} & 0 & 0 & 0 & 0 & -\frac{1}{8} & 0 \\ -\frac{1}{8} & 0 & 0 & \frac{1}{4} & 0 & 0 & 0 & 0 & 0 \\ -\frac{1}{8} & 0 & 0 & 0 & \frac{1}{4} & 0 & 0 & 0 & 0 \\ 0 & 0 & 0 & 0 & 0 & \frac{1}{8} & 0 & 0 & -\frac{1}{8} \\ 0 & -\frac{1}{8} & 0 & 0 & 0 & 0 & \frac{1}{4} & 0 & 0 \\ 0 & 0 & -\frac{1}{8} & 0 & 0 & 0 & 0 & \frac{1}{4} & 0 \\ 0 & 0 & 0 & 0 & 0 & -\frac{1}{8} & 0 & 0 & \frac{1}{4} \end{bmatrix},$$

$$\hat{\beta} = \begin{bmatrix} 83.125 \\ 2.625 \\ 3.125 \\ 3.750 \\ -2.000 \\ -4.375 \\ 0 \\ 1.500 \\ -0.250 \end{bmatrix}, \qquad \begin{aligned} SSE &= 368, \\ s^2 &= 52.57, \\ s &= 7.25. \end{aligned}$$

Testing the hypothesis, $\beta_5 = 0$, where β_5 as before is the coefficient of $x_1 x_2$, we obtain

$$t = \frac{\hat{\beta}_5}{s\sqrt{c_{55}}} = \frac{-4.375}{7.25\sqrt{\frac{1}{8}}} = -1.71$$

Since the calculated value of t is less than the value $t_{.05} = 2.365$, there is not sufficient evidence to indicate that β_5 differs from zero.

Note that β_5 for both analyses is the coefficient of $x_1 x_2$. Why do we observe the apparent contradiction in the results for the two statistical tests of the hypothesis, $\beta_5 = 0$? One rejects the null hypothesis and the other does not. Are the conclusions derived from the analysis dependent upon the method of coding? The discussion that follows should help to answer this question.

9.2 The Effect of Coding on the Orientation of the Response Surface

If an experimental investigation involves one or more quantitative independent variables, the experimenter will be concerned with the properties of response curves or surfaces. For example, he may wish to obtain a good approximation to the response surface over the experimental region so as to assist in locating a maximum response, minimum response, or the response for some specific settings of the independent variables. If one of the independent variables is qualitative (treatments), the single linear model will actually describe a separate response surface for each of the treatments when the appropriate values are substituted for the dummy variables. Thus a comparison of treatments will be, in effect, a comparison of the mean responses (elevation) of the response surfaces for a fixed setting of the independent variables or, perhaps, a more complicated comparison of the surfaces themselves. The analysis of covariance, described in Exercise 32, Chapter 7, involves a comparison of treatments adjusted for a single covariate and represents a simple example of this type of problem.

In studying response surfaces, one should give thought to the ultimate objective of the experimental investigation and avoid the temptation to mechanically test hypotheses concerning each individual parameter in the linear model. Thus it would seem that emphasis should be directed toward the functional relation describing the response surface, particularly the expected value of y for given values of the independent variables, and also the values of the partial derivatives which measure surface slope. The apparent inconsistency of Sec. 9.1 is caused by the fact that the corresponding coded independent variables representing catalysts and blocks are not equivalent and hence that the β_5 for the linear model using coding method

1 is not the same as that for method 2. Thus if we denote the independent variables for methods 1 and 2 as (x_1, x_2, x_3, x_4) and $(x_1^*, x_2^*, x_3^*, x_4^*)$, respectively,

$$x_1^* = x_1, \quad x_2^* = x_2, \quad x_3^* = \frac{x_3 + 1}{2}, \quad x_4^* = \frac{x_4 + 1}{2}.$$

For example, when the catalyst is set at $C = 7$, $x_3 = x_3^* = 1$. However, when $C = 5$, $x_3 = -1$ and $x_3^* = 0$.

We can see the exact relation between the coefficients of $x_1 x_2$ for the two methods of coding by examining the partial derivatives of $E(y)$. (The reader unfamiliar with the calculus may omit this discussion and move to the concluding remarks.) Thus

$$E(y) = \beta_0 + \beta_1 x_1 + \beta_2 x_2 + \beta_3 x_3 + \beta_4 x_4$$
$$+ \beta_5 x_1 x_2 + \beta_6 x_1 x_3 + \beta_7 x_2 x_3 + \beta_8 x_1 x_2 x_3$$

and

$$\frac{\partial^2 E(y)}{\partial x_1 \, \partial x_2} = \beta_5 + \beta_8 x_3.$$

Note that this partial derivative, measuring the rate of change of the slope of the surface (in a direction parallel to the x_1-axis) with respect to a change in x_2, is dependent upon x_3 and is equal to β_5 when $x_3 = 0$ (or a catalyst level, $C = 6$). This will be the value of $\partial^2 E(y)/\partial x_1 \, \partial x_2$ at the center of the experimental region.

The second partial derivative of $E(y)$ expressed in terms of $(x_1^*, x_2^*, x_3^*, x_4^*)$ is

$$\frac{\partial^2 E(y)}{\partial x_1^* \, \partial x_2^*} = \beta_5^* + \beta_8^* x_3^*.$$

Evaluated at the same point in the experimental region ($x_3 = 0$ corresponds to $x_3^* = \frac{1}{2}$),

$$\frac{\partial^2 E(y)}{\partial x_1^* \, \partial x_2^*} = \beta_5^* + \tfrac{1}{2}\beta_8^*.$$

Thus it is clear that $\beta_5 = \beta_5^* + \tfrac{1}{2}\beta_8^*$ and that $\beta_5 \neq \beta_5^*$.

The interpretation of β_5^* can be obtained by letting $x_3^* = 0$. Then β_5^* equals $\partial^2 E(y)/\partial x_1^* \, \partial x_2^*$ evaluated at the point $x_3^* = 0$ or catalyst level $C = 5$. Since β_5^* is the value of the second partial derivative located at a point on the perimeter of the experimental region (as opposed to the center for β_5), it is not surprising that its estimator, $\hat{\beta}_5^*$, possesses a larger variance than that associated with $\hat{\beta}_5$. Both β_5 and β_5^* are values of the same second partial derivative *but at different points in the experimental region*. Estimates of $E(y)$ or its partial derivatives will be unaffected by the system of coding when evaluated at a given point in the experimental region. Similarly, the variance of these estimators will be independent of the coding.

The reason for not rejecting the hypothesis, $\beta_5^* = 0$, may be either the larger variance of $\hat{\beta}_5^*$ (relative to $V[\hat{\beta}_5]$) or the fact that β_5^* is smaller (in absolute value) than β_5 and more difficult to detect.

The example of Sec. 9.1 tells us that coding has no effect on the conclusions that one might draw from an analysis but it does change the interpretation of the model parameters. Thus a test of an hypothesis $H_0 \colon \beta_5 = 0$ associated with coding method 1 is the same as the hypothesis

$$H_0 \colon \ \beta_5^* + \tfrac{1}{2}\beta_8^* = 0$$

for coding method 2. The example also illustrates the importance of interpreting model parameters in terms of $E(y)$ or partial derivatives of $E(y)$ *defined at some particular point* in the experimental region rather than simply as certain types of "interactions."

9.3 Orthogonal Systems of Coding

The X matrix for coding method 1 of Sec. 9.1 possesses very special properties. Particularly, $(X'X)$ is a diagonal matrix and hence its inversion is a very simple operation. A similar result was observed for Example 7.7. Since the elements in the columns of the X matrix are determined by the method of coding, we would be interested in the properties required of the coding (and hence the X matrix) such that $(X'X)$ be diagonal.

Let us regard the columns of the $[n \times (k+1)]$-dimensional X matrix as $(n \times 1)$ submatrices (called *vectors*) such that

$$\underset{n \times 1}{\mathbf{x}_0}, \quad \underset{n \times 1}{\mathbf{x}_1}, \quad \ldots, \quad \underset{n \times 1}{\mathbf{x}_k}$$

represent the first, second, . . . , and the last columns of the X matrix. For example, $\mathbf{x}_0$, the vector corresponding to the n values of the dummy independent variable, $\mathbf{x}_0$, would be

$$\underset{n \times 1}{\mathbf{x}_0} = \begin{bmatrix} 1 \\ 1 \\ 1 \\ 1 \\ \cdot \\ \cdot \\ \cdot \\ 1 \\ 1 \end{bmatrix}.$$

Definition *Two vectors, $\mathbf{x}_i$, $\mathbf{x}_j$, are said to be* orthogonal *if* $\mathbf{x}_i'\mathbf{x}_j = 0$.

Example 9.1 Let

$$\mathbf{x}_1 = \begin{bmatrix} 1 \\ 1 \\ 1 \end{bmatrix} \quad \text{and} \quad \mathbf{x}_2 = \begin{bmatrix} -1 \\ 0 \\ 1 \end{bmatrix}.$$

Then

$$\mathbf{x}_1'\mathbf{x}_2 = \begin{bmatrix} 1 & 1 & 1 \end{bmatrix} \begin{bmatrix} -1 \\ 0 \\ 1 \end{bmatrix} = 0$$

and $\mathbf{x}_1$ and $\mathbf{x}_2$ are orthogonal.

It is apparent that all pairs of columns of the X matrix for Example 7.7 are orthogonal, so that all off-diagonal elements of $(X'X)$ equal zero.

Example 9.2 Let

$$X = \begin{bmatrix} 1 & -1 & -1 \\ 1 & -1 & 1 \\ 1 & -1 & 0 \\ 1 & 1 & 0 \\ 1 & 1 & 1 \\ 1 & 1 & -1 \end{bmatrix}.$$

Multiplying, $\mathbf{x}_0'\mathbf{x}_1 = 0$, $\mathbf{x}_0'\mathbf{x}_2 = 0$, and $\mathbf{x}_1'\mathbf{x}_2 = 0$. Also, $(X'X)$ is a diagonal matrix. Thus all pairs of vectors in X are orthogonal.

Definition *The vectors* $\mathbf{x}_0, \mathbf{x}_1, \mathbf{x}_2, \ldots, \mathbf{x}_k$ *are said to be mutually orthogonal if*

$$\mathbf{x}_i'\mathbf{x}_j = 0 \qquad \text{for all } i \text{ and } j, \, i \neq j.$$

Two facts concerning mutually orthogonal vectors are pertinent to our discussion. First, it can be shown that one can construct *at most* n mutually orthogonal vectors (where n is the number of elements in each vector). The second fact is stated in the following theorem, the proof of which is left to the reader.

Theorem 9.1 *Let the columns of an X matrix be denoted by the vectors* $\mathbf{x}_0,$ $\mathbf{x}_1, \mathbf{x}_2, \ldots, \mathbf{x}_k$. *If* $\mathbf{x}_0, \mathbf{x}_1, \mathbf{x}_2, \ldots, \mathbf{x}_k$ *form a mutually orthogonal set of vectors, then* $(X'X)$ *will be a diagonal matrix.*

It is interesting to note that if the linear model contains a parameter, β_0, and hence the first column, $\mathbf{x}_0$, is the $(n \times 1)$ matrix with transpose $\mathbf{x}_0' = \begin{bmatrix} 1 & 1 & 1 & \ldots & 1 \end{bmatrix}$, then the sum of the elements in each of the columns, $x_1, x_2, x_3, \ldots, x_k$, must equal zero in order that these column vectors be orthogonal to x_0.

To reduce the labor involved in the inversion of $(X'X)$ it is desirable to code so that most or all of the column vectors of the X matrix are orthogonal. A second consideration unrelated to orthogonality would imply that the coding should be such that the elements of the $(X'X)$ matrix are approximately of the same order of magnitude. This will tend to reduce rounding errors in the inversion of $(X'X)$.

9.4 Independent Linear Functions of a Set of Variables

It will be helpful at this point to indulge in an aside concerning linear algebra. The reader will recall from elementary algebra that a necessary condition for a unique solution to a set of p simultaneous linear equations in p unknowns is that the equations be *linearly independent*. Thus, the pair of simultaneous linear equations in x_1 and x_2,

$$(1) \quad 2x_1 + \ x_2 = 3,$$
$$(2) \quad 6x_1 + 3x_2 = 9,$$

does not possess a unique solution because equation (2) is equal to a multiple (3) of equation (1). Similarly, the equations

$$(1) \quad 2x_1 + x_2 + \ x_3 = 4,$$
$$(2) \quad \ x_1 + x_2 + 2x_3 = 3,$$
$$(3) \quad \ x_1 \qquad - \ x_3 = 1,$$

do not possess a unique solution because equation (3) is equal to the difference between equations (1) and (2). Thus they are *linearly dependent*. Note that we are speaking of dependence and independence in an algebraic rather than a probabilistic sense.

The concept of linear independence and its relation to linear functions can be easily illustrated using this last example. Let

$$l_1 = 2x_1 + x_2 + \ x_3,$$
$$l_2 = \ x_1 + x_2 + 2x_3,$$
$$l_3 = \ x_1 \qquad - \ x_3.$$

The linear dependence of the corresponding linear equations was indicated by the fact that

$$l_1 - l_2 = l_3$$

or

$$l_1 - l_2 - l_3 = 0.$$

And it is intuitively clear that linear independence of a set of three linear equations would imply the impossibility of expressing any one as a linear function of the others. Or, equivalently, the only values for c_1, c_2, and c_3 for which

$$c_1 l_1 + c_2 l_2 + c_3 l_3 = 0$$

identically for all values of x_1, x_2, and x_3 are $c_1 = c_2 = c_3 = 0$.

Definition   *Let $l_1, l_2, \ldots, l_p$ be a set of p linear functions of a set of variables, $x_1, x_2, x_3, \ldots, x_n$, $n \geq p$. Then $l_1, l_2, l_3, \ldots, l_p$ are said to be* linearly independent *if the function*

$$c_1 l_1 + c_2 l_2 + c_3 l_3 + \cdots + c_p l_p$$

vanishes for all $x_1, \ldots, x_n$ (identically in $x_1, \ldots, x_n$) only when $c_1 = c_2 = c_3 = \ldots = c_p = 0$.

For example, for the simultaneous linearly independent equations

$$\begin{aligned}
x_1 + x_2 + x_3 &= 5, \\
x_1 - x_2 + 3x_3 &= 7, \\
4x_1 - 3x_2 + x_3 &= -1,
\end{aligned}$$

and the associated linear functions

$$\begin{aligned}
l_1 &= x_1 + x_2 + x_3, \\
l_2 &= x_1 - x_2 + 3x_3, \\
l_3 &= 4x_1 - 3x_2 + x_3,
\end{aligned}$$

it is impossible to satisfy the equation

$$c_1 l_1 + c_2 l_2 + c_3 l_3 = 0$$

for values of c_1, c_2, and c_3 other than

$$c_1 = c_2 = c_3 = 0.$$

We will apply the above material in a discussion dealing with linearly independent functions of the parameters $\beta_0, \beta_1, \beta_2, \ldots, \beta_k$ of the general linear model.

9.5 Estimators of Linear Functions of the Model Parameters

Suppose that the general linear model for an experiment contains $(k + 1)$ estimable parameters, $\beta_0, \beta_1, \beta_2, \ldots, \beta_k$, with estimators, respectively, $\hat{\beta}_0, \hat{\beta}_1, \hat{\beta}_2, \ldots, \hat{\beta}_k$ (that is, the least-squares equations are linearly independent and hence $(X'X)$ possesses an inverse). Then it can be shown that the least-squares estimator of any linear function of the model parameters, say,

$$L = a_0\beta_0 + a_1\beta_1 + a_2\beta_2 + \cdots + a_k\beta_k,$$

is

$$\hat{L} = a_0\hat{\beta}_0 + a_1\hat{\beta}_1 + a_2\hat{\beta}_2 + \cdots + a_k\hat{\beta}_k.$$

Coding has the effect of making the parameters associated with one method equal to linear functions of the parameters of a second method. Hence, a generalization of the above statement follows. If one possesses the least-squares estimators of any $(k + 1)$ linearly independent functions of the model parameters, say,

$$L_0 = a_{00}\beta_0 + a_{01}\beta_1 + a_{02}\beta_2 + \cdots + a_{0k}\beta_k,$$
$$L_1 = a_{10}\beta_0 + a_{11}\beta_1 + a_{12}\beta_2 + \cdots + a_{1k}\beta_k,$$
$$\vdots$$
$$L_k = a_{k0}\beta_0 + a_{k1}\beta_1 + a_{k2}\beta_2 + \cdots + a_{kk}\beta_k,$$

then it can be shown that any other linear function of the parameters, say L_{k+1}, is equal to a linear function of $L_1, L_2, \ldots, L_k$ and the least-squares estimator of L_{k+1} is equal to the corresponding linear function of the estimators of $L_0, L_1, \ldots, L_k$.

Thus, if one acquires the least-squares estimators of one set of $(k + 1)$ independent linear functions of the model parameters, the least-squares estimators for any other linear function may be obtained by utilizing some linear combination of the $(k + 1)$ estimators. The experimenter often applies this interesting result by selecting a method of coding that leads to orthogonality of the vectors of the X matrix and consequent simplicity of computation even though the resulting model parameters may be nonsensical linear functions of the experimental parameters of interest. Estimates of these latter parameters may easily be obtained as linear functions of the estimates of the model parameters. For example, if one has obtained estimates $\hat{\beta}_1$ and $\hat{\beta}_2$ of the differences between treatments B and A and C and A, respectively, then an estimate of the difference between the mean response for treatments B and C is given by the linear function, $(\hat{\beta}_1 - \hat{\beta}_2)$. The application of the above procedure to simplify computation in fitting a linear model and in calculating the sums of squares for an analysis of variance will be apparent in the following sections.

Linear functions of random variables play an important role in fitting a general linear model to a set of points by the method of least squares. Indeed it can be shown that the least-squares estimator of any linear function of the parameters of the general linear model is a linear function of the n response measurements, $y_1, y_2, y_3, \ldots, y_n$.

It was mentioned in Sec. 7.7 that this estimator will be normally distributed in repeated sampling, a result that would follow directly from Theorem 1.3 concerning linear functions of normally distributed random variables.

9.6 Orthogonal Linear Contrasts

A particular class of independent linear functions are those which are *orthogonal*.

Definition   *Let l_1 and l_2 be two linear functions of the n response measurements associated with an experiment, $y_1, y_2, \ldots, y_n$—that is,*

$$l_1 = a_1 y_1 + a_2 y_2 + \cdots + a_n y_n,$$
$$l_2 = b_1 y_1 + b_2 y_2 + \cdots + b_n y_n.$$

Then l_1 and l_2 are said to be orthogonal if the covariance of l_1 and l_2, Cov (l_1, l_2), is equal to zero. A set of p linear functions, $l_1, l_2, \ldots, l_p$, $p \leq n$, are said to be mutually orthogonal if l_i is orthogonal to l_j for all i and j, $i \neq j$.

Expanding the expression for the covariance,

$$\text{Cov } (l_1, l_2) = E\{[l_1 - E(l_1)][l_2 - E(l_2)]\},$$

one can prove the following theorem concerning the necessary and sufficient condition for the orthogonality of l_1 and l_2.

Theorem 9.2   *Let l_1 and l_2 be linear functions of the response measurements $y_1, y_2, y_3, \ldots, y_n$. Then a necessary and sufficient condition for l_1 and l_2 to be orthogonal is that*

$$\sum_{i=1}^{n} a_i b_i = 0.$$

Since it is well known that two uncorrelated normally distributed random variables are statistically independent, the following theorem holds:

Theorem 9.3   *If l_1 and l_2 are orthogonal and $y_1, y_2, \ldots, y_n$ are independent and normally distributed, then l_1 and l_2 will be statistically independent. (Note: l_1 and l_2 will be normally distributed by Theorem 1.3 and Cov $(l_1, l_2) = 0$ because of the orthogonality of l_1 and l_2.)*

The reader will observe that the matrix product, $X'Y$, acquired in estimating the parameters of the linear model, is a $[(k + 1) \times 1]$ matrix, where each element is a linear function of $y_1, y_2, \ldots, y_n$. Thus

$$(X'Y) = \begin{bmatrix} l_0 \\ l_1 \\ l_2 \\ \cdot \\ \cdot \\ \cdot \\ l_k \end{bmatrix} = \begin{bmatrix} \mathbf{x}_0'Y \\ \mathbf{x}_1'Y \\ \mathbf{x}_2'Y \\ \cdot \\ \cdot \\ \cdot \\ \mathbf{x}_k'Y \end{bmatrix},$$

where the vectors $\mathbf{x}_0, \mathbf{x}_1, \mathbf{x}_2, \ldots, \mathbf{x}_k$ represent the columns of the X matrix as defined in Sec. 9.3, and the linear functions of $y_1, y_2, \ldots, y_n$ are $l_0 = \mathbf{x}_0'Y$, $l_1 = \mathbf{x}_1'Y$, $l_2 = \mathbf{x}_2'Y, \ldots, l_k = \mathbf{x}_k'Y$. The elements in a vector, $\mathbf{x}_i$ will be the coefficients of the variables in the linear function, l_i.

Then by Theorem 9.2 two linear functions, $l_i = \mathbf{x}_i'Y$ and $l_j = \mathbf{x}_j'Y$, $i \neq j$, will be orthogonal if the vectors $\mathbf{x}_i'$ and $\mathbf{x}_j'$ satisfy the property

$$\mathbf{x}_i'\mathbf{x}_j = 0$$

or, equivalently, if the vectors $\mathbf{x}_i$ and $\mathbf{x}_j$ are orthogonal. If this is true for all i and j, $i \neq j$, then $l_0, l_1, \ldots, l_k$ form a mutually orthogonal set of linear functions.

Definition *A linear function of $y_1, y_2, \ldots, y_n$, $l = a_1y_1 + a_2y_2 + a_3y_3 + \cdots + a_ny_n$, is called a linear contrast of $y_1, y_2, y_3, \ldots, y_n$ if*

$$\sum_{i=1}^{n} a_i = 0.$$

Since $\mathbf{x}_0$ will be of the form $\mathbf{x}_0' = \begin{bmatrix} 1 & 1 & 1 & \cdots & 1 \end{bmatrix}$ for all linear models containing the constant, β_0, it is necessary that $\mathbf{x}_0'\mathbf{x}_j$, the sum of the elements in the vector $\mathbf{x}_j$, equal zero in order for $\mathbf{x}_j$ to be orthogonal to $\mathbf{x}_0$. Thus a mutually orthogonal set of vectors, $\mathbf{x}_0, \mathbf{x}_1, \mathbf{x}_2, \ldots, \mathbf{x}_k$, representing the columns of the X matrix will be such that $l_1 = \mathbf{x}_1'Y, l_2 = \mathbf{x}_2'Y, \ldots, l_k = \mathbf{x}_k'Y$ will be a mutually orthogonal set of linear contrasts. Also, the diagonal elements of $(X'X)$ will be $\mathbf{x}_0'\mathbf{x}_0, \mathbf{x}_1'\mathbf{x}_1, \ldots, \mathbf{x}_k'\mathbf{x}_k$, respectively, where $\mathbf{x}_i'\mathbf{x}_i$ is equal to the sum of squares of the elements in the column $\mathbf{x}_i$. The reader may verify that the X matrix for Example 7.7 is constructed so that the sum of the elements in the ith columns, $i = 1, 2, 3, \ldots, k$, is equal to zero and the diagonal elements of $(X'X)$ are the sums of squares of the elements in the columns of the X matrix.

Proof is omitted, but it can be shown that one can construct n mutually orthogonal linear functions of the response measurements, $y_1, y_2, \ldots, y_n$, where $(k + 1)$ will be employed for estimating $(k + 1)$ independent linear functions of the model parameters (see Sec. 9.5) and $[n - (k + 1)]$ will be utilized for estimating σ^2. Orthogonal linear contrasts of the response measurements simplify the computations in fitting a linear model by diagonalizing $(X'X)$, and they assume a major role in the analysis of variance.

The following three theorems present the theory necessary for practical applications that follow. The first, relating to estimation, is not necessary for the discussion but it is of interest.

The theorems will be stated without proof, but a verification may be acquired by an examination of Example 7.7 or the example for coding method 1, Sec. 9.1.

Theorem 9.4 *If the X matrix is such that $l_1, \ldots, l_k$ represent a mutually orthogonal set of linear contrasts, then it can be shown that the estimator of β_i is*

$$\hat{\beta}_i = \frac{l_i}{x_i' x_i} = \frac{x_i' Y}{x_i' x_i}, \qquad i = 0, 1, 2, \ldots, k.$$

Note that l_i is the element in the ith row of the $(X'Y)$ matrix. Similarly, $x_i' x_i$ is the diagonal element in the ith row of the $(X'X)$ matrix and is equal to the sum of squares of the coefficients in the linear function l_i. Thus if

$$l_i = a_1 y_1 + a_2 y_2 + \cdots + a_n y_n$$

then

$$\hat{\beta}_i = \frac{l_i}{\sum\limits_{i=1}^{n} a_i^2}.$$

Example 9.3 Estimate β_1 for Example 7.7 by construction of the appropriate linear contrast of $y_1, y_2, \ldots, y_n$.

Solution: The second column of the X matrix is represented by the vector x_1 where

$$x_1' = [-1 \quad -1 \quad 1 \quad 1 \quad -1 \quad -1 \quad 1 \quad 1].$$

Then

$$l_1 = x_1' Y = -y_1 - y_2 + y_3 + y_4 - y_5 - y_6 + y_7 + y_8 = 4,$$

$$x_1' x_1 = \sum_{j=1}^{n} x_{1j}^2 = (-1)^2 + (-1)^2 + (1)^2 + (1)^2 + \cdots + (1)^2 = 8,$$

and

$$\hat{\beta}_1 = \frac{l_1}{x_1' x_1} = \frac{4}{8} = 0.50.$$

Theorem 9.5 *Refer to the conditions of Theorem 9.4. The sum of squares associated with a parameter β_i estimated by a linear contrast $l_i / x_i' x_i$ is*

$$SS(l_i) = \frac{l_i^2}{x_i' x_i}.$$

Theorem 9.5 can be justified by examination of the procedure for computing SS(l_i). These computations are simplified for the conditions stated above—that is, when $l_0, l_1, l_2, \ldots, l_k$ represent mutually orthogonal linear functions of $y_1, y_2, \ldots, y_n$.

The drop in sums of squares associated with β_i will equal

$$\text{SSE}_1 - \text{SSE}_2 = (Y'Y - \hat{\beta}'_* X'_* Y) - (Y'Y - \hat{\beta}'X'Y)$$
$$= \hat{\beta}'X'Y - \hat{\beta}'_* X'_* Y$$

when X_* is the reduced data matrix obtained from the X matrix by deleting the vector $\mathbf{x}_i$. Since the only difference between $\hat{\beta}X'Y$ and $\hat{\beta}_* X'_* Y$ would be the product, $\hat{\beta}_i \mathbf{x}'_i Y$, the sum of squares associated with the parameter β_i (or, one might say, with the linear contrast l_i) is

$$\hat{\beta}_i \mathbf{x}'_i Y = \frac{l_i^2}{\mathbf{x}'_i \mathbf{x}_i}.$$

Example 9.4   Find the sum of squares associated with β_i, Example 7.7.

Solution: From Theorem 9.5, this sum of squares is

$$\text{SS}(l_i) = \frac{l_i^2}{\mathbf{x}'_1 \mathbf{x}_1}.$$

From Example 9.3, $l_1 = 4$ and $\mathbf{x}'_1 \mathbf{x}_1 = 8$. Then

$$\text{SS}(l_1) = \frac{(4)^2}{8} = 2.$$

This result may be verified by employing the procedure of Sec. 8.2, fitting the complete and reduced linear models (the reduced linear model may be obtained by deleting $\beta_1 x_1$ from the complete linear model), and calculating the drop in the sum of squares for error.

Theorem 9.6   *Let $\beta_{g+1}, \beta_{g+2}, \ldots, \beta_k$ be $(k - g)$ parameters of the linear model estimated by the mutually orthogonal linear contrasts,*

$$\hat{\beta}_i = \frac{l_i}{\mathbf{x}'_i \mathbf{x}_i},$$

where $l_i = \mathbf{x}'_i Y$ and the sum of squares associated with the parameter β_i is

$$\text{SS}(l_i) = \frac{l_i^2}{\mathbf{x}'_i \mathbf{x}_i} . \dagger$$

If SST *represents the sum of squares associated with the set of parameters β_{g+1}, $\beta_{g+2}, \ldots, \beta_k$, then (it can be shown that)*

$$\text{SST} = \text{SS}(l_{g+1}) + \text{SS}(l_{g+2}) + \cdots + \text{SS}(l_k),$$

†These conditions will hold when the $\mathbf{x}_i$, $i = g + 1, g + 2, \ldots, k$, are mutually orthogonal and are orthogonal to the remaining vectors in the X matrix.

where $\text{SS}(l_{g+1})$, $\text{SS}(l_{g+2})$, . . . , $\text{SS}(l_k)$ *each possess one degree of freedom.*

Theorem 9.6 states that the sums of squares of orthogonal linear contrasts of the response measurements are additive and will apply to *any* mutually orthogonal set of contrasts that one may wish to construct. Particularly note that $l_1, l_2, \ldots, l_g$, the remaining linear functions, need not be mutually orthogonal. In effect, we may partition the sum of squares, SST, based upon $(k - g)$ degrees of freedom into $(k - g)$ sums of squares each possessing a single degree of freedom. Since the method of coding will determine the estimated linear function of the model parameters, we may ignore the X matrix and construct any set of orthogonal linear contrasts for the estimation of a set of independent linear functions of a specified set of model parameters. The sum of squares associated with a specific linear contrast,

$$l_1 = a_1 y_1 + a_2 y_2 + \cdots + a_n y_n,$$

will always equal

$$\text{SS}(l_1) = \frac{(l_i)^2}{\sum\limits_{i=1}^{n} a_i^2}.$$

Theorem 9.6 is particularly useful for partitioning the sums of squares for a set of parameters, say treatments, into sums of squares based on single degrees of freedom. These are unimportant from the standpoint of hypothesis testing because we have noted that a single-degree-of-freedom t-test is equivalent to an F-test based upon 1 and ν degrees of freedom (see Sec. 8.10). Such a test is important, however, for computing single-degree-of-freedom sums of squares required in the analysis of variance so that SSE can be easily acquired by subtracting various factor and interaction sums of squares from the "total"

$$\sum_{i=1}^{n} (y_i - \bar{y})^2.$$

This technique for calculating the sums of squares for the linear component of speed and the (linear speed) $\times$ (insulation) interaction for Example 8.6 would have eliminated the need for repeated fittings of the linear model to calculate the sum of squares for "lack of fit." Linear contrasts estimating linear, quadratic, cubic, and higher-order effects associated with quantitative variables will be discussed in Sec. 9.8.

Example 9.5   Refer to the randomized block design, Example 7.8. Construct a mutually orthogonal set of three linear contrasts of the treatment means such that the sum of their respective sums of squares will equal the sum of squares for treatments.

Solution: The experiment contained four treatments and therefore three parameters in the linear model representing treatment differences. We may therefore construct a set of three orthogonal linear contrasts for the treatment means. The contrasts constructed will usually be meaningful from a practical point of view but they need not be. For example, one might use

$$l_1 = \bar{T}_A - \bar{T}_B,$$
$$l_2 = \bar{T}_C - \bar{T}_D,$$
$$l_3 = \bar{T}_A + \bar{T}_B - \bar{T}_C - \bar{T}_D.$$

(We will leave the verification of the orthogonality of $l_1, l_2,$ and l_3 as an exercise for the reader.)

Since each treatment mean contains three observations, it is clear that

$$l_1 = \frac{y_{A1} + y_{A2} + y_{A3} - y_{B1} - y_{B2} - y_{B3}}{3},$$

$$l_2 = \frac{y_{C1} + y_{C2} + y_{C3} - y_{D1} - y_{D2} - y_{D3}}{3},$$

$$l_3 = \frac{y_{A1} + y_{A2} + y_{A3} + y_{B1} + y_{B2} + y_{B3} - y_{C1} - y_{C2} - y_{C3} - y_{D1} - y_{D2} - y_{D3}}{3}.$$

Therefore, the sum of squares of the coefficients of the variables in the linear function l_1 will be

$$\mathbf{x}_1'\mathbf{x}_1 = (\tfrac{1}{3})^2 + (\tfrac{1}{3})^2 + \cdots + (\tfrac{1}{3})^2 = 6(\tfrac{1}{9}) = \tfrac{2}{3}.$$

Similarly, $\mathbf{x}_2'\mathbf{x}_2 = \tfrac{2}{3}$ and $\mathbf{x}_3'\mathbf{x}_3 = \tfrac{4}{3}$. Then

$$\mathrm{SS}(l_1) = \frac{l_1^2}{\mathbf{x}_1'\mathbf{x}_1} = \frac{(11.4 - 12.3333)^2}{\tfrac{2}{3}} = 1.307,$$

$$\mathrm{SS}(l_2) = \frac{l_2^2}{\mathbf{x}_2'\mathbf{x}_2} = \frac{(12.8 - 11.2)^2}{\tfrac{2}{3}} = 3.840,$$

$$\mathrm{SS}(l_3) = \frac{l_3^2}{\mathbf{x}_3'\mathbf{x}_3} = \frac{(11.4 + 12.3333 - 11.2 - 12.8)^2}{\tfrac{4}{3}} = 0.053.$$

The sums of squares for treatments, Example 7.8, was found to equal 5.2. It is easy to see that addition of the sums of squares for the single degrees of freedom is equal to the sum of squares for treatments. Thus

$$\mathrm{SS}(l_1) + \mathrm{SS}(l_2) + \mathrm{SS}(l_3) = 1.307 + 3.840 + 0.053 = 5.2.$$

9.7 Orthogonal Linear Contrasts for Main Effects in a k-way Classification

Orthogonal linear contrasts associated with the main-effects parameters for a factor in a k-way classification, say factor A, can be constructed by forming orthogonal linear contrasts of the factor totals or means (recall that all cell totals are assumed to be based upon the same number of measurements). The resulting contrasts can be shown to estimate the same orthogonal linear functions of the expected values of the factor totals.

For example, suppose that three degrees of freedom are associated with factor A (four levels for factor A) and we wish to construct three corresponding orthogonal linear contrasts. The first is easily chosen by observation, say,

$$l_1 = a_1 A_1 + a_2 A_2 + a_3 A_3 + a_4 A_4 = A_1 - A_2,$$

where $a_1 = 1$, $a_2 = -1$, $a_3 = 0$, and $a_4 = 0$. Then a contrast orthogonal to l_1 will be

$$l_2 = b_1 A_1 + b_2 A_2 + b_3 A_3 + b_4 A_4,$$

where b_1, b_2, b_3, and b_4 must satisfy the relations

$$\sum_{i=1}^{4} b_i = 0 \qquad \text{or} \qquad b_1 + b_2 + b_3 + b_4 = 0,$$

$$\sum_{i=1}^{4} a_i b_i = 0 \qquad \text{or} \qquad b_1 - b_2 = 0.$$

These two simultaneous linear equations in four unknowns, b_1, b_2, b_3, and b_4, clearly do not possess a unique solution; therefore we must place two additional linearly independent restrictions upon the unknowns, say $b_1 = 1$ and $b_4 = 0$, and solve for $b_2 = 1$ and $b_3 = -2$. Hence the second linear contrast is

$$l_2 = A_1 + A_2 - 2A_3.$$

A quick check will indicate that l_2 is a contrast and is orthogonal to l_1.

Finally, let

$$l_3 = c_1 A_1 + c_2 A_2 + c_3 A_3 + c_4 A_4,$$

where, in order for l_3 to be a linear contrast orthogonal to both l_1 and l_2, we require

$$\sum_{i=1}^{4} c_i = 0 \qquad \text{or} \qquad c_1 + c_2 + c_3 + c_4 = 0,$$

$$\sum_{i=1}^{4} a_i c_i = 0 \qquad \text{or} \qquad c_1 - c_2 = 0,$$

$$\sum_{i=1}^{4} b_i c_i = 0 \qquad \text{or} \qquad c_1 + c_2 - 2c_3 = 0.$$

With three equations in four unknowns, we must add a fourth linearly independent restriction on the unknowns, say $c_1 = 1$, and solve for $c_2 = 1$, $c_3 = 1$, and $c_4 = -3$. Then $l_3 = A_1 + A_2 + A_3 - 3A_4$ and l_1, l_2, and l_3 are mutually orthogonal.

Noting the pattern in the orthogonal linear functions,

$$l_1 = A_1 - A_2,$$
$$l_2 = A_1 + A_2 - 2A_3,$$
$$l_3 = A_1 + A_2 + A_3 - 3A_4,$$

we might suppose that a set of k mutually orthogonal linear contrasts of k means, $A_1, A_2, \ldots, A_k$, could be constructed by using

$$l_4 = A_1 + A_2 + A_3 + A_4 - 4A_5,$$
$$l_5 = A_1 + A_2 + A_3 + A_4 + A_5 - 5A_6,$$

and, in general,

$$l_i = A_1 + A_2 + \cdots + A_i - (i)A_{i+1}, \qquad i \leq k.$$

A check of the coefficients of these linear functions will reveal that they satisfy the necessary condition for orthogonality and that they are contrasts and form a mutually orthogonal set.

The procedure described above for constructing sets of orthogonal linear contrasts is direct but tedious. In most practical problems the experimenter

Figure 9.1 X-matrix showing coefficients for orthogonal contrasts

(a)

$$Y = \begin{bmatrix} y_{11} \\ y_{12} \\ \cdot \\ \cdot \\ \cdot \\ \hline y_{21} \\ y_{22} \\ \cdot \\ \cdot \\ \cdot \\ \hline y_{31} \\ y_{32} \\ \cdot \\ \cdot \\ \cdot \\ \hline y_{41} \\ y_{42} \\ \cdot \\ \cdot \\ \cdot \end{bmatrix} \qquad X = \begin{bmatrix} 1 & 1 & 1 & 1 & \cdots \\ 1 & 1 & 1 & 1 & \cdots \\ \cdot & \cdot & \cdot & \cdot & \\ \cdot & \cdot & \cdot & \cdot & \\ \cdot & \cdot & \cdot & \cdot & \\ 1 & 1 & 1 & 1 & \cdots \\ \hline 1 & -1 & 1 & 1 & \cdots \\ 1 & -1 & 1 & 1 & \cdots \\ \cdot & \cdot & \cdot & \cdot & \\ \cdot & \cdot & \cdot & \cdot & \\ \cdot & \cdot & \cdot & \cdot & \\ 1 & -1 & 1 & 1 & \cdots \\ \hline 1 & 0 & -2 & 1 & \cdots \\ 1 & 0 & -2 & 1 & \cdots \\ \cdot & \cdot & \cdot & \cdot & \\ \cdot & \cdot & \cdot & \cdot & \\ \cdot & \cdot & \cdot & \cdot & \\ 1 & 0 & -2 & 1 & \cdots \\ \hline 1 & 0 & 0 & -3 & \cdots \\ 1 & 0 & 0 & -3 & \cdots \\ \cdot & \cdot & \cdot & \cdot & \\ \cdot & \cdot & \cdot & \cdot & \\ \cdot & \cdot & \cdot & \cdot & \\ 1 & 0 & 0 & -3 & \cdots \end{bmatrix}$$

Figure 9.1   (continued)

(b)

	X_1	X_2	X_3
A_1	1	1	1
A_2	-1	1	1
A_3	0	-2	1
A_4	0	0	-3

will have one (or perhaps more) linear contrasts of practical interest. With a bit of experience he can add the other orthogonal linear contrasts to the set by trial and error as long as the number is not too large.

Keep in mind that selecting the coefficients for a linear contrast is *equivalent* to choosing the elements of a column of the X matrix. The orthogonal vectors for the three contrasts for factor A, indicated as x_1, x_2, x_3, would appear in the X matrix as shown in Fig. 9.1(a). The associated Y matrix showing the treatment responses is also included in Fig. 9.1(a).

A simplified method for constructing the contrasts is indicated in Fig. 9.1(b). Since each total contains the same number of observations and each response in a total *receives the same coefficient*, all of the information concerning the linear contrasts given in the Y and X matrices of Fig. 9.1(a) is contained in Fig. 9.1(b). The first column of Fig. 9.1(b) showing the totals, A_1, A_2, A_3, and A_4, provides a condensation of the pertinent information (concerning the ordering of the response measurements $y_1, y_2, \ldots, y_n$) contained in the Y matrix. Similarly, the information contained in the three vectors, x_1, x_2, and x_3, is indicated in columns 2, 3, and 4.

9.8 Orthogonal Linear Contrasts for Interactions in a k-way Classification

The calculation of single-degree-of-freedom contrasts associated with factor interactions in a k-way classification can be easily illustrated by expanding upon the previous example. Suppose that two of the factors are A (at four levels) and B (at three levels) and that the three orthogonal contrasts for A are identified with the orthogonal vectors x_1, x_2, and x_3 as shown in Fig. 9.1(a). Two orthogonal linear contrasts of the factor-B totals, B_1, B_2, and B_3, are

$$l_4 = B_1 - B_2,$$

and

$$l_5 = B_1 + B_2 - 2B_3.$$

The reader will recall that interaction terms in the factorial linear model are those involving cross products of the main-effect variables (such as $x_1 x_2$, $x_1 x_2 x_3^2$, and so on). Two-way cross products represent two-way interactions and, in general, k-way cross products are associated with k-way interactions. (See Sec. 5.3.) Furthermore, the elements in the vector of the X matrix corresponding to the x_1x_2 interaction term are obtained by multiplying corresponding elements in the vectors $\mathbf{x}_1$ and $\mathbf{x}_2$. With this in mind, we can find the coefficients for orthogonal linear contrasts for interactions by constructing a table similar to Fig. 9.1(b).

Let $(AB)_{ij}$ represent the total of observations measured at the ith level of A and the jth level of B. These twelve totals are shown in the first column of Fig. 9.2 and correspond to the ordering of the response measurements, y, in the Y matrix. The second, third, and fourth columns correspond to the x_1, x_2, and x_3 columns of the X matrix, Fig. 9.1(a); the fifth and sixth columns, x_4 and x_5, identify the elements that would appear in the two orthogonal vectors for the two linear contrasts for factor B.

Figure 9.2   Condensed representation of the
Y and X matrices for a k-way classification

$(AB)_{ij}$	x_1	x_2	x_3	x_4	x_5	(x_1x_4)
$(AB)_{11}$	1	1	1	1	1	1
$(AB)_{12}$	1	1	1	-1	1	-1
$(AB)_{13}$	1	1	1	0	-2	0
$(AB)_{21}$	-1	1	1	1	1	-1
$(AB)_{22}$	-1	1	1	-1	1	1
$(AB)_{23}$	-1	1	1	0	-2	0
$(AB)_{31}$	0	-2	1	1	1	0
$(AB)_{32}$	0	-2	1	-1	1	0
$(AB)_{33}$	0	-2	1	0	-2	0
$(AB)_{41}$	0	0	-3	1	1	0
$(AB)_{42}$	0	0	-3	-1	1	0
$(AB)_{43}$	0	0	-3	0	-2	0

Six columns would appear in the X matrix, Fig. 9.1(a), corresponding to the six degrees of freedom for the AB interactions (and the six terms in the linear model). These vectors would be obtained by multiplying corresponding elements in the vector pairs, $(\mathbf{x}_1, \mathbf{x}_4)$, $(\mathbf{x}_1, \mathbf{x}_5)$, $(\mathbf{x}_2, \mathbf{x}_4)$, $(\mathbf{x}_2, \mathbf{x}_5)$, $(\mathbf{x}_3, \mathbf{x}_4)$, and $(\mathbf{x}_3, \mathbf{x}_5)$. A condensation of this information for one of the interaction contrasts, (x_1x_4), is shown as the seventh column of Fig. 9.2. Thus, the orthogonal contrast corresponding to the (x_1x_4) interaction, denoted as l_6, is

$$l_6 = (AB)_{11} - (AB)_{12} - (AB)_{21} + (AB)_{22}.$$

The other five linear contrasts can be obtained in a similar manner.

Example 9.6   A manufacturing concern producing individual job-lot orders for the chemical, steel, and petroleum industries wished to compare the profit per job per unit time expended (hereinafter called "profit") for two different salesmen for each of the types of industry. Each salesman was responsible for estimating the cost of a job, and it was therefore possible for a sizable difference in expected profit to exist between two salesmen.

The two salesmen, A_1 and A_2, and the three industries, B_1, B_2, B_3, form a 2×3 factorial arrangement. Four contracts previously negotiated were randomly selected for each salesman-industry combination. The recorded profit is shown in the accompanying table.

	B_1	B_2	B_3
A_1	8.4	10.3	9.8
	7.1	7.4	7.5
	6.0	7.1	11.9
	9.9	8.9	9.1
A_2	4.6	7.7	12.1
	7.8	9.3	14.7
	5.9	8.2	9.3
	8.0	6.6	10.9

It is thought that salesman A_1 is likely to achieve a higher average profit than A_2 in the chemical industry (B_1) but that the reverse is true for the petroleum industry (B_3). Do the data present sufficient evidence to indicate an interaction between the difference between salesman and the difference between the chemical and petroleum industries?

Solution: Let

$$l_1 = A_1 - A_2$$

and

$$l_2 = B_1 - B_3$$

be two linear contrasts of the salesmen and industry totals, respectively, with associated vectors in the X matrix, $\mathbf{x}_1$ and $\mathbf{x}_2$. Failure of the expected difference in profit between the salesmen, estimated by $l_1/\mathbf{x}_1'\mathbf{x}_1$ (see Theorem 9.4), to be the same from chemical industry to petroleum industry would imply an interaction between the l_1 and l_2 contrasts. Hence one would wish to test the hypothesis that $\beta_3 = 0$, where β_3 is the coefficient of $x_3 = x_1 x_2$ in the linear model.

The single-degree-of-freedom sum of squares for the l_1 by l_2 interaction will be calculated by constructing a condensed representation of a portion of the Y and X matrices (corresponding to Fig. 9.2). This is shown in Figure 9.3.

Then l_3, the linear contrast for the single degree of freedom for the $x_3 = x_1 x_2$ interaction, is

$$l_3 = (AB)_{11} - (AB)_{13} - (AB)_{21} + (AB)_{23}$$
$$= 31.4 \quad - \quad 38.3 \quad - \quad 26.3 \quad + \quad 47.0$$
$$= 13.8.$$

Figure 9.3 Condensed representation of a portion
of the Y and X matrices for Example 9.6

i, j	$(AB)_{ij}$	x_1	x_2	$x_3 = x_1 x_2$
1, 1	31.4	1	1	1
1, 2	33.7	1	0	0
1, 3	38.3	1	-1	-1
2, 1	26.3	-1	1	-1
2, 2	31.8	-1	0	0
2, 3	47.0	-1	-1	1

Each $(AB)_{ij}$ is a total of four measurements. Therefore, the columns in the complete X matrix corresponding to x_1, x_2, and $x_3 = x_1 x_2$ would imply four replications of the columns of Fig. 9.3, and each would contain 24 elements (since $n = 24$). Then the sum of squares of the elements in the $x_3 = x_1 x_2$ column would equal $\mathbf{x}_3' \mathbf{x}_3 = 16$ and

$$SS(l_3) = \frac{l_3^2}{\mathbf{x}_3' \mathbf{x}_3} = \frac{(13.8)^2}{16} = 11.90.$$

It may be verified that $s^2 = 2.90$ for this example. Then, since l_3 is based upon a single degree of freedom, $SS(l_3) = MS(l_3)$ and the F-statistic for testing the hypothesis, $\beta_3 = 0$, is

$$F = \frac{11.90}{2.90} = 4.10.$$

The computed value of F, based on $\nu_1 = 1$ and $\nu_2 = 18$ degrees of freedom, exceeds $F_{.10} = 3.01$ but is less than $F_{.05} = 4.41$. Hence there is sufficient evidence to reject the null hypothesis at the $\alpha = .10$ (but not at the $\alpha = .05$) level of significance. Thus it appears that this interaction does exist, and salesman A_1 appears to be better than A_2 in the chemical industry but the reverse is true in the petroleum industry. Since the test was not statistically significant at the $\alpha = .05$ level, we might wish to confirm the observed results with more data.

The primary objective of Example 9.6 is to illustrate the method for calculating the sums of squares for a single-degree-of-freedom interaction contrast. In addition, the example demonstrates an alternative procedure (the analysis-of-variance F-test) for testing the hypothesis that $\beta_3 = 0$. With the coding implied by l_1 and l_2, the Student's t-test could have been employed to give the same result. From Sec. 7.4,

$$\hat{\beta}_3 = \frac{l_3}{\mathbf{x}_3' \mathbf{x}_3}, \qquad c_{33} = \frac{1}{\mathbf{x}_3' \mathbf{x}_3},$$

and

$$t = \frac{\hat{\beta}_3}{s\sqrt{\dfrac{1}{\mathbf{x}_3' \mathbf{x}_3}}}.$$

Note that

$$F = \frac{\text{MS}(l_3)}{s^2} = \frac{\frac{l_3^2}{\mathbf{x}_3' \mathbf{x}_3}}{s^2} = t^2.$$

9.9 Orthogonal Polynomials

Coding a set of independent variables requires a transformation from the existing or uncoded variables to a new and coded set. If we denote the original and the coded variables as $v_1, v_2, \ldots, v_p$, and $x_1, x_2, \ldots, x_p$, respectively, the transformation expresses each x_i as a function of $v_1, v_2, \ldots, v_p$—that is,

$$x_1 = \Phi_1(v_1, v_2, \ldots, v_p),$$
$$x_2 = \Phi_2(v_1, v_2, \ldots, v_p),$$
$$\cdot$$
$$\cdot$$
$$\cdot$$
$$x_p = \Phi_p(v_1, v_2, \ldots, v_p).$$

The simple codings of Chapters 6 and 7 for equally spaced variables were linear transformations applied to translate the origin to the center of the experimental region and achieve orthogonality between some vectors in the X matrix. And although the functional relations expressing the coded variables in terms of the uncoded in Sec. 9.6 were not given explicitly, the substitution of orthogonal vectors representing linear contrasts for the original nonorthogonal vectors associated with some factor in an orthogonal design implied a transformation of the independent variables.

We now consider the problem of constructing orthogonal contrasts for the main-effect terms of *quantitative* variables that will simplify the computation involved in fitting a polynomial to a set of data or including polynomial terms in a model containing both qualitative and quantitative variables. Since a vector of the X matrix is associated with each dummy variable (representing one degree of freedom) for a qualitative variable, we will expect to transform the main-effect terms for a quantitative variable, say $x_1 = x$, $x_2 = x^2$, $x_3 = x^3$, and so on, so that the vectors for $x, x^2, x^3, \ldots$, are mutually orthogonal.

The new independent variables are known as *orthogonal polynomials* and the method is due to the Russian mathematician, Tchebysheff (who is also responsible for Theorem 1.1, Chapter 1, to which his name is attached). The method which we describe is appropriate for equally spaced independent variables with the same number of measurements at each level, but orthogonal polynomials can be constructed to apply to any spacing.

Let x be a quantitative independent variable investigated at t equally spaced levels, and for the sake of simplicity assume that the response is measured once at each level. Then, as noted in Chapter 5, the main-effect terms in the linear model associated with x may include $x_1 = x$, $x_2 = x^2$, $x_3 = x^3, \ldots, x_{t-1} = x^{t-1}$, or any subset of these terms (in case we wish to omit some). Then Tchebysheff's transformation expresses $x_1, x_2, x_3, \ldots, x_{t-1}$ in terms of new independent variables, $u_1, u_2, u_3, \ldots, u_{t-1}$, where the response y may be written as a function of either the old or new independent variables,

$$y = \beta_0 x_0 + \beta_1 x + \beta_2 x^2 + \beta_3 x^3 + \cdots + \beta_{t-1} x^{t-1} + \epsilon$$
$$= \alpha_0 u_0 + \alpha_1 u_1 + \alpha_2 u_2 + \alpha_3 u_3 + \cdots + \alpha_{t-1} u_{t-1} + \epsilon$$

and

$$u_0 = x_0 = 1,$$
$$u_1 = C_{10} + C_{11} x,$$
$$u_2 = C_{20} + C_{21} x + C_{22} x^2,$$
$$u_3 = C_{30} + C_{31} x + C_{32} x^2 + C_{33} x^3,$$

$$\cdot$$
$$\cdot$$
$$\cdot$$

$$u_{t-1} = C_{t-1,0} + C_{t-1,1} x + C_{t-1,2} x^2 + C_{t-1,3} x^3 + \cdots + C_{t-1,t-1} x^{t-1}.$$

Having transformed to a new set of independent variables, we now wish to estimate the parameters, $\alpha_0, \alpha_1, \ldots, \alpha_{t-1}$. The new data matrix, the U matrix, corresponds to the X matrix, and gives the values of $u_0, u_1, u_2, u_3, \ldots, u_{t-1}$ for each of the n data points. The elements $C_{10}, C_{11}, \ldots$, and, in general, C_{ij}, $i = 1, 2, \ldots, (t-1)$ and $j \leq i$, are selected so that the columns of the U matrix, represented by the vectors $u_0, u_1, \ldots, u_{t-1}$, will be mutually orthogonal and hence $U'U$ will be diagonal. Letting

$$C = \begin{bmatrix} 1 & 0 & 0 & 0 & 0 & \cdots & 0 \\ C_{10} & C_{11} & 0 & 0 & 0 & \cdots & 0 \\ C_{20} & C_{21} & C_{22} & 0 & 0 & \cdots & 0 \\ \cdot & & & & & & \\ \cdot & & & & & & \\ C_{t-1,0} & C_{t-1,1} & C_{t-1,2} & \cdot & \cdot & \cdot & C_{t-1,t-1} \end{bmatrix}$$

we can see that the original and transformed data matrices, X and U, are related as

$$U = XC'.$$

Thus one wishes to choose the elements of the C matrix so that $U'U$ is a diagonal matrix.

The detail of the calculation of the values of the orthogonal polynomials, $u_1, u_2, \ldots, u_{t-1}$ is not essential to our discussion since the polynomials have been tabulated. The interested reader will find a treatment of this topic in Anderson and Bancroft (1952). The values of the elements of the C matrix as well as the computed values of the orthogonal polynomials for equal spacing and $t = 3$ to 52 levels are given in the *Biometrika Tables for Statisticians*. Since polynomials higher than the sixth power are rarely required, these reproduced tables give the values of only the first six orthogonal polynomials, $u_1, u_2, u_3, \ldots, u_6$, where the number of levels of the independent variable, x, is greater than or equal to seven. A similar table by Anderson and Houseman (1942) provides for a larger number of equally spaced values of the independent variable ($t = 3$ to 104) with u_i, $i = 1$ to 5.

In order to relate the new independent variables, $u_1, u_2, \ldots, u_{t-1}$, to the independent variable, x, one must locate the origin and the units of measurement for x. We will assume that x is coded so that it assumes values $1, 2, 3, 4, \ldots, t$. Then it can be shown that

$$u_1 = \lambda_1(x - \bar{x}),$$

$$u_2 = \lambda_2\left[(x - \bar{x})^2 - \frac{t^2 - 1}{12}\right],$$

$$u_3 = \lambda_3\left[(x - \bar{x})^3 - (x - \bar{x})\frac{3t^2 - 7}{20}\right],$$

$$u_4 = \lambda_4\left[(x - \bar{x})^4 - (x - \bar{x})^2\left(\frac{3t^2 - 13}{14}\right) + \frac{3(t^2 - 1)(t^2 - 9)}{560}\right],$$

$$u_5 = \lambda_5\left[(x - \bar{x})^5 - (x - \bar{x})^3\left(\frac{5}{18}\right)(t^2 - 7) + \frac{(x - \bar{x})(15t^4 - 230t^2 + 407)}{1008}\right],$$

$$u_6 = \lambda_6\left[(x - \bar{x})^6 - \frac{5}{44}(x - \bar{x})^4(3t^2 - 31) + (x - \bar{x})^2\frac{(5t^4 - 110t^2 + 329)}{176}\right.$$
$$\left. - \frac{5}{14{,}784}(t^2 - 1)(t^2 - 9)(t^2 - 25)\right],$$

where t is the number of levels of x (or equally spaced points), and $\lambda_1, \lambda_2, \ldots, \lambda_6$ are constants that are functions of t and are tabulated along with values of the orthogonal polynomials.

To predict particular values of y or $E(y)$ for a given value of x, one could substitute x into the above expressions and obtain specific values of $u_1, u_2, \ldots, u_6$ to substitute into the fitted prediction function,

$$\hat{y} = \hat{\alpha}_0 + \hat{\alpha}_1 u_1 + \hat{\alpha}_2 u_2 + \cdots + \hat{\alpha}_6 u_6.$$

If $\hat{y}$ is desired in terms of the original independent variable, x, the polynomials $u_1, u_2, \ldots, u_6$ given in the preceding paragraph may be substituted into the expression for $\hat{y}$. Clearly, this is a tedious procedure and provides a strong argument for utilizing the prediction equation expressed in terms of the orthogonal polynomials, $u_1, u_2, \ldots, u_6$.

The tabulated values of the orthogonal polynomials for $t = 3$ to $t = 10$ are given in Table 7, Appendix III.

Example 9.7   Fit a cubic polynomial to the following data points.

y	5.8	3.1	3.2	6.0	7.3	8.1	6.2
x	1	2	3	4	5	6	7

Solution: The linear model for this example is

$$y = \alpha_0 + \alpha_1 u_1 + \alpha_2 u_2 + \alpha_3 u_3 + \epsilon,$$

where, from the preceding discussion,

$$u_0 = 1,$$

$$u_1 = (x - \bar{x}),$$

$$u_2 = (x - \bar{x})^2 - \frac{t^2 - 1}{12},$$

$$u_3 = \frac{1}{6}\left[(x - \bar{x})^3 - (x - \bar{x})\frac{3t^2 - 7}{20}\right].$$

The values of $\lambda_1, \lambda_2,$ and λ_3 were obtained from the bottom line of Table 7 for $t = 7$.

The Y matrix is given below with the corresponding U matrix, the columns of which were obtained from Table 7. The reader may verify that these elements are correct by substituting the various values for x into the expressions for $u_1, u_2,$ and u_3 given in the preceding paragraph.

$$Y = \begin{bmatrix} 5.8 \\ 3.1 \\ 3.2 \\ 6.0 \\ 7.3 \\ 8.1 \\ 6.2 \end{bmatrix}, \qquad U = \begin{bmatrix} 1 & -3 & 5 & -1 \\ 1 & -2 & 0 & 1 \\ 1 & -1 & -3 & 1 \\ 1 & 0 & -4 & 0 \\ 1 & 1 & -3 & -1 \\ 1 & 2 & 0 & -1 \\ 1 & 3 & 5 & 1 \end{bmatrix}.$$

Then

$$\hat{\alpha} = \begin{bmatrix} \hat{\alpha}_0 \\ \hat{\alpha}_1 \\ \hat{\alpha}_2 \\ \hat{\alpha}_3 \end{bmatrix} = (U'U)^{-1}U'Y.$$

The computation of the matrix products is not required since it is clear that the vectors $\mathbf{u}_0$, $\mathbf{u}_1$, $\mathbf{u}_2$, and $\mathbf{u}_3$ are mutually orthogonal. Then from Theorem 9.6

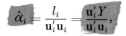

$$\hat{\alpha}_i = \frac{l_i}{\mathbf{u}_i'\mathbf{u}_i} = \frac{\mathbf{u}_i'Y}{\mathbf{u}_i'\mathbf{u}_i},$$

were omitted

where the values of $\mathbf{u}_i'\mathbf{u}_i$ are given in the next-to-last line of Table 7. The computations are given in Table 9.2.

Table 9.2 Computed values of parameters for Example 9.7

i	$l_i = \mathbf{u}_i'Y$	$\mathbf{u}_i'\mathbf{u}_i$	α_i
0	39.7	7	5.671
1	15.3	28	.546
2	4.5	84	.054
3	−8.7	6	−1.450

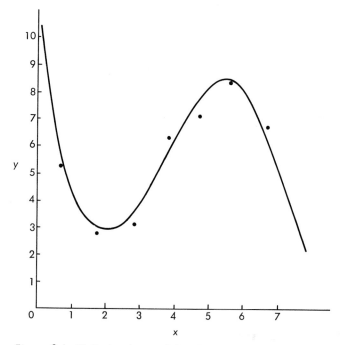

Figure 9.4 Plotted points and fitted cubic curve for Example 9.7

The fitted polynomial is

$$\hat{y} = 5.671 + .546u_1 + .054u_2 - 1.450u_3.$$

The plotted points and a graph of $\hat{y}$ are shown in Fig. 9.4.

Example 9.8   Refer to Example 9.7 and predict y for $x = 2.5$.

Solution: For Example 9.7, $\bar{x} = 4$, $x = 2.5$,

$$u_1 = (2.5 - 4) = -1.500,$$

$$u_2 = (2.5 - 4)^2 - \frac{(7)^2 - 1}{12} = -1.750,$$

$$u_3 = \frac{1}{6}\left[(2.5 - 4)^3 - (2.5 - 4)\frac{3(7)^2 - 7}{20}\right] = 1.187.$$

Then

$$\hat{y} = \hat{\alpha}_0 + \hat{\alpha}_1 u_1 + \hat{\alpha}_2 u_2 + \hat{\alpha}_3 u_3$$
$$= 5.671 + (.546)(-1.500) + (.054)(-1.750) - (1.450)(1.187)$$
$$= 3.032.$$

This value of $\hat{y}$ can be checked with the graph, Fig. 9.4, for $x = 2.5$.
A 95 per cent prediction interval for y would be

$$\hat{y} \pm t_{.025}s\sqrt{1 + a'(U'U)^{-1}a},$$

where

$$a' = [1 \quad -1.500 \quad -1.750 \quad 1.187], \qquad t_{.025} = 3.182,$$

$$(U'U)^{-1} = \begin{bmatrix} \frac{1}{7} & 0 & 0 & 0 \\ 0 & \frac{1}{28} & 0 & 0 \\ 0 & 0 & \frac{1}{84} & 0 \\ 0 & 0 & 0 & \frac{1}{6} \end{bmatrix},$$

and s, based upon three degrees of freedom, is computed from SSE. We will leave this computation as an exercise for the reader.

It was necessary to utilize two sets of symbols to distinguish and establish the relationship between the original independent variable and the orthogonal polynomials. Now that this relationship is understood, we will discard the symbols $u_1, u_2, \ldots, u_k$ and revert to the use of $x_1, x_2, \ldots, x_k$ to indicate the variables in the general linear model. We will understand that some of these could represent orthogonal polynomials, and thus a subset of the vectors in the X matrix for an experiment might correspond to orthogonal polynomials associated with some quantitative variable. It is quite clear from Table 7 that the vectors associated with the tabulated orthogonal polynomials will provide linear contrasts of the response measurements and hence that the sum of squares associated with a model parameter is given by Theorem 9.5. We will illustrate with an example.

Example 9.9 Calculate the sums of squares for the linear component of speed for Example 8.6.

Solution: The quantitative variable, speed, was investigated at three levels (hence $t = 3$) with six observations at each point. Since we only wish to fit a linear term, we will be concerned only with the polynomial, u_1, in Table 7, $t = 3$. Since the tabulated values of u_1 are $-1, 0, 1$, it is clear that the vector x_1' will contain $n = 18$ elements of which six each will assume the values, $-1, 0,$ and 1, respectively. The response totals at the low, medium, and high speeds are, respectively,

$$S_1 = 26.6, \qquad S_2 = 32.4, \qquad S_3 = 41.5.$$

Then, if the contrast for linear speed is denoted as l_1,

$$l_1 = (-1)S_1 + (0)S_2 + (1)S_3 = 14.9$$

and

$$\mathrm{SS}(l_1) = \frac{l_1^2}{\mathbf{x}_1'\mathbf{x}_1} = \frac{(14.9)^2}{12} = 18.50.$$

Example 9.10 Calculate the linear speed by insulation sum of squares for Example 8.6.

Solution: The sum of squares for this single-degree-of-freedom contrast may be obtained by the method of Sec. 9.8. We will denote the insulation totals as I_A and I_B and the single-degree-of-freedom contrast associated with insulations as

$$l_2 = I_B - I_A.$$

Then a condensation of the X matrix analogous to Fig. 9.2 is given in Fig. 9.5. The six (speed-insulation) totals $(SI)_{ij}$ are indicated in the second column, while the third, fourth, and fifth columns give a condensation of the vectors associated with linear speed, differences between insulations, and the linear speed by insulation interaction, respectively.

From column five of Fig. 9.5 it is clear that the linear contrast, l_3, associated with the linear speed by insulation interaction is

$$\begin{aligned}
l_3 &= (SI)_{1A} - (SI)_{3A} - (SI)_{1B} + (SI)_{3B} \\
&= (14.7) - (23.3) - (11.9) + (18.2) \\
&= -2.3.
\end{aligned}$$

Since each total in l_3 is the sum of three observations, the vector associated with (x_1x_2) will actually contain $n = 18$ elements, which will be three replications of the six elements indicated in the x_1x_2 column of Fig. 9.5; then $\mathbf{x}_3'\mathbf{x}_3 = 12$ and

$$\mathrm{SS}(l_3) = \frac{l_3^2}{\mathbf{x}_3'\mathbf{x}_3} = \frac{(-2.3)^2}{12} = 0.441.$$

Figure 9.5 Condensed representation of the
Y and X matrices for Example 8.6

i, j	$(SI)_{ij}$	X_1	X_2	$X_1 X_2$
1, A	14.7	-1	-1	1
2, A	18.1	0	-1	0
3, A	23.3	1	-1	-1
1, B	11.9	-1	1	-1
2, B	14.3	0	1	0
3, B	18.2	1	1	1

The sum of squares for the single degree of freedom associated with insulations may be calculated by the method of Sec. 8.7. The reader may verify that these sums of squares agree with the results given in the analysis-of-variance table for Example 8.6.

9.10 The Relation between Two Systems of Coding

We have indicated in earlier discussion that coding has the effect of changing from one set of $(k + 1)$ estimable parameters, $\beta_0, \beta_1, \beta_2, \ldots, \beta_k$, to a second set, $\beta_0^*, \beta_1^*, \beta_2^*, \ldots, \beta_k^*$, which are independent linear functions of the original parameters. For example, in order to achieve orthogonality of the X matrix and thereby a reduction in computation, we coded so that the new main-effect parameters for a k-way classification were orthogonal contrasts of the expected values of the factor totals. Similarly, the use of orthogonal polynomials transformed the parameters of a linear model associated with a quantitative independent variable, x, from $\beta_0, \beta_1, \beta_2, \ldots, \beta_k$ to $\alpha_0, \alpha_1, \alpha_2, \ldots, \alpha_k$, the latter being independent linear functions of $\beta_0, \beta_1, \beta_2, \ldots, \beta_k$.

Unfortunately, the experimenter is often interested in the original parameters, $\beta_i, i = 1, 2, \ldots, k$ rather than the new transformed parameters, $\beta_i^*, i = 1, 2, \ldots, k$, which may be meaningless from a practical point of view. Thus coding simplifies the acquisition of estimators of the β_i^* parameters, but the problem of obtaining estimates of the original parameters remains. This poses little difficulty in many practical situations. We have previously stated that β_i will be a linear function of the new parameters and $\hat{\beta}_i$ will be the same linear function of their estimates. Thus, if the linear relations between the old and new parameters are known, one can easily substitute into these expressions and compute $\hat{\beta}_i$ in terms of $\hat{\beta}_0^*, \hat{\beta}_1^*, \hat{\beta}_2^*, \ldots, \hat{\beta}_k^*$.

For many experimental designs the linear relations between old and new parameters will be known but may or may not be obvious to the beginner.

For this reason we present a discussion of the relation between two systems of coding and thereby acquire a mechanical procedure for moving from one set of parameters to another.

Let the new parameters be expressed as $(k + 1)$ independent linear functions of the old. Thus

$$\beta_0^* = a_{00}\beta_0 + a_{01}\beta_1 + a_{02}\beta_2 + \cdots + a_{0k}\beta_k,$$
$$\beta_1^* = a_{10}\beta_0 + a_{11}\beta_1 + a_{12}\beta_2 + \cdots + a_{1k}\beta_k,$$

.
.
.

$$\beta_k^* = a_{k0}\beta_0 + a_{k1}\beta_1 + a_{k2}\beta_2 + \cdots + a_{kk}\beta_k.$$

Denoting

$$\beta' = [\beta_0 \quad \beta_1 \quad \beta_2 \quad \cdots \quad \beta_k], \qquad \beta^{*'} = [\beta_0^* \quad \beta_1^* \quad \cdots \quad \beta_k^*]$$

and the transformation matrix,

$$A = \begin{bmatrix} a_{00} & a_{01} & a_{02} & \cdots & a_{0k} \\ a_{10} & a_{11} & a_{12} & \cdots & a_{1k} \\ \cdot & & & & \\ \cdot & & & & \\ \cdot & & & & \\ a_{k0} & a_{k1} & a_{k2} & \cdots & a_{kk} \end{bmatrix},$$

then, in matrix notation, $\beta^* = A\beta$.

Regardless of the system of coding, the predicted values of the n response measurements must remain unchanged, and therefore

$$\hat{y} = X\hat{\beta}$$
$$= X^*\hat{\beta}^*,$$

where X^* is the coded data matrix corresponding to the new parameters in β^*. But since $\hat{\beta}^* = A\hat{\beta}$,

$$\hat{y} = X^*(A\hat{\beta})$$
$$= (X^*A)\hat{\beta},$$

and it is apparent that $X = X^*A$. Or, given the X matrix, $X^* = XA^{-1}$. (The A matrix will possess an inverse because $\beta_0^*, \beta_1^*, \beta_2^*, \ldots, \beta_k^*$ are independent linear functions of $\beta_0, \beta_1, \beta_2, \ldots, \beta_k$.)

The A matrix can also be obtained from the preceding expression. Thus

$$X = X^*A,$$
$$X^{*'}X = X^{*'}X^*A,$$

and

$$A = (X^{*'}X^*)^{-1}X^{*'}X.$$

Note that if the new coding produces mutual orthogonality in the vectors of the X^* matrix, $(X^{*\prime}X^*)$ will be diagonal and can easily be inverted.

Finally, since $\hat{\beta}^* = A\hat{\beta}$, the estimates of the old parameters can be obtained from

$$\hat{\beta} = A^{-1}\hat{\beta}^* = (X^{*\prime}X)^{-1}(X^{*\prime}X^*)\hat{\beta}^*.$$

The relationship between the independent variables for the two systems of coding can also be established. Thus if we define two matrices containing these variables,

$$x' = [1 \quad x_1 \quad x_2 \quad x_3 \quad \cdots \quad x_k]$$

and

$$x^{*\prime} = [1 \quad x_1^* \quad x_2^* \quad x_3^* \quad \cdots \quad x_k^*],$$

$$x^* = (A')^{-1}x \qquad \text{and} \qquad x = A'x^*.$$

We leave the proof of this statement as an exercise for the reader.

Example 9.11   Given a randomized block design with two blocks and three treatments and the following two methods of coding:

Method 1:

$$y = \beta_0 + \beta_1 x_1 + \beta_2 x_2 + \beta_3 x_3 + \epsilon,$$

where

$$\begin{aligned} x_1 &= 1 \quad \text{if block 2,} \\ x_1 &= -1 \quad \text{if not;} \\ x_2 &= 1 \quad \text{if treatment 2,} \\ x_2 &= -1 \quad \text{if not;} \\ x_3 &= 1 \quad \text{if treatment 3,} \\ x_3 &= -1 \quad \text{if not.} \end{aligned}$$

Method 2:

$$y = \beta_0^* + \beta_1^* x_1^* + \beta_2^* x_2^* + \beta_3^* x_3^* + \epsilon,$$

where

$$\begin{aligned} x_1^* &= 1 \quad \text{if block 2,} \\ x_1^* &= 0 \quad \text{if not;} \\ x_2^* &= 1 \quad \text{if treatment 2,} \\ x_2^* &= 0 \quad \text{if not;} \\ x_3^* &= 1 \quad \text{if treatment 3,} \\ x_3^* &= 0 \quad \text{if not.} \end{aligned}$$

Find the A matrix that relates the two methods of coding.

Solution: $A = (X^{*\prime}X^*)^{-1}X^{*\prime}X,$

where

$$X = \begin{bmatrix} 1 & -1 & -1 & -1 \\ 1 & -1 & 1 & -1 \\ 1 & -1 & -1 & 1 \\ 1 & 1 & -1 & -1 \\ 1 & 1 & 1 & -1 \\ 1 & 1 & -1 & 1 \end{bmatrix}, \qquad X^* = \begin{bmatrix} 1 & 0 & 0 & 0 \\ 1 & 0 & 1 & 0 \\ 1 & 0 & 0 & 1 \\ 1 & 1 & 0 & 0 \\ 1 & 1 & 1 & 0 \\ 1 & 1 & 0 & 1 \end{bmatrix},$$

$$(X^{*\prime}X^*) = \begin{bmatrix} 6 & 3 & 2 & 2 \\ 3 & 3 & 1 & 1 \\ 2 & 1 & 2 & 0 \\ 2 & 1 & 0 & 2 \end{bmatrix}, \qquad (X^{*\prime}X^*)^{-1} = \begin{bmatrix} \frac{2}{3} & -\frac{1}{3} & -\frac{1}{2} & -\frac{1}{2} \\ -\frac{1}{3} & \frac{2}{3} & 0 & 0 \\ -\frac{1}{2} & 0 & 1 & \frac{1}{2} \\ -\frac{1}{2} & 0 & \frac{1}{2} & 1 \end{bmatrix},$$

$$X^{*\prime}X = \begin{bmatrix} 6 & 0 & -2 & -2 \\ 3 & 3 & -1 & -1 \\ 2 & 0 & 2 & -2 \\ 2 & 0 & -2 & 2 \end{bmatrix},$$

and

$$A = (X^{*\prime}X^*)^{-1}X^{*\prime}X = \begin{bmatrix} 1 & -1 & -1 & -1 \\ 0 & 2 & 0 & 0 \\ 0 & 0 & 2 & 0 \\ 0 & 0 & 0 & 2 \end{bmatrix}.$$

Thus $\beta^* = A\beta$, or

$$\beta_0^* = \beta_0 - \beta_1 - \beta_2 - \beta_3,$$
$$\beta_1^* = 2\beta_1,$$
$$\beta_2^* = 2\beta_2,$$
$$\beta_3^* = 2\beta_3.$$

The purpose of this example was to illustrate the mechanical, although somewhat tedious, procedure for finding the A matrix. It is interesting to note that these last equations might have been obtained by inspection of the two linear models and their defined codings. If this were done, the A matrix would be the coefficient matrix for the β parameters.

Example 9.12 Consider a randomized block design containing three blocks and four treatments with the linear model

$$y = \beta_0 + \underbrace{\beta_1 x_1 + \beta_2 x_2}_{\text{Block effects}} + \underbrace{\beta_3 x_3 + \beta_4 x_4 + \beta_5 x_5}_{\text{Treatment effects}} + \epsilon.$$

As a first method of coding, let

$x_1 = 1$ if block 2,
$x_1 = 0$ if not;
$x_2 = 1$ if block 3,
$x_2 = 0$ if not;
$x_3 = 1$ if treatment 2 is applied,
$x_3 = 0$ if not;
$x_4 = 1$ if treatment 3 is applied,
$x_4 = 0$ if not;
$x_5 = 1$ if treatment 4 is applied,
$x_5 = 0$ if not.

Most texts on the design of experiments present the model for a randomized block design as

$$y_{ij} = \mu + \beta_i^* + \tau_j + \epsilon_{ij}, \qquad i = 1, 2, 3, \qquad j = 1, 2, 3, 4,$$

where y_{ij} is the response in the ith block receiving treatment j and

$$\sum_{i=1}^{3} \beta_i^* = \sum_{j=1}^{4} \tau_j = 0.$$

This latter restriction means that $\beta_3^* = -\beta_1^* - \beta_2^*$ and $\tau_4 = -\tau_1 - \tau_2 - \tau_3$ and therefore that the model contains only two linearly independent block and three linearly independent treatment parameters. Thus both models contain the same number of linearly independent estimable parameters. The dummy variables for this second method of coding are rarely ever shown in the linear model, and the associated X matrix, identifying the particular values assigned to each dummy variable for the n response measurements, is likewise rarely given.

(a) Give the linear model with associated dummy variables for this second method of coding.

(b) Find either the transformation matrix, A, or its inverse.

(c) Find the matrix, X^*, for the second linear model, thus identifying the values assumed by the dummy variables for specific response measurements.

Solution: (a) The linear model showing the dummy variables can be written as

$$y = \mu + \beta_1^* x_1^* + \beta_2^* x_2^* + \tau_1 x_3^* + \tau_2 x_4^* + \tau_3 x_5^* + \epsilon.$$

The specific values assigned to the dummy variables $x_1^*, x_2^*, \ldots, x_5^*$ for a particular block-treatment response will be given in the X^* matrix of part (c).

(b) Since $\sum_{i=1}^{3} \beta_i^* = 0$, it is clear that the average of the three response measurements receiving treatment (j) estimates $(\mu + \tau_j)$. And since β_3 (model 1) is the difference in the expected response between treatments 2 and 1,

$$\beta_3 = (\mu + \tau_2) - (\mu + \tau_1) = \tau_2 - \tau_1.$$

Similarly,

$$\beta_4 = (\mu + \tau_3) - (\mu + \tau_1) = \tau_3 - \tau_1,$$
$$\beta_5 = (\mu + \tau_4) - (\mu + \tau_1) = \tau_4 - \tau_1$$
$$= -2\tau_1 - \tau_2 - \tau_3.$$

Likewise, since $\sum_{j=1}^{4} \tau_j = 0$, the average of the four response measurements in block i will estimate $(\mu + \beta_i^*)$. Therefore, since β_1 is the difference in the expected response between blocks 2 and 1,

$$\beta_1 = (\mu + \beta_2^*) - (\mu + \beta_1^*) = \beta_2^* - \beta_1^*.$$

Similarly,

$$\beta_2 = (\mu + \beta_3^*) - (\mu + \beta_1^*) = \beta_3^* - \beta_1^*$$
$$= -2\beta_1^* - \beta_2^*.$$

Finally, since β_0 is the expected response for treatment 1 in block 1,

$$\beta_0 = \mu + \beta_1^* + \tau_1.$$

The reader will note that we have expressed each of the parameters of model 1 as a linear function of the parameters of model 2.

Summarizing,

$$\beta_0 = \mu + \beta_1^* + \tau_1,$$
$$\beta_1 = \beta_2^* - \beta_1^*,$$
$$\beta_2 = -2\beta_1^* - \beta_2^*,$$
$$\beta_3 = \tau_2 - \tau_1,$$
$$\beta_4 = \tau_3 - \tau_1,$$
$$\beta_5 = -2\tau_1 - \tau_2 - \tau_3.$$

where

$$\beta = \begin{bmatrix} \beta_0 \\ \beta_1 \\ \beta_2 \\ \beta_3 \\ \beta_4 \\ \beta_5 \end{bmatrix} \quad \text{and} \quad \beta^* = \begin{bmatrix} \mu \\ \beta_1^* \\ \beta_2^* \\ \tau_1 \\ \tau_2 \\ \tau_3 \end{bmatrix}.$$

Since $\beta^* = A\beta$ and $\beta = A^{-1}\beta^*$, the coefficients of the parameters of the β^* matrix appearing in the above linear equations must define the matrix, A^{-1}. Therefore,

$$A^{-1} = \begin{bmatrix} 1 & 1 & 0 & 1 & 0 & 0 \\ 0 & -1 & 1 & 0 & 0 & 0 \\ 0 & -2 & -1 & 0 & 0 & 0 \\ 0 & 0 & 0 & -1 & 1 & 0 \\ 0 & 0 & 0 & -1 & 0 & 1 \\ 0 & 0 & 0 & -2 & -1 & -1 \end{bmatrix}.$$

(c) The X^* matrix corresponding to the second method of coding can be obtained from the matrix product,

$$X^* = XA^{-1}.$$

Since the X matrix for coding method 1 is well known to the reader, we leave the acquisition of the product, XA^{-1}, as an exercise.

9.11 Summary

Sections 9.1 and 9.2 illustrate the necessity for carefully formed statistical hypotheses rather than the automatic and mechanical application of statistical test procedures. If one or more of the independent variables are quantitative, parameters of the linear model (excepting β_0) represent partial derivatives of $E(y)$ evaluated at some point in the experimental region, which will depend upon the method of coding of the independent variables. Thus a test of an hypothesis associated with an interaction term might show statistical significance for one method of coding and not for another simply because the parameters are not equivalent.

Sections 9.3 through 9.9 are primarily concerned with orthogonal systems of coding and with the effect of these systems on reducing the computation involved in fitting a linear model and in calculating the sums of squares for single degrees of freedom in the analysis of variance. Particularly, the procedures for calculating the sums of squares associated with orthogonal linear contrasts are often useful for completing the analysis-of-variance table so that one may obtain SSE by subtraction.

Exercises

1. In defining the orthogonality of two linear functions (definition, Section 9.6), what properties are implied for the n random variables y_1, $y_2, \ldots, y_n$?

2. Given the properties of Exercise 1, what is the necessary and sufficient condition for two linear functions of $y_1, y_2, \ldots, y_n$ to be orthogonal?

3. Let $l_1 = y_1 + y_2 + y_3 + y_4$. Find a linear function l_2 of $y_1, y_2, y_3,$ and y_4, such that l_1 and l_2 are orthogonal.

4. Refer to Exercise 3. Find a third and a fourth linear function, l_3 and l_4, such that $l_1, l_2, l_3,$ and l_4 will form a mutually orthogonal set.

5. Refer to Exercise 4. If the coefficients of l_1 are all equal to unity, what property must the coefficients $a_1, a_2, a_3, a_4,$ of $l_i = a_1y_1 + a_2y_2 + a_3y_3 + a_4y_4$ satisfy in order that l_i be orthogonal to l_1? What is l_i called?

6. Let $l_1 = 2y_1 + y_2 - y_3 - y_4 + y_5$. Find a linear function l_2 of $y_1, y_2, \ldots, y_5$ that is orthogonal to l_1. Show that l_2 is or is not a linear contrast.

7. Prove Theorem 9.2.

8. What is meant by an orthogonal experimental design?

9. Note that the least-squares solution, $\hat{\beta} = (X'X)^{-1}X'Y$ implies that all of the parameter estimators appearing in the $\hat{\beta}$ matrix are linear functions of $y_1, y_2, \ldots, y_n$ appearing in the Y matrix. (The linear functions can also be shown to be mutually independent. Note that we refer to algebraic rather than probabilistic independence.) Now consider an orthogonal design, for example a 3×3 Latin square, and let $\hat{\beta}_i$ represent the estimator of a row parameter and $\hat{\beta}_j$ an estimator of a column parameter. Thus,

$$\hat{\beta}_i = a_1y_1 + a_2y_2 + \cdots + a_ny_n$$

and

$$\hat{\beta}_j = b_1y_1 + b_2y_2 + \cdots + b_ny_n,$$

where $a_1, a_2, \ldots, a_n$ and $b_1, b_2, \ldots, b_n$ are specific rows of $(X'X)^{-1}X'$ for the Latin square design. Define the two matrices, $a' = [a_1a_2 \cdots a_n]$ and $b' = [b_1b_2 \cdots b_n]$. Find the value of the matrix product, $a'b$, and justify your answer.

10. Write the X matrix for the 3×3 Latin square design, Exercise 9, using a $(0, 1)$ coding for the dummy variables. Are the column vectors of this X matrix mutually orthogonal? Should these vectors be mutually orthogonal for an orthogonal design?

11. Let $y = \beta_0 + \beta_1X_1 + \beta_2X_2 + \cdots + \beta_kX_k + \epsilon$ represent a general linear model. What conditions must be satisfied in order that $\hat{\beta}_0 = c_0x'_0Y$, $\hat{\beta}_1 = c_1x'_1Y$, and, in general, $\hat{\beta}_i = c_ix'_iY$, $i = 0, 1, 2, \ldots, k$, where $c_0, c_1, c_2, \ldots, c_k$ are constants? Give the value of c_i.

12. Let the column vectors of the X matrix be a mutually orthogonal set for the general linear model of Exercise 11. Show that the analysis-

of-variance sum of squares associated with β_i is

$$SS(l_i) = \frac{(x_i'Y)^2}{x_i'x_i},$$

where $l_i = x_i'Y$.

13. Calculate the sum of squares associated with β_1 for Example 7.7.

14. Assume the conditions of Exercise 12 and prove that

$$\sum_{i=1}^{n} (y_i - \bar{y})^2 = SSE + SS(l_1) + SS(l_2) + \cdots + SS(l_k).$$

Note that this is proof of a special case of Theorem 9.6 where $g = 0$. The result is a justification of the additivity of the analysis-of-variance sums of squares for this type of design. Those readers wishing to justify the above identity numerically can do so by computing the necessary sums of squares for Example 7.7.

15. Refer to the 3×3 Latin square mentioned in Exercise 9, and recode the dummy independent variables so that the column vectors associated with each factor are orthogonal to x_0, are mutually orthogonal, and hence that all of the vectors of the X matrix are mutually orthogonal. Apply this result to fit the linear model to the following data. Find SSE.

		Columns		
		1	2	3
	1	A	B	C
		23	13	15
Rows	2	B	C	A
		16	17	15
	3	C	A	B
		21	23	15

16. Refer to Exercise 15. Compute the total sum of squares of deviations about the mean and the sums of squares for each of the parameters, $\beta_1, \beta_2, \ldots, \beta_6$. Then, using the value of SSE calculated in Exercise 15, show numerically that

$$\sum_i (y_i - \bar{y})^2 = SSE + SS(l_1) + SS(l_2) + \cdots + SS(l_6).$$

17. Use the results of Exercise 16 to construct an analysis-of-variance table to test the following hypotheses:
    (a) There is no difference among the mean responses for treatments.
    (b) There is no difference among the mean responses for rows.
    (c) There is no difference among the mean responses for columns.

18. Refer to Exercise 15.

(a) Is it possible to find a confidence interval for the mean response due to treatment A? Explain.

(b) Find a 95 per cent confidence interval for the difference in mean response between treatments B and A.

19. Compare the treatment means of Exercise 15 using Tukey's method of multiple comparison.

20. Consider the randomized block design presented earlier in Exercise 14, Chapter 8.

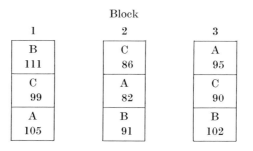

Block

1	2	3
B 111	C 86	A 95
C 99	A 82	C 90
A 105	B 91	B 102

(a) Code the independent variables so that the column vectors for treatments imply parameters which are orthogonal linear contrasts of the treatment means.

(b) Repeat this process for the block independent variables, and hence make the vectors of the X matrix a mutually orthogonal set. Verify that this last condition is satisfied.

(c) Use (a) and (b) to fit a linear model to the data and obtain SSE. Compare with the result of Exercise 14, Chapter 8. (Note: The easy way to analyze this data is by using the analysis-of-variance formulas. This problem is intended only as an exercise to assist the student in learning to construct orthogonal contrasts of treatment means.)

(d) Suppose that the linear model for this experiment is

$$y = \beta_0 + \beta_1 x_1 + \beta_2 x_2 + \beta_3 x_3 + \beta_4 x_4 + \epsilon,$$

where x_1 and x_2 are the block dummy variables and x_3 and x_4 are those corresponding to treatments. What values will x_1, x_2, x_3 and x_4 assume if you wish to estimate the mean response for treatment A in block 1?

21. Refer to Exercise 38, Chapter 7. Code the independent variables for treatments so that the column vectors of the X matrix are associated with orthogonal linear contrasts of the treatment means. Then complete the X matrix by adding the treatment-time interaction vectors.

(a) Fit the linear model and calculate SSE. As a check on your calculations, compare with the SSE of Exercise 38, Chapter 7. Note the simplicity of the computations as compared with those utilized in Chapter 7.

(b) Find the sum of squares (based on two degrees of freedom) associated with the chemical-time interaction.

(c) Do the data present sufficient evidence to indicate a difference in the rates of reaction for the three chemicals? Compare the conclusions with those of Exercise 38, Chapter 7, part (g).

(d) Utilizing the complete model, estimate the mean response of chemical C at time equal to 1.5, using a 95 per cent confidence interval.

22. Refer to Exercise 24, Chapter 6. Code the two block independent variables so that the corresponding vectors of the X matrix are associated with mutually orthogonal contrasts of the block means.

(a) Fit the linear model using these coded variables. (Note that $(X'X)$ is a diagonal matrix, and observe the simplicity of the calculations in comparison to the difficulty encountered when solving Exercise 24, Chapter 6.)

(b) Predict the mean response in block 2 when $x_1 = -1$, $x_2 = 1$, and $x_3 = 1$. Compare with the results of Exercise 24, Chapter 6, part (c).

23. (Note: this problem involves some computation.) A comparison was made between three feeds using four animals per feed. The initial weight of the animals was expected to affect the gain in weight and was included as a covariate. (The resulting analysis is called an *analysis of covariance*.)

Feeds	A				B				C			
Initial Weight x	40	36	37	42	48	41	46	38	35	43	44	40
Gain in Weight y	5.9	5.4	5.8	6.1	6.1	5.5	5.7	5.1	6.1	6.5	6.6	6.4

(a) Do the data present sufficient evidence to indicate a difference between treatments if the covariate is ignored? Run an analysis of variance.

(b) Answer (a) taking the covariate into account. (Note: This requires fitting the complete linear model. Some of the computational labor can be eliminated by coding the treatment of independent variables so that the corresponding vectors of the X matrix imply orthogonal linear contrasts of the treatment means.)

(c) Do the data present sufficient evidence to indicate that initial weight affects gain in weight over the weight range indicated in this experiment?

24. Refer to Exercise 23. How would one determine whether the data present sufficient evidence to indicate that initial weight affects the growth differently from one feed to another?

(a) Assuming that it does, write a linear model for the experiment.

(b) Indicate computational procedure for acquiring the sum of squares to test this hypothesis. The sum of squares, attributable to the newly added parameters associated with this difference, is included for the reader with sufficient interest to cope with the computations.

25. Refer to Exercise 23. (Note: this exercise also involves rather laborious computations.) Suppose that the animals had been blocked on litters. That is, three animals selected from a particular litter formed the three experimental units for a block. One each of these was assigned to feeds A, B, and C for four litters.

Block

	1			2			3			4	
	x	y		x	y		x	y		x	y
A	43	7.5	A	37	4.9	A	40	5.2	A	38	6.4
B	40	5.2	B	39	4.2	B	41	4.2	B	42	5.1
C	44	6.1	C	36	3.3	C	42	3.8	C	40	5.5

(a) Do the data present sufficient evidence to indicate a difference in feeds? (To simplify the computation, code so that the block and treatment vectors in the X matrix are mutually orthogonal.

(b) Is the covariate an important consideration in analyzing the data?

26. Suppose that the yield of chemical is related to temperature in what appears to be a parabolic manner. An experiment was conducted at five equally spaced temperature levels with two replications at each temperature level. The results are shown below.

Yield, y	1.0, 1.6	2.9, 3.2	3.6, 3.5	3.0, 3.9	3.1, 2.8
Temperature, x	1	2	3	4	5

(a) Fit a quadratic polynomial to the data using orthogonal polynomials.

(b) Estimate the mean yield of chemical when $x = 2$, using a 95 per cent confidence interval.

(c) Do the data present sufficient evidence to indicate that a parabola is an inadequate model for $E(y)$?

27. The sales, y, of a corporation (in millions of dollars) were recorded over a ten-year period with the following results:

Sales y	.3	.6	1.0	1.6	2.3	2.8	3.4	3.6	3.9	4.0
Time x	1	2	3	4	5	6	7	8	9	10

(a) Fit a cubic polynomial to this data using orthogonal polynomials.

(b) Plot the data and graph the fitted curve obtained in part (a).

28. The efficiency for three internal combustion engines was compared at five levels of speed (revolutions per minute) for a fixed load. The data, with efficiencies measured in per cent, are shown below:

	Speeds				
Engines	1	2	3	4	5
A	30	54	52	63	58
B	28	32	43	37	42
C	23	40	42	53	48

Suppose that the speed levels are equally spaced and that it is known that the efficiency curve for a given engine will be approximately parabolic.

(a) Do the data present sufficient evidence to indicate a difference in the efficiency curves for the three engines? (Note: The error sum of squares will be based upon 6 degrees of freedom.)

(b) Find a 95 per cent confidence interval for the difference in expected efficiency between engines A and B at speed level 3.

(c) How many complete replications of the experiment would be required to estimate the difference in the expected efficiency between engines A and B at speed level 3 correct to within plus or minus 5 per cent?

29. Paper is produced by distributing wood fiber onto a screen where the distribution is made at two points, the primary and secondary headboxes. "Rushing" occurs when the velocity at the head box exceeds the velocity of the screen. Thus rushing is expected to affect the strength of the finished paper (called mullen). The effect of rush at the primary and the secondary headboxes of a paper machine were investigated on the mullen of finished paper using a 3 × 3 factorial experiment.

	Rush at Primary Head Box x_1		
	-1	0	1
Rush at Secondary Head Box x_2 +1	105.2	108.9	95.2
0	103.7	108.2	97.6
-1	104.4	105.9	96.9

(a) Fit the linear model

$$y = \beta_0 + \beta_1 x_1 + \beta_2 x_2 + \beta_3 x_1 x_2 + \beta_4 x_1^2 + \beta_5 x_2^2 + \epsilon$$

to the data using orthogonal polynomials for both quantitative variables.

(b) Do the data present sufficient evidence to indicate an $x_1 x_2$ interaction?

(c) Find a 95 per cent confidence interval for the mean response when $x_1 = x_2 = -1$.

(d) What assumptions must be made to justify the validity of the confidence intervals of part c?

30. Consider the following two methods of coding for a randomized block design with three treatments and four blocks.

(a) Write the linear model for the randomized block design using a $(0, 1)$ coding for all dummy variables except $x_0 = 1$. Denote the parameters as $\beta_0, \beta_1, \beta_2, \ldots, \beta_5$.

(b) Consider the same linear model, except let the dummy variables, denoted as $x_1^*, \ldots, x_5^*$, take a $(-1, 1)$ coding and let the corresponding parameters be $\beta_0^*, \beta_1^*, \ldots, \beta_5^*$. Express the parameters of model (b) as linear functions of the parameters of model (a).

(c) Define the matrices $\beta' = [\beta_0, \beta_1, \beta_2, \beta_3, \beta_4, \beta_5]$ and $\beta^{*\prime} = [\beta_0^*, \beta_1^*, \beta_2^*, \beta_3^*, \beta_4^*, \beta_5^*]$ and let the linear equations of part (b) be expressed as a matrix product $\beta^* = A\beta$, where A is a (6×6) matrix. Find A. Note that the A matrix (transform matrix) expresses the parameters $\beta_0^*, \beta_1^*, \ldots, \beta_5^*$ in terms of $n = 6$ independent linear functions of the parameters $\beta_0, \beta_1, \ldots, \beta_5$.

31. Refer to Exercise 30. Give the variances of $\hat{\beta}_1$ and $\hat{\beta}_1^*$.

32. (a) Relate the independent variables for the two systems of coding, Exercise 30. Thus $x_0^* = x_0 = 1$. Express $x_1^*, x_2^*, \ldots, x_5^*$ as linear functions of $x_1, x_2, \ldots, x_5$.

(b) Given the matrices $x' = [1 \; x_1 \; x_2 \cdots x_5]$ and $x^{*\prime} = [1 \; x_1^* \; x_2^* \cdots x_5^*]$, then the linear equations of (a) can be expressed as

$$x^* = Bx.$$

Find B.

33. Refer to Exercise 30. Let $x' = [1 \; x_1 \; x_2 \cdots x_5]$ and $x^{*\prime} = [1 \; x_1^* \; x_2^* \cdots x_5^*]$ and note that $E(y)$ may be written as $E(y) = x'\beta$ and also as $E(y) = x^{*\prime}\beta^*$. For a given point in the experimental region, $E(y) = x'\beta = x^{*\prime}\beta^*$. Using this relationship, show that the independent variables of models (a) and (b) are related by the expression,

$$x^* = (A')^{-1}x,$$

where A is the transformation matrix obtained in 30 (c). (Note: The transpose of a matrix product is given by the relation, $(CD)' = (D'C')$. Thus the B matrix of 32 (b) is $B = (A')^{-1}$. Confirm this result by showing that the product $BA' = (A')(A')^{-1} = I$, where B and A are obtained from Exercises 30 (b) and 32 (b), respectively.

34. Refer to the example, Section 9.1. Let the independent variables and parameters associated with model 2 be denoted as $x_0^*, x_1^*, \ldots, x_8^*$ and $\beta_0^*, \beta_1^*, \ldots, \beta_8^*$, respectively. Relate the independent variables of

model 2 to those of model 1. That is, find the matrix, B, such that $x^* = Bx$.

35. Refer to Exercise 34. Let the parameters for the two models be related by the matrix expression

$$\beta^* = A\beta.$$

Find A and then specifically give β^* as a linear function of β_0, $\beta_1, \ldots, \beta_8$. Note that Exercises 1 to 6 imply that if one can relate the two sets of independent variables corresponding to two systems of coding, then the transformation matrix, A, relating the two sets of parameters can easily be determined. Or, if A is known, then B can be determined.

From 32 (b) we find that $\beta_1^* = \frac{1}{2}\beta_1$. Also, $\hat{\beta}_1^*$ can be shown to be equal to $\hat{\beta}_1^* = \frac{1}{2}\hat{\beta}_1$. Since $V(\hat{\beta}_1^*) = V(\frac{1}{2}\hat{\beta}_1)$, use this relationship to check the answer to part (a).

36. Refer to Exercise 28.
   (a) Find $V(\hat{y})$ for engine A at speed 1.
   (b) Give the formula for a 95 per cent prediction interval for the efficiency reading for a test on engine A at speed 1 to be conducted at some future date.
   (c) Suppose that we wish to compare the *rate* of *change* of efficiencies with respect to a change in speed between engines B and A at speed 2. Give the estimation of this difference and its variance. Give a test statistic to test the hypothesis that the difference in rate of change of efficiencies is equal to zero.

37. Derive linear and quadratic orthogonal polynomials for six equally spaced values of x.

38. Suppose that a quantitative independent variable investigated at three levels is unequally spaced, say $x = 1, 2, 4$.
   (a) Find orthogonal polynomials which may be employed to fit a second-degree polynomial to the response.
   (b) When is it useful to develop orthogonal polynomials for unequal spacing?
   (c) Suppose that two response measurements are recorded for each value of x, with the following result:

x	y	
1	7.1	7.4
2	7.8	7.7
4	10.3	9.9

   Use the results of (a) to fit a second-degree polynomial to the response.

(d) Refer to (c). Find a 95 per cent confidence interval for $E(y)$ when $x = 1$.

39. Two linear models for a 2×2 factorial experiment in factors A and B may be written as

(1) $y = \beta_0 + \beta_1 x_1 + \beta_2 x_2 + \beta_3 x_1 x_2 + \epsilon$,

where $x_1 = 1$ if high level of A,

$\quad\quad\;\; x_1 = -1$ if low level of A,

$\quad\quad\;\; x_2 = 1$ if high level of B,

$\quad\quad\;\; x_2 = -1$ if low level of B.

(2) $y_{ij} = \mu + \alpha_i + \beta_j + (\alpha\beta)_{ij} + \epsilon_{ij}$,

where y_{ij} is the response for the observation receiving the ith level of A and the jth level of B, $i = 1,2$, and $j = 1,2$, where

$$\sum_{i=1}^{2} \alpha_i = \sum_{j=1}^{2} \beta_i = \sum_{i=1}^{2} (\alpha\beta)_{ij} = \sum_{j=1}^{2} (\alpha\beta)_{ij} = 0.$$

Find the transformation matrix relating the two systems of coding.

References

Anderson, R. L., and T. A. Bancroft, *Statistical Theory in Research*. New York: McGraw-Hill Book Company, 1952.

Anderson, R. L., and E. E. Houseman, *Tables of Orthogonal Polynomial Values Extended to N = 104*, Iowa State College, Agricultural Experiment Station Research Bulletin 297, 1942.

Pearson, E. S., and H. O. Hartley, *Biometrika Tables for Statisticians*, 3rd. ed., Vol. I. London: Cambridge University Press, 1966.

10

Seeking a Maximum or Minimum Response

10.1 Introduction

One of the most frequent objectives of an experimental investigation is the location of the maximum or minimum of a response surface where the response is a function of a number of independent variables. Thus one may wish to determine the conditions which imply a minimum cost or maximum profit in a manufacturing operation, the combination of fertilizer application and soil treatment that yields maximum profit in the production of wheat, or the combination of drugs in conjunction with variables that measure the physical condition of a patient that produce minimum cholesterol build-up in the blood vessels.

In many situations a mathematical expression for the response function is developed from existing theory, often by the use of differential equations, and then the well-known methods of the differential calculus are employed to locate the maximum or minimum. This solution is often thought to be exact; indeed, it does represent an exact maximum or minimum for the *derived function* which is an approximation to the true functional relation.

267

Thus the error involved in locating the maximum or minimum will be determined by the chain of approximating assumptions imbedded in the underlying theory and their effect on the final result viewed from the standpoint of the propagation of errors.

As in earlier discussion, we will assume that the true response function is unknown, that we are able to obtain measurements on the response subject to a random error, and that the general linear model, along with associated assumptions (Chapter 7), is an appropriate model for the response over the experimental region.

Seeking a maximum is analogous to searching for a mountain peak, while a minimum would correspond to an earthly valley or depression of minimum elevation. Conducting an experiment for a particular combination of values of the independent variables is analogous to requesting and viewing the elevation of the earth's surface at some given latitude and longitude.

Thus, since each request (experimental point) costs a fixed quantity of money and time, we wish to know how many points would be required before the general position of the mountain peak (maximum) could be determined. What design should be selected for the first few experimental points, and how would the responses at these points be utilized to move toward the maximum? What is the best procedure for augmenting the points of the original design in order to progress to the maximum with a minimum of additional points? In brief, what is the best experimental strategy for seeking a maximum?

The infinitely large number of possible surfaces that the experimenter might encounter and the equally large number of alternatives for selecting the experimental points indicate the complexity of selecting a "best" strategy for seeking a maximum or minimum. As yet this problem is unsolved. However, a number of intuitively appealing procedures are available, and it is toward these that we direct our attention.

10.2 Approximating Surfaces

Since the true functional relation between the response and the independent variables is unknown, the linear model selected for a given experimental situation will simply approximate the actual response surface over the restricted confines of the experimental region. And although the true response function may be quite complex over the domain of the independent variables, it generally will be well behaved and often may be approximated by a simple polynomial expression over a relatively small experimental region. Indeed, when the experimental region is sufficiently small, the response surface may be approximated by a plane. The history of the exploration of the earth's surface provides an excellent illustration of this point. Before the discovery of America the earth was thought to be flat; knowledgeable people of the fifteenth century observed the excellent planar fit to the earth's surface (at sea level) within the limited confines of their view and mentally extrapolated this plane to fit the entire surface of the earth. Columbus and subsequent explorers indicated the fallacy of this extrapolation, an historical event that contains two important lessons for the experimenter. First, a low-order polynomial can often be utilized to approximate a response surface over a relatively small experimental region. Second, it is dangerous to employ an approximating surface to extrapolate beyond the confines of an experimental region.

As noted, the simplest approximating surface to a response function of independent variables, $x_1, x_2, \ldots, x_k$, is given by the model

$$y = \beta_0 + \beta_1 x_1 + \beta_2 x_2 + \cdots + \beta_k x_k + \epsilon,$$

where $E(y)$ is the equation of a plane. Particularly, the reader will recognize this model as the linear model for a 2^k factorial experiment with interaction terms omitted.

If curvature is present, the response surface possibly may be described by a polynomial with highest-order terms of the second degree. The resulting smooth curved surface is called a *second-order surface* or, sometimes, a conic surface. Thus the second-order model for two independent variables, x_1 and x_2, is

$$y = \beta_0 + \beta_1 x_1 + \beta_2 x_2 + \beta_3 x_1 x_2 + \beta_4 x_1^2 + \beta_5 x_2^2 + \epsilon.$$

The second-order surface traced by $E(y)$ will be a paraboloid, an hyperboloid, a cone, or some other conic surface. These surfaces are smooth without reversal of curvature and hence provide good approximations to an experimental response surface if the region of experimentation is not too large. If the true response surface can be represented by a Taylor's series over the region of experimentation, the second-order model utilizes the terms of the series up to and including those involving second-order partial derivatives. For the special case where this truncated series exactly describes the response, the parameters of the second-order model (excepting β_0) represent the various partial derivatives of the response function evaluated at the origin.

We will note in later discussion that in seeking a maximum or minimum, one attempts to select the region of experimentation so that a first- or second-order model will adequately represent the response. When these models provide a poor approximation to the response surface—for example, where reversal in curvature in the response surface occurs—higher-order models can be constructed which include polynomial terms of higher than the second degree and which will generally provide a better model for the response.

10.3 Contour Maps

A contour map provides a simple method for studying variation in response as a function of two independent variables. Thus, as the geographer maps curves of equal elevation of the earth's surface, the experimenter plots contours of equal response. In doing so, he gains insight into the changes in elevation of the response surface and hopefully, if seeking a maximum, is directed toward a region of higher response.

For example, suppose that the experimenter has conducted a 2×2 factorial experiment and that the fitted prediction equation is

$$\hat{y} = 7 + 3x_1 - x_2.$$

Points with coordinates (x_1, x_2) implying a constant response, say $\hat{y} = 6$, must satisfy the equation

$$6 = 7 + 3x_1 - x_2$$

or

$$x_2 = 3x_1 + 1.$$

The reader will recognize this as the equation which defines a locus of points falling on a straight line as indicated in Fig. 10.1.

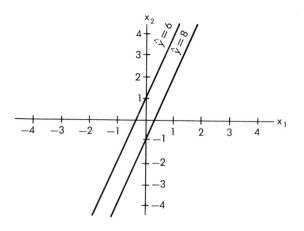

Figure 10.1   Contour map for the surface defined by $\hat{y} = 7 + 3x_1 - x_2$

Similarly, all points (x_1, x_2) yielding a constant response, $\hat{y} = 8$, must satisfy the equation

$$8 = 7 + 3x_1 + x_2$$

or

$$x_2 = 3x_1 - 1.$$

This line is also shown on Fig. 10.1. Note that the yield is increasing as one moves toward the lower right-hand quadrant in Fig. 10.1.

Suppose that a second-order linear model has been fitted to data over an experimental region defined by the unit square $(-1 \le x_1 \le 1$ and $-1 \le x_2 \le 1)$ and that the fitted prediction equation is

$$\hat{y} = 10 + x_1 - .7x_2 + x_1x_2 + 1.2x_1^2 + 2x_2^2.$$

The corresponding contour map of constant response is indicated in Fig. 10.2. For example, the contour for $\hat{y} = 10$ would yield points that satisfy the equation

$$10 = 10 + x_1 - .7x_2 + x_1x_2 + 1.2x_1^2 + 2x_2^2.$$

The utility derived from the construction of contour maps is not restricted to experiments involving two independent variables. Three-dimensional constant-response figures can be constructed of plaster or other material, or a series of two-dimensional response contours can be developed for fixed values of the other independent variables included in the experiment.

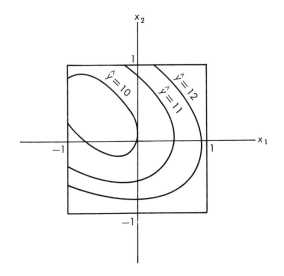

Figure 10.2   Contour map for a second-order linear model

It should particularly be noted 'that all of the information provided by a contour map is contained in the underlying prediction equation. Thus contour maps do not yield additional information pertinent to the response surface; rather, they present the information contained in a prediction equation in a pictorial and thereby a more understandable form.

10.4 The Method of Steepest Ascent

The method of steepest ascent is a procedure for moving, through sequential experimentation, to a region of higher (or lower) response when seeking a maximum (or minimum). The logic behind the procedure is relatively easy to see. Experimental points are selected over a relatively small experimental region so that a plane provides a reasonably good fit to the surface. The tilt of the plane is then examined to determine the direction of movement that will imply maximum surface slope, and this is called the direction of steepest ascent. The experimental region is then moved in the direction of steepest ascent, more experimental points are selected, and a new plane is fitted to the surface. In order to avoid overextending the experimental region and thereby inducing curvature in the surface, only the points contained within the limited confines of the second experimental design are used to fit the new plane. The direction of steepest ascent for the second plane is determined and a new experimental region is established in that direction. The process of fitting a plane is repeated until, through sequential experimentation, the experimenter moves to the vicinity of the maximum.

The direction of steepest ascent for a given planar fit can easily be seen by viewing the two-independent-variable example of Fig. 10.1. The constant-response curves for $\hat{y} = 6$ and $\hat{y} = 8$ are parallel straight lines. Furthermore, it is clear that the substitution of a new response will only change the intercept of the constant-response line with the x_2-axis and will leave the slope unchanged. Thus constant-response curves for a planar fit will be parallel lines equidistantly spaced for equal changes in the response.

See Fig. 10.3, which is similar to Fig. 10.1 except that the equal-response lines for $\hat{y} = 9$ and $\hat{y} = 10$ are added. Note that the equal-response lines are parallel and that the distance between a pair of lines is proportional to the change in response. The direction of steepest ascent, indicated by the arrow in Fig. 10.3, is perpendicular to the constant-response lines and will imply movement in the x_1 and x_2 directions proportional to the coefficients of x_1 and x_2. Thus, since the prediction equation is

$$\hat{y} = 7 + 3x_1 - x_2,$$

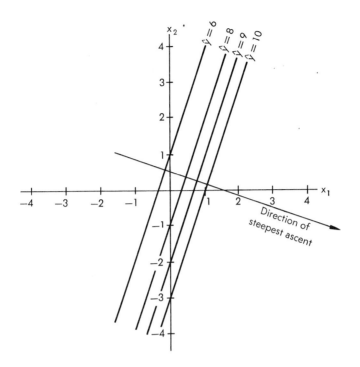

Figure 10.3 Direction of steepest ascent for the plane $\hat{y} = 7 + 3x_1 - x_2$

the direction of steepest ascent would be obtained by increasing x_1 by three units for every one-unit decrease in x_2. The direction of steepest descent would require a move in the opposite direction and consequently a three-unit decrease in the x_1 direction for every one unit increase in x_2.

The results implied by the contour map of Fig. 10.3 hold in general. If a response y is a function of k variables, $x_1, x_2, \ldots, x_k$, and a hyperplane is fitted to the response surface, yielding

$$\hat{y} = \hat{\beta}_0 + \hat{\beta}_1 x_1 + \hat{\beta}_2 x_2 + \cdots + \hat{\beta}_k x_k,$$

the direction of steepest ascent will be achieved by moving along the x_1, $x_2, \ldots, x_k$ axes in an amount proportional to $\hat{\beta}_1, \hat{\beta}_2, \ldots, \hat{\beta}_k$, respectively. Thus if $k = 3$ and

$$\hat{y} = 2 + x_1 - x_2 + 2x_3,$$

the direction of steepest ascent will imply movement proportional to one unit along the x_1-axis, minus one unit along the x_2-axis and two units along the x_3-axis.

It should be noted that the changing curvature of the response surface will imply changes in the direction of steepest ascent in sequential experimentation, and this condition is further aggravated by experimental error. That is, the estimators of the parameters indicating the direction of steepest ascent, $\beta_1, \beta_2, \beta_3, \ldots, \beta_k$, are subject to the usual errors of estimation and hence the sequential fitting of planes to seek a higher yield will give directions of steepest ascent that often seem to vary, to contradict and correct one another. One might argue that this should not be too disturbing as long as movement to a region of higher yield is achieved, but this point of view is unsatisfactory when experimental costs are considered. Thus the specter of "experimental strategy" looms before us, and we wonder whether a particular sequence of experiments led us to a maximum response at minimum cost.

For example, what kind of experimental design is best for each stage of the sequential experimental route to the maximum? When is it desirable to replicate experimental design points to obtain better estimates of the coefficients of the linear model and thereby reduce the error in determining the direction of steepest ascent? Once the direction of steepest ascent has been determined at a given stage, how far should one move to establish the new experimental points? Most of these questions remain unanswered. Certainly one must have a fair degree of accuracy in the estimation of the model parameters so that the error of estimating the direction of steepest ascent is not too large. We have given procedures in Chapter 7 for placing confidence intervals on the model parameters. The half-width of these intervals will measure the error of estimating a particular slope parameter.

A local maximum, minimum, or saddle point will be achieved at a point where the partial derivatives of $E(y)$, namely, $\beta_1, \beta_2, \ldots, \beta_k$, are equal to zero. Thus the magnitude of the change in the independent variables should be somewhat proportional to the overall magnitude of the parameter estimates. When the parameter estimates are large, a relatively large shift would be made to locate the new experimental region. In contrast, small values of the estimates would suggest that one is near a local maximum where, in most cases, smaller shifts would be made in locating a new experimental region.

As one gets nearer the maximum, the parameters become smaller in absolute value and consequently difficult to estimate with accuracy. When this occurs, a second-order experimental design is often employed. The maximum (or minimum) of the fitted second-order prediction equation is then acquired (using the calculus) with the expectation that this will provide a solution relatively near the true local maximum or minimum. The reader will note that we refer to a "local" maximum or minimum because one never knows for certain that multiple humps do not exist in the response surface.

10.5 First-Order Experimental Designs

We have noted in Sec. 5.3 that a two-level factorial experiment provides sufficient information to fit a plane to a response surface. For example, the complete model for a 2^3 factorial experiment with independent variables x_1, x_2, and x_3 is

$$y = \beta_0 + \beta_1 x_1 + \beta_2 x_2 + \beta_3 x_3 + \beta_4 x_1 x_2 + \beta_5 x_1 x_3 + \beta_6 x_2 x_3 + \beta_7 x_1 x_2 x_3 + \epsilon.$$

If no interactions exist, thus permitting the deletion of the terms involving $\beta_4, \beta_5, \beta_6$, and β_7, the resulting model would imply an $E(y)$ that would trace a hyperplane in the space defined by the independent variables, x_1, x_2, and x_3.

First-order experimental designs are those which permit the estimation of the parameters in a planar model. In addition to the 2^k factorial experiment, fractional replicates of the 2^k factorial (discussed in Chapter 11) and the *simplex* design are first-order experimental designs. A simplex design utilizes a minimum number of experimental points by placing one point at each vertex of a simplex figure symmetrically situated with respect to the origin. Simplex figures in two and three dimensions are the equilateral triangle and the equilateral tetrahedron, respectively. A similar equilateral figure containing $(k + 1)$ vertices in k dimensions can be used to form a simplex design in k dimensions. All three of these designs are part of a larger class of designs presented by Box (1952). All are orthogonal designs, can easily be expanded to form a second-order design, and all provide minimum-variance estimators of the slope parameters that are used in the method of steepest ascent.

Further familiarity with the simplex designs will be developed in the exercises at the end of this chapter.

10.6 An Augmented 2^k Factorial Experiment

Unfortunately, the experimenter rarely knows for certain that the selected experimental region is small enough to permit a planar fit. The fact that the 2^k factorial experiment provides for the estimation or tests of hypotheses concerning the interaction parameters yields an additional check to test for twist in the response surface (represented by the interaction terms) if an estimate of σ^2 is available either through replication or prior experimentation.

Checks to detect lack of fit in a planar model are very desirable because they may indicate that a second-order model would provide a better approximation to the response surface over the experimental region. For example, the 2^k factorial experiment does not provide information for the estimation of the coefficients of the second-degree terms $x_1^2, x_2^2, \ldots, x_k^2$, and therefore it is often convenient to acquire this information by augmenting the design with one or more experimental points at the origin (the center of the experimental region). Thus the configuration for a 2×2 factorial experiment with a center point at the origin would require five experimental points (factor combinations) as shown in Fig. 10.4.

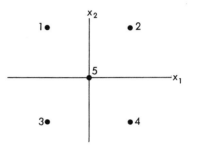

Figure 10.4 Augmented 2×2 factorial experiment

The additional information contributed by the center point of the augmented 2×2 factorial experiment can be seen by comparison of the two-variable second-order model,

$$y = \beta_0 + \beta_1 x_1 + \beta_2 x_2 + \beta_3 x_1 x_2 + \beta_4 x_1^2 + \beta_5 x_2^2 + \epsilon,$$

with the corresponding model for the 2×2 factorial experiment. Since the only difference between the two models will be the terms $\beta_4 x_1^2$ and $\beta_5 x_2^2$, we would expect the increase in information to measure the contribution of these terms in predicting the response and thereby provide a test of the hypothesis that $\beta_4 = \beta_5 = 0$. Thus we recall that one can form at most four orthogonal linear contrasts of the five response measurements and consequently can estimate at most five parameters in a linear model (including β_0). The first three orthogonal contrasts estimate the parameters of the 2×2 factorial model associated with the linear effects due to x_1 and x_2, and the parameter associated with the $x_1 x_2$ interaction. The fourth and remaining orthogonal contrast will imply a comparison of the response at the center point with the responses at the four exterior points of the design and will employ the contrast,

$$l_4 = y_1 + y_2 + y_3 + y_4 - 4y_5.$$

(The subscripts correspond with the experimental points of Fig. 10.4.)

The Y and X matrices for the augmented 2×2 factorial experiment are shown in Fig. 10.5. The first through the fourth columns of the X matrix correspond to x_0, x_1, x_2, and $x_1 x_2$ respectively, and the fifth column is the vector $\mathbf{x}_4$ used to construct the linear contrast l_4.

Figure 10.5 Y and X matrices for a 2×2 factorial experiment with center point

$$Y = \begin{bmatrix} y_1 \\ y_2 \\ y_3 \\ y_4 \\ y_5 \end{bmatrix} \qquad X = \begin{bmatrix} 1 & -1 & 1 & -1 & 1 \\ 1 & 1 & 1 & 1 & 1 \\ 1 & -1 & -1 & 1 & 1 \\ 1 & 1 & -1 & -1 & 1 \\ 1 & 0 & 0 & 0 & -4 \end{bmatrix}$$

The expected value of l_4 is

$$E(l_4) = E(\mathbf{x}_4' y) = E(y_1 + y_2 + y_3 + y_4 - 4y_5)$$
$$= 4\beta_4 + 4\beta_5,$$

thereby indicating that l_4 may be used to estimate or test hypotheses concerning $4(\beta_4 + \beta_5)$. Denoting the parameter of the linear model associated with the vector $\mathbf{x}_4$ as β_4^*, we recall (Sec. 9.6) that the estimator of β_4^* is

$$\hat{\beta}_4^* = \frac{l_4}{\mathbf{x}_4' \mathbf{x}_4} = \frac{l_4}{20}.$$

It would follow that the expected value of this estimator is

$$\beta_4^* = E(\hat{\beta}_4^*) = \tfrac{1}{20} E(l_4) = \tfrac{1}{5}(\beta_4 + \beta_5)$$

and hence that $\hat{\beta}_4^*$ is an unbiased estimator of $\tfrac{1}{5}(\beta_4 + \beta_5)$.

Similarly, if we seek a lack-of-fit test to detect curvature in the response surface of the type implied by the quadratic terms x_1^2 and x_2^2, we may test the hypothesis

$$\beta_4^* = \tfrac{1}{5}(\beta_4 + \beta_5) = 0$$

with the t-statistic

$$t = \frac{\hat{\beta}_4^*}{s\sqrt{c_{44}}} = \frac{\hat{\beta}_4^*}{s\sqrt{1/(\mathbf{x}_4' \mathbf{x}_4)}} = \frac{l_4}{20s\sqrt{1/(20)}}$$
$$= \frac{y_1 + y_2 + y_3 + y_4 - 4y_5}{s\sqrt{20}}$$

(Note that $c_{44} = (\mathbf{x}_4' \mathbf{x}_4)^{-1}$ because the columns of the X matrix are mutually orthogonal and hence $X'X$ is diagonal.) If the null hypothesis is rejected, we would conclude that there is sufficient evidence to indicate that either β_4, β_5, or both differ from zero and to indicate that a second-order model would yield an improvement over the planar model in fitting the response surface. Note that a least-squares estimate of σ^2 must be obtained either by replication or from prior experimentation in order to conduct this test.

As one might suspect, the addition of a single experimental point does not provide sufficient information to test for the existence of both parameters β_4 and β_5. Indeed, the quantity $(\beta_4 + \beta_5)$ might equal zero when β_4 and β_5 differ in sign but are both large and equal in absolute value. Thus a rejection of the null hypothesis does imply lack of fit. Nonrejection could be due either to a difference in sign of β_4 and β_5 or to the fact that the data provide insufficient information to detect the departure of $\frac{1}{5}(\beta_4 + \beta_5)$ from zero, or it could imply that the null hypothesis is true. As such, the test is a useful test of lack of fit that is based upon a minimal number of experimental points, but it is not a substitute for a second-order design.

Why then does one not always employ a second-order design and thereby improve the lack-of-fit test? The answer, of course, is that the second-order design requires more experimental points and is therefore more costly. The 3×3 factorial experiment is a second-order design that illustrates this point.

The preceding discussion will apply to any two-level factorial experiment augmented by a center point. Thus a 2^k factorial experiment with a center point will require $(2^k + 1)$ runs and will provide the lack-of-fit contrast,

$$l_p = y_1 + y_2 + \cdots + y_{(2^k)} - (2^k)y_p,$$

where y_p is the response at the center point. Then the parameter associated with this contrast, say β_p, is estimated by

$$\hat{\beta}_p = \frac{l_p}{\mathbf{x}_p' \mathbf{x}_p} = \frac{l_p}{2^k(1 + 2^k)}.$$

(Note that the transpose of the vector, $\mathbf{x}_p$, would be $[1, 1, 1, 1, \ldots, 1, -2^k]$, where the first 2^k elements would be identical and equal to unity.)

If, for the sake of discussion, the coefficients of $x_1^2, x_2^2, \ldots, x_k^2$ are denoted as $\beta_1, \beta_2, \ldots, \beta_k$, it can be shown by Theorem 1.4 that the expected value of $\hat{\beta}_p$ is

$$E(\hat{\beta}_p) = \frac{\beta_1 + \beta_2 + \cdots + \beta_k}{(1 + 2^k)}.$$

Hence, the test statistic

$$t = \frac{\hat{\beta}_p}{s\sqrt{c_{pp}}} = \frac{\hat{\beta}_p}{s(\mathbf{x}_p' \mathbf{x}_p)^{-1/2}} = \frac{\hat{\beta}_p[2^k(1 + 2^k)]^{1/2}}{s} = \frac{l_p}{s[2^k(1 + 2^k)]^{1/2}}$$

could be employed to test the null hypothesis

$$H_0: \beta_1 + \beta_2 + \ldots + \beta_k = 0.$$

If the t-statistic falls in the rejection region, we conclude that at least one of the coefficients of the second-degree terms $x_1^2, x_2^2, \ldots, x_k^2$ differs from zero.

If the test does not imply rejection, one must be cautious in drawing conclusions, because this situation could occur owing to differing signs of the coefficients when in fact $\beta_1, \beta_2, \ldots, \beta_k$ actually differ from zero.

Example 10.1   A 2×2 factorial experiment augmented with a center point produced the responses indicated in Fig. 10.6. Do the data present sufficient evidence to indicate that the second-degree terms, x_1^2 and x_2^2, are important for the prediction of y? Assume that $s = .8$, an estimate of σ based upon 30 degrees of freedom, was obtained from earlier experimentation.

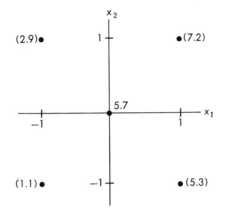

Figure 10.6   Response for Example 10.1

Solution: The contrast for testing an hypothesis concerning the curvature term, β_4^*, is

$$l_4 = y_1 + y_2 + y_3 + y_4 - 4y_5 = -6.3.$$

Then, to test the null hypothesis that $\beta_4^* = 0$,

$$t = \frac{l_4}{s\sqrt{20}} = \frac{-6.3}{.8\sqrt{20}} = -1.76$$

The rejection region for $\alpha = .05$ is $|t| \geq 2.04$. Since the calculated value of $|t|$ does not exceed 2.04, we cannot reject H_0 and hence there is not sufficient evidence to indicate that β_4^* differs from zero at the $\alpha = .05$ level of significance. Note that this conclusion could be due to lack of sufficient data or to a difference of signs of the two quadratic parameters when in fact they are really large from a practical point of view. Whether the five experimental data points provide sufficient information depends upon the magnitude of the quadratic parameters that the experimenter considers to be of practical importance and hence wishes to detect.

10.7 Second-Order Experimental Designs

The goodness of first-order designs is measured primarily by their ability to provide precise estimates of the slope coefficients which are used to determine the direction of steepest ascent. A second consideration is the bias introduced into these estimates when the surface is curved and a second- or higher-order model would be more appropriate for describing the surface. A third measure of goodness might be the ease with which first-order designs can be augmented by experimental points to form second-order designs.

The selection of criteria of goodness for evaluating an experimental design is arbitrary and may vary from experimenter to experimenter and from one experimental situation to another. Nevertheless, we would suggest that in general the criteria of goodness for evaluating first- and second-order experimental designs will be quite different. Minimum-variance estimation of model parameters is no longer of major importance because the model parameters no longer possess a simple directional interpretation; and the experimental objective is no longer determination of the direction of steepest ascent. Rather, we wish to estimate $E(y)$ at various points in the experimental region, compare $E(y)$ at two different points, and estimate its value in the vicinity of the maximum. Thus it would be desirable to select a second-order experimental design that will in some sense minimize the variance of $\hat{y}$, the estimator of $E(y)$, at various points in the experimental region. Also, if a second-order model is an inadequate description for the response surface, we would like to minimize the bias in estimating $E(y)$. An excellent discussion of these objectives is given by Box and Hunter (1957).

At this point we will concern ourselves primarily with the variance of $\hat{y}$ where, from Sec. 7.8,

$$V(\hat{y}) = [a'(X'X)^{-1}a]\sigma^2.$$

The coordinates $(x_1, x_2, x_3, \ldots)$, appearing in the matrix, a, identify some point in the experimental region; hence $V(\hat{y})$ is a function of $(x_1, x_2, x_3, \ldots)$. Thus the variance of $\hat{y}$ will vary over the experimental region, and the pattern will differ from one design to another. For example, $V(\hat{y})$ for the two-factor second-order model,

$$y = \beta_0 + \beta_1 x_1 + \beta_2 x_2 + \beta_3 x_1 x_2 + \beta_4 x_1^2 + \beta_5 x_2^2 + \epsilon,$$

will be

$$V(\hat{y}) = [a'(X'X)^{-1}a]\sigma^2, \qquad \text{where } a = \begin{bmatrix} 1 \\ x_1 \\ x_2 \\ x_1 x_2 \\ x_1^2 \\ x_2^2 \end{bmatrix}.$$

Then we can evaluate $V(\hat{y})$ at a particular point in the experimental region, say ($x_1 = 2$, $x_2 = 1$), by substituting these values for x_1 and x_2 in the vector, a, and obtaining the matrix product,

$$V(\hat{y}) = [a'(X'X)^{-1}a]\sigma^2.$$

The X matrix and, consequently, the $(X'X)^{-1}$ matrix are determined by the design employed in fitting the second-order model to the observed data.

The 3^k factorial experiment is an example of a k-factor second-order design. Particularly, for $k = 2$, the X matrix and $(X'X)^{-1}$ matrices are shown in Fig. 10.7.

Figure 10.7   Design matrix and $(X'X)^{-1}$ matrix for a 3×3 factorial experiment

$$
\begin{array}{ccccccc}
 & x_0 & x_1 & x_2 & x_1x_2 & x_1^2 & x_2^2 \\
\end{array}
$$

$$
X = \begin{bmatrix}
1 & -1 & -1 & 1 & 1 & 1 \\
1 & -1 & 0 & 0 & 1 & 0 \\
1 & -1 & 1 & -1 & 1 & 1 \\
1 & 0 & -1 & 0 & 0 & 1 \\
1 & 0 & 0 & 0 & 0 & 0 \\
1 & 0 & 1 & 0 & 0 & 1 \\
1 & 1 & -1 & -1 & 1 & 1 \\
1 & 1 & 0 & 0 & 1 & 0 \\
1 & 1 & 1 & 1 & 1 & 1
\end{bmatrix}
$$

$$
(X'X)^{-1} = \begin{bmatrix}
\frac{5}{9} & 0 & 0 & 0 & -\frac{1}{3} & -\frac{1}{3} \\
0 & \frac{1}{6} & 0 & 0 & 0 & 0 \\
0 & 0 & \frac{1}{6} & 0 & 0 & 0 \\
0 & 0 & 0 & \frac{1}{4} & 0 & 0 \\
-\frac{1}{3} & 0 & 0 & 0 & \frac{1}{2} & 0 \\
-\frac{1}{3} & 0 & 0 & 0 & 0 & \frac{1}{2}
\end{bmatrix}
$$

For convenience suppose that $\sigma^2 = 1$. Then, using the $(X'X)^{-1}$ matrix of Fig. 10.7 and the vector, a, for the second-order model, we find $V(\hat{y})$ for the 3×3 factorial experiment to be

$$V(\hat{y}) = a'(X'X)^{-1}a = \tfrac{5}{9} - \tfrac{1}{2}x_1^2 - \tfrac{1}{2}x_2^2 + \tfrac{1}{4}x_1^2x_2^2 + \tfrac{1}{2}x_1^4 + \tfrac{1}{2}x_2^4.$$

For example, $V(\hat{y})$ at the point ($x_1 = 1$, $x_2 = 1$) in the experimental region will be

$$V(\hat{y}) = \tfrac{29}{36}.$$

Note that $V(\hat{y})$ for the 3×3 factorial experiment is a fourth-degree polynomial function of the coordinates of a point in the experimental region, and this will clearly be true for *all* second-order models and their corresponding designs. The expressions for $V(\hat{y})$ will vary for two experimental designs because of their differing X matrices and, consequently, their differing $(X'X)^{-1}$ matrices.

A convenient way to characterize the behavior of $V(\hat{y})$ for a particular experimental design is to construct a contour map of constant $V(\hat{y})$ over the experimental region. Thus for the 3×3 factorial experiment, setting $V(\hat{y}) = .8$, we have

$$.8 = \tfrac{5}{9} - \tfrac{1}{2}x_1^2 - \tfrac{1}{2}x_2^2 + \tfrac{1}{4}x_1^2 x_2^2 + \tfrac{1}{2}x_1^4 + \tfrac{1}{2}x_2^4.$$

Graphing this function, we obtain a contour curve giving all points in the experimental region for which $V(\hat{y}) = .8$. To illustrate, contours of constant variance are plotted for the 3×3 factorial experiment in Fig. 10.8. The nine experimental points are indicated on the graph.

A second method of indicating the properties of $V(\hat{y})$ for a design is to graph $V(\hat{y})$ as a function of d, the distance from the center of the experimental design. For most designs this function will depend upon the direc-

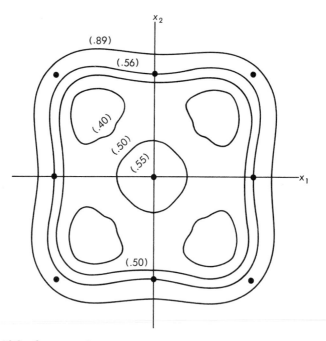

Figure 10.8 Contours of constant variance for a 3×3 factorial experiment
$\sigma^2 = 1$, $V(\hat{y}) = .40, .50, .56, .89$

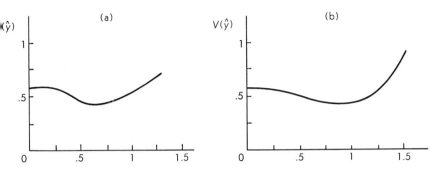

Figure 10.9   Graph of $V(\hat{y})$ as a function of the distance, d, from the center of the design (a) along the x_1-axis, (b) at a 45-degree angle to the x_1-axis

tion of movement away from the origin. For example, $V(\hat{y})$ as a function of d is given for the 3×3 factorial experiment in Fig. 10.9 for two directions, (a) along the x_1-axis and (b) at a 45-degree angle to the x_1-axis. Note that $V(\hat{y})$ increases very rapidly as d increases beyond the confines of the ex- perimental region.

We have indicated in the preceding discussion that the quartic polynomial $V(\hat{y})$, defined over the experimental region, should provide a measure of goodness of a second-order experimental design, but we have not indicated the particular form of $V(\hat{y})$ that might generally be considered optimal.

Since the purpose of the design is to explore a response surface and often to locate a maximum or minimum, the orientation of the response surface with respect to the experimental region is unknown. For example, one does not know whether the maximum occurs in the center, off in one corner, or completely outside of the experimental region. For this reason it would seem desirable to select an experimental design which provides uniform information—that is, constant $V(\hat{y})$—throughout the experimental region while minimizing the bias introduced by lack of fit of the second-order model. If attainable, this design would give $V(\hat{y}) =$ constant (ignoring the bias) as a function of d, regardless of the direction of movement away from the center of the design. This ideal variance function would appear as indi- cated in Fig. 10.10.

Unfortunately, exactly uniform information designs do not exist, but some designs give nearly uniform information on $E(y)$ over the experimental region and these would appear to be preferable to many response-surface explorations.

One additional comment should be made concerning a "nearly uniform

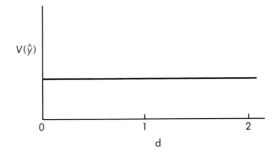

Figure 10.10 $V(\hat{y})$ as a function of d for a uniform information design

information" criterion for evaluating the goodness of a design. Actually, one should attempt to achieve near uniformity of the mean-square error of $\hat{y}$ rather than $V(\hat{y})$. The mean-square error for estimating $E(y)$,

$$E\{[\hat{y} - E(y)]^2\} = V(\hat{y}) + (\text{bias})^2,$$

takes into account both the bias and the variance of the estimator of $E(y)$. We have neglected the bias in this elementary discussion because it will depend upon the true functional form of the response surface, which is unknown, and also because one would not expect this bias to be too serious in many experimental situations as long as $E(y)$ is estimated within the confines of the experimental region. Most response functions would be expected to be reasonably well behaved over the experimental region and hence suitable for approximation by a second-order model. Some exceptions to this statement undoubtedly exist, and the risk of this occurrence will increase as the experimental region is expanded.

In addition to the criterion of a "nearly uniform information design," other useful criteria for evaluating the goodness of a second-order experimental design have been suggested. Box and Hunter (1957) have proposed the concept of *rotatability*. *Rotatable* designs are those for which $V(\hat{y})$ is constant at a fixed distance from the center of the design. These designs create spheres of equal information about the origin and, under certain conditions, achieve near uniformity of information throughout the experimental region.

For some unusual experimental situations, one may wish to select the design points and then estimate $E(y)$ at some extrapolated point outside the experimental region. Both $V(\hat{y})$ and the bias induced by lack of fit of the second-order model will generally increase rapidly as d, the distance from the design center, increases. However, the bias in estimating $E(y)$ at an extrapolated point will not likely be great if the point is not too far from the boundary of the experimental region. Designs which minimize the error of estimating $E(y)$ at an extrapolated point will differ from those which provide nearly uniform information on $E(y)$ throughout the experimental region.

To summarize, second-order experimental designs might be compared by examining their contours of constant variance over relatively equivalent experimental regions or by comparing the form of $V(\hat{y})$ as a function of d, the distance from the center of the design. What constitutes a desirable pattern of $V(\hat{y})$ over the experimental region will vary depending upon the specific objective of the experimenter. Assuming equivalent experimental regions and more or less the same general level of information on $E(y)$, the acquisition of uniform information on $E(y)$ throughout the experimental region would seem to be a suitable objective.

10.8 Additional Comments on the 3^k Factorial Experiment

The 3^k factorial experiment permits the estimation of the parameters for some terms of higher order than the second degree. If these can be regarded as negligible, the associated degrees of freedom can be employed to estimate σ^2. For example, six parameters appear in the two-factor second-order model, leaving three degrees of freedom for the estimator of σ^2. These may be supplemented by the addition of experimental points—for example, at the *center* of the design.

The reader may verify that points added at the origin of an experimental design do not disturb the orthogonality of the design. All independent variables will assume values equal to zero at the origin, and hence the addition of center points will add zeros in all vectors of the X matrix with the exception of the $\mathbf{x}_0$ vector.

For example, if a second-order model is fitted to the data generated by a 3×3 factorial experiment augmented by h experimental points at the origin, the X and $(X'X)^{-1}$ matrices are as indicated in Fig. 10.11.

If we let $\sigma^2 = 1$, $V(\hat{y})$ is equal to

$$
\begin{aligned}
V(\hat{y}) &= a'(X'X)^{-1}a \\
&= \frac{5}{5h+9} + \frac{5h-27}{6(5h+9)}x_1^2 + \frac{5h-27}{6(5h+9)}x_2^2 + \frac{9-3h}{4(5h+9)}x_1^2x_2^2 \\
&\quad + \frac{3(h+3)}{2(5h+9)}x_1^4 + \frac{3(h+3)}{2(5h+9)}x_2^4.
\end{aligned}
$$

The effect of the addition of center points to the 3×3 factorial experiment can be seen if we plot $V(\hat{y})$ as a function of d for various values of h

Figure 10.11 X and $(X'X)^{-1}$ matrices for a 3×3 factorial experiment with $(h+1)$ points at the origin

$$
\begin{array}{cccccc}
x_0 & x_1 & x_2 & x_1x_2 & x_1^2 & x_2^2
\end{array}
$$

$$
X = \left.\begin{bmatrix}
1 & -1 & -1 & 1 & 1 & 1 \\
1 & -1 & 0 & 0 & 1 & 0 \\
1 & -1 & 1 & -1 & 1 & 1 \\
1 & 0 & -1 & 0 & 0 & 1 \\
1 & 0 & 0 & 0 & 0 & 0 \\
1 & 0 & 1 & 0 & 0 & 1 \\
1 & 1 & -1 & -1 & 1 & 1 \\
1 & 1 & 0 & 0 & 1 & 0 \\
1 & 1 & 1 & 1 & 1 & 1 \\
\hline
1 & 0 & 0 & 0 & 0 & 0 \\
1 & 0 & 0 & 0 & 0 & 0 \\
\cdot & \cdot & \cdot & \cdot & \cdot & \cdot \\
\cdot & \cdot & \cdot & \cdot & \cdot & \cdot \\
\cdot & \cdot & \cdot & \cdot & \cdot & \cdot \\
1 & 0 & 0 & 0 & 0 & 0 \\
1 & 0 & 0 & 0 & 0 & 0 \\
1 & 0 & 0 & 0 & 0 & 0
\end{bmatrix}\right\} \begin{array}{l} \text{Original } 3 \times 3 \text{ factorial experiment} \\ \\ \\ \\ \\ \\ \\ \\ \\ h \text{ augmented points at origin} \end{array}
$$

$$
(X'X)^{-1} = \begin{bmatrix}
\dfrac{5}{5h+9} & 0 & 0 & 0 & \dfrac{-3}{5h+9} & \dfrac{-3}{5h+9} \\[2ex]
0 & \dfrac{1}{6} & 0 & 0 & 0 & 0 \\[2ex]
0 & 0 & \dfrac{1}{6} & 0 & 0 & 0 \\[2ex]
0 & 0 & 0 & \dfrac{1}{4} & 0 & 0 \\[2ex]
\dfrac{-3}{5h+9} & 0 & 0 & 0 & \dfrac{3(h+3)}{2(5h+9)} & \dfrac{-h}{5h+9} \\[2ex]
\dfrac{-3}{5h+9} & 0 & 0 & 0 & \dfrac{-h}{5h+9} & \dfrac{3(h+3)}{2(5h+9)}
\end{bmatrix}
$$

(ideally, we would compare the contours of constant variance), where, for convenience, we will permit d to vary in a positive direction along the x_1-axis. The curves of $V(\hat{y})$ as a function of d are shown in Fig. 10.12.

Note that the addition of center points lowers $V(\hat{y})$ near the origin but

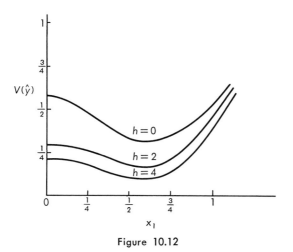

Figure 10.12

does little to stabilize $V(\hat{y})$ as one moves away from the origin along a major axis.

10.9 Orthogonal Composite Designs

Box and Wilson (1951) proposed a second-order experimental design that utilizes a 2^k factorial experiment augmented by points on each of the axes of the independent variables as well as one at the design center. This selection of experimental points, called a *composite design*, permits the experimenter to supplement the experimental points of a first-order design if a planar fit is found to be inadequate. A two-factor composite design with points added on each axis at a distance, α, from the origin is shown in Fig. 10.13.

The points which augment the 2^k factorial experiment on the variable axes need not be at the same distance from the origin. Particularly, various selections of these distances change the constant $V(\hat{y})$ contours as well as the bias involved in the estimation of $E(y)$ if the true response is not of second order. For the special case where the experimental points on the axes are equidistant from the origin, we can modify the form of the second order model and select α so that all vectors of the X matrix are mutually orthogonal. This produces an *orthogonal composite design*.

For example, here is the X matrix for fitting the standard second-order model to the data generated by the two-factor composite design, Fig. 10.13.

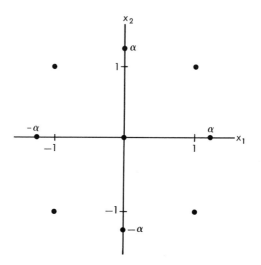

Figure 10.13

$$X = \begin{array}{cccccc} x_0 & x_1 & x_2 & x_1x_2 & x_1^2 & x_2^2 \\ \end{array}$$

	x_0	x_1	x_2	x_1x_2	x_1^2	x_2^2	
	1	-1	-1	1	1	1	
	1	-1	1	-1	1	1	Points for 2×2 basic factorial experiment
	1	1	-1	-1	1	1	
	1	1	1	1	1	1	
$X =$	1	$-\alpha$	0	0	α^2	0	
	1	α	0	0	α^2	0	
	1	0	$-\alpha$	0	0	α^2	
	1	0	α	0	0	α^2	
	1	0	0	0	0	0	

The reader may verify that the vectors of the X matrix corresponding to x_1^2 and x_2^2 are not orthogonal to the x_0 vector. However, by coding,

$$x_1^* = x_1^2 - \frac{\sum\limits_{j=1}^{9} x_{1j}^2}{9} = x_1^2 - \frac{4 + 2\alpha^2}{9},$$

$$x_2^* = x_2^2 - \frac{\sum\limits_{j=1}^{9} x_{2j}^2}{9} = x_2^2 - \frac{4 + 2\alpha^2}{9},$$

and fitting the second-order model,

$$y = \beta_0 + \beta_1 x_1 + \beta_2 x_2 + \beta_3 x_1 x_2 + \beta_4 x_1^* + \beta_5 x_2^* + \epsilon,$$

the sum of the elements in the vectors, x_1^* and x_2^*, will equal zero. Then it is possible to select α so that

$$\mathbf{x_1^{*'} x_2^*} = \sum_{j=1}^{9} x_{1j}^* x_{2j}^* = 0$$

and thereby achieve complete orthogonality of the vectors of the coded X matrix. It can be seen that $\alpha = 1$ will satisfy these relations and hence that the two-factor orthogonal composite design is a 3×3 factorial experiment.

Similarly, an orthogonal composite design in k factors will utilize either a complete 2^k factorial experiment or some fractional replicate as a basis with one point added at the origin and two points added on each variable axis at a distance of (α) and $(-\alpha)$ from the origin. As noted earlier, α will depend upon the basic design and the number of factors. For example, if the basic design is a 2^k factorial experiment, the total number of experimental points will be $n = (2^k + 2k + 1)$. The coded quadratic variables will be

$$x_i^* = x_i^2 - \frac{\sum_{j=1}^{n} x_{ij}^2}{n}, \qquad i = 1, 2, \ldots, k,$$

$$= x_i^2 - \frac{2^k + 2\alpha^2}{n}.$$

Since the vectors of the X matrix will be mutually orthogonal, the only nonzero elements in $X'X$ will be the diagonal elements, which are sums of squares of the vector elements and can easily be visualized by observation of the X matrix for a two-factor orthogonal composite design. Thus the sum of squares of the elements in the vectors associated with the first-order terms, $x_1, x_2, \ldots$, will be $(2^k + 2\alpha^2) = 2(2^{k-1} + \alpha^2)$. Similarly, the sums of squares of the elements in the vectors associated with the two-way cross-product terms will be 2^k. The somewhat more complicated expression for the sums of squares of the elements of one of the vectors, $x_1^*, x_2^*, x_3^*, \ldots$, is

$$\sum (x_i^*)^2 = (2^k + 2\alpha^4) - \frac{(2^k + 2\alpha^2)^2}{n}.$$

The values of α required to achieve orthogonality will be those which make the elements of the vectors of the second-degree variables,

$$x_i^* = x_i^2 - \frac{\sum_{j=1}^{n} x_{ij}^2}{n}, \qquad i = 1, 2, \ldots, k,$$

such that $\mathbf{x}_i^{*\prime} \mathbf{x}_j^* = 0$. If a 2^k factorial experiment is the basic first-order design, it is easy to show that

$$\mathbf{x}_i^{*\prime} \mathbf{x}_j^* = 2^k - \frac{(2^k + 2\alpha^2)^2}{n}$$

and the values of α for the two-, three-, and four-factor orthogonal composite designs are $\alpha = 1$, 1.215, and 1.414, respectively. The values of α for other multifactor designs can be calculated as indicated in Example 10.2.

Example 10.2 Calculate the value of α for a five-factor orthogonal composite design which uses a 2^5 factorial experiment as the basic first-order design.

Solution: Setting

$$\mathbf{x}_i^{*\prime} \mathbf{x}_j^* = 2^k - \frac{(2^k + 2\alpha^2)^2}{n} = 0,$$

where $n = 2^k + 2k + 1 = 43$ $(k = 5)$, and solving for α, we have

$$32 - \frac{(32 + 2\alpha^2)^2}{43} = 0$$

or

$$2\alpha^2 = \sqrt{(43)(32)} - 32,$$
$$\alpha = 1.60$$

It should be observed that a fractional replicate of a 2^k factorial experiment (see Chapter 11) may be used as the basic first-order design if k is large, and this will modify the form of the product, $\mathbf{x}_i^{*\prime} \mathbf{x}_i^*$. The interested reader can consult Box and Wilson (1951).

Example 10.3 Fit a three-factor second-order model to the data of the orthogonal composite design shown below.

x_1	x_2	x_3	Response
-1	-1	-1	20.65
-1	-1	1	20.25
-1	1	-1	25.65
-1	1	1	26.35
1	-1	-1	13.35
1	-1	1	17.75
1	1	-1	20.95
1	1	1	24.65
0	0	0	16.15
$-\alpha$	0	0	23.51
α	0	0	18.25
0	$-\alpha$	0	14.38
0	α	0	21.47
0	0	$-\alpha$	16.81
0	0	α	19.04

Solution: For the three-factor orthogonal composite design,

$$\alpha = 1.215 \quad \text{and} \quad \left(\sum_{j=1}^{15} \frac{x_{ij}^2}{n}\right) = .730163, \quad i = 1, 2, 3.$$

The second-order linear model is

$$y = \beta_0 + \beta_1 x_1 + \beta_2 x_2 + \beta_3 x_3 + \beta_4 x_1 x_2 + \beta_5 x_1 x_3 + \beta_6 x_2 x_3$$
$$+ \beta_7 x_1^* + \beta_8 x_2^* + \beta_9 x_3^* + \epsilon,$$

where

$$x_i^* = x_i^2 - \frac{\sum_{j=1}^{15} x_{ij}^2}{n} = x_i^2 - .730163.$$

The acquisition of the Y and X matrices for the design is not necessary because we already know that $(X'X)$ is a diagonal matrix with the diagonal elements given by formulas in the preceding discussion. They are presented to permit the reader to numerically check these results.

$$Y = \begin{bmatrix} 20.65 \\ 20.25 \\ 25.65 \\ 26.35 \\ 13.35 \\ 17.75 \\ 20.95 \\ 24.65 \\ 16.15 \\ 23.51 \\ 18.25 \\ 14.38 \\ 21.47 \\ 16.81 \\ 19.04 \end{bmatrix}$$

$X =$	1	-1	-1	-1	1	1	1	.2698	.2698	.2698
	1	-1	-1	1	1	-1	-1	.2698	.2698	.2698
	1	-1	1	-1	-1	1	-1	.2698	.2698	.2698
	1	-1	1	1	-1	-1	1	.2698	.2698	.2698
	1	1	-1	-1	-1	-1	1	.2698	.2698	.2698
	1	1	-1	1	-1	1	-1	.2698	.2698	.2698
	1	1	1	-1	1	-1	-1	.2698	.2698	.2698
	1	1	1	1	1	1	1	.2698	.2698	.2698
	1	0	0	0	0	0	0	$-.7301$	$-.7301$	$-.7301$
	1	-1.215	0	0	0	0	0	.7461	$-.7301$	$-.7301$
	1	1.215	0	0	0	0	0	.7461	$-.7301$	$-.7301$
	1	0	-1.215	0	0	0	0	$-.7301$	.7461	$-.7301$
	1	0	1.215	0	0	0	0	$-.7301$	.7461	$-.7301$
	1	0	0	-1.215	0	0	0	$-.7301$	$-.7301$	.7461
	1	0	0	1.215	0	0	0	$-.7301$	$-.7301$	.7461

The $(X'X)^{-1}$, $X'Y$, and $\hat{\beta}$ matrices are

$$(X'X)^{-1} = \begin{bmatrix} \frac{1}{15} & 0 & 0 & 0 & 0 & 0 & 0 & 0 & 0 & 0 \\ 0 & .0913 & 0 & 0 & 0 & 0 & 0 & 0 & 0 & 0 \\ 0 & 0 & .0913 & 0 & 0 & 0 & 0 & 0 & 0 & 0 \\ 0 & 0 & 0 & .0913 & 0 & 0 & 0 & 0 & 0 & 0 \\ 0 & 0 & 0 & 0 & .125 & 0 & 0 & 0 & 0 & 0 \\ 0 & 0 & 0 & 0 & 0 & .125 & 0 & 0 & 0 & 0 \\ 0 & 0 & 0 & 0 & 0 & 0 & .125 & 0 & 0 & 0 \\ 0 & 0 & 0 & 0 & 0 & 0 & 0 & .2293 & 0 & 0 \\ 0 & 0 & 0 & 0 & 0 & 0 & 0 & 0 & .2293 & 0 \\ 0 & 0 & 0 & 0 & 0 & 0 & 0 & 0 & 0 & .2293 \end{bmatrix}$$

$$X'Y = \begin{bmatrix} 299.21 \\ -22.59 \\ 34.21 \\ 11.11 \\ 3.40 \\ 7.80 \\ .40 \\ 12.78 \\ 4.05 \\ 4.05 \end{bmatrix}, \quad \hat{\beta} = (X'X)^{-1}X'Y = \begin{bmatrix} 19.947 \\ -2.062 \\ 3.123 \\ 1.014 \\ .425 \\ .975 \\ .050 \\ 2.930 \\ .928 \\ .928 \end{bmatrix}$$

and the fitted model is

$$\hat{y} = 19.947 - 2.062x_1 + 3.123x_2 + 1.014x_3 + .425x_1x_2$$
$$+ .975x_1x_3 + .050x_2x_3 + 2.930x_1^* + .928x_2^* + .928x_3^*.$$

The sum of squares for error is equal to

$$\text{SSE} = Y'Y - \hat{\beta}'X'Y = 6187.9881 - 6187.0580 = .9301$$

and

$$s^2 = \frac{\text{SSE}}{n - (k + 1)} = \frac{.9301}{5} = .18602.$$

Tests of hypotheses concerning model parameters as well as a confidence interval for $E(y)$ can be constructed depending upon the objectives of the experimenter.

Supplemental center points may be added to orthogonal composite designs, thereby reducing $V(\hat{y})$ in the center of the experimental region. To illustrate, the variance of $\hat{y}$ for the three-factor orthogonal composite design with $(h + 1)$ center points is

$$V(\hat{y}) = \frac{1}{15 + h} + .0913x_1^2 + .0913x_2^2 + .0913x_3^2 + .2293x_1^{*2}$$
$$+ .2293x_2^{*2} + .2293x_3^{*2} + \tfrac{1}{8}x_1^2x_2^2 + \tfrac{1}{8}x_1^2x_3^2 + \tfrac{1}{8}x_2^2x_3^2,$$

where σ^2 is assumed to equal 1.

A plot of $V(\hat{y})$ as a function of d for $h = 1, 3, 5$ augmented center points is shown in Fig. 10.14, where the direction of movement from the origin is along one of the major axes.

The k-factor orthogonal composite design would appear to be an improvement over the 3^k factorial experiment for fitting a second-order model to a response surface because it requires fewer experimental points and

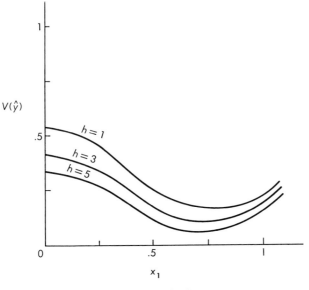

Figure 10.14

because of its computational simplicity. A comparison of $nV(\hat{y})$, where n is equal to the number of experimental points in a design, would adjust for the unequal number of experimental points for two different designs and permit a comparison of their variance contours. Properly, an adjustment should also be made to compensate for the slightly larger volume included in the experimental region for the orthogonal composite design. A comparison of the two designs will reveal that both lack uniformity of $V(\hat{y})$ over the experimental region and that a modification in $V(\hat{y})$ can be attained by the addition of center points without destroying the orthogonal properties of the designs. Thus, generally speaking, we would prefer the orthogonal composite design to the 3^k factorial experiment for fitting a second-order model to a response surface.

10.10 Rotatable Designs

Rotatable designs which provide constant $V(\hat{y})$ at points equidistant from the center of the experimental region were first proposed by Box and Hunter (1957). In particular, this paper presents the properties which are necessary for a design to be rotatable as well as some rotatable designs of first and second order. A discussion of these topics is beyond the scope of this text, but a few summarizing remarks will be made concerning first- and second-order rotatable designs since these have the greatest utility.

Comments concerning first-order rotatable designs tend to be somewhat academic since the primary objective of first-order designs is usually the estimation of the individual slope parameters rather than $E(y)$. Nevertheless, it is interesting to note that 2^k factorial experiments as well as fractional replicates (Chapter 11) of 2^k factorials are part of a much broader class of first-order rotatable designs.

Box and Hunter (1957) show that second-order experimental designs may be obtained from several geometric configurations of points in the experimental region. One of particular interest is a generalization of the composite design of Sec. 10.9 obtained by utilizing n_0 points at the center. Letting n_c denote the number of experimental points associated with the basic 2^k or fractional replicate of a 2^k factorial experiment, Box and Hunter (1957) show that the value of α necessary for rotatability is $\alpha = n_c^{1/4}$. Both orthogonality and rotatability can be achieved by selecting $\alpha = n_c^{1/4}$ and the appropriate value of n_0. Box and Hunter (1957) give $n_0 = 8$, 9, 12, and 17 as the number of center points necessary to achieve orthogonality for 2, 3, 4, and 5 factors, respectively.

Note that a combination of rotatability and orthogonality for a design will not necessarily satisfy the criterion of "near uniformity" of $V(\hat{y})$ over the experimental region, nor will these designs be best in minimizing the

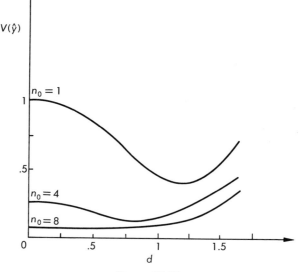

Figure 10.15

bias in estimating $E(y)$ in case the actual response surface is of third or higher order. The variation in $V(\hat{y})$ over the experimental region can be demonstrated as in the case of other second-order designs by expressing $V(\hat{y})$ as a function of d, the distance from the center of the design. A graph of $V(\hat{y})$ as a function of d is given for a two-factor second-order rotatable design for $n_0 = 1$, 4, and 8 in Fig. 10.15.

10.11 An Evolutionary Operation

An interesting sidelight to a discussion of response-surface exploration is the problem of investigating a response in an operating industrial process. The objective of the experimentation is the attainment of maximum yield, profit, a quality characteristic or some combination thereof; and the obstacle is the reluctance of the production superintendent to permit experimentation and thereby risk a loss in production and profit in an operation for which he is responsible. The solution to this apparent impasse, proposed by Box (1952), follows readily from our discussion in Chapter 2.

In order to satisfy the production superintendent, only very small changes may be made in the process independent variables so that any day-to-day changes in the response will be negligible. Thus any changes in the mean response as a result of a change in the independent variables will be very small and result in *a very weak signal to the experimenter* that will be obscured by the noise contributed by other process variables. Compensation for this very low signal-to-noise ratio can be achieved by an increase in volume obtained by replication. Thus, if one is running a 2^2 factorial experiment, the error of estimating the model parameters can be reduced to any desired value by replicating the experimental points over and over again. The trick then is to continue the process, varying the process variables over an experimental design, and patiently collecting the data for replication after replication over time. As the process produces a salable product, it also produces information which can be employed to move to a setting of process variables that will maximize yield or some other important characteristic of the process.

The procedure just described is called an evolutionary operation because it is an "in-process" response-surface study with the objective of creeping toward a maximum over time and doing so without disturbing the productive output of the process. Thus one uses the information of an operating process, which is a by-product of the production process, to move slowly but surely to a more desirable set of operating conditions over time.

The number of variables included in an evolutionary operation study is usually small. The objective is not to explore the effect of all of the variables in a process but rather to investigate only a few and achieve an improvement in the process yield.

The experimental designs often employed for studies of this type are 2^k factorial experiments, fractional replicates of 2^k factorials, or an augmented 2^k factorial experiment as described in Sec. 10.6. This latter design is particularly desirable because it detects humps or depressions in the center of the experimental region and, consequently, a departure from planarity.

The linear model for the augmented 2^k factorial experiment, Sec. 10.6, can be fitted to the data generated by an evolutionary operation by the methods of Chapter 6 (and Sec. 10.6), and tests of hypotheses and estimation of model parameters follow readily from Chapter 7.

Box and Hunter (1959) note that it is often convenient to have process foremen perform the necessary calculations to determine whether a process change is statistically significant and give simple range tests which are easy to compute and which may be taught to factory foremen unfamiliar with statistics. These procedures lack the efficiency of the t-tests of Chapter 7. The psychological advantage obtained by the participation of production personnel in evaluating the success of an evolutionary operation may outweigh the loss of information created by the use of a range estimator of σ rather than the least-squares estimator. However, for many situations, the small amount of knowledge and labor required to calculate s^2 for the simple 2^k or augmented 2^k factorial experiment is a small price to pay for the savings in labor and time involved in collecting additional data to compensate for the loss of information incurred in using the range estimator. For example, if the response is the daily yield of a production process, it takes twenty-four hours to generate a single new response and very few minutes to calculate s^2 if running totals of the necessary quantities used in the calculations are recorded.

10.12 Summary and Comments

The visualization of a response function as a surface defined over the experimental region is a very useful concept which leads to a characterization of the surface by means of contours of equal response and provides a simple intuitive justification for the method of steepest ascent (descent) which is employed in seeking a maximum (minimum). It also explains the utility of the first-order model in the method of steepest ascent as well as its general use in approximating a response function over a limited portion of the experimental region.

Second- or higher-order models take curvature into account and are used to approximate the response surface when the experimental region is relatively large or when it is in the neighborhood of a maximum or minimum.

First-order experimental designs usually attempt to provide minimum-variance estimation of the first-order parameters with a minimum of bias, an objective that might be translated to mean that one wishes to minimize the mean square error of the estimators. Secondary objectives would be the ability of the design to detect lack of fit of the linear model as well as the ease with which the design might be augmented to form a second-order design.

Second-order designs usually seek the estimation of $E(y)$ with minimum variance and bias and with some degree of uniformity over the experimental region. Contours or surfaces of constant variance defined over the experimental region are very helpful in assessing the utility of a design.

Graphs of $V(\hat{y})$ as a function of d, the distance from the origin, are easier to construct and interpret but have less utility because the function will depend upon the direction of movement away from the origin as well as upon the distance, d.

The estimated parameters of the first-order planar model are easy to interpret as slopes indicating the direction of steepest ascent; consequently they permit one to visualize the location of the response plane. A similar interpretation and visualization of the form of a second-order model is not so simple. Sketches of constant response contours in the plane of two of the independent variables for fixed values of the others are helpful but are cumbersome when the number of independent variables is large.

A second approach would be suggested by the elementary methods of analytic geometry and, particularly, by the characterization of simple conic equations in two variables in canonical form. Thus the discriminant of the second-degree equation in two variables indicates whether the corresponding curve is an ellipse, parabola, hyperbola, or some degenerate form of one of these. Proper rotation of the variable axes and translation reduces the second-degree equation to the canonical form for an ellipse, parabola, or hyperbola and permits a simple visualization of the conic section.

Second-degree polynomial functions of more than two variables can be similarly treated by rotation of axes to get the multidimensional conic surface into canonical form. Although rotation makes the surface easier to visualize for two independent variables, it is considerably more difficult to interpret when the number of independent variables is large. A discussion of rotation of axes is given in Davies (1956).

Perhaps the easiest method for study of the response surface is to employ the traditional methods of analysis. Thus the calculus may be used to locate maxima and minima of the fitted surface and to investigate slopes of the surface and other rates of change of response at various points in the experimental region. In some respects this is much more direct and simpler than a transformation of the independent variables to achieve the canonical form of the conic surface.

Exercises

1. What is a first-order response surface model?

2. Write a second-order model for $E(y)$ as a function of three independent variables, x_1, x_2, and x_3.

3. Suppose that $E(y) = 5 + 2x_1 - x_1^2 - x_1x_2$, where $-1 \leq x_2 \leq 1$. Draw a contour map of $E(y)$ showing the constant response curves for $E(y) = 1, 3, 5,$ and 6.

4. Refer to Exercise 3 and find the approximate location of the maximum of $E(y)$ within the domain of x_1 and x_2.

5. Suppose that a first-order model is used to approximate a response surface and that $\hat{y} = 10 + x_1 - .5x_2$. Draw a graph showing the lines of constant response for $\hat{y} = 8, 10,$ and 12. Give the direction of steepest ascent.

6. How is the direction of steepest ascent related to the parameters of the first-order model?

7. Refer to Exercise 3 and imagine $E(y)$ as the true response function, where $\sigma^2 = 0$. Then to simulate "experimentation," all that we need to do is to substitute values of x_1 and x_2 and compute $E(y)$. Consider the portion of the experimental region in each of the four quadrants (half-unit squares) in the (x_1, x_2) plane and run a 2×2 factorial experiment in each square. Find the direction of steepest ascent and indicate each of these four directions on the contour map. (Pass the direction line through the center of each square.) Do they point toward the approximate maximum $E(y)$ found in Exercise 4?

8. What two factors cause an experimentally determined direction of steepest ascent to point in a direction other than the maximum?

9. Test your skill in experimentally locating a maximum by simulating a response function. Choose $E(y)$ equal to some second-order function in two independent variables (like that in Exercise 3), and add a random error, ϵ, to each observed response. Then select four experimental points

in the experimental region and conduct your experiment by generating the four response measurements. Assume that σ^2 is unknown. Continue "experimenting" until you near the vicinity of the maximum, and count the number of points (and hence the cost) of locating the maximum using your experimental strategy. (Random errors with a near normal probability distribution can be obtained by tossing a die five times, averaging the observations, and subtracting 3.5. The variance of ϵ could be changed by multiplying each deviation by a constant, K. Far more sophisticated procedures are available for approximate random sampling from a normal population, but the procedure described above is simple, adequate for our purposes, and easy to describe).

10. A simplex design in two variables can be constructed by utilizing an X matrix of dimensions (3×3), where $x_0' = \begin{bmatrix} 1 & 1 & 1 \end{bmatrix}$ and x_1 and x_2 are mutually orthogonal contrast vectors that satisfy the condition $x_1'x_1 = x_2'x_2 = c$, where c is a constant. For example, a two-dimensional simplex design is indicated by the following X matrix.

$$ X = \begin{bmatrix} 1 & \dfrac{-1}{\sqrt{2}} & \dfrac{1}{\sqrt{6}} \\[2ex] 1 & \dfrac{1}{\sqrt{2}} & \dfrac{1}{\sqrt{6}} \\[2ex] 1 & 0 & \dfrac{-2}{\sqrt{6}} \end{bmatrix} $$

(a) Plot the three points implied by this X matrix in the (x_1, x_2) plane.

(b) Show analytically that the vertices are equidistant and hence that the vertices define an equilateral triangle. The distance between two points i and j is

$$ d = \sqrt{(x_{1i} - x_{1j})^2 + (x_{2i} - x_{2j})^2}. $$

(c) Construct another two-dimensional simplex design, plot the experimental points, and verify that they define an equilateral triangle. Note that the simplex design utilizes a minimum number of points in providing estimates of the parameters of a first-order model.

11. Refer to Exercise 10 (a). Fit a first-order linear model to the response measurements for this simplex design if they are given by the Y matrix, $Y' = \begin{bmatrix} 3 & 7 & 2 \end{bmatrix}$. How many degrees of freedom are available for estimating σ^2?

12. When might the simplex design be particularly useful in the method of steepest ascent?

13. Give a 4×4 matrix appropriate for a three-dimensional simplex design, where the vectors x_1, x_2, and x_3 are mutually orthogonal, and $x_1'x_1 = x_2'x_2 = x_3'x_3 = c$, where c is a constant. For this example, let $c = 1$. Show that the points identifying the vertices of the simplex are equidistant and hence that the figure forms an equilateral tetrahedron. Note that the procedure for constructing a simplex design utilized in Exercises 10 and 13 may be used for any number of dimensions.

14. What is the effect of adding experimental points at the center of a simplex? How might these points be used?

15. The following experiment is a 2×2 factorial augmented with two center points. Do the data present evidence to indicate lack of planarity of the response surface?

x_1 \ x_2	-1	0	1
-1	44		78
0		63, 69	
1	21		39

16. Refer to Exercise 15. Do the data indicate an x_1x_2 interaction?

17. Refer to Exercise 15. Do the data present sufficient evidence to indicate that the coefficients of the quadratic terms of the second-order model differ from zero?

18. Consider the two-dimensional simplex design of Exercise 10, with a fourth point located at the origin. Suppose that the four response measurements are given by the vector $Y' = [3 \quad 7 \quad 2 \quad 3.8]$ and that σ^2 is known to equal .4. Test for lack of fit of the first-order model.

19. Consider a two-factor experiment and a pentagonal configuration of points equidistant from the origin. Show that this is or is not an orthogonal first-order design.

20. Refer to Exercise 19. Let the points be located on a circle of radius $r = 1$, and let $\sigma^2 = 1$. Find $V(\hat{y})$ as a function of (x_1, x_2), a point in the experimental region. Describe the contours of constant $V(\hat{y})$. Graph $V(\hat{y})$ as a function of d, the distance from the origin.

21. What criteria of goodness are usually used to evaluate and compare first-order designs?

22. What criterion of goodness is usually used to evaluate and compare second-order designs?

23. Consider a six-point, two-factor experimental design obtained by superimposing two simplex designs with the origin in the center of the configuration. The points of the first and second simplex designs are located on circles with radii r_1 and r_2, respectively, and are separated angularly by 60 degrees. Let $r_2 = r_1 = 1$ and show that the design is or is not an orthogonal first-order design.

24. Refer to Exercise 23. Let $r_2 = 1$ with $r_1 < 1$. Find $V(\hat{y})$ and graph as a function of d for several values of r_1. What can be said about contours of constant $V(\hat{y})$ in the (x_1, x_2) plane?

25. Refer to Exercise 24. Find $V(\hat{\beta}_1)$ as a function of r_1 and graph the function. What is the best value of r_1 if one wishes to estimate the directional slopes—for example, β_1?

26. Refer to Exercise 23. Suppose that this design is used as a second-order design for $r_1 = r_2$. Give an intuitive explanation why the coefficients of x_1^2 and x_2^2 in the second-order model are or are not estimable.

27. What is meant by a rotatable design? A uniform information design?

28. Prove the result of Exercise 26. To simplify the problem, code the second-degree variables x_1^2 and x_2^2 as

$$x_i^* = x_i^2 - \frac{\sum\limits_{j=1}^{n} x_{ij}^2}{n}, \quad i = 1, 2.$$

29. Refer to Exercise 23. Let $r_1 = 1$ and $r_2 = r \leq 1$, and consider the following six points:

Point	x_1	x_2	
1	0	1	
2	$-\cos 30°$	$-\sin 30°$	simplex no. 1
3	$\cos 30°$	$-\sin 30°$	
4	0	$-r$	
5	$r \cos 30°$	$r \sin 30°$	simplex no. 2
6	$-r \cos 30°$	$r \sin 30°$	

(a) Verify that the first three points define a simplex design with vertices on a circle of radius, $r_1 = 1$.

(b) Verify that the second three points form a simplex design with vertices on a circle of radius $r_2 = r$.

(c) Note that the points of simplex 2 were obtained by multiplying the coordinates of simplex 1 by $(-r)$. Show that this method for generating the second simplex will locate the vertices on radii that are separated by 60° angles. Note also that this design utilizes a minimum number of points in providing estimates of the parameters of a second-order model.

30. It can be shown that the design of Exercise 29 is a second-order design when $r < 1$. Show that all of the parameters of the second-order design are estimable for the special case where $r = .5$. (Hint: Show that the least-squares equations possess a unique solution.)

31. (a) Find $V(\hat{y})$ for the design, Exercise 29, where $r = .5$. Hint: $a' = [1, x_1, x_2, x_1 x_2, x_1^*, x_2^*]$,

where $x_i^* = x_i^2 - \dfrac{\sum\limits_{j=1}^{6} x_{ij}^2}{6}$,

and

$$(X'X)^{-1} = \begin{bmatrix} .167 & 0 & 0 & 0 & 0 & 0 \\ 0 & 1.259 & 0 & 2.074 & 0 & 0 \\ 0 & 0 & 1.259 & 0 & 1.037 & -1.037 \\ 0 & 2.074 & 0 & 5.926 & 0 & 0 \\ 0 & 0 & 1.037 & 0 & 2.667 & -.296 \\ 0 & 0 & -1.037 & 0 & -.296 & 2.667 \end{bmatrix}$$

(b) Is the design rotatable?
(c) Let $\sigma^2 = 1$. Graph $V(\hat{y})$ as a function of x_1 when $x_2 = 0$.

32. Suppose that h points are added at the origin for the design, Exercise 31.
(a) Does this disturb any orthogonal aspects of the design?
(b) Graph $V(\hat{y})$ for $h = 0$ and $h = 3$ $(\sigma^2 = 1)$. How does the addition of centerpoints affect $V(\hat{y})$?

33. The design, Exercise 29, was employed in an experiment with $r = .5$. The observed-response measurements are given in the matrix $Y' = [10 \quad 7 \quad 9 \quad 11 \quad 10 \quad 12]$.
(a) Fit a second-order model to the data.
(b) If $\sigma^2 = .4$, find a 95 per cent confidence interval for $E(y)$ at the origin.

34. What is a composite second-order design? An orthogonal composite second-order design?

35. Fit a second-order model to the data for the following four-factor, orthogonal composite design. Assume that x_1 cannot interact with any other factors (note that this design would be unsuitable if this assumption was not satisfied due to aliasing of two-way interactions.)

y	x_1	x_2	x_3	x_4
70.3	-1	-1	-1	-1
84.5	1	1	-1	-1
67.9	-1	-1	1	1
82.9	1	1	1	1
66.3	1	-1	1	-1
66.7	1	-1	-1	1
73.3	-1	1	1	-1
76.1	-1	1	-1	1
78.1	-1.3537	0	0	0
82.3	1.3537	0	0	0
65.7	0	-1.3537	0	0
79.9	0	1.3537	0	0
80.1	0	0	-1.3537	0
83.5	0	0	1.3537	0
84.7	0	0	0	-1.3537
84.3	0	0	0	1.3537
83.9	0	0	0	0

36. Find $V(\hat{y})$ for the orthogonal composite design in Exercise 35, and graph as a function of d, the distance from the origin, when $x_1 = x_2 = x_3 = 0$.

37. Refer to Exercise 35 and find a 95 per cent confidence interval for $E(y)$ when $x_1 = .5$ and $x_2 = x_3 = x_4 = 1$.

38. Show that $\alpha = 1.414$ for an orthogonal composite design in four factors where a 2^4 factorial is used as the basic design.

39. A one-half replicate of a 2^4 factorial experiment (discussed in Chapter 11) is given by the following points in the experimental region:

x_1	x_2	x_3	x_4
-1	-1	-1	-1
-1	-1	1	1
-1	1	-1	1
-1	1	1	-1
1	-1	-1	1
1	-1	1	-1
1	1	-1	-1
1	1	1	1

Augment this basic configuration with axial points to form an orthogonal composite design. Find α.

40. Give the allocation of experimental points that define a composite

rotatable design in three dimensions. Assume that the basic design is a 2^3 factorial experiment and utilize $n_0 = 6$ centerpoints.

41. It will be shown in Chapter 11 that a half-replicate of a 2^k factorial experiment will require 2^{k-1} experimental points. Assume that the vectors in the X matrix associated with $x_1, x_2, x_3, \ldots, x_k$ and all cross products $x_i x_j$ for all i and j, $i \neq j$, are mutually orthogonal. Further assume that all are contrast vectors with elements equal to (1) or (-1) as in the case for the complete 2^k factorial (see Exercise 37 for an example). If this design is augmented by axial points at a distance α and $(-\alpha)$ from the origin and a point at the center to form an orthogonal composite design, show that $2^{k-1} - (2^{k-1} + 2\alpha^2)^2/n = 0$.

42. Use the formula in Exercise 41, to calculate α for the composite design of Exercise 35. Compare with the value of α used in Exercise 35.

43. Find $V(\hat{y})$ and consequently show that the design of Exercise 40 is rotatable.

44. Graph $V(\hat{y})$ as a function of d, the distance from the origin, for Exercise 40. Assume that $\sigma^2 = 1$.

45. Modify the design of Exercise 40 by placing a total of $n_0 = 9$ points at the origin. Graph $V(\hat{y})$ as a function of d (letting $\sigma^2 = 1$), and compare with the results of Exercise 42. What is the effect of the modification?

46. What is an evolutionary operation?

47. Suppose that the design of Exercise 40 is to be employed in an experimental situation and it is known that $\sigma^2 = 1$. Approximately how many replications of this design will be required in order to estimate $E(y)$ with an error of less than .2 within a region bounded by a circle with radius equal to 1 and center at the origin?

48. Repeat Exercise 47, except assume that the basic design is that of Exercise 45.

49. Would blocking be important when using composite and rotatable designs? See Chapter 11 for a discussion of confounding; also see Box and Hunter (1957).

References

Box, G. E. P., "Evolutionary Operation: A Method for Increasing Industrial Productivity," *Applied Statistics*, **6**, 3–23 (1957).

———, "Multifactor Designs of First Order," *Biometrika*, **39**, 49–57 (1952).

———, "The Exploration and Exploitation of Response Surfaces: Some General Considerations and Examples," *Biometrics*, **10**, 16–60 (1954).

————, and D. W. Behnken, "Simplex-Sum Designs: A Class of Second Order Rotatable Designs Derivable from Those of First Order," *Annals of Mathematical Statistics*, **31**, 838–864 (1960).

————, "Some New Three Level Designs for the Study of Quantitative Variables," *Technometrics*, **2**, 455–475 (1960).

————, and J. S. Hunter, "A Confidence Region for the Solution of a Set of Simultaneous Equations with an Application to Experimental Design," *Biometrika*, **41**, 190–199 (1954).

————, and J. S. Hunter, "Condensed Calculations for Evolutionary Operation Programs," *Technometrics*, **1**, 77–95 (1959).

————, and J. S. Hunter, "Multifactor Experimental Designs for Exploring Response Surfaces," *Annals of Mathematical Statistics*, **28**, 195–241 (1957).

————, and K. B. Wilson, "On the Experimental Attainment of Optimum Conditions," *Journal of the Royal Statistical Society*, Ser. B, **13**, 1–45 (1951).

Davies, O. L., *Design and Analysis of Industrial Experiments*, 2nd ed. New York: Hafner Publishing Company, Inc., 1956. Chapter 11.

DeBaun, R. M., "Block Effects in the Determination of Optimum Conditions," *Biometrics*, **12**, 20–22 (1956).

————, "Response Surface Designs for Three Factors at Three Levels," *Technometrics*, **1**, 1–8 (1959).

Draper, N. R., "Third Order Rotatable Designs in Three Dimensions," *Annals of Mathematical Statistics*, **31**, 865–874 (1960).

————, "Third Order Rotatable Designs in Three Dimensions: Some Specific Designs," *Annals of Mathematical Statistics*, **32**, 910–913 (1961).

————, "Third Order Rotatable Designs in Three Factors: Analysis," *Technometrics*, **4**, 219–234 (1962).

Gardiner, D. A., A. H. E. Grandage, and R. J. Hader, "Third Order Rotatable Designs for Exploring Response Surfaces," *Annals of Mathematical Statistics*, **30**, 1082–1096 (1959).

Plackett, R. L., and J. P. Burman, "The Design of Multifactorial Experiments," *Biometrika*, **33**, 305–325 (1946).

11

Fractional Factorial Experiments and Incomplete Block Designs

11.1 Introduction

In earlier chapters we have identified designs as being either "noise-reducers" or "volume-increasers," depending upon their major function. Thus the randomized block design and the Latin square permitted comparison of treatments under relatively homogeneous experimental conditions and created noise reduction in the presence of trends in one and two directions, respectively. The factorial experiment was primarily a volume-increaser in that it shifted information to focus on factor interactions and main effects in multivariable experimentation. Multivariable experimentation usually requires a blend of these two types of designs in that the factorial combinations are the treatments applied to the experimental units and these in turn are laid out in some type of blocked design.

A problem that early confronts the experimental designer is that of squeezing all the necessary factor combinations of the complete factorial experiment into a single block, as would be implied by a randomized block design. As the block is increased in size to incorporate the required experimental units, the within-block variability increases and the noise reduction of the randomized block design is reduced. This is because small blocks of experimental material, time, and so on are usually more homogeneous than large.

Two methods are available for circumventing this difficulty. One procedure is to partition the complete factorial experiment into what are known as fractional replicates, laying each fractional replicate out in a block. Using this procedure, one can employ small blocks and still run the complete factorial experiment.

A second method of reducing the block size is to use an incomplete block design in which the number of experimental units in a block is less than the number of treatments. By proper assignment of groups of treatments to each block, the block effect can be eliminated in the comparison of treatments with a consequent reduction in noise.

The theory underlying the construction of fractional replicates of complete factorial experiments and incomplete block designs rests heavily on modern algebra and geometry and is beyond the scope of this introductory text. Fortunately for the user, knowledge of the theory of construction of these designs is beneficial but not a necessity since most of the common fractional factorial experiments and incomplete block designs have been constructed and may be found tabulated in the references at the end of this chapter.

We will commence our study of fractional factorial experiments by pointing to their role in fitting planes in the method of steepest ascent; then we will discuss their most important applications, the reduction of block size and their use in screening experiments. The method of construction of some of the simpler fractional factorial experiments will be illustrated by example, and the consequences of fractionalization will be observed. A more extensive discussion of the theory of construction of these two types of designs will be found in Davies (1960) and Finney (1960). The construction of incomplete block designs is much more complex and will be omitted. An example of an incomplete block design will be sufficient to convey the basic idea involved.

11.2 Fractional Factorial Experiments

We have noted in Sec. 5.3 that a two-level factorial experiment provides sufficient information to fit a plane to a response surface and also permits the estimation of the parameters associated with certain interaction terms in case a planar fit is inadequate. For example, the model for a 2^3 factorial experiment is

$$Y = \beta_0 + \beta_1 x_1 + \beta_2 x_2 + \beta_3 x_3 + \beta_4 x_1 x_2 + \beta_5 x_1 x_3 + \beta_6 x_2 x_3 + \beta_7 x_1 x_2 x_3 + \epsilon.$$

Now suppose that an estimate of σ^2 is available from earlier experimentation, that the experimental region is small enough to permit a planar fit, and that the experimental error is relatively small, thereby permitting estimation of parameters with a minimum number of experimental points. We would then wonder whether a subset of the eight experimental points necessary for the complete 2^3 factorial would permit the estimation of the planar parameters, $\beta_0, \beta_1, \beta_2,$ and β_3, thereby reducing the cost of the experiment. Such a selection of experimental points would yield a *fractional factorial experiment.* For experimental situations which satisfy the conditions specified, the fractional factorial experiment would be useful for fitting the planes necessary for the method of steepest ascent.

The method for constructing a fractional factorial experiment will be illustrated for the 2^3 factorial experiment, whose Y and X matrices are shown in Fig. 11.1.

Figure 11.1   Y and X matrices for a 2^3 factorial experiment

$$
Y = \begin{bmatrix} y_1 \\ y_2 \\ y_3 \\ y_4 \\ y_5 \\ y_6 \\ y_7 \\ y_8 \end{bmatrix}
\qquad
X = \begin{bmatrix}
x_0 & x_1 & x_2 & x_3 & x_1x_2 & x_1x_3 & x_2x_3 & x_1x_2x_3 \\
1 & -1 & -1 & -1 & 1 & 1 & 1 & -1 \\
1 & -1 & 1 & -1 & -1 & 1 & -1 & 1 \\
1 & -1 & -1 & 1 & 1 & -1 & -1 & 1 \\
1 & -1 & 1 & 1 & -1 & -1 & 1 & -1 \\
1 & 1 & -1 & -1 & -1 & -1 & 1 & 1 \\
1 & 1 & 1 & -1 & 1 & -1 & -1 & -1 \\
1 & 1 & -1 & 1 & -1 & 1 & -1 & -1 \\
1 & 1 & 1 & 1 & 1 & 1 & 1 & 1
\end{bmatrix}
$$

One of the vectors of the X matrix is selected as the *defining contrast* that will partition the eight experimental points into two groups of four experimental points each. For example, one might choose the three-way interaction vector indicated by the last column of the X matrix as the defining contrast. The partitioning is then accomplished by placing all experimental points identified by a plus sign in the defining contrast vector into one group and all those with a minus sign into another. Each of the two sets of four experimental points is called a *half-replicate* of the 2^3 factorial. Thus the four points which would generate $y_2, y_3, y_5,$ and y_8 would form one half-replicate and the remaining points would form another. The four experimental points indicating the half-replicate identified by the plus sign in the defining contrast are shown in Fig. 11.2. The reader may verify that the Y and X matrices for either of the two half-replicates—for example

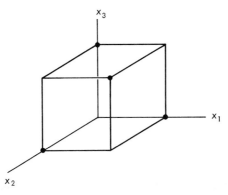

Figure 11.2

that one defined by the plus signs in the defining contrast

$$Y = \begin{bmatrix} y_2 \\ y_3 \\ y_5 \\ y_8 \end{bmatrix}, \qquad X = \begin{matrix} & x_0 & x_1 & x_2 & x_3 \\ & \begin{bmatrix} 1 & -1 & 1 & -1 \\ 1 & -1 & -1 & 1 \\ 1 & 1 & -1 & -1 \\ 1 & 1 & 1 & 1 \end{bmatrix} \end{matrix}$$

—will permit estimation of the parameters in the planar linear model,

$$Y = \beta_0 + \beta_1 x_1 + \beta_2 x_2 + \beta_3 x_3 + \epsilon.$$

Two-level factorial experiments may be fractionalized any number of times by selecting an appropriate number of defining contrasts. For example, a 2^4 fractional factorial experiment may be partitioned into four quarter-replicates by selecting two defining contrasts. One quarter-replicate would be defined as the collection of all experimental points for which the elements in both defining contrasts were positive $(+, +)$. A second quarter-replicate would comprise those which gave a positive element in the first defining contrast and a negative element in the second $(+, -)$. The other two quarter-replicates would be defined by the combinations $(-, +)$ and $(-, -)$. The four experimental points for the $(+, +)$ quarter-replicate for a 2^4 factorial experiment are shown in Fig. 11.3. The defining contrasts were the $x_1 x_2$ and the $x_3 x_4$ interaction vectors. (The Y matrix is omitted.)

We emphasize that caution must be employed in utilizing fractional factorial experiments for fitting planes in the method of steepest ascent. Their utility is limited because they provide no information for the estima-

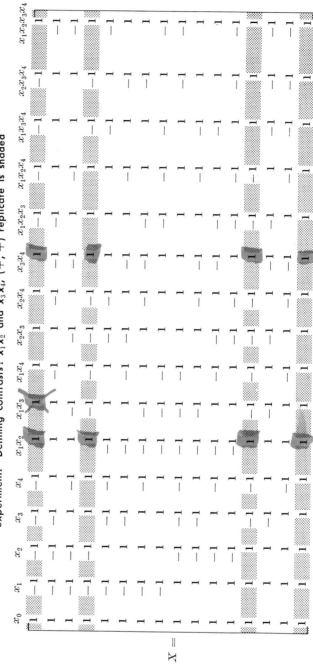

Figure 11.3 The experimental points for a quarter-replicate of a 2^4 factorial experiment. Defining contrasts: $x_1 x_2$ and $x_3 x_4$, $(+, +)$ replicate is shaded

tion of σ^2, and, particularly, they must be restricted to experimentation where the error of estimation of the model parameters is relatively small.

11.3 Confounded Factorial Experiments

If the number of factor combinations in a 2^k factorial experiment exceeds the number of experimental units in a block, which is often the case, a complete randomized block design is impossible and one must resort to an incomplete block design (Sec. 11.6) or some other procedure. One method for circumventing this difficulty is to partition the complete 2^k factorial experiment into fractional replicates, randomly assigning the factorial combinations of each fractional replicate to a block. For example, the two half-replicates of the 2^3 factorial experiment of Fig. 11.1 would be randomly assigned to two blocks as indicated in Fig. 11.4. The subscripts on the responses indicate the specific experimental points as identified in Fig. 11.1.

Figure 11.4   Two half-replicates of a 2^3 factorial experiment placed in two randomized blocks

Block 1   Block 2

y_2 y_4

y_8 y_7

y_3 y_1

y_5 y_6

In order to simplify the identification of the experimental points assigned to each block, we will adopt a convention found in most texts on the design of experiments. Suppose that the three factors are denoted as A, B, and C (we have previously used x_1, x_2, and x_3, respectively, to denote the levels of these factors). Then the symbol abc will be used to denote the experimental point for which all three factors are at the high level. The symbol ab will identify the point where a and b are at the high level and c is at the low level. Thus if a letter appears, that factor is at the high level; otherwise it is at its low level. For example, the responses for Fig. 11.4 would be identified with the experimental points (all at low level)

$$y_1 \longrightarrow 1, \qquad y_5 \longrightarrow a,$$

$$y_2 \longrightarrow b, \qquad y_6 \longrightarrow ab,$$

$$y_3 \longrightarrow c, \qquad y_7 \longrightarrow ac,$$

$$y_4 \longrightarrow bc, \qquad y_8 \longrightarrow abc.$$

In some cases it may be convenient to equate these symbols with the actual responses, and this will be apparent from the context in which they are used.

Similarly, one might randomly assign the factorial combinations of each of the four quarter-replicates of the 2^4 factorial experiment (Fig. 11.3) to a block so that the complete experiment will require four blocks, each containing four experimental units. These would be randomly assigned to the blocks as shown in Fig. 11.5.

Figure 11.5 Four quarter-replicates of a 2^4 factorial experiment laid out in four blocks

1	d	b	bd
cd	c	bcd	bc
ab	abd	a	ad
$abcd$	abc	acd	ac

As one might suspect, fractional replicates of a complete factorial experiment laid out in blocks will not provide the same quantity of information as a complete factorial experiment placed in a single block. For example, the linear model for the two half-replicates of the 2^3 factorial experiment laid out in the two blocks, Fig. 11.4, would contain the eight parameters of the complete 2^3 factorial plus one parameter representing the difference between the blocks. And it is clearly impossible to fit a model containing nine parameters with only eight points. What information is lost?

The answer to this question can easily be seen by observing the X matrix for the complete 2^3 factorial experiment, Fig. 11.1. Recall that the three-way interaction vector was the defining contrast used to fractionalize the experiment, and note that the estimation of the three-way interaction parameter involves a comparison of the four responses for the experimental points indicated by the plus signs in the three-way interaction vector with the four identified by the minus signs. Since the four with plus signs, representing one of the two fractional replicates, are all in block 1 and the other four are in block 2, the estimation of the three-way interaction parameter will involve a comparison of the two block totals. Hence the estimator of the block differences is the same as the estimator of the three-way interaction parameter, and we say that these two effects are confounded. For example, if the three-way interaction parameter tests significantly different from zero, one would not know whether it was due to a three-way interaction of the factors or to a difference between blocks.

A complete 2^k factorial experiment fractionalized and laid out in blocks will always confound the block parameters with those of the defining contrasts, and the greater the fractionalization, the more parameters will be confounded. For example, one can construct three independent linear contrasts of the block effects for the fractionalized 2^4 factorial laid out in four blocks, Fig. 11.5. Two independent comparisons of the blocks will be confounded with the parameters associated with the defining contrasts, the x_1x_2 and the x_3x_4 interactions, and the third will be confounded with the $x_1x_2x_3x_4$ interaction. For example, the reader may verify (see Fig. 11.5) that the $x_1x_2x_3x_4$ contrast involves a comparison of the responses in blocks 1 and 4 versus 2 and 3.

Given two defining contrasts as for the 2^4 factorial experiment, Fig. 11.3, one can easily find the third effect confounded with blocks by utilizing the following symbolic multiplicative device. Multiply the terms x_1x_2 and x_3x_4 associated with the two defining contrasts and obtain $x_1x_2x_3x_4$. If any of the variables in the resulting product occurs to the second power, delete that variable. Of course, this did not happen for the confounding of Fig. 11.5. The resulting product, $x_1x_2x_3x_4$, will be a third defining contrast. Any two of the three defining contrasts will give the same fractionalization pattern for the design and any two will generate the third by symbolic multiplication. For example, if one partitioned a 2^5 factorial into quarter-replicates using the defining contrast, $x_1x_2x_3x_4$ and $x_3x_4x_5$, then the third defining contrast, which will be confounded with blocks, is the $x_1x_2x_5$ interaction term. This is obtained by the symbolic multiplication

$$(x_1x_2x_3x_4)(x_3x_4x_5) = x_1x_2x_3^2x_4^2x_5,$$

which, by our convention, is equal to $x_1x_2x_5$.

Example 11.1 Suppose that a 2^6 factorial experiment involves factors A, B, C, D, E, and F and that the $ABCDEF$ and the ABC interactions are used as defining contrasts to construct quarter-replicates of the experiment.

(a) Give the third defining contrast.

(b) If the four quarter-replicates are laid out in four blocks, give the treatment contrasts that are confounded with the block contrasts.

Solution: (a) The symbolic multiplication for the six factors may be accomplished by using either the symbols A, B, C, D, E, F or $x_1, x_2, \ldots, x_6$ denoting their levels. We will use the former for this example. Using symbolic multiplication, the third defining contrast is

$$(ABC)(ABCDEF) = A^2B^2C^2DEF$$
$$= DEF$$

(b) The three treatment contrasts confounded with the block contrasts will be the three defining contrasts, the ABC, $ABCDEF$, and DEF interactions. These, of course, will correspond to the $x_1x_2x_3$, the $x_1x_2x_3x_4x_5x_6$, and the $x_4x_5x_6$ terms in the linear model.

We have illustrated that a fractionalization of a 2^k factorial experiment into two half-replicates requires one defining contrast. Quarter-replicates require two defining contrasts to accomplish the partitioning, and these two defining contrasts automatically imply a third which is obtained by symbolic multiplication. As one might suspect, one-eighth replicates are constructed by selecting three defining contrasts, placing all experimental points with plus signs in all three vectors $(+, +, +)$ into one one-eighth replicate, all $(+, +, -)$ into a second, and so on for the other six combinations of plus and minus signs. These eight fractional replicates would be placed in eight blocks and would confound seven treatment contrasts with the seven block contrasts. The confounded contrasts can be shown to be the original defining contrasts plus four additional (giving a total of seven) which are obtained by symbolic multiplication of the original three defining contrasts taking them two at a time and then three at a time. Higher fractionalization and confounding will follow a similar pattern with the number of defining contrasts equal to one less than the number of fractional replicates.

Thus, fractionalization of a 2^k factorial experiment into 2^p fractional replicates $(k > p)$ will require p original defining contrasts to create the partition and will generate $2^p - 1$ defining contrasts. Any p of these contrasts could be used to fractionalize the experiment, and any p will generate the remaining defining contrasts by symbolic multiplication taking the original p defining contrasts two at a time, three at a time, four at a time, and so on.

Example 11.2   Suppose that three defining contrasts, ABC, ADE, and BCF, are used to confound a 2^6 factorial experiment in eight blocks of eight treatment combinations each. Give the four additional defining contrasts that will be confounded with the block contrasts.

Solution: The four additional defining contrasts confounded with the block contrasts are obtained by symbolic multiplication of the original three defining contrasts taken two at a time and then three at a time. These are

$$(ABC)(ADE) = A^2BCDE = BCDE,$$
$$(ABC)(BCF) = AB^2C^2F = AF,$$
$$(ADE)(BCF) = ABCDEF,$$
$$(ABC)(ADE)(BCF) = A^2B^2C^2DEF = DEF.$$

In confounding a factorial experiment in blocks, the objective is to select the defining contrast so as to confound high-order interactions, which one expects to be negligible. This can be done with a bit of practice. A general discussion of the procedure for locating the confounding pattern for higher degrees of fractionalization will be found in the references previously cited. One can also obtain fractional replicates of factorial experiments with factors at more than two levels. Fractional factorials for two, three, and a mixture of two and three levels are given by the National Bureau of Standards (1957, 1959, and 1961, respectively).

Example 11.3 Suppose that one is confounding a 2^4 factorial experiment in four blocks and that the AB interaction is known to be negligible as well as all higher-order interactions. Find two defining contrasts for fractionalizing and confounding the experiment.

Solution: If the AB interaction is negligible, we would select the AB vector as one of the defining contrasts. For a second defining contrast, we might select the ACD interaction. The third defining contrast would then be

$$(AB)(ACD) = A^2BCD = BCD.$$

This would confound the AB, ACD, and BCD interactions with the block contrasts, all of which are assumed to be negligible for this experiment.

11.4 Screening Experiments

The third application of fractional factorial experiments is their use in screening experiments. As mentioned in Chapter 5, screening experiments are those constructed to investigate a large number of independent variables in an attempt to identify some (preferably, all) of the variables affecting the response. This kind of experimentation precedes more extensive response-surface studies and poses an extremely difficult problem for the statistician because of the many experimental points involved and the consequent high cost of the experiment. Particularly when the number of independent variables included in an investigation is large, it often becomes economically impossible to conduct all of the 2^k experimental points in the complete factorial experiment.

One way to circumvent this difficulty is to run a fractional replicate of the complete factorial experiment. For example, a quarter-replicate of a 2^7 would reduce the number of experimental points from 128 to 32. This evasive action thereby reduces the cost of the screening experiment and creates two new difficulties, which fortunately are manageable in many circumstances.

The first difficulty is the creation of *aliases* between parameter estimators, which is to say that *a single contrast may be the estimator for several parameters*. The parameters estimated by the same contrast are called *aliases*.

The pattern of aliases for the half-replicate of the 2^3 factorial experiment, Fig. 11.1, can be seen if we write the Y and X matrices for only the half-replicate.

$$Y = \begin{bmatrix} y_2 \\ y_3 \\ y_5 \\ y_8 \end{bmatrix}, \quad X = \begin{matrix} x_0 & x_1 & x_2 & x_3 & x_1x_2 & x_1x_3 & x_2x_3 & x_1x_2x_3 \\ \begin{bmatrix} 1 & -1 & 1 & -1 & -1 & 1 & -1 & 1 \\ 1 & -1 & -1 & 1 & 1 & -1 & -1 & 1 \\ 1 & 1 & -1 & -1 & -1 & -1 & 1 & 1 \\ 1 & 1 & 1 & 1 & 1 & 1 & 1 & 1 \end{bmatrix} \end{matrix}.$$

We first note that the vector for the defining contrast is the same as x_0 and hence that *the three-way interaction parameter cannot be estimated.* Secondly, note that the vector x_1 is the same as that for x_2x_3 and therefore that the contrast estimating the main-effect parameter for x_1 is the same as the estimator of the parameter for the x_2x_3 interaction. Thus these two are said to be aliases.

Other easily identifiable aliases are the main effect due to x_2 and the x_1x_3 interaction, also the main effect due to x_3 and the x_1x_2 interaction. The pattern of aliases can easily be determined by our earlier symbolic multiplication of the defining contrast. Since the $x_1x_2x_3$ vector was the defining contrast for this fractionalization, we find that the alias of x_1 is

$$(x_1)(x_1x_2x_3) = x_1^2x_2x_3 = x_2x_3.$$

Likewise, the alias of x_3 is

$$(x_3)(x_1x_2x_3) = x_1x_2x_3^2 = x_1x_2.$$

If more than one defining contrast is involved, the aliases of some effect are obtained by symbolically multiplying *each* of the defining contrasts by the effect. For example, a quarter-replicate of the 2^4 factorial, Fig. 11.3, was constructed using two defining contrasts, x_1x_2 and x_3x_4—and, as noted earlier, this automatically made $x_1x_2x_3x_4$ into a third defining contrast. Hence the aliases of x_1 would be

$$(x_1)(x_1x_2) = x_1^2x_2 = x_2,$$
$$(x_1)(x_3x_4) = x_1x_3x_4,$$
$$(x_1)(x_1x_2x_3x_4) = x_1^2x_2x_3x_4 = x_2x_3x_4.$$

Thus x_1, x_2, $x_1x_3x_4$, and $x_2x_3x_4$ are aliases and estimated by the same linear contrast. Similarly, the aliases of $x_1x_2x_3$ are

$$(x_1x_2x_3)(x_1x_2) = x_1^2x_2^2x_3 = x_3,$$
$$(x_1x_2x_3)(x_3x_4) = x_1x_2x_3^2x_4 = x_1x_2x_4,$$
$$(x_1x_2x_3)(x_1x_2x_3x_4) = x_1^2x_2^2x_3^2x_4 = x_4.$$

Confirmation of these aliases may be obtained by observation of the vectors in the X matrix, Fig. 11.3, after deleting the experimental points for all but a single fractional replicate.

Example 11.4 Refer to Example 11.1. For a single fractional replicate of this 2^6 factorial experiment, give the aliases of (a) the main effect due to A, (b) the AB interaction.

Solution: (a) The aliases for an effect are determined by the symbolic multiplication of the effect and the three defining contrasts. Thus the three aliases of A are

$$A(ABC) = A^2BC = BC,$$

$$A(ABCDEF) = A^2BCDEF = BCDEF,$$

$$A(DEF) = ADEF.$$

(b) The three aliases of the AB interaction are

$$(AB)(ABC) = A^2B^2C = C,$$

$$(AB)(ABCDEF) = A^2B^2CDEF = CDEF,$$

$$(AB)(DEF) = ABDEF.$$

The effect of fractionalization on estimation is very important. We have noted that the same linear contrast will be the estimator of each member of an alias set. *Actually, it can be shown that the expected value of a contrast is a linear function of the parameters of its alias set.* Hence if main effects are aliases of two-way interactions and a fractional replicate is used to fit a plane to a response surface, the estimator of a slope parameter will actually estimate a linear function of the parameters associated with slope and the two-way interaction. If the surface really is of second order, the estimator of slope will be biased because the two-way interaction parameter differs from zero. Thus the estimator of a parameter of an alias set will be biased by its aliases unless they actually equal zero. The reader will note that these biases could seriously distort the estimates of the direction parameters used in fitting a plane and establishing the direction of steepest ascent in response-surface exploration.

The effect of fractionalization on testing an hypothesis concerning some parameter of the linear model is equally disturbing. Since the expected value of a contrast is a linear function of the parameters in an alias set, the hypothesis could be rejected when any one of the parameters is large. Thus if the null hypothesis, $E(l) = 0$, is rejected, one would not know which member of the alias set caused the rejection. On the other hand, nonrejection could imply that the parameters of the alias set were small, say negligible, or it could mean that they were very large and of differing sign so that they canceled one another in $E(l)$.

As in confounding, it is clear that one would select as defining contrasts those effects which one would expect to be negligible. These are usually interactions of high order. Secondly, since the defining contrasts control the alias pattern, they must be chosen so as to create aliases between a single effect of interest and high-order interactions which we hope may be negligible. The alias pattern for the 2^4 factorial, Fig. 11.3, is completely unsatisfactory because it creates an alias between main effects (for example, x_1 and x_2). Thus if a test of an hypothesis, $\beta_1 = 0$, were rejected, one would not know whether the rejection was due to x_1 or x_2. Clearly, one cannot use a quarter-replicate of a 2^4 factorial and estimate β_0 and the four parameters associated with the four main effects. A quarter-replicate of a 2^5 can be constructed to estimate all five main-effect parameters, but some of these will have two-way interaction parameters for aliases. Heavy fractionalization can be dangerous, and the consequences should be borne in mind.

Example 11.5 Refer to Example 11.2. For a single fractional replicate, give the aliases of (a) the main effect due to C, (b) the BD interaction.

Solution: (a) Recalling that the aliases of an effect can be obtained by the symbolic product of an effect and the defining contrasts, we have

$$C(ABC) = ABC^2 = AB,$$

$$C(ADE) = ACDE,$$

$$C(BCF) = BC^2F = BF,$$

$$C(BCDE) = BC^2DE = BDE,$$

$$C(AF) = ACF,$$

$$C(ABCDEF) = ABC^2DEF = ABDEF,$$

$$C(DEF) = CDEF.$$

(b) The aliases of the BD interaction are

$$BD(ABC) = AB^2CD = ACD,$$

$$BD(ADE) = ABD^2E = ABE,$$

$$BD(BCF) = B^2CDF = CDF,$$

$$BD(BCDE) = B^2CD^2E = CE,$$

$$BD(AF) = ABDF,$$

$$BD(ABCDEF) = AB^2CD^2EF = ACEF,$$

$$BD(DEF) = BD^2EF = BEF.$$

A second drawback of the fractional factorial is that one must often either replicate some of the experimental points or obtain an estimate of σ^2 from some other experiment in order to conduct a valid t or F-test. In some cases high-order interactions may have only other high-order interactions for aliases. If considered to be negligible, these may be used to estimate σ^2.

The two difficulties that we have just described have caused some criticism of the use of fractional factorial experiments in experimental situations when a large number of factors are involved and the experimenter has resorted to rather heavy fractionalization of the complete factorial experiment. An old statement concerning affairs of the heart draws attention to a parallel between love and fractional factorial experimentation—in that it is better to fractionalize experiments once than not to experiment at all. Many experiments are abandoned because of the large number of factors involved. It would seem a much better experimental strategy to experiment, even if heavy fractionalization is necessary, thereby creating aliases of some important effects rather than not to experiment at all. If one of these statistical tests resulted in rejection of the null hypothesis, the experimenter would not know *which* of the effects were actually causing rejection but he would have *narrowed his choice to those in the alias group*. These could be checked with further experimentation. Keep in mind that a screen test is like a large net. We do not expect to detect all of the important variables in an experiment with a single screen test. We are simply trying to catch the big fish in the pond. If the holes in the net are too large, we will reduce their size with replication.

Failure to possess an estimate of σ^2 is a second cause for criticism of fractional factorial experiments. Once again, it would seem that an inflated estimate based on interactions or simply a crude estimate based upon replication at only one or two points will provide a useful yardstick to judge the importance of various effects. If no estimate is available, the *least* that one can do is to construct a histogram of the values of the contrasts. Since all have the same variance and expected value equal to zero when the effects are nonexistent, the histogram of contrasts might indicate outliers and hence point to main effects and interactions that are important in the process.

The theory of construction of fractional replicates, the generation of defining contrasts, and the pattern of aliasing can be presented in terms of the mathematical theory of finite groups. One may also fractionalize 3^k factorial experiments, certain mixtures of two- and three-level factorial experiments, as well as some other experimental designs. The references indicated at the end of this chapter offer a discussion of these topics.

11.5 The Analysis of Fractional Factorial Experiments

The fractional factorial experiment is analyzed in exactly the same manner as the complete factorial experiment. That is, one may use the analysis of variance, Chapter 8, or may fit a linear model as described in Chapter 7. The two-level fractional factorial experiments described in this chapter are particularly easy to analyze. If we use a $(+1, -1)$ coding for each of the independent variables, the $(X'X)$ and $(X'X)^{-1}$ matrices will be diagonal, indicating that the vectors of the X matrix form a mutually orthogonal set. Parameter estimates may obtained easily by the methods of Chapter 7 from $\hat{\beta} = (X'X)^{-1}X'Y$ or by the formulas of Sec. 9.6.

The parameters of the linear model may be tested or estimated using the procedures based on Student's t, or, equivalently, the sums of squares may be calculated for each of the parameters using the formula given in Sec. 9.5 and the tests performed using the F-statistic.

The major consideration in the analysis of fractional factorial experiments is not in the computation but rather in the interpretation of the results. If a complete 2^k factorial is fractionalized and laid out in blocks, it is well to remember that the defining contrasts are confounded with the block effects. If the data provide sufficient evidence to indicate that these effects differ from zero, one would not know whether the rejection was due to the defining contrast, a block difference, or both.

If a single fractional replicate is employed, the experimenter should keep the alias pattern in mind. In effect, the members of an alias set are confounded with one another, and, while we may like to think that all but one of an alias set are negligible effects, the possibility of lack of satisfaction of this condition and the consequent confounding should not be overlooked.

11.6 Incomplete Block Designs

The reduction of block size by fractionalization and confounding is not always possible, because all treatment contrasts may be important and therefore none would be available as defining contrasts suitable for confounding. For instance, if one wishes to compare the yields for eight different varieties of wheat, the eight varieties represent eight treatments and these would be analogous to the eight factor combinations of 2^3 factorial experiment. Now, we might be willing to sacrifice the three-way interaction term for a defining contrast in the 2^3 factorial experiment, but we certainly would not wish to confound *any* of the seven variety treatment contrasts with the block effects. One might accidentally confound the most important variety comparison if this were attempted.

The alternative to confounding fractional factorials in blocks is the use of *incomplete* block designs, where the number of elements in a block is less than the total number of treatments. These designs rely on a particular assignment of the treatments to the blocks and can be classed as either *balanced* or *partially balanced*. We will confine our discussion to balanced incomplete block designs, using an example for purposes of illustration, and will give the analysis of variance for any balanced incomplete block design.

11.7 Balanced Incomplete Block Designs

An incomplete block design is said to be *balanced* if every pair of treatments appear together in a block the same number of times. Thus, if A appears with B in three blocks, every other pair of treatments must appear together in exactly three blocks in order for the design to be balanced.

If the experiment involves p treatments and each block contains k experimental units, then one type of balanced incomplete block design would place all combinations of the p treatments taken k at a time in C_k^p blocks. Unfortunately, this incomplete block design may involve a large number of blocks and hence an inordinately large and costly number of experimental units. Balanced incomplete block designs may in many situations be constructed with a smaller number of blocks, but the illustration above points to the major shortcoming of incomplete block designs. To achieve balance, or even what might be called a partial balance, the experiment may require too many blocks and hence too many experimental units.

As an example of an incomplete block design, consider the assignment of $p = 4$ treatments, A, B, C, and D, to $b = 6$ blocks each containing $k = 2$ experimental units as shown in Fig. 11.6. The treatments would be randomly assigned within each block.

Figure 11.6   An incomplete block design. $p=4$, $k=2$, $b=6$

Blocks

1	2	3	4	5	6
A	A	A	B	B	C
B	C	D	C	D	D

As in the case of the randomized block design, this experiment involves two qualitative variables, treatments and blocks. The five independent block differences and the three independent treatment differences would enter the linear model with five and three dummy variables, respectively. Thus the linear model might be written as

$$y = \beta_0 + \underbrace{\beta_1 x_1 + \beta_2 x_2 + \beta_3 x_3 + \beta_4 x_4 + \beta_5 x_5}_{\text{Block differences}} + \underbrace{\beta_6 x_6 + \beta_7 x_7 + \beta_8 x_8}_{\text{Treatment differences}} + \epsilon,$$

where

$x_1 = 1$ if the response is measured in block 2,

$x_1 = 0$ if not;

$x_2 = 1$ if the response is measured in block 3,

$x_2 = 0$ if not;

$x_3 = 1$ if the response is measured in block 4,

$x_3 = 0$ if not;

$x_4 = 1$ if the response is measured in block 5,

$x_4 = 0$ if not;

$x_5 = 1$ if the response is measured in block 6,

$x_5 = 0$ if not;

$x_6 = 1$ if treatment B is applied,

$x_6 = 0$ if not;

$x_7 = 1$ if treatment C is applied,

$x_7 = 0$ if not;

$x_8 = 1$ if treatment D is applied,

$x_8 = 0$ if not.

With this specification of dummy variables, it is clear that when $x_1 = x_2 = \ldots = x_8 = 0$, β_0 must be the mean response for treatment A in block 1. The parameters $\beta_1, \beta_2, \beta_3, \beta_4$, and β_5 represent the comparison of blocks 2, 3, 4, 5, and 6, respectively, with block 1, while β_6, β_7, and β_8 are the differences in mean response between treatments B and A, C and A, and D and A, respectively.

The linear model for a balanced incomplete block design is of limited interest because it is unlikely that one would wish to estimate a mean response for this experiment and because the formulas for the sums of squares for treatments and blocks are well known. However, it is interesting to note that the balanced incomplete block design *is not* an orthogonal design, and this can be verified by examination of the Y and X matrices for the experiment. (See Sec. 8.4 for a definition of orthogonal designs.) Thus if one were to transform the block variables (see Sec. 9.6) so that the five block vectors in the X matrix were mutually orthogonal, and if the same were done to the treatment variables, the block vectors would not be orthogonal to the treatment vectors. This would produce off-diagonal elements in the $X'X$ and the $(X'X)^{-1}$ matrices, which would imply a nonzero covariance between the estimators of the block and treatment parameters. It will also imply that the sums of squares for treatments (the drop in SSE obtained by fitting a complete and reduced model) plus the sums of squares for blocks will not add to the total sums of squares associated with the complete set of treatment and block parameters.

11.8 The Analysis of Variance for a Balanced Incomplete Block Design

Since sums of squares involving the block and treatment totals appear in the analysis of variance for a balanced incomplete block design, it will be desirable to make a distinction between the sum of squares for treatments obtained by fitting complete and reduced linear models and a sum of squares involving the block totals. The former, which will be used to test hypotheses concerning treatment differences, will be called the sum of squares for treatments *adjusted* for blocks or, SST(adj). We will also calculate a sum of squares for blocks which will *not* be equal to the drop in SSE obtained by fitting linear models with and without the block effects. This quantity, which simply enters into the analysis of variance, will be called the unadjusted sum of squares for blocks and denoted by the symbol SSB(unadj). Since we are primarily interested in treatments, we will not bother to calculate the adjusted sums of squares for blocks, although this could be done if desired.

We will employ the following symbols in the analysis of variance:

p = number of treatments,

r = number of replications of a given treatment,

b = number of blocks,

k = number of experimental units per block,

λ = number of times two particular treatments occur together in the same block,

T_i = total of all observations receiving treatment i,

$B_{(i)}$ = sum of all block totals receiving treatment i,

B_j = total of all observations in the jth block,

$Q_i = kT_i - B_{(i)}$.

The number of times that two treatments appear together in the same block, λ, can easily be expressed in terms of r, k, and p. Thus if a given treatment is replicated r times, it will appear in r blocks. Since each block contains k experimental units, $(k - 1)$ will remain in each block, giving a total of $r(k - 1)$ experimental units to distribute equally among the remaining $(p - 1)$ treatments.

Hence,

$$\lambda = \frac{r(k - 1)}{p - 1},$$

and since $n = bk = pr$, we obtain by substitution

$$\lambda = \frac{r(k - 1)}{p - 1} = \frac{n(k - 1)}{p(p - 1)}.$$

The analysis of variance for a balanced incomplete block design is shown in Table 11.1, where the sums of squares are computed as shown below.

Table 11.1 Analysis-of-variance table for a balanced incomplete block design

Source	d.f.	SS	MS
Treatments (adj)	$p - 1$	SST (adj)	SST (adj)/$(p - 1)$
Blocks (unadj)	$(b - 1)$	SSB (unadj)	
Error	$n - p - b + 1$	SSE	$\dfrac{\text{SSE}}{n - p - b + 1}$
Total	$n - 1$	$\sum\limits_{j=1}^{n} (y_i - \bar{y})^2$	

$$\text{Total SS} = \sum_{j=1}^{n} (y_i - \bar{y})^2 = \sum_{i=1}^{n} y_i^2 - \text{CM},$$

where

$$\text{CM} = \frac{\left(\sum\limits_{i=1}^{n} y_i \right)^2}{n},$$

$$\text{SSB(unadj)} = \frac{\sum\limits_{j=1}^{b} B_j^2}{k} - \text{CM}$$

$$\text{SST(adj)} = \frac{(p - 1)}{nk(k - 1)} \sum_{i=1}^{p} Q_i^2,$$

$$\text{SSE} = \text{Total SS} - \text{SSB(unadj)} - \text{SST(adj)}$$

The mean squares necessary for the analysis-of-variance F-test for testing a hypothesis of "no difference between treatments" are shown in the fourth column of Table 11.1.

In addition to conducting the analysis-of-variance F-test, the experi-

menter will very likely wish to estimate the parameters representing individual treatment differences with a confidence interval. The estimator of the
difference in mean response between a pair of treatments, say treatments
i and j, can be shown to be

$$\hat{\theta} = \frac{Q_i - Q_j}{p\lambda},$$

when $(\bar{y} + Q_i/p\lambda)$ is the estimator of the mean response for treatment i
(recall that $\bar{y}$ is the grand mean of all n observations).

The estimator, $(Q_i - Q_j)/p\lambda$, is not a simple difference between a pair
of uncorrelated means, and hence its variance will be different from the
variance of the differences between treatment means previously encountered.
If we substitute the model for each response appearing in Q_i and Q_j and
apply Theorem 1.4, the variance of the estimator of the difference in treatment means can be shown to be

$$\sigma_{\hat{\theta}}^2 = \left(\frac{2k}{\lambda p}\right)\sigma^2$$

and the $(1 - \alpha)$ confidence interval for the difference in mean treatment
response is

$$\frac{Q_i - Q_j}{p\lambda} \pm t_{\alpha/2} s \sqrt{\frac{2k}{\lambda p}}.$$

We will illustrate with an example.

Example 11.6 An experiment was conducted to compare the effect of
$p = 7$ chemical substances on the skin of male rats. The area of experimentation on an animal's skin was confined to a region which was known to be
relatively homogeneous, but this restricted the experimenter to three experimental units (patches of skin) per animal. Hence to eliminate the rat-
to-rat variability for the comparison of treatments, the experiment was
blocked on rats using the balanced incomplete block design shown below
($k = 3$, $r = 3$, $b = 7$, and $\lambda = 1$). The seven blocks correspond to seven
rats.

Blocks

1	2	3	4	5	6	7
A 10.2	D 12.9	C 11.7	E 9.1	B 8.8	E 9.2	A 11.3
B 6.9	F 14.1	B 12.1	G 7.7	G 8.6	F 15.2	C 9.7
D 14.2	C 9.9	E 8.6	D 14.3	F 16.3	A 13.1	G 6.2

(a) Do the data present sufficient evidence to indicate a real difference in the effect of the chemical substances on the skin of rats?

(b) Find a 95 per cent confidence interval for the difference in mean response between treatments A and B.

Solution: The various required totals are given below.

i, j	1	2	3	4	5	6	7
B_j	31.3	36.9	32.4	31.1	33.7	37.5	27.2
T_i	34.6	27.8	31.3	41.4	26.9	45.6	22.5
$B_{(i)}$	96.0	97.4	96.5	99.3	101.0	108.1	92.0
Q_i	7.8	-14.0	-2.6	24.9	-20.3	28.7	-24.5

$$\text{CM} = \frac{\left(\sum_{i=1}^{n} y_i \right)^2}{n} = \frac{(230.1)^2}{21} = 2521.238,$$

$$\text{Total SS} = \sum_{i=1}^{n} (y_i - \bar{y})^2 = \sum_{i=1}^{n} y_i^2 - \text{CM} = 2684.97 - 2521.238 = 163.732,$$

$$\text{SSB(unadj)} = \frac{\sum_{j=1}^{7} B_j^2}{k} - \text{CM} = \frac{7640.05}{3} - 2521.238 = 25.445,$$

$$\text{SST(adj)} = \frac{(p-1)}{nk(k-1)} \sum_{i=1}^{7} Q_i^2 = \frac{6}{(21)(3)(2)} (2719.64) = 129.507,$$

$$\text{SSE} = \text{Total SS} - \text{SSB(unadj)} - \text{SST(adj)} = 8.780.$$

The analysis of variance is given below.

	d.f.	SS	MS
Blocks (unadj)	6	25.445	4.241
Treatments (adj)	6	129.507	21.585
Error	8	8.780	1.098
Total	20	163.732	

(a) To test an hypothesis of "no difference between treatments" we would use the test statistic

$$F = \frac{\text{MST(adj)}}{s^2} = \frac{21.585}{1.098} = 19.66.$$

The tabulated value of F based upon $\nu_1 = 6$ and $\nu_2 = 8$ degrees of freedom is $F = 3.58$. Since the computed value of F exceeds this value, we reject the hypothesis of "no difference between treatments."

(b) A 95 per cent confidence interval for the difference between the mean responses for treatments B and A is

$$\frac{Q_b - Q_a}{p\lambda} \pm ts\sqrt{\frac{2k}{\lambda p}},$$

$$\frac{(-14.0) - (7.8)}{(7)(1)} \pm (2.306)(1.048)\sqrt{\frac{(2)(3)}{(1)(7)}},$$

or

$$-3.11 \pm 2.235.$$

11.9 Other Incomplete Block Designs

Because balanced incomplete block designs often require a large number of blocks and hence a large number of experimental units, they may, for some experimental situations, be impractical from the standpoint of cost. Partially balanced incomplete block designs may solve this problem in some cases.

Recall that for a balanced incomplete block design, any one treatment will occur in the same block with another treatment λ times, and this must be true for any pair. This will cause the variance of the estimator of the difference between a pair of treatment means to be the same for all pairs. Now suppose that a blocking is constructed in which the property of balance is not satisfied, thereby permitting a reduction in the required number of blocks. For example, some pairs of treatments might occur together λ_1 times in the same block while other pairs occur together λ_2 times. A general class of designs which lack complete balance but still readily permit the estimation of treatment differences are the *partially balanced incomplete block designs*.

One of the more elementary partially balanced incomplete block designs is the *simple lattice design*, which requires the number of treatments to be a perfect square. For example, suppose that the number of treatments is $p = 9$. To form a simple lattice design, the nine treatments are randomly assigned to the nine cells of a 3×3 arrangement as indicated in Fig. 11.7.

Figure 11.7 Assignment of treatments
to form a simple lattice design

A	H	C
G	B	I
D	F	E

The first, second, and third rows give the treatment assignment for three blocks and the three columns give the assignment for three more. The six blocks, in which the treatments are randomly assigned, are shown below.

Blocks

1	*2*	*3*	*4*	*5*	*6*
A	B	C	H	G	E
D	F	I	A	I	D
G	H	E	C	B	F

The simple lattice design clearly replicates each treatment twice. Some treatments occur together $\lambda_1 = 1$ times in the same block with some treatments and $\lambda_2 = 0$ times with others. Consequently the block effects will cancel for all treatment comparisons, but the variance-of-treatment differences will differ for those which do or do not appear in the same block.

We shall not give the analysis of variance for the simple lattice design, but rather we shall use it as an elementary example of a partially balanced incomplete block design and suggest the consequences of partial balancing of treatments within blocks. Partially balanced incomplete block designs represent a large class of designs which, like balanced incomplete block designs, do not exist for every b, k, r, p combination. Many of these designs are given in Cochran and Cox (1957) along with the formulas for their analysis of variance. Another less common group is presented in a publication by Bose, Clatworthy, and Shrikhande (1954).

A second reason for not giving the analysis for partially balanced incomplete block designs is that all can be analyzed by the method of least squares as described in Chapters 7 and 8. Unfortunately, lack of complete orthogonality of these designs produces $X'X$ matrices which are cumbersome to invert. Although this computation could be done on an electronic computer, it is often much simpler to use the formulas for the various estimators and the analysis-of-variance sums of squares, which are readily available. Since these formulas vary from one class of partially balanced incomplete block designs to another, it is convenient to refer the reader to a text or a handbook in which various specialized analyses are tabulated.

In addition to being balanced or partially balanced, incomplete block designs may or may not be *resolvable*. Resolvability of an incomplete block design means that the blocks of the complete design may be partitioned into subgroups, each representing a replication of the complete set of treatments. Thus the original blocks may be laid out in large blocks or replications if the incomplete block design is resolvable.

For example, the incomplete block design, Fig. 11.6, is resolvable as is indicated by the arrangement of blocks, Fig. 11.8, with block 1 and 6 representing one replication, 2 and 5 another, and 3 and 4 providing the third.

Figure 11.8   Grouping of the resolvable incomplete block design, Fig. 11.6, into three replications

Replications

1		2		3	
Blocks		Blocks		Blocks	
1	6	2	5	3	4
A	C	A	B	A	B
B	D	C	D	D	C

Replications might be time or the levels of some third factor. The blocks within each replicate should be randomly assigned.

Similarly, a simple lattice design is resolvable by grouping the blocks constructed from the rows of the n^2 configuration (for example, Figure 11.7) into one replication and those derived from the columns into a second.

Thus resolvable incomplete block designs permit a blocking within the overall design and enable the experimenter to separate this sum of squares, say a sum of squares for replication, from the sum of squares for error.

11.10 Summary and Comments

Chapter 11 provides a supplement to the general discussion of blocking designs (Chapter 4) and factorial experiments (Chapter 5) by introducing the fractional factorial experiment and the balanced incomplete block design. These designs are connected by a common thread in that they provide means for comparing a large number of treatments, p, in blocks, where k, the number of experimental units per block, is less than p. A complete factorial experiment may be conducted by laying fractional replicates in blocks, thereby confounding the defining contrasts with block effects. Incomplete block designs, as the name implies, require a specific assignment of treatments to the block in order to remove the block effect in making treatment comparisons. The major disadvantage of incomplete block designs is the relatively large number of blocks, and hence experimental units, required to achieve balance.

Finally, we note that the fractional factorial experiment is useful in response surface exploration and is particularly important in screening experiments involving a large number of independent variables.

We have made no attempt to list or catalogue the very large number of different types of incomplete block designs or the fractionalizations of 2^k factorial experiments. Instead, we have concentrated on the practical objectives of these two types of designs, their analyses, and their limitations.

Exercises

1. Give the experimental points (factorial combinations) for each of the two half-replicates of a 2^4 factorial experiment where the $x_1x_2x_3x_4$ interaction is the defining contrast.

2. Give the experimental points for each of the two half-replicates of a 2^5 factorial experiment where the $x_1x_2x_3$ interaction is the defining contrast.

3. Refer to Exercise 2. Define the four quarter-replicates of the 2^5 factorial experiment using $x_1x_2x_3$ and $x_3x_4x_5$ as the defining contrasts.

4. Find the third defining contrast for the fractionalization of Exercise 3.

5. Use $x_1x_2x_3$ and the third defining contrast of Exercise 4 to partition the 2^5 factorial experiment into four quarter-replicates. Note that the resulting replicates are identical to those of Exercise 3. Repeat using $x_3x_4x_5$ and the defining contrast of Exercise 4 to obtain the same result, and thereby show that any two of the defining contrasts give the same partitioning into quarter-replicates.

6. Suppose that the two half-replicates of Exercise 1 are randomly assigned within blocks, a half-replicate per block. Write a linear model for the complete factorial experiment of Exercise 1 and include a parameter representing the difference in mean response between the two blocks. In what sense is part of the factorial information "confounded" with blocks?

7. Refer to Exercise 6. Find the expected value of the defining contrast, and note the effect of confounding.

8. Refer to Exercise 3. Find the expected values of the three defining contrasts. Note that these expected values represent three independent linear functions of the block parameters if the three factorial interaction parameters associated with the defining contrasts are assumed equal to zero.

9. Assume that interaction does not exist between the pairs of independent variables (x_1, x_2) and (x_3, x_4) and that all three- and four-way interac-

tions are negligible for the confounded factorial experiment, Figure 11.5.
The data for the experiment is shown below.

Block

1		2		3		4	
(1)	9.9	d	9.7	b	9.1	bd	8.9
cd	15.8	c	14.8	bcd	14.2	bc	13.0
ab	7.9	abd	11.6	a	12.3	ad	12.1
$abcd$	13.5	abc	12.4	acd	18.3	ac	15.6

Analyze the experiment and draw pertinent conclusions concerning the effect of x_1, x_2, x_3, and x_4 on the response.

10. Find the expected values of the three defining contrasts, Exercise 9. Note that no confounding exists because the $x_1 x_2$ and $x_3 x_4$ interactions are assumed equal to zero.

11. If a complete 2^8 factorial experiment in $x_1, x_2, \ldots, x_8$ is partitioned into eight one-eighth-replicates using the defining contrasts $x_1 x_2 x_3$, $x_3 x_4 x_5$, and $x_5 x_6 x_7$, give the factorial contrasts confounded with blocks.

12. Suppose it is known that the $x_1 x_6$ interaction is negligible and the experimenter wishes to conduct a 2^6 factorial experiment with eighth-replicates laid out in blocks. Give three defining contrasts that can be used to partition the complete experiment so that no main effect or two-way interaction parameters (except $x_1 x_6$) are confounded with blocks. Then list all factorial parameters confounded with blocks.

13. How can a confounded factorial experiment increase the quantity of information in an experiment? What are the limitations of this type of design?

14. What is the smallest fraction of a 2^5 factorial experiment that will permit the estimation of the parameters of a first-order model? Give the defining contrasts for the fractionalization.

15. What is a screening experiment?

16. What is meant by an "alias set" as applied to a fractional factorial experiment?

17. Suppose that the $x_1 x_2 x_3$ interaction vector is used as the defining contrast to construct a half-replicate of a 2^3 factorial experiment.
    (a) What can be said regarding the estimation of the parameter associated with the defining contrast?
    (b) Give the aliases of the main effect due to x_1.

18. Use the complete 2^3 factorial model to find the expected value of $\hat{\beta}_1$ for the $(+)$ half-replicate of the experiment, Exercise 17. Note that

this expected value is a function only of β_1 and the parameter of its alias.

19. If a half-replicate of the 2^5 factorial experiment in Exercise 2 is used as a fractional factorial experiment, give the aliases of each of the following effects: (a) x_1, (b) x_4, (c) x_2x_4, and (d) x_4x_5.

20. If a quarter replicate of the 2^5 factorial experiment in Exercise 3 is used as a fractional factorial experiment, give the aliases of (a) x_1, (b) x_3, (c) x_2x_4, (d) x_1x_4, (e) $x_1x_3x_4$.

21. Consider a quarter-replicate of the complete factorial experiment, Figure 11.5, and give the aliases of x_1. Use the complete factorial model to find the expected value of $\hat{\beta}_1$ computed from the data of the $(+, +)$ quarter replicate. Note the result of using the fractional replicate.

22. Suppose that a test of the hypothesis, $\beta_1 = 0$, for the fractional factorial experiment in Exercise 21 is not statistically significant and that the probability of a type II error is very small. Could this result occur when, in fact, β_1 is very large? Explain.

23. What is an incomplete block design? A balanced incomplete block design?

24. Give a balanced incomplete block design for five treatments in blocks containing three experimental units each. Use a minimum number of blocks. How many blocks will be required? Find λ.

25. The density of cakes prepared from four different mixes, A, B, C, and D, were compared after baking. Unfortunately, the special temperature-controlled ovens could only accommodate three cakes at a time and consequently required an incomplete block design to remove baking to baking variability. The density measurements made on twelve cakes are shown below in a balanced incomplete block design. The blocks correspond to a single baking or overheat.

Blocks

1	2	3	4
D 13.1	C 11.7	B 10.6	D 14.9
A 13.5	B 10.0	D 13.0	C 13.7
C 12.2	A 13.0	A 12.7	B 10.8

(a) Write a linear model for this experiment.
(b) Do the data present sufficient evidence to indicate a difference between mixes?

(c) Estimate the difference in mean density between mixes A and B, using a 95 per cent confidence interval.

26. The experiment of Exercise 25 was replicated in order to obtain a better estimate of the difference in mean density for the mixes. Assume that the eight oven heats (blocks) were run in random order. (Note that the replicates could have been laid out in two blocks of time. This design is considered in Exercise 35.)

Blocks

5	6	7	8
C 13.7	A 13.2	B 11.7	A 14.0
B 11.4	D 14.0	C 13.6	B 9.2
D 15.3	C 13.0	A 15.9	D 13.5

(a) Write a linear model for the combined experiment that includes the data of Exercise 25.

(b) Give the analysis of variance.

(c) Do the data present sufficient evidence to indicate a difference in the mean density for the mixes?

(d) Estimate the difference in mean density between mixes A and B, using a 95 per cent confidence interval.

27. Refer to Exercise 25 and find the expected value of the estimator of the mean density for mix A, $\bar{y} + Q_A/p\lambda$

28. Refer to Exercise 25 and find the expected value of the estimator of the difference in mean density between mixes A and B,

$$\frac{Q_A - Q_B}{p\lambda}.$$

29. Refer to Exercise 25 and find the expected value of $\bar{T}_A - \bar{T}_B$. Note that this estimator of the difference in mean density for mixes A and B is biased.

30. Approximately how many replications of the experiment in Exercise 25 would be required to estimate the difference in mean density for a pair of mixes correct to within .55 with probability .95?

31. Six methods for performing a painting operation in a manufacturing plant were compared, using ten men. Each man was assigned only three methods because the experimental material could be partitioned into three relatively homogeneous experimental units. Larger blocks of experimental material were much more variable. The average thickness

of the paint film measured at five specified points on the experimental unit was the response measurement. The observed response measurements for methods A, B, C, D, E, and F are shown in the following randomized incomplete block design.

Block

1	2	3	4	5
C 5.5	B 3.8	B 3.0	E 3.9	B 3.9
A 4.2	C 5.2	F 4.6	B 4.1	D 3.2
F 5.4	E 3.4	A 4.6	A 4.6	C 4.8

6	7	8	9	10
D 4.1	D 3.7	F 5.8	B 3.2	E 3.7
E 3.4	A 4.3	C 6.2	D 3.4	A 4.0
F 4.6	C 6.1	E 3.8	F 4.0	D 3.9

(a) Find λ.

(b) Do the data present evidence of a difference between treatments?

(c) Find a 95 per cent confidence interval for the difference in mean response between treatments B and C.

32. An experiment was conducted to investigate the penetration rate of meteorites through the skin of a space vehicle for four thicknesses of metal, A, B, C, and D. In order to work with an adequate area per thickness, the total area of a satellite was equally allocated to three thicknesses, but this required the use of an incomplete block design. Eight satellites were employed in the experiment, as shown below. The recorded response is the number of penetrations per square foot.

Satellite

1	2	3	4
B 3.0	D .8	C 3.4	D 1.0
D .1	A 5.1	B 3.3	C 2.9
A 1.9	C 1.1	A 7.3	B 3.6

5	6	7	8
A 6.0	D 3.9	B 3.4	D .8
D 1.9	C 6.8	A 3.2	B 2.7
C 2.6	B 6.1	C .6	A 5.1

(a) Give λ.

(b) Note that the number of penetrations per square foot will likely follow a Poisson probability distribution. Will the variances of the responses vary from one thickness to another?

(c) Give the transformation to stabilize the variance and perform the transformation on the data.

(d) Suppose that the four thicknesses A, B, C, and D correspond to .01, .02, .03, and .04 inches, respectively, and that it is known that a second-degree polynomial will adequately represent the relation between the transformed response and thickness. Write the linear model for the experiment.

(e) How many degrees of freedom will be available for the estimation of σ^2?

(f) Refer to (d). Do the data present sufficient evidence to indicate that the mean penetration rate varies with thickness?

33. Refer to Exercise 32 and estimate the change in the expected value of the transformed penetration rate as the thickness varies from .01 to .03 inches. Give an approximate confidence interval for the difference in the expected penetration rate for these two thicknesses.

34. Describe a simple lattice design. Construct a simple lattice design for $t = 16$ treatments. Is this a balanced incomplete block design?

35. Refer to Exercise 26 and assume that the first four heats (blocks) were conducted one month and the last four a month later.

(a) Write a linear model for the experiment.

(b) Find the unadjusted pooled sum of squares for blocks within replications. Note that this will possess six degrees of freedom. What happened to the seventh degree of freedom?

(c) Find the sum of squares for replications.

(d) Give the complete analysis of variance. Note that SST remains unchanged. Compare with the results of Exercise 26.

(e) Do the data present evidence of a difference between replications?

References

Addelman, S., "Irregular Fractions of the 2^n Factorial Experiments," *Technometrics*, **3**, 479–496 (1961).

Bose, R. C., W. H. Clatworthy, and S. S. Shrikhande, *Tables of Partially Balanced Designs with Two Associate Classes*. North Carolina State College Publication, 1954.

Cochran, W. G., and G. M. Cox, *Experimental Design*, 2nd ed. New York: John Wiley & Sons, Inc., 1957.

Davies, O. L., *The Design and Analysis of Industrial Experiments*, 2nd ed. New York: Hafner Publishing Company, Inc., 1960.

Finney, D. J., *An Introduction to the Theory of Experimental Design*. Chicago: University of Chicago Press, 1960.

Hunter, J. S., and G. E. P. Box, "The 2^{k-p} Fractional Factorial Designs, I," *Technometrics*, **3**, 333 (1961).

———, "The 2^{k-p} Fractional Factorial Designs, II," *Technometrics*, **3**, 449–458 (1961).

John, P. W. M., "Blocking of $3(2^{n-k})$ Designs," *Technometrics*, **6**, 371–376 (1964).

———, "Three-Quarter Replicates of 2^4 and 2^5 Designs," *Biometrics*, **17**, 319–321 (1961).

———, "Three-Quarter Replicates of 2^n Designs," *Biometrics*, **18**, 172–184 (1962).

National Bureau of Standards, *Contributions on Partially Balanced Incomplete Block Designs with Two Associate Classes*. Washington, D.C.: U.S. Government Printing Office, 1956.

———, *Fractional Factorial Experiment Designs for Factors at Two Levels*. Washington, D.C.: U.S. Government Printing Office, 1957.

———, *Fractional Factorial Designs for Experiments with Factors at Two and Three Levels*. Washington, D.C.: U.S. Government Printing Office, 1961.

———, *Fractional Factorial Experiment Designs for Factors at Three Levels*. Washington, D.C.: U.S. Government Printing Office, 1959.

Whitwell, J. C. and Morbey, G. K., "Reduced Designs of Resolution Five," *Technometrics*, **3**, 459–477 (1961).

12

An Example of a Completely
Random Model

12.1 Introduction

The linear statistical model discussed in the preceding chapters expressed a response, y, as a linear function of a set of unknown parameters, β_0, β_1, $\beta_2, \ldots, \beta_k$, and a single random component, ϵ. The random component, ϵ, which might have been due to a number of contributing sources, explained the failure of repeated measurements on y to be the same for fixed values of the independent variables. The practical problems associated with this model involved studies to locate important information-contributing variables for the prediction of y, making inferences concerning linear functions of the model parameters and the prediction of a particular value of y. Thus, we visualized a response that traced a surface over the domain of the independent variables.

In many practical situations some of the major sources contributing to the random error are known, and it is desirable to add a random component to the model for each source of variability. One will then be interested in the magnitude of the error associated with each source as measured by its variance and the effect of various sampling procedures on the error incurred in predicting the expected value of y.

If the linear model contains more than one random component but the number of independent variables, k, equals zero, the model is said to be a *completely random* or *variance-component* model. Thus if we have three sources of random error with random components α, γ, and ϵ, respectively, a completely random model might be written as

$$y = \mu + \alpha + \gamma + \epsilon,$$

where α, γ, and ϵ are independent random variables and

$$E(\alpha) = 0, \qquad V(\alpha) = \sigma_\alpha^2,$$
$$E(\gamma) = 0, \qquad V(\gamma) = \sigma_\gamma^2,$$
$$E(\epsilon) = 0, \qquad V(\epsilon) = \sigma^2.$$

To complete the model the probability distribution for α, γ, and ϵ should be specified. Note that we have assumed that the expected value of each random component is equal to zero and, hence, $E(y) = \mu$. Thus μ corresponds to the constant, β_0, in the general linear model. And since y is a linear function of independent random variables, by Theorem 1.4, the variance of y is

$$V(y) = \sigma_\alpha^2 + \sigma_\gamma^2 + \sigma^2.$$

If the linear model contains one or more nonrandom independent variables plus more than one component of error, it is called a *mixed model*. For example,

$$y = \beta_0 + \beta_1 x_1 + \beta_2 x_2 + \cdots + \beta_k x_k + \alpha + \gamma + \epsilon$$

combines the general linear model of the preceding chapters with the three random components α, γ, and ϵ. To complete the model, assumptions regarding the dependence and probability distributions of α, γ, and ϵ would be required. (Properly, the joint probability distribution of the three random variables α, γ, and ϵ should be specified.) The reader will observe that the completely random model is the special case of the mixed model where $k = 0$.

We shall not deal extensively with the completely random and mixed models but will give one of the more important examples of the completely random model in Chapter 12 and a few examples of the mixed model in Chapter 13. In doing so, we hope to suggest the method for writing models of this type for any experimental situation for which they are appropriate and to give insight into the method of analysis of the resulting experimental data.

12.2 Nested Sampling

Suppose that we wish to sample a large vat of antibiotic in order to estimate the mean potency, $E(y)$. Variation in the potency is known to occur from one part of the vat to another, hence it is desirable to select n_1 random one-ounce samples of the antibiotic within the vat using a mechanical sampler. After each one-ounce sample has been obtained, it can be partitioned into a fixed number of subsamples, say n_2 subsamples, and the potency of these less costly units may be measured. Finally, it is quite inexpensive to make repeated measurements, say n_3, on each subsample to attempt to "average out" the error of the measuring instrument. Thus the resulting experiment produces $n = n_1 n_2 n_3$ measurements on the response y and is called a *nested sampling* experiment, the term "nested" deriving from the subsampling *within* units at various sampling stages.

Nested sampling experiments with an equal number of subsamples per unit imply the random selection of n_1 prime units. Then a random subsample of n_2 measurements is selected within each prime unit, and this subsampling may be continued to any number of stages. (In our discussion we assume that the number of subsamples per unit at each sampling stage is constant, but this restriction is not in general required.) Finally, assume that samples at each stage may be regarded as randomly selected from a relatively large population and hence that large-sample assumptions about the probability distributions of the random errors will adequately approximate reality. (For example, there are a very large number of ways to partition a one-ounce antibiotic sample into n_2 subunits.)

Nested sampling experiments are common to many fields of study and are particularly evident in surveys and industrial experiments similar to the sampling of the antibiotic just described. In some situations, particularly genetics, the objective of the experiment may be the estimation of the variances of the sources of error, which are known as *variance components*. In others, the ultimate objective will be the estimation of the expected value of y, μ, with given precision and at minimum cost. Since the cost per sampling unit will vary from stage to stage, one would wish to select the subsample sizes per unit at the various stages of sampling so as to minimize the cost of a fixed quantity of information concerning μ. This quantity will be measured by $V(\bar{y})$, where $\bar{y}$ is the estimator of μ. It is this problem concerning the economics of sampling that we particularly consider in Chapter 12.

12.3 The Linear Model for a Nested Sampling Experiment

Suppose that a nested sampling experiment involves two stages with $n_1 = 2$ and $n_2 = 3$ as shown in Fig. 12.1. Then y_{ij} denotes the jth subsample measurement recorded on the ith prime sampling unit.

Each y_{ij} is assumed to be composed of three parts, a constant, μ, a random component, α_i, associated with the ith prime sampling unit, and a random

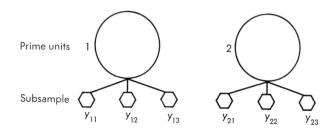

Figure 12.1

component ϵ_{ij} attached to the jth subsample within the ith prime sampling unit. Thus

$$y_{ij} = \mu + \alpha_i + \epsilon_{ij},$$

where all random components within or between observations are assumed to be independent with

$$E(\alpha_i) = 0, \qquad V(\alpha_i) = \sigma_\alpha^2,$$
$$E(\epsilon_{ij}) = 0, \qquad V(\epsilon_{ij}) = \sigma^2.$$

The linear model for a three-stage nested sampling experiment would be

$$y_{ijk} = \mu + \alpha_i + \gamma_{ij} + \epsilon_{ijk},$$

where y_{ijk} is the measurement of response on the ith prime sampling unit, the jth subsampling unit within prime unit i, and the kth third-stage sampling unit within subsampling unit j. The random components α_i, γ_{ij}, and ϵ_{ijk} are assumed to be independent with

$$E(\alpha_i) = 0, \qquad V(\alpha_i) = \sigma_\alpha^2,$$
$$E(\gamma_{ij}) = 0, \qquad V(\gamma_{ij}) = \sigma_\gamma^2,$$
$$E(\epsilon_{ijk}) = 0, \qquad V(\epsilon_{ijk}) = \sigma^2.$$

The method for writing the linear model for nested sampling experiments with more than three stages would simply be an extension of the procedure indicated above.

12.4 The Analysis of Variance for a Nested Sampling Experiment

Suppose that a two-stage nested sampling experiment has been conducted to estimate the variance components in sampling mineral deposits. A total of n_1 ore samples, representing the first sampling stage, were randomly selected over the given terrain and then n_2 chemical analyses were made on each ore sample. To simplify the computations we will give the data for $n_1 = 4$ and $n_2 = 3$, although one would wish n_1 to be much larger in a practical situation. The twelve recorded chemical analyses are given in Table 12.1. The model for the two-stage sampling experiment would be

$$y_{ij} = \mu + \alpha_i + \epsilon_{ij},$$

where y_{ij} is the response measured for the jth analysis for the ore sample obtained from location i. The random components would be independent, have expected values equal to zero, and have variances σ_α^2 and σ^2, respectively.

Table 12.1   Chemical analyses on ore content

Locations	Analysis 1	Analysis 2	Analysis 3	Totals L_i
1	50.1	49.6	51.2	150.9
2	45.6	46.1	45.5	137.2
3	47.0	46.0	46.4	139.4
4	44.7	43.1	42.9	130.7
Total	187.4	184.8	186.0	558.2

If $\bar{y}$ denotes the average of the $n = n_1 n_2 = 12$ observations in the experiment, then it can be shown that the total sum of squares of deviations of the observations about this mean partitions into two quantities; the first is a multiple of the sum of squares of deviations of the location means about $\bar{y}$ and the second is the pooled sum of squares of deviations of analyses within locations. The former sum of squares is called the sum of squares *between* locations and the latter is called the sum of squares *within* locations. Thus

$$\text{Total SS} = \sum_{i=1}^{n} (y_i - \bar{y})^2 = \text{SS (locations)} + \text{SS (within locations)}$$

$$= n_2 \sum_{i=1}^{n_1} (\bar{L}_i - \bar{y})^2 + \sum_{i=1}^{n_1} \sum_{j=1}^{n_2} (y_{ij} - \bar{L}_i)^2.$$

Note that the multiplier of $\sum_{i=1}^{n} (\bar{L}_i - \bar{y})^2$ is n_2, the number of observations in a location total.

The sum of squares between locations for the data of Table 12.1 is

$$\text{SS (locations)} = 3 \sum_{i=1}^{4} (\bar{L}_i - \bar{y})^2 = \frac{\sum_{i=1}^{4} L_i^2}{3} - \text{CM}$$

$$= 26{,}036.50 - 25{,}965.60$$

$$= 70.90,$$

where L_i and $\bar{L}_i$ are the total and average, respectively, of the measurements made on the ore sample obtained from location i.

The sum of squares within locations is

$$\text{SS (within locations)} = \sum_{i=1}^{4} \sum_{j=1}^{3} (y_{ij} - \bar{L}_i)^2$$

$$= \sum_{j=1}^{3} (y_{1j} - \bar{L}_1)^2 + \sum_{j=1}^{3} (y_{2j} - \bar{L}_2)^2 + \cdots + \sum_{j=1}^{3} (y_{4j} - \bar{L}_4)^2$$

$$= \sum_{i=1}^{12} (y_i - \bar{y})^2 - \text{SS (locations)}$$

$$= 74.90 - 70.90 = 4.00.$$

Or, one could obtain SS(within locations) by calculating the sums of squares within each of the four locations and adding. For example, the sum of squares within location 1 would be

$$\sum_{j=1}^{3} (y_{1j} - \bar{L}_1)^2 = \sum_{j=1}^{3} y_{1j}^2 - \frac{L_1^2}{3}$$

$$= (50.1)^2 + (49.6)^2 + (51.2)^2 - \frac{(150.9)^2}{3}.$$

The sums of squares within the other three locations could be calculated in like manner, and the sum of these four quantities would equal 4.00. Of course, it is much simpler to obtain SS(within locations) by subtraction.

The analysis-of-variance table for the data of Table 12.1 is shown in Table 12.2. Since there are $n_1 = 4$ locations, the degrees of freedom for locations will be $(n_1 - 1) = 3$. Similarly, each sum of squares within a location will provide $(n_2 - 1)$ degrees of freedom, hence the pooled sum of squares for the $n_1 = 4$ locations will possess $n_1(n_2 - 1) = 4(2) = 8$ degrees of freedom. The mean squares in the table will be used to estimate the variance components, σ_α^2 and σ^2, in Sec. 12.4 and 12.5.

Table 12.2 ANOVA table for the two-stage nested sampling experiment of Table 12.1

Source	d.f.	SS	MS
Locations	3	70.90	23.63
Analysis within locations	8	4.00	.50
Total	11	74.90	

The procedure for calculating the analysis of variance for a nested sampling experiment with an equal number of subunits per unit at each stage can be obtained by extending the procedures described above for the two-stage experiment. To illustrate, the sums of squares for a three-stage nested sampling experiment with n_1 units in the first stage, A, n_2 subunits per prime unit in the second stage, B, and n_3 measurements per second-stage unit in the third stage, C, will be

$$\text{SS (total)} = \sum_{i=1}^{n} (y_i - \bar{y})^2 = \sum_{i=1}^{n} y_i^2 - \text{CM}, \qquad n = n_1 n_2 n_3,$$

$$\text{SS}A = n_2 n_3 \sum_{i=1}^{n_1} (\bar{A}_i - \bar{y})^2 = \sum_{i=1}^{n_1} \frac{A_i^2}{n_2 n_3} - \text{CM},$$

where $A_1, A_2, \ldots, A_{n_1}$ are the n_1 totals of the first stage, $\bar{A}_1, \bar{A}_2, \ldots, \bar{A}_{n_1}$ are the corresponding means, and $n_2 n_3$ is the number of observations in an A_i total.

$$\text{SS } (B \text{ in } A) = n_3 \sum_{i=1}^{n_1} \sum_{j=1}^{n_2} (\bar{B}_{ij} - \bar{A}_i)^2$$

$$= n_3 \left[\sum_{j=1}^{n_2} (\bar{B}_{1j} - \bar{A}_1)^2 + \sum_{j=1}^{n_2} (\bar{B}_{2j} - \bar{A}_2)^2 + \cdots + \sum_{j=1}^{n_2} (\bar{B}_{n_1 j} - \bar{A}_{n_1})^2 \right]$$

$$= \sum_{i=1}^{n_1} \sum_{j=1}^{n_2} \frac{B_{ij}^2}{n_3} - \sum_{i=1}^{n_1} \frac{A_i^2}{n_2 n_3},$$

where B_{ij} and $\bar{B}_{ij}$ are the total and the mean, respectively, for the observations in subsample j of first-stage sampling unit i and n_3 is the number of observations in a B_{ij} total.

$$\text{SS } (C \text{ in } B) = \sum_{i=1}^{n_1} \sum_{j=1}^{n_2} \sum_{k=1}^{n_3} (y_{ijk} - \bar{B}_{ij})^2$$

$$= \sum_{i=1}^{n} y_i^2 - \sum_{i=1}^{n_1} \sum_{j=1}^{n_2} \frac{B_{ij}^2}{n_3}$$

$$= \text{SS (total)} - \text{SS}A - \text{SS } (B \text{ in } A).$$

The analysis of variance is shown in Table 12.3. The expected mean squares, shown in the fifth column of Table 12.3, will be discussed in Sec. 12.5.

Table 12.3   ANOVA table for a three-stage nested sampling experiment

Source	d.f.	SS	MS	E(MS)
A	$n_1 - 1$	SSA	SS$A/(n_1 - 1)$	$\sigma^2 + n_3 \sigma_\gamma^2 + n_2 n_3 \sigma_\alpha^2$
B in A	$n_1(n_2 - 1)$	SS(B in A)	SS(B in A)/$n_1(n_2 - 1)$	$\sigma^2 + n_3 \sigma_\gamma^2$
C in B	$n_1 n_2(n_3 - 1)$	SS(C in B)	SS(C in B)/$n_1 n_2(n_3 - 1)$	σ^2
Total	$n_1 n_2 n_3 - 1$	$\sum_{i=1}^{n} (y_i - \bar{y})^2$		

The term "degrees of freedom" associated with a sum of squares for the completely random model possesses identically the same significance as it did for the fixed-effect model of Chapters 1 through 9 in that it determines the probability distribution of the sum of squares. We will have more to say on this point in Sec. 12.6.

The rule for determining the number of degrees of freedom for some independent variable by taking one less than the number of its parameters in the linear model would no longer appear to apply, since the components of the model are now assumed to be random. Actually, if one constructs a corresponding fixed-effect model to interpret the data and determines the degrees of freedom in accordance with the rules of Chapter 8, the correct number of degrees of freedom for the completely random model will be obtained. For example, if the n_1 units of first sampling stage are regarded as n_1 levels of a qualitative variable, then it would require $(n_1 - 1)$ degrees of freedom for the sum of squares associated with the first sampling stage. Similarly, for each subsample of n_2 subsets within a prime unit, it would require $(n_2 - 1)$ parameters to describe the subunit differences and would therefore imply $n_1(n_2 - 1)$ parameters associated with subunit differences within units. The reader will observe that $n_1(n_2 - 1)$ is equal to the number of degrees of freedom for the pooled $(B$ within $A)$ sum of squares for the nested sampling experiment.

Finally, it is interesting to note that the sums of squares for a source of variability in the completely random model can be computed by fitting the reduced and complete linear models as described in Chapter 8, where the models are written as though the effects were fixed. This procedure is tedious and unnecessary, since the formulas for the sums of squares for most completely random models are well known.

We conclude this section with an example of a three-stage nested sampling experiment for the antibiotic sampling of Sec. 12.2.

Example 12.1   The data for $n_1 = 4$ one-ounce samples, $n_2 = 2$ subsamples (partitions) per sample, and $n_3 = 2$ analyses per subsample are shown below. Construct the analysis-of-variance table with appropriate calculated sums and mean squares.

	Sample A			
Subsample B	1	2	3	4
1	4.12	3.76	3.64	4.03
	4.11	3.78	3.65	4.00
2	4.06	3.80	3.59	3.96
	4.07	3.82	3.54	3.96
Totals	16.36	15.16	14.42	15.92

Solution: Denote the three stages of sampling as A, B, and C with the completely random model

$$y_{ijk} = \mu + \alpha_i + \gamma_{ij} + \epsilon_{ijk}$$

as defined in Sec. 10.3. Then

$$\text{SS (total)} = \sum_{i=1}^{n} y_i^2 - \text{CM} = 239.9693 - \frac{(61.89)^2}{16} = 0.57105,$$

$$\text{SS}A = \frac{\sum_{i=1}^{n_1} A_i^2}{n_2 n_3} - \text{CM} = 239.95352 - \text{CM} = 0.55527,$$

$$\text{SS } (B \text{ in } A) = \frac{\sum_{i=1}^{n_1} \sum_{j=1}^{n_2} B_{ij}^2}{n_3} - \frac{\sum_{i=1}^{n_1} A_i^2}{n_2 n_3} = 239.96705 - 239.95352$$

$$= 0.01353,$$

$$\text{SS } (C \text{ in } B) = \text{SS (total)} - \text{SS}A - \text{SS } (B \text{ in } A)$$
$$= 0.57105 - 0.55527 - 0.01353$$
$$= 0.00225.$$

The analysis of variance is shown below. As indicated, the mean squares are obtained by dividing the respective sums of squares by their degrees of freedom.

Source	d.f.	SS	MS	E(MS)
A	3	0.55527	0.18509	$\sigma^2 + 2\sigma_\gamma^2 + 4\sigma_\alpha^2$
B in A	4	0.01353	0.003382	$\sigma^2 + 2\sigma_\gamma^2$
C in B	8	0.00225	0.000281	σ^2
Total	15	0.57105		

12.5 Mean Squares—Their Expectation and Probability Distribution

The mean squares of the analysis of variance, Table 12.3, estimate functions of the variance components of the completely random model; therefore it is important to know the probability distributions and expectations of the various mean squares. We will give the expected mean squares for a three-stage nested sampling experiment and the rule for obtaining the expected mean squares for a nested sampling experiment containing any number of stages.

Let

$$y_{ijk} = \mu + \alpha_i + \gamma_{ij} + \epsilon_{ijk}$$

be the completely random model for the three-stage nested sampling experiment as defined in Sec. 12.3. The totals of observations, A_i and B_{ij}, utilized in calculating the sums of squares for the analysis of variance will be as defined in Sec. 12.4.

Then $\bar{y}$ and $\bar{A}_i$, expressed in terms of the linear model, are

$$\bar{y} = \mu + \frac{\sum\limits_{i=1}^{n_1} \alpha_i}{n_1} + \frac{\sum\limits_{i=1}^{n_1} \sum\limits_{j=1}^{n_2} \gamma_{ij}}{n_1 n_2} + \frac{\sum\limits_{i=1}^{n_1} \sum\limits_{j=1}^{n_2} \sum\limits_{k=1}^{n_3} \epsilon_{ijk}}{n_1 n_2 n_3}$$

and

$$\bar{A}_i = \mu + \alpha_i + \frac{\sum\limits_{j=1}^{n_2} \gamma_{ij}}{n_2} + \frac{\sum\limits_{j=1}^{n_2} \sum\limits_{k=1}^{n_3} \epsilon_{ijk}}{n_2 n_3}.$$

Note that

$$\bar{\alpha} = \frac{\sum\limits_{i=1}^{n_1} \alpha_i}{n_1}$$

is the average of the n_1 randomly selected α components, hence its expected value and variance are zero and σ_α^2/n_1, respectively. Likewise, the expected value and variance of

$$\bar{\gamma} = \frac{\sum\limits_{i=1}^{n_1} \sum\limits_{j=1}^{n_2} \gamma_{ij}}{n_1 n_2}$$

are zero and $\sigma_\gamma^2/n_1 n_2$, respectively. Similar statements may be made concerning the other sums appearing in $\bar{y}$ and $\bar{A}_i$.

Noting that all covariances of *different* random elements will equal zero because of their independence, the variances of $\bar{y}$ and $\bar{A}_i$ are, respectively,

$$V(\bar{y}) = \frac{\sigma_\alpha^2}{n_1} + \frac{\sigma_\gamma^2}{n_1 n_2} + \frac{\sigma^2}{n_1 n_2 n_3}$$

and

$$V(\bar{A}_i) = \sigma_\alpha^2 + \frac{\sigma_\gamma^2}{n_2} + \frac{\sigma^2}{n_2 n_3}.$$

Then the expected mean square for A is

$$E[\text{MSA}] = \frac{1}{(n_1 - 1)} E[\text{SSA}] = \frac{1}{(n_1 - 1)} E\left[n_2 n_3 \sum_{i=1}^{n_1} (\bar{A}_i - \bar{y})^2 \right].$$

Noting that $E(\bar{A}_i) = E(\bar{y}) = \mu$, add and subtract μ within the parentheses to obtain

$$E[\text{MSA}] = \frac{1}{(n_1 - 1)} E\left[n_2 n_3 \sum_{i=1}^{n_1} [(\bar{A}_i - \mu) - (\bar{y} - \mu)]^2 \right]$$

$$= \frac{1}{(n_1 - 1)} E\left[n_2 n_3 \left[\sum_{i=1}^{n_1} (\bar{A}_i - \mu)^2 - n_1(\bar{y} - \mu)^2 \right] \right]$$

$$= \frac{1}{(n_1 - 1)} \left[n_2 n_3 \sum_{i=1}^{n_1} V(\bar{A}_i) - n_1 n_2 n_3 V(\bar{y}) \right].$$

And, since $V(\bar{A}_i)$ is the same for $i = 1, 2, \ldots, n_1$,

$$E(\text{MS}A) = \frac{n_1 n_2 n_3}{(n_1 - 1)}[V(\bar{A}_i) - V(\bar{y})].$$

Substituting for $V(\bar{A}_i)$ and $V(\bar{y})$,

$$E(\text{MS}A) = \frac{n_1 n_2 n_3}{(n_1 - 1)}\left[\frac{(n_1 - 1)}{n_1}\sigma_\alpha^2 + \frac{(n_1 - 1)}{n_1 n_2 n_3}\sigma_\gamma^2 + \frac{(n_1 - 1)}{n_1 n_2 n_3}\sigma^2\right]$$

or

$$E(\text{MS}A) = n_2 n_3 \sigma_\alpha^2 + n_3 \sigma_\gamma^2 + \sigma^2.$$

If we use the same procedure as that employed for finding $E(\text{MS}A)$, it is easy to show that

$$E[\text{MS}(B \text{ in } A)] = n_3 \sigma_\gamma^2 + \sigma^2$$

and

$$E[\text{MS}(C \text{ in } B)] = \sigma^2.$$

Note the very simple pattern assumed by the expected mean squares. The expected mean square for a given stage will contain the variance component for that stage as well as those for all *lower* stages. The coefficient of the variance component of a particular stage will always equal the number of observations contained in a total for that stage. Thus the coefficient of the variance component for the second stage of a three-stage experiment, σ_γ^2, is n_3, the number of elements in a B_{ij} total.

Example 12.2 Write the expected mean squares for a four-stage nested sampling experiment with n_1, n_2, n_3, and n_4 units, respectively, in the first, second, third, and fourth stages.

Solution: The completely random model for the experiment is

$$y_{ijkl} = \mu + \alpha_i + \gamma_{ij} + \delta_{ijk} + \epsilon_{ijkl}$$

with variance components σ_α^2, σ_γ^2, σ_δ^2, and σ^2, respectively. Then we have the results tabulated below.

Mean square	*Expected mean square*
A	$\sigma^2 + n_4 \sigma_\delta^2 + n_3 n_4 \sigma_\gamma^2 + n_2 n_3 n_4 \sigma_\alpha^2$
B in A	$\sigma^2 + n_4 \sigma_\delta^2 + n_3 n_4 \sigma_\gamma^2$
C in B	$\sigma^2 + n_4 \sigma_\delta^2$
D in C	σ^2

The expected mean squares derived in the preceding paragraphs do not depend upon the form of the distribution of the random components. As such, they clearly indicate that unbiased estimators of the variance components can be constructed by utilizing a linear combination of the mean squares. In order to say something about the goodness of these estimators, we must have information concerning the probability distributions of the mean squares, and these, in turn, depend upon the probability distributions of the random components in the completely random model.

Existing methodology is based upon the assumption that the random components possess normal probability distributions, an assumption that would appear to fit satisfactorily many practical situations. With the assumption of normality, it can be shown that the mean squares of the analysis of variance are statistically independent and that

$$\chi^2 = \frac{\nu(\text{MS})}{E(\text{MS})}$$

will follow a chi-square probability distribution with ν degrees of freedom. The symbol MS is employed to denote the mean square for a particular sampling stage, $E(\text{MS})$ is its expected value, and ν represents its degrees of freedom. Thus for a three-stage nested sampling experiment,

$$\frac{(n_1 - 1)\text{MS}A}{\sigma^2 + n_3\sigma_\gamma^2 + n_2 n_3\sigma_\alpha^2}$$

possesses a χ^2 distribution with $(n_1 - 1)$ degrees of freedom.

12.6 A Test of an Hypothesis Concerning a Variance Component

An F-statistic is properly defined as the ratio of two independent chi-square variables times the reciprocal of the ratio of their degrees of freedom. Thus

$$F = \frac{\chi_1^2}{\chi_2^2} \cdot \frac{\nu_2}{\nu_1}$$

when χ_1^2 and χ_2^2 are independent and possess ν_1 and ν_2 degrees of freedom, respectively. The F-statistic utilized in the analysis of variance, Sec. 8.2, satisfies the requirements implied by this definition when the null hypothesis, $\beta_g = \beta_{g+1} = \beta_{g+2} = \cdots = \beta_k = 0$, is true.

Not too surprisingly, the F-statistic plays an equally important role in testing hypotheses concerning the variance components of the completely random model. Since multiples of the mean squares in the analysis of variance for the nested sampling experiment possess independent chi-square distributions as stated in Sec. 12.5, ratios of the mean squares can be used to form F-statistics.

Thus for a three-stage sampling experiment with MSA and MSB representing the mean squares for the first and second stages, respectively,

$$F = \frac{\chi_A^2 \nu_B}{\chi_B^2 \nu_A} = \left(\frac{\nu_A \dfrac{MSA}{E(MSA)}}{\nu_B \dfrac{MSB}{E(MSB)}}\right)\frac{\nu_B}{\nu_A}$$

$$= \frac{MSA}{MSB}\left(\frac{\sigma^2 + n_3\sigma_\gamma^2}{\sigma^2 + n_3\sigma_\gamma^2 + n_2 n_3 \sigma_\alpha^2}\right)$$

may be employed to construct a test of the null hypothesis,

$$H_0: \sigma_\alpha^2 = 0.$$

It is clear that the ratio of the mean squares,

$$F = \frac{MSA}{MSB},$$

provides a test statistic. When H_0 is true ($\sigma_\alpha^2 = 0$), $E(MSA) = E(MSB)$ and

$$F = \frac{MSA}{MSB}$$

will follow an F distribution with $\nu_A = (n_1 - 1)$ and $\nu_B = n_1(n_2 - 1)$ degrees of freedom. When H_0 is false, $E(MSA)$ will be larger than $E(MSB)$ and MSA will tend (in probability) to be larger than expected. Therefore, the null hypothesis would be rejected for large values of F.

Likewise, $F = MSB/MSC$ would form a test statistic to test the null hypothesis, $H_0: \sigma_\gamma^2 = 0$. And, in general, if σ_i^2 is the variance component associated with the ith stage of a nested sampling experiment, we may test the hypothesis, $\sigma_i^2 = 0$, by utilizing the ratio of the mean squares for the ith and $(i + 1)$st stages.

Example 12.3   Refer to Table 12.2 and test the hypothesis that $\sigma_\alpha^2 = 0$, where σ_α^2 is the variance component associated with locations.

Solution:

$$H_0: \sigma_\alpha^2 = 0.$$

The test statistic is

$$F = \frac{MS \text{ (locations)}}{MS \text{ (within locations)}} = \frac{23.63}{.5} = 47.26.$$

Since $F_{.05}$, based upon $(n_1 - 1) = 3$ and $n_1(n_2 - 1) = 8$ degrees of freedom, is 4.07, it is clear that the null hypothesis should be rejected. There is ample evidence to indicate variation between locations.

12.7 Estimation of the Variance Components

As noted earlier, the purpose of this chapter is to illustrate the utility of a completely random model as it relates to the economics of sampling. Since knowledge of the variance components is essential to this problem, point estimation of the components, which depends upon the analysis of variance and the expected mean squares, is a necessary precedent to a discussion of optimal sampling procedures. And since the optimal sampling procedure is dependent upon the true values of the variance components, which are generally unknown and must be estimated from the mean squares of the analysis of variance, it is important to acquire a measure of goodness of these estimates. For this reason it is important to consider procedures for constructing confidence intervals for the variance components.

It is a relatively simple matter to obtain unbiased estimators of the variance components, but the construction of associated confidence intervals is a much more difficult problem. Consider the three-stage nested sampling experiment as an example. Since

$$E(\text{MS}A) = \sigma^2 + n_3\sigma_\gamma^2 + n_2 n_3 \sigma_\alpha^2,$$
$$E(\text{MS}B) = \sigma^2 + n_3\sigma_\gamma^2,$$
$$E(\text{MS}C) = \sigma^2,$$

it is clear that

$$\hat{\sigma}^2 = \text{MS}C,$$
$$\hat{\sigma}_\gamma^2 = \frac{\text{MS}B - \text{MS}C}{n_3},$$
$$\hat{\sigma}_\alpha^2 = \frac{\text{MS}A - \text{MS}B}{n_2 n_3}$$

are unbiased estimators of σ^2, σ_γ^2, and σ_α^2, respectively. Since

$$\chi^2 = \frac{\nu_c \text{MS}C}{\sigma^2}$$

is a chi-square variable with $\nu_c = n_1 n_2(n_3 - 1)$ degrees of freedom, we may select tabulated values, χ_L^2 and χ_U^2, such that

$$P(\chi_L^2 < \chi^2 < \chi_U^2) = 1 - \alpha,$$
$$P\left(\chi_L^2 < \frac{\nu_c \text{MS}C}{\sigma^2} < \chi_U^2\right) = 1 - \alpha,$$

or

$$P\left(\frac{\nu_c \text{MS}C}{\chi_U^2} < \sigma^2 < \frac{\nu_c \text{MS}C}{\chi_L^2}\right) = 1 - \alpha$$

to provide a $(1 - \alpha)$ confidence interval for σ^2.

Confidence intervals for the other variance components are more difficult to obtain. The reader will note that the estimators of σ_α^2 and σ_γ^2 are linear functions of the mean squares and hence linear functions of chi-square variables. To illustrate, the estimator of σ_α^2 for a three-stage sampling experiment is

$$\hat{\sigma}_\alpha^2 = \frac{\text{MS}A - \text{MS}B}{n_2 n_3}.$$

Since

$$\frac{\nu_A \text{MS}A}{E(\text{MS}A)} = \chi_A^2 \quad \text{and} \quad \frac{\nu_B \text{MS}B}{E(\text{MS}B)} = \chi_B^2.$$

$$\hat{\sigma}_\alpha^2 = \frac{\dfrac{\chi_A^2 E(\text{MS}A)}{\nu_A} - \dfrac{\chi_B^2 E(\text{MS}B)}{\nu_B}}{n_2 n_3}$$

$$= a_1 \chi_A^2 + a_2 \chi_B^2,$$

where

$$a_1 = \frac{E(\text{MS}A)}{n_2 n_3 \nu_A} \quad \text{and} \quad a_2 = -\frac{E(\text{MS}B)}{n_2 n_3 \nu_B}.$$

An explicit expression cannot be obtained for the probability distribution of a linear function of chi-square variables, but several large-sample approximations are available and the probability distribution for small samples may be obtained to any degree of accuracy by a series approximation. We will give approximate procedures for the confidence interval for a variance component due to Satterthwaite (1946) and Welch (1956). The reader interested in other approximate procedures may consult the original papers indicated in the references or the summarizations given in Anderson and Bancroft (1952) and Graybill (1961).

Let $\text{MS}_1, \text{MS}_2, \ldots, \text{MS}_k$ be k independent mean squares of the nested sampling experiment with $\nu_1, \nu_2, \ldots, \nu_k$ degrees of freedom, respectively. Then l, a linear function of the mean squares,

$$l = a_1 \text{MS}_1 + a_2 \text{MS}_2 + \cdots + a_k \text{MS}_k,$$

is an unbiased estimator of a variance component or some linear function of the variance components. Thus we wish to construct a $(1 - \alpha)$ interval for $E(l)$, where

$$E(l) = a_1 E(\text{MS}_1) + a_2 E(\text{MS}_2) + \cdots + a_k E(\text{MS}_k).$$

For example, the estimator of σ_α^2 for the three-stage sampling experiment is

$$l = \hat{\sigma}_\alpha^2 = \left(\frac{1}{n_2 n_3}\right) \text{MS}A - \left(\frac{1}{n_2 n_3}\right) \text{MS}B$$

and $E(l) = \sigma_\alpha^2$.

Satterthwaite (1946) constructed an approximation to the distribution of l using a chi-square distribution. Thus

$$\frac{\nu l}{E(l)}$$

is approximately distributed as a chi-square variable with

$$\nu = \frac{l^2}{\sum_{i=1}^{k} \frac{a_i^2 MS_i^2}{\nu_i}}$$

degrees of freedom. Utilizing this approximation, a $(1 - \alpha)$ confidence interval for $E(l)$ is

$$\frac{\nu l}{\chi_U^2} < E(l) < \frac{\nu l}{\chi_L^2}$$

where χ_L^2 and χ_U^2 are defined by

$$P(\chi^2 > \chi_L^2) = 1 - \frac{\alpha}{2} \qquad \text{and} \qquad P(\chi^2 > \chi_U^2) = \frac{\alpha}{2}$$

Example 12.4 Construct an approximate 95 per cent confidence interval for σ_α^2, the variance component for the first stage of a three-stage nested sampling experiment. Assume that $n_1 = 20$, $n_2 = 10$, $n_3 = 5$ and that MSA, MSB, and MSC are, respectively, 12.7, 3.6, and 1.2.

Solution:

$$l = \hat{\sigma}_\alpha^2 = \frac{MSA - MSB}{n_2 n_3} = \frac{12.7 - 3.6}{50} = .182$$

where

$$a_1 = \frac{1}{n_2 n_3} = \frac{1}{50} \qquad \text{and} \qquad a_2 = -\frac{1}{n_2 n_3} = -\frac{1}{50};$$

$$\nu = \frac{(.182)^2}{\frac{(\frac{1}{50})^2(12.7)^2}{19} + \frac{(-\frac{1}{50})^2(3.6)^2}{180}} = 9.673.$$

Hence we will take $\nu = 10$. Therefore, the 95 per cent confidence interval for $E(l) = \sigma_\alpha^2$ is

$$\frac{\nu l}{\chi_U^2} < \sigma_\alpha^2 < \frac{\nu l}{\chi_L^2}.$$

Substituting,

$$\frac{(10)(.182)}{20.483} < \sigma_\alpha^2 < \frac{10(.182)}{3.247}$$

and

$$.089 < \sigma_\alpha^2 < 0.56.$$

Satterthwaite (1946) indicates that the chi-square approximation to the distribution of a linear function of chi-square variables is good except for the case where the degrees of freedom associated with some of the mean squares are so small that one obtains negative estimates of the variance components. He notes that when this occurs, little information is available in the data for the estimation of the variance components.

Graybill (1961), in commenting on the chi-square approximation procedure, states that the resulting confidence intervals are probably adequate if $\nu \geq 30$, where

$$\nu = \frac{l^2}{\displaystyle\sum_{i=1}^{k} \frac{a_i^2 \mathrm{MS}_i^2}{\nu_i}}.$$

It is clear (Example 12.4) that this condition may not be satisfied for many practical problems.

Welch (1956) indicates a number of situations where the confidence intervals based upon the chi-square approximation will be quite close to those obtained from the exact distribution of $[\nu l/E(l)]$. However, he gives a correction to χ_L^2 and χ_U^2 which, while tedious to calculate, gives a better approximation to the confidence interval for $E(l)$.

Welch calculates the $(1 - \alpha)$ confidence interval,

$$\frac{\nu l}{A_U} < E(l) < \frac{\nu l}{A_L}$$

where ν is as previously defined and

$$A_L = \chi_{(1-\alpha/2)}^2 - \frac{2}{3}(2z_{(1-\alpha/2)}^2 + 1)\left[\frac{l \displaystyle\sum_{i=1}^{k} \frac{a_i^3 \mathrm{MS}_i^3}{\nu_i^2}}{\left(\displaystyle\sum_{i=1}^{k} \frac{a_i^2 \mathrm{MS}_i^2}{\nu_i}\right)^2} - 1 \right]$$

$$= \chi_{(1-\alpha/2)}^2 - \frac{2}{3}(2z_{(1-\alpha/2)}^2 + 1)\left[\frac{\nu^2}{l^3} \sum_{i=1}^{k} \frac{a_i^3 \mathrm{MS}_i^3}{\nu_i^2} - 1 \right].$$

A_U is obtained by substituting $\chi_{\alpha/2}^2$ in the above expression in place of $\chi_{(1-\alpha/2)}^2$. Note that the correction to the chi-square critical value, the second term in the expression for A_L, is the same for both A_U and A_L because $z_{\alpha/2} = |z_{(1-\alpha/2)}|$.

Example 12.5 See Example 12.4. Calculate a 95 per cent confidence interval for σ_α^2 using Welch's method.

Solution:

$$\sum_{i=1}^{k} \frac{a_i^3 MS_i^3}{\nu_i^2} = \left(\frac{1}{50}\right)^3 \frac{(12.7)^3}{(19)^2} - \left(\frac{1}{50}\right)^3 \frac{(3.6)^3}{(180)^2}$$
$$= (4.5382)(10^{-5}).$$

Then

$$A_L = \chi_{(1-\alpha/2)}^2 - \frac{2}{3}[2z_{(1-\alpha/2)}^2 + 1]\left(\frac{\nu^2}{l^3} \sum_{i=1}^{k} \frac{a_i^3 MS_i^3}{\nu_i^2} - 1\right)$$
$$= 3.247 - \frac{2}{3}[2(-1.96)^2 + 1]\left[\frac{(9.673)^2}{(.182)^3}(4.538 \times 10^{-5}) - 1\right]$$
$$= 3.247 + 1.712 = 4.959,$$
$$A_U = \chi_{\alpha/2}^2 + 1.712$$
$$= 20.486 + 1.712 = 22.198.$$

Then the 95 per cent confidence interval for σ_α^2 is

$$\frac{\nu l}{A_U} < \sigma_\alpha^2 < \frac{\nu l}{A_L}.$$

Substituting, we have

$$\frac{(10)(.182)}{22.198} < \sigma_\alpha^2 < \frac{(10)(.182)}{4.959}$$

or

$$.082 < \sigma_\alpha^2 < .367.$$

12.8 Selecting the Number of Units per Stage

The preceding discussion has been a necessary preface to the practical problem of selecting the optimal number of units per stage to acquire a fixed quantity of information pertinent to a population parameter, μ. As noted earlier, $\bar{y}$ is an unbiased estimator of μ and therefore $V(\bar{y})$ will serve as an adequate measure of the quantity of information available for estimating μ. Then the problem will be to select the number of units per stage, $n_1, n_2, n_3, \ldots$, so as to minimize the sampling cost subject to the restraint that $V(\bar{y})$ is less than or equal to some bound, say B, specified by the experimenter.

Suppose that a nested sampling experiment has k stages with $n_1, n_2, \ldots, n_k$ subunits per unit with the cost of a sampling unit in the ith stage equal to $c_i, i = 1, 2, \ldots, k$. Then, assuming a linear cost function, the total sampling cost is

$$C = c_1 n_1 + c_2 n_1 n_2 + c_3 n_1 n_2 n_3 + \cdots + c_k n_1 n_2 \cdots n_k.$$

Thus we wish to minimize C subject to the condition that

$$V(\bar{y}) = B,$$

where, as we have seen, $V(\bar{y})$ is a function of the variance components and $n_1, n_2, \ldots, n_k$. We will illustrate this minimization procedure with an example.

Example 12.6 Suppose that we wish to predict the average amount of mineral contained in ore over the region implied in the nested sampling experiment, Table 12.2. While better estimates of the variance components would be desired in a practical situation, for purposes of illustration assume that these estimates are reasonably accurate and find the optimal sample sizes, n_1 and n_2, to estimate μ correct to within two units with probability equal to .95. Assume that $C_1 = \$100$ and $C_2 = \$1$.

Solution: The 95 per cent confidence interval for μ is

$$\bar{y} \pm t \text{ (estimated standard deviation of } \bar{y}).$$

Letting t be approximately equal to 2, we desire

$$2\sigma_{\bar{y}} \leq 2 \quad \text{or} \quad V(\bar{y}) \leq 1.$$

From Sec. 12.5,

$$V(\bar{y}) = \frac{\sigma_\alpha^2}{n_1} + \frac{\sigma^2}{n_1 n_2}.$$

To minimize the cost function,

$$C = c_1 n_1 + c_2 n_1 n_2,$$

subject to the restriction,

$$V(\bar{y}) = \frac{\sigma_\alpha^2}{n_1} + \frac{\sigma^2}{n_1 n_2} = 1,$$

one might solve for n_1 in terms of n_2 in the relation, $V(\bar{y}) = 1$. This could then be substituted into the cost function, C, to obtain a function of a single variable, n_2. Then, from the ordinary calculus, a maximum, minimum, or point of inflection would be obtained by setting the derivative of C with respect to n_2 equal to zero and solving for n_2. It can be shown that the solution will yield a minimum for the situation described.

An alternative procedure, the method of Lagrange multipliers, is described in many calculus texts. Thus a function,

$$\phi = C + \lambda[.V(\bar{y}) - B],$$

is constructed which represents the original function to be minimized plus (or minus) a constant, λ, times the restriction, where the restriction must be in the form,

$$V(\bar{y}) - B = 0.$$

The constant, λ, is called a Lagrange multiplier.

It is well known that the values of the three variables, n_1, n_2, and λ, that minimize ϕ will give the same values of n_1 and n_2 that minimize C. Thus we will set the three partial derivatives,

$$\frac{\partial \phi}{\partial n_1}, \quad \frac{\partial \phi}{\partial n_2} \quad \text{and} \quad \frac{\partial \phi}{\partial \lambda},$$

equal to zero and solve the resulting equations simultaneously.

For example,

$$\phi = c_1 n_1 + c_2 n_1 n_2 + \lambda\left(\frac{\sigma_\alpha^2}{n_1} + \frac{\sigma^2}{n_1 n_2} - B\right).$$

Taking partial derivatives of ϕ with respect to n_1, n_2 and setting each equal to zero, we obtain

$$\frac{\partial \phi}{\partial n_1} = c_1 + c_2 n_2 - \frac{\lambda}{n_1^2}\left(\sigma_\alpha^2 + \frac{\sigma^2}{n_2}\right) = 0,$$

$$\frac{\partial \phi}{\partial n_2} = c_2 n_1 - \frac{\lambda \sigma^2}{n_1 n_2^2} = 0,$$

$$\frac{\partial \phi}{\partial \lambda} = \frac{\sigma_\alpha^2}{n_1} + \frac{\sigma^2}{n_1 n_2} - B = 0.$$

From Table 12.2 we see that

$$\hat{\sigma}_\alpha^2 = \frac{\text{MSA} - \text{MSB}}{n_2} = \frac{23.63 - .50}{3} = 7.71 \quad \text{and} \quad \hat{\sigma}^2 = .50.$$

Substituting $c_1 = \$100$, $c_2 = \$1$, $\hat{\sigma}_\alpha^2 = 7.71$, $\hat{\sigma}^2 = .50$, and $B = 1$ into the preceding set of simultaneous equations,

$$(1) \quad 100 + n_2 - \frac{\lambda}{n_1^2}\left(7.71 + \frac{.50}{n_2}\right) = 0,$$

$$(2) \qquad\qquad n_1 - \frac{\lambda(.50)}{n_1 n_2^2} = 0,$$

$$(3) \qquad\qquad \frac{7.71}{n_1} + \frac{.50}{n_1 n_2} = 1.$$

From equation (2),

$$\lambda = \frac{n_1^2 n_2^2}{.50}.$$

Substituting in (1), we have

$$100 + n_2 - \frac{n_1^2 n_2^2}{n_1^2(.50)}\left(7.71 + \frac{.50}{n_2}\right) = 0$$

or

$$n_2^2 = \frac{100}{15.42} = 6.49 \qquad \text{and} \qquad n_2 = 2.55.$$

Then, substituting in (3),

$$\frac{7.71}{n_1} + \frac{.50}{n_1(2.55)} = 1$$

or

$$n_1 = 7.91.$$

Thus, one might choose $n_1 = 8$ and $n_2 = 3$ to acquire the desired information concerning μ at minimum cost. Since n_1 and n_2 must assume integral values, it would be desirable to check values of n_1 and n_2 in the neighborhood of the approximate solution, $n_1 = 7.91$ and $n_2 = 2.55$, to locate the actual optimal sample size for each sampling stage. If the equations of Example 12.6 are solved directly before substitution of numerical values for $c_1, c_2, \sigma_\alpha^2$, and σ^2, we find the values of n_1 and n_2 that minimize the linear cost function, C, to be

$$n_1 = \frac{1}{B}\left\{\sigma_\alpha^2 + \frac{\sigma^2}{\sqrt{\frac{\sigma^2 c_1}{\sigma_\alpha^2 c_2}}}\right\},$$

$$n_2 = \frac{\sigma}{\sigma_\alpha}\sqrt{\frac{c_1}{c_2}}.$$

The verification of this result is left as an exercise for the reader.

The method of Lagrange multipliers may be used for $k > 2$ stages in a manner similar to that employed in Example 12.6. In general, one will be concerned with only one restriction, $V(\bar{y}) = B$, and therefore only a single multiplier, λ. However, k stages will imply the solution of $(k + 1)$ simultaneous equations,

$$\frac{\partial \phi}{\partial n_1} = 0,$$

$$\frac{\partial \phi}{\partial n_2} = 0,$$

$$\cdot$$
$$\cdot$$
$$\cdot$$

$$\frac{\partial \phi}{\partial n_k} = 0,$$

$$\frac{\partial \phi}{\partial \lambda} = 0,$$

in the unknowns $n_1, n_2, \ldots, n_k$ and λ. Thus the procedure is straightforward, but the complexity and tedium of solving the equations increases with the number of sampling stages.

12.9 Summary

Variance-component (completely random) models are those in which all elements of the linear model are assumed to be random with the exception of the constant μ. And, although completely random models may be appropriate for randomized block designs and many other situations, emphasis in Chapter 12 is focused on a single illustration, the nested sampling experiment.

The estimation of the variance components, the variances of the random elements in the linear model, may be the primary objective of the experiment. Thus we present the procedures of Satterthwaite and Welch, Sec. 12.7. For others, the investigator is primarily concerned with the estimation of the population mean, μ, where, in this case, the variance components indicate the magnitude of the variability contributed by various sources. Thus one wishes to select the number of units per stage, $n_1, n_2, \ldots, n_k$, so as to minimize the overall sampling cost.

Exercises

1. What is a completely random model? A mixed model?

2. Show algebraically that the sums of squares between locations and within locations add to the total sum of squares $\sum\limits_{i=1}^{n} (y_i - \bar{y})^2$ for the two-stage nested sampling experiment, Section 12.4. Assume that the formulas for the between and within sums of squares are as indicated in Section 12.4.

3. Consider the three-stage nested sampling experiment of Table 12.3 and show algebraically that

$$n_3 \sum_{i=1}^{n_1} \sum_{j=1}^{n_2} (\bar{B}_{ij} - \bar{A}_i)^2 = \sum_{i=1}^{n_1} \sum_{j=1}^{n_2} \frac{B_{ij}^2}{n_3} - \sum_{i=1}^{n_1} \frac{A_i^2}{n_2 n_3}$$

is an identity. Note that this quantity is SS $(B$ in $A)$.

4. The mean porosity of paper emerging from a production line was evaluated by selecting ten paper samples at random from the finished product and taking three porosity measurements on each. The data are shown on next page.

Paper Sample	Porosity		
1	994	993	998
2	987	987	982
3	1001	1006	1003
4	1004	1002	998
5	990	991	991
6	1011	1007	1015
7	1000	1005	1006
8	981	988	980
9	999	998	999
10	1009	1010	1004

Calculate the sums of squares and give the analysis of variance for this data.

5. The response to stimulus in a psychological conditioning experiment was subject to three sources of variability. The responses varied between subjects, between measurements taken at different times (usually separated by at least one hour) within a subject, and in repeated measurements taken on a given subject at a particular point in time. Each of ten subjects was tested at three different times, and two response measurements were taken at testing time. The results are shown below with the two measurements per test shown in the cells of the table:

Subject	Time		
	1	2	3
1	33	30	31
	35	29	34
2	39	44	41
	38	46	43
3	29	32	35
	31	35	34
4	41	43	42
	41	46	40
5	34	38	30
	36	39	32
6	26	30	31
	23	39	33
7	40	36	41
	37	38	40

Subject	Time		
	1	2	3
8	49	43	46
	46	45	43
9	29	31	33
	32	30	33
10	36	37	40
	38	33	42

Calculate the sums of squares and give the analysis of variance for this design.

6. Write a completely random model for Exercise 5 and state assumptions associated with the elements in the model.

7. Give the expected mean squares for Exercise 4 and state the assumptions necessary to achieve these results.

8. Give the expected mean squares for Exercise 5.

9. Show that the expected value of MS(B in A) for the three-stage sampling experiment in Section 12.6 is $(n_3\sigma_\gamma^2 + \sigma^2)$.

10. Show that the expected value of MS(C in B) for the three-stage sampling experiment in Section 12.6 is equal to σ^2.

11. Do the data in Exercise 4 present sufficient evidence to indicate a between-sample variation in porosity that cannot be attributed to the measuring instrument?

12. Do the data in Exercise 5 present sufficient evidence to indicate that the between-subject variance component differs from zero? Do the data present sufficient evidence to indicate that the between-test time-variance component differs from zero?

13. How is the F-statistic related to the Chi-square variable? Of what importance is this in testing hypotheses concerning variance components in the nested sampling experiment?

14. Find a 95 per cent confidence interval for the expected mean square between samples in Exercise 4.

15. Find a 95 per cent confidence interval for the expected mean square for measurements within samples in Exercise 4.

16. Find a 95 per cent confidence interval for $E(y)$ in Exercise 4.

17. Why is it impossible to obtain an exact confidence interval for some of the variance components of the nested sampling experiment? Find an

approximate 95 per cent confidence interval for the between-sample variance component in Exercise 4.

18. Use Welch's approximation to obtain an improved confidence interval for the variance component in Exercise 17.

19. Estimate the variance components for Exercise 5 using Satterthwaite's approximation.

20. Find a 95 per cent confidence interval for $E(y)$ in Exercise 5.

21. Suppose that it costs $50.00 to prepare for testing a single paper sample and $1.00 per porosity measurement once a paper sample is acquired. Give approximately the number of paper samples and measurements per sample necessary to estimate the true mean porosity of the production correct to within plus or minus 10.0 on the porosity scale. (Assume that the number of porosity measurements is the same for all paper samples.) Give the approximate total cost of the experiment.

22. Refer to Exercise 5. Suppose that it costs approximately $300 per subject, an additional $20 for each test time per subject, and $1.00 per test measurement. Approximately how many subjects, test times, and measurements per test time will be required to estimate the expected response correct to within plus or minus 3. Give the approximate cost of the experiment.

23. The yield of wheat per acre was sampled over $n_1 = 30$ counties in a given state, $n_2 = 5$ townships per county, and $n_3 = 10$ farms per township. The results of this nested sampling experiment are shown below:

Source	d.f.	SS
Between Counties	29	50,207
Townships Within Counties	120	25,920
Farms Within Townships	1350	21,600
Total	1499	97,727

(a) Write a linear model for this nested sampling experiment.
(b) Find an approximate 95 per cent confidence interval for the "between counties" variance component.
(c) Find an approximate 95 per cent confidence interval for the "between townships within counties" variance component.
(d) Find a 95 per cent confidence interval for the "farms within townships" variance component.

24. Suppose that $\bar{y} = 40$ in Exercise 23. Find a 95 per cent confidence interval for the expected yield of wheat for the state.

25. Refer to Exercise 23 and find $V(\bar{y})$, where $\bar{y}$ is the estimator of the mean yield of wheat per acre for the state. If it costs $C_1 = \$1600$ to sample

a county, $200 additional to sample a township within a county, and $30 per farm, find n_1, n_2, and n_3 necessary to estimate $E(y)$ correct to within 5 bushels per acre with probability equal to .95.

26. (a) Write the linear model for a four-stage nested sampling experiment, and give the assumed properties of the random components.
   (b) Suppose that n_i, $i = 1, 2, 3, 4$ for the four stages, and let $\bar{y}$ be the mean of all $n = n_1 n_2 n_3 n_4$ observations. Find $V(\bar{y})$.
   (c) Let $\bar{y}_i$ be the average of the observations in the ith first stage sampling unit. Find $V(\bar{y}_i)$.

27. Complete the analysis-of-variance table shown below for a four-stage nested sampling experiment by giving the degrees of freedom and expected mean squares.

Source	d.f.	$E(MS)$
A		
B in A		
C in B		
D in C		
Total		

28. Give the formulas for the sums of squares for the four-stage nested sampling experiment in Exercise 26.

29. The number of bricks laid per day on a construction job is approximately normally distributed and will vary independently from day to day. Unfortunately, the actual number laid per day is difficult to determine exactly and hence must be estimated by each of three human "estimators." Let y_{ij} denote the number of bricks estimated by the jth estimator on the ith day and $\bar{y}_i$ be the average of the three estimates for the ith day. The objective of the estimation is to keep track of construction progress and, particularly, to use the results in the early stages of construction to predict the total number of bricks laid at some point in the future. Thus one wishes to use $\sum_{i=1}^{n_1} \bar{y}_i$, the estimated total number of bricks laid in the first n_1 days to predict the estimated total, $\sum_{i=1}^{n_1+d} \bar{y}_i$, d days in the future. Averages rather than sums could be used to detect a change in the mean rate of production.

(a) Write a linear model for the observed results of the first n_1 days. (Note that this data will involve $3n_1$ measurements, y_{ij}, $i = 1, 2, \ldots, n_1; j = 1, 2, 3$.) Assume the "estimator" errors are independently normally distributed, with mean and variance equal to zero and σ^2, respectively.

(b) The results of the first seven days of construction are shown below, with the response measured in units of one thousand bricks. Give the analysis of variance for the data.

Day	Estimates		
	1	2	3
1	107.2	108.1	105.7
2	105.9	103.2	104.1
3	98.6	99.4	96.3
4	110.9	111.3	110.2
5	96.7	97.8	99.0
6	102.1	103.0	102.9
7	104.8	102.7	105.1

30. Refer to Exercise 29 and let $\bar{y}_{n_k} = \dfrac{\sum\limits_{i=1}^{n_k} \bar{y}_i}{n_k}$

   (a) Find the expected value and variance of $\bar{y}_{n_1}$.
   (b) Find the expected value and variance of $(\bar{y}_{n_1+d} - \bar{y}_{n_1})$. Note that these averages are correlated. Also note that if $\bar{y}_{n_1}$ is used to predict $\bar{y}_{n_1+d}$, then the difference is the "error of prediction."

31. Use the results of Exercise 30 to derive a prediction interval for the "estimated" number of bricks that will be laid in $n_1 + d$ days.

32. Refer to Exercises 29 and 31. Find a prediction interval for $\sum\limits_{i=1}^{n_1+d} \bar{y}_i$, where $n_1 = 7$ and $d = 3$.

33. Suppose that $\bar{y}_{n_1}$ is the average of $\bar{y}_i$ over n_1 days and $\bar{y}_{n_2}$ is the average over the *succeeding* n_2 days.
   (a) Find the expected value and variance of $(\bar{y}_{n_1} - \bar{y}_{n_2})$.
   (b) Use the results of (a) to construct a test statistic to detect a change in the mean number of bricks laid over the two time periods.

34. The data for Exercise 29 for the eighth through the fourteenth days is given below:

Day	Estimates		
	1	2	3
8	102.1	99.9	101.2
9	97.4	95.2	96.7
10	101.3	100.1	102.3
11	95.0	96.1	94.8
12	97.8	98.9	96.2
13	92.7	92.8	94.6
14	100.2	99.7	98.9

Do these data and the data of Exercise 29 provide sufficient evidence to indicate a change in the mean production rate over time?

35. An experiment was conducted to estimate the mean radioactivity of soil sampled over a specified area where the response was the number of radioactive counts per minute. It was known that the radioactivity varied from one point in the experimental region to another and hence n_1 soil samples were randomly selected over the area. The number of radioactive counts per minute was expected to follow a Poisson probability distribution, and it was therefore decided to measure the number of radioactive counts over n_2 one-minute time periods per soil sample. Does this experiment satisfy the assumptions of the nested sampling experiment of Section 12.3? Explain.

36. (Only for students having had a course in basic statistical theory and familiar with conditional expectation.) Refer to Exercise 35. Let y_{ij} represent the number of radioactive counts for the jth one-minute interval for soil sample i, and let y_{ij} follow a Poisson probability distribution with mean m_i. Secondly, assume that $y_{ij} = m_i + e_{ij}$, where m_i, the mean radioactivity count at a given point in the experimental region, possesses mean μ and variance σ_m^2.
   (a) Show that $V(y_{ij}) = \mu + \sigma_m^2$.
   (b) Show that $E(\bar{y}_i)$ and $V(\bar{y}_i)$ are μ and $\left(\dfrac{\mu}{n_2} + \sigma_m^2\right)$, respectively, where
   $$\bar{y}_i = \frac{\sum\limits_{j=1}^{n_2} y_{ij}}{n_2}.$$
   (c) Show that $E(\bar{y})$ and $V(\bar{y})$, where $\bar{y}$ is the average of the $n_1 n_2$ response measurements, are μ and $\left(\dfrac{\mu}{n_1 n_2} + \dfrac{\sigma_m^2}{n_1}\right)$, respectively.

37. Refer to Exercise 36. Suppose that it costs C_1 dollars per soil sample and C_2 additional dollars per each one-minute time interval measured. Find the ratio of n_1 and n_2 that will minimize the cost of a specified quantity of information relative to $E(y)$.

38. Refer to Exercise 35 and find
$$E\left\{\sum_{i=1}^{n_1} \frac{(\bar{y}_i - \bar{y})^2}{n_1 - 1}\right\}.$$

Find an unbiased estimator of σ_m^2. Give an unbiased estimator of $V(\bar{y})$, where $\bar{y}$ is the unbiased estimator of μ, the mean radioactive counts per minute over the experimental region.

39. The data for the experiment in Exercise 35 is shown below. Find estimates of μ and σ_m^2.

Radioactivity Counts
$n_2 = 30$ minutes

Sample	Counts per Minute/Kilogram
1	505.1
2	548.1
3	533.3
4	681.0
5	491.1
6	588.4
7	461.2
8	511.2
9	530.7
10	526.0
11	493.0
12	429.0
13	528.6
14	480.0
15	474.4

40. Refer to Exercise 35 and find n_1 and n_2 such that the cost of estimating $E(y)$ with an error less than 2 units with probability approximately equal to .95 is a minimum. Assume that $C_1 = \$100$ and $C_2 = \$20$.

41. Suppose that n_1 and n_2 are moderately large. Give the approximate probability distribution of $\dfrac{\sum\limits_{i=1}^{n_1} (\bar{y}_i - \bar{y})^2}{\sigma_m^2 + \dfrac{\mu}{n_2}}$. Find an approximate 95 per cent confidence interval for μ. Apply to the data of Exercise 39.

42. Truck loads of oranges are sampled to ascertain the mean sugar content of the juice per load, with a sampling of boxes and oranges within boxes. The analysis of variance for an experiment is given below.

Source	d.f.	SS
Between boxes	19	1410
Oranges within boxes	40	400
Total	59	1810

Estimate the variance components using 95 per cent confidence intervals.

43. Refer to Exercise 29. Suppose that each "estimator" possessed a bias

(in contrast to the assumptions of Exercise 29) and that the estimators were assumed to have been randomly selected from a population of estimators. Write a completely random model for this case. Note that we can no longer use a nested sampling model for the response. Give the analysis of variance and the expected mean squares for this model.

References

Anderson, R. L., and T. A. Bancroft, *Statistical Theory in Research*. New York: McGraw-Hill Book Company, 1952. Chapter 22.

Bross, I., "Fiducial Intervals for Variance Components," *Biometrics*, **6**, 136–144 (1950).

Graybill, F. A., *An Introduction to Linear Statistical Models*. New York: McGraw-Hill Book Company, 1961.

Huitson, A., "A Method of Assigning Confidence Limits to Linear Combinations of Variances," *Biometrika*, **42**, 471–479 (1955).

Satterthwaite, F. E., "An Approximate Distribution of Estimates of Variance Components," *Biometrics Bulletin*, **2**, 110–114 (1946).

Welch, B. L., "On Linear Combinations of Several Variances," *Journal of the American Statistical Association*, **51**, 132–148 (1956).

13

Mixed Models

13.1 Introduction

Mixed models contain a mixture of fixed and random elements and therefore represent a blend of the fixed-effect model of Chapters 2 to 11 and the completely random model of Chapter 12. They are associated with the familiar experimental designs encountered earlier in the text except that some of the experimental variables are now assumed to generate a random contribution (rather than a constant or "fixed effect") to the response y. This produces in the model a mixture of fixed and random components which are assumed to be additive and whose sum is equal to y. Consequently, a qualitative variable, blocks, viewed as a fixed effect in the comparison of treatment means, may now be regarded as randomly selected from a population of blocks, thereby contributing a second source of variability to a response. This additional variability, as well as others which may be present, will affect the variance of an estimated treatment mean and may be reflected in the variance of the difference between a pair of treatment means. These ideas are best illustrated with an example.

Suppose that a randomized block design is used to compare the effect of three different fertilizers on yield of corn, with each of the three fertilizer "treatments" randomly assigned to a plot within each of four fields. If the sole objective of the experiment is a comparison of treatments, one may employ the fixed-effect model of Chapter 5,

$$y = \beta_0 + \underbrace{\beta_1 x_1 + \beta_2 x_2 + \beta_3 x_3}_{\substack{\text{Block} \\ \text{differences}}} + \underbrace{\tau_1 x_4 + \tau_2 x_5}_{\substack{\text{Treatment} \\ \text{differences}}} + \epsilon,$$

which contains parameters τ_1 and τ_2, the two linearly independent treatment differences, and β_1, β_2, and β_3, the three linearly independent block effects. When treatments are compared, the block effects cancel and permit an unbiased estimate of treatment differences.

On the other hand, suppose that the objective of the experiment is not only the comparison of treatments but also the estimation of the expected yield of a given fertilizer for some soil and seed combinations for which the four fields (blocks) are representative. Thus the four blocks are assumed to be randomly selected from a population of blocks with a block effect, β_i, varying from block to block in a random manner. Hence any error of estimation of $E(y)$ for general field conditions will be influenced not only by the plot-seed random error, ϵ, but also by the random component due to blocks. This would account for the variations in fertility and soil conditions, which are partly removed by blocking for a comparison of treatments.

The mixed model for the randomized block experiment consisting of three treatments and four blocks, treating block effects as random, is

$$y_{ij} = \beta_0 + \tau_1 x_1 + \tau_2 x_2 + \beta_i + \epsilon_{ij},$$

where

$x_1 = 1$ if treatment B is applied,
$x_1 = 0$ if not;
$x_2 = 1$ if treatment C is applied,
$x_2 = 0$ if not;
$y_{ij} =$ response on the experimental unit in block i receiving treatment j;
   $i = 1, 2, 3, 4; j = 1, 2, 3;$
$\beta_i =$ random component contributed by block i, where β_i is normally distributed with $E(\beta_i) = 0$, $V(\beta_i) = \sigma_b^2$, and $\text{Cov}(\beta_i, \beta_j) = 0$ for $i \neq j$ and $\text{Cov}(\beta_i, \epsilon_j) = 0$;
$\epsilon_{ij} =$ random component contributed by the ith plot in block j. As in earlier models, assume ϵ_{ij} is normally distributed, $E(\epsilon_{ij}) = 0$, $V(\epsilon_{ij}) = \sigma^2$, and any pair of ϵ's, say ϵ_i, ϵ_j, are uncorrelated.

Similarly, imagine four people randomly selected to compare the reaction to three different drugs in a medical experiment where the drugs, A, B, and C, are randomly assigned to the subjects. Assuming no carryover effect of the drugs, the resulting experiment is the same randomized block design as that used for the comparison of the fertilizers. If the sole objective of the experiment is the comparison of the difference in the effect of the drugs, it does not matter whether the block effects are regarded as fixed or random since they cancel for a given treatment comparison. However, if one wished to estimate the expected response for a drug, the error of estimation would necessarily be influenced by both person-to-person variability and the variation within a person.

13.2 Analysis of a Randomized Block Design: Blocks Random

In order to simplify the presentation of the analysis of a randomized block design where the block effects are assumed to be random, we will give the analysis without derivation along with an example in this section. Various expectations which justify parts of the analysis will be given in Sec. 13.3 but may be omitted if desired. The following statements concerning methodology are based upon the mixed model of Sec. 13.1.

Suppose that the design consists of b randomly selected blocks with p treatments randomly assigned to the experimental units within a block. Then, with the assumptions of Sec. 13.1, it can be shown that $\bar{T}_i$ and $(\bar{T}_i - \bar{T}_j)$ provide unbiased estimators of the expected response for treatment i and the difference between the expected response for treatments i and j, respectively. Furthermore, it can be shown that

$$V(\bar{T}_i) = \frac{\sigma_b^2 + \sigma^2}{b}$$

and

$$V(\bar{T}_i - \bar{T}_j) = \frac{2\sigma^2}{b}.$$

The familiar analysis of variance for a k-way classification provides the necessary mean squares for estimating σ_b^2 and σ^2 and for testing an hypothesis of "no difference between treatments." The sums of squares are calculated in the same way as for the fixed-effect model (Chapter 8) and will possess the same number of degrees of freedom. The only difference will be the expected mean squares, which are shown in the analysis of variance, Table 13.1.

Table 13.1   Analysis-of-variance table for a randomized block design, blocks random

Source	d.f.	SS	MS	E(MS)
Treatments	$p - 1$	SST	$MST = SST/(p - 1)$	$\sigma^2 + \theta_\tau$
Blocks	$b - 1$	SSB	$MSB = SSB/(b - 1)$	$\sigma^2 + p\sigma_b^2$
Error	$bp - p - b + 1$	SSE	s^2	σ^2
Total	$bp - 1$	SS (total)		

The quantity θ_τ appearing in $E(\mathrm{MST})$ was defined in Sec. 8.5 and is a function of the sum of squares of deviations of the treatment parameters about their mean.

Under the null hypothesis that all treatment parameters simultaneously equal zero, $\theta_\tau = 0$ and SST/σ^2 is distributed as a chi-square variable with $(p-1)$ degrees of freedom. Similarly, $\mathrm{SSB}/(\sigma^2 + p\sigma_b^2)$ and SSE/σ^2 are distributed as independent chi-square variables with $(b-1)$ and $(bp - p - b + 1)$ degrees of freedom, respectively, and both are independent of SST. Hence the F-statistic

$$F = \frac{\mathrm{MST}}{s^2} \qquad \text{with } \nu_1 = (p-1) \text{ and } \nu_2 = (bp - p - b + 1) \text{ d.f.}$$

can be employed to test the hypothesis of no difference between treatments as in the case of the fixed-effect model.

To test an hypothesis, $\sigma_b^2 = 0$, one can use the test statistic,

$$F = \frac{\mathrm{MSB}}{s^2}, \qquad [\nu_1 = (b-1),\ \nu_2 = (bp - p - b + 1)].$$

An unbiased estimator of σ_b^2 is obtained from

$$\hat{\sigma}_b^2 = \frac{\mathrm{MSB} - s^2}{p}$$

but, as in the case of the completely random model, the exact probability distribution of $\hat{\sigma}_b^2$ is unknown. An approximate confidence interval for σ_b^2 can be obtained using Satterthwaite's approximation to the probability distribution of $\hat{\sigma}_b^2$ and the methods of Sec. 12.7.

A $(1 - \alpha)$ confidence interval for the difference between a pair of means is the same as for the fixed-effect model—that is,

$$(\bar{T}_i - \bar{T}_j) \pm t_{\alpha/2}\, s \sqrt{\frac{2}{b}}.$$

The variance of a single treatment mean can be estimated by substituting $\hat{\sigma}_b^2$ and s^2 for σ_b^2 and σ^2, respectively, in the formula for $V(\bar{T}_i)$. Thus,

$$\hat{V}(\bar{T}_i) = \frac{\hat{\sigma}_b^2 + \hat{\sigma}^2}{b} = \frac{(p-1)s^2 + \mathrm{MSB}}{bp}$$

$$= \frac{(p-1)}{bp} s^2 + \frac{\mathrm{MSB}}{bp}$$

is a linear function of the mean squares and its distribution may be approximated by using a chi-square distribution as indicated in Sec. 12.7. Then an approximate $(1 - \alpha)$ confidence interval for $E(\bar{T}_i)$ is given by

$$\bar{T}_i \pm t_{\alpha/2} \sqrt{\frac{(p-1)s^2 + \mathrm{MSB}}{bp}},$$

where $t_{\alpha/2}$ is based upon

$$\nu = \frac{\left[\dfrac{(p-1)s^2 + \text{MSB}}{bp}\right]^2}{\dfrac{\left[\dfrac{(p-1)s^2}{bp}\right]^2}{bp - p - b + 1} + \dfrac{\left(\dfrac{\text{MSB}}{bp}\right)^2}{b-1}}.$$

Note that ν is calculated from the formula

$$\nu = \frac{l^2}{\displaystyle\sum_{i=1}^{k} \frac{a_i^2 \text{MS}_i^2}{\nu_i}},$$

where $l = \sum\limits_{i=1}^{k} a_i \text{MS}_i$ is a linear function of mean squares satisfying the assumptions stated in Sec. 12.7.

Example 13.1 Two chemicals, A and B, developed to increase the strength of paperboard were compared by making comparisons within 60 samples randomly selected from production. Each paperboard sample was divided and the two chemicals, A and B, were randomly assigned, one to each half. The resulting strength measurements gave sample averages $\bar{y}_A = 32.2$ and $\bar{y}_B = 35.8$ and the analysis of variance shown in Table 13.2.

Table 13.2 Analysis of variance for data, Example 13.2

Source	d.f.	SS	MS	E(MS)
Treatments	1	388.80	388.80	$\sigma^2 + \theta_\tau$
Blocks	59	5130.60	86.96	$\sigma^2 + 2\sigma_b^2$
Error	59	2240.30	37.97	σ^2
Total	119	7759.70		

(a) Find a 95 per cent confidence interval for the difference in mean strength for paper samples treated by the two chemicals.

(b) Find an approximate 95 per cent confidence interval for σ_b^2, the measure of variation between the paper samples.

(c) What can be said about the minimum strength measurement for paperboard treated with one of the chemicals, say chemical A?

Solution: (a) A 95 per cent confidence interval for the difference in mean strength for the two samples is

$$(\bar{T}_i - \bar{T}_j) \pm t_{\alpha/2} s \sqrt{\frac{2}{b}},$$

$$(32.2 - 35.8) \pm (1.96)\sqrt{37.97}\sqrt{\frac{2}{60}},$$

$$-3.6 \pm 2.22.$$

(b) $\hat{\sigma}^2 = \text{MSE} = 37.97$, $\hat{\sigma}^2 + 2\hat{\sigma}_b^2 = \text{MSB} = 86.96$. Then

$$l = \hat{\sigma}_b^2 = \frac{\text{MSB} - \text{MSE}}{2} = \frac{86.96 - 37.97}{2} = 24.50.$$

To obtain a 95 per cent confidence interval for σ_b^2, we will use Satterthwaite's chi-square approximation to the distribution of $l = \hat{\sigma}_b^2$. The degrees of freedom for the approximating chi-square distribution will be

$$\nu = \frac{l^2}{\sum\limits_{i=1}^{k} \dfrac{a_i^2 MS_i^2}{\nu_i}}$$

$$= \frac{(24.50)^2}{\dfrac{(\frac{1}{2})^2(86.96)^2}{59} + \dfrac{(\frac{1}{2})^2(37.97)^2}{59}} = 15.7$$

And, since the tabulated values of χ^2 are given for integral values of ν, we will use $\nu = 16$. Then an approximate 95 per cent confidence interval for σ_b^2 is

$$\frac{\nu l}{\chi^2_{(.025)}} < \sigma_b^2 < \frac{\nu l}{\chi^2_{(.975)}},$$

$$\frac{(16)(24.50)}{28.84} < \sigma_b^2 < \frac{(16)(24.50)}{6.908},$$

$$13.59 < \sigma_b^2 < 56.74.$$

(c) Although the mean strength of paperboard is important, the manufacturer is more concerned with the actual distribution of strength of individual pieces of board since these will be used to construct shipping containers. It is of little value to manufacture paperboard with a high mean strength if a substantial number of individual containers possess low strength and hence burst in shipping. Thus we are interested in a prediction interval for an individual response, y.

A Student's t may be defined as the statistic

$$t = \frac{z}{\sqrt{\chi^2/\nu}},$$

where z is a normally distributed random variable with mean and variance equal to 0 and 1, respectively, χ^2 is a chi-square variable with ν degrees of freedom, and z and χ^2 are independent. Then if y_A is a new response on a paperboard sample treated with chemical A and $\bar{T}_A$ is the average of those measurements included in the randomized block experiment, then

$$E(y_A - \bar{T}_A) = 0, \qquad V(y_A - \bar{T}_A) = \frac{(b+1)}{b}(\sigma_b^2 + \sigma^2),$$

and

$$z = \frac{y_A - \bar{T}_A}{\sqrt{\frac{(b+1)}{b}(\sigma_b^2 + \sigma^2)}}.$$

Using Satterthwaite's approximation,

$$\frac{\nu\left[\frac{(b+1)}{b}(\hat{\sigma}_b^2 + \hat{\sigma}^2)\right]}{\frac{(b+1)}{b}[\sigma_b^2 + \sigma^2]} = \frac{\nu[(p-1)s^2 + \text{MSB}]}{p(\sigma_b^2 + \sigma^2)}$$

is approximately distributed as a chi-square variable with ν degrees of freedom and is independent of z. Substituting into the expression for t, we obtain the statistic

$$t = \frac{y_A - \bar{T}_A}{\sqrt{\frac{(b+1)}{bp}[(p-1)s^2 + \text{MSB}]}},$$

which is approximately distributed as a Student's t with ν degrees of freedom, where

$$l = \hat{V}(y_A - \bar{T}_A) = \frac{(b+1)}{bp}[(p-1)s^2 + \text{MSB}] = 63.51,$$

and

$$\nu = \frac{l^2}{\sum\limits_{i=1}^{k} \frac{a_i^2 MS_i^2}{\nu_i}} = \frac{(63.51)^2}{\left[\frac{61}{(60)(2)}\right]^2 \frac{(37.97)^2}{59} + \left[\frac{61}{(60)(2)}\right]^2 \frac{(86.96)^2}{59}} = 102.$$

Then, using the method of Sec. 7.9, one can construct an approximate one-sided prediction interval for y_A,

$$y_A \geq \bar{T}_A - t_\alpha \sqrt{\frac{(b+1)}{bp}[(p-1)s^2 + \text{MSB}]}.$$

Substituting,

$$y_A \geq 32.2 - (1.645)\sqrt{\frac{(61)[(1)(37.97) + (86.96)]}{(60)(2)}}$$

or

$$y_A \geq 19.1.$$

The number of degrees of freedom, ν, is very large for this example, hence $t_{\alpha/2} \approx z_{\alpha/2}$. Note also that the confidence interval for a single treatment mean (presented in this section) is derived in a manner similar to that employed for the prediction interval given above.

13.3 Expectations for the Randomized Block Design, Blocks Random

The linear model for the randomized block design with p treatments will contain p parameters corresponding to β_0 and the $(p-1)$ linearly independent treatment differences. And, as noted in Chapter 9, it is possible to code so as to estimate p linearly independent functions of the original p estimable parameters. Consequently, we will take the liberty in this section of writing the mixed model for a response in block i receiving treatment j as

$$y_{ij} = \mu + \beta_i + \tau_j + \epsilon_{ij}, \qquad i = 1, 2, \ldots, b, \quad j = 1, 2, \ldots, p,$$

where

$$\sum_{j=1}^{p} \tau_j = 0, \quad E(\beta_i) = 0, \quad V(\beta_i) = \sigma_b^2, \quad E(\epsilon_{ij}) = 0, \quad V(\epsilon_{ij}) = \sigma^2,$$

and all random components are assumed to be mutually independent. Note that the coding of the fixed qualitative variable, treatments, corresponds to that employed in Example 9.12.

Using this model,

$$\bar{T}_j = \mu + \tau_j + \bar{\beta} + \bar{\epsilon}_j,$$

where $\bar{\beta}$ is the average of the b random block components entering in $\bar{T}_j$, and $\bar{\epsilon}_j$ is the average of the b random components associated with the experimental units receiving treatment j. Then, regarding $\bar{T}_j$ as a linear function of independent random variables, we have

$$V(\bar{T}_j) = V(\bar{\beta}) + V(\bar{\epsilon}_j) = \frac{1}{b}(\sigma_b^2 + \sigma^2),$$

where all covariances equal zero since $\beta_i, \beta_j, \epsilon_k, \epsilon_l$ are independent for $i \neq j$ and $k \neq l$.

Similarly, the estimator of the difference between the expected yields for treatments i and j is

$$(\bar{T}_i - \bar{T}_j) = (\tau_i - \tau_j) + \bar{\epsilon}_i - \bar{\epsilon}_j,$$

where the random components entering into $\bar{\epsilon}_i$ and $\bar{\epsilon}_j$ are independent of one another. Then

$$V(\bar{T}_i - \bar{T}_j) = V(\bar{\epsilon}_i) + V(\bar{\epsilon}_j) = \frac{2\sigma^2}{b}.$$

The expected mean square for treatments will equal $(\sigma^2 + \theta_\tau)$ as calculated in Sec. 8.5, since the block effects cancel when we are making treatment comparisons. The following is a derivation of the expected mean square for blocks:

$$E(\text{MSB}) = \frac{1}{(b-1)} E(\text{SSB}) = \frac{1}{(b-1)} E\left[\sum_{i=1}^{b} \frac{B_i^2}{p} - \frac{\left(\sum_{i=1}^{n} y_i\right)^2}{n}\right]$$

$$= \frac{1}{(b-1)} E\left[p \sum_{i=1}^{b} (\bar{B}_i - \bar{y})^2\right]$$

$$= \frac{p}{(b-1)} \sum_{i=1}^{b} E[(\bar{B}_i - \bar{y})^2] = \frac{p}{(b-1)} \sum_{i=1}^{b} V(\bar{B}_i - \bar{y})$$

and, since $E(\bar{B}_i - \bar{y}) = 0$,

$$E[(\bar{B}_i - \bar{y})^2] = V(\bar{B}_i - \bar{y}).$$

The quantity $(\bar{B}_i - \bar{y})$ is a linear function with the variance the same for all i. Thus

$$V(\bar{B}_i - \bar{y}) = V(\bar{B}_i) + V(\bar{y}) - 2 \text{ Cov } (\bar{B}_i, \bar{y}),$$

where

$$\text{Cov } (\bar{B}_i, \bar{y}) = E(\bar{B}_i \bar{y}) - [E(\bar{B}_i)][E(\bar{y})] = \frac{\sigma_b^2}{b} + \frac{\sigma^2}{n}.$$

Then

$$E(\text{MSB}) = \frac{bp}{(b-1)}\left[\left(\sigma_b^2 + \frac{\sigma^2}{p}\right) + \left(\frac{\sigma_b^2}{b} + \frac{\sigma^2}{bp}\right) - 2\left(\frac{\sigma_b^2}{b} + \frac{\sigma^2}{n}\right)\right]$$

$$= \sigma^2 + p\sigma_b^2.$$

Another way to achieve the same result is to note that

$$\text{MSB} = p\left[\sum_{i=1}^{b} \frac{(\bar{B}_i - \bar{y})^2}{b-1}\right] = p[\text{unbiased estimator of } V(\bar{B}_i)].$$

Therefore

$$E(\text{MSB}) = pV(\bar{B}_i) = p\left(\sigma_b^2 + \frac{\sigma^2}{p}\right) = \sigma^2 + p\sigma_b^2.$$

Showing that $E(\text{MSE}) = \sigma^2$ is a tedious procedure, particularly since SSE was obtained by subtraction in the analysis of variance. Thus

$$\sum_i \sum_j (y_{ij} - \bar{y})^2 = \text{SSE} + \text{SSB} + \text{SST}$$

and

$$E(\text{SSE}) = E[\sum_i \sum_j (Y_{ij} - \bar{y})^2] - E(\text{SSB}) - E(\text{SST}),$$

where $E(\text{SSB})$ and $E(\text{SST})$ are given above. The only unknown quantity in $E(\text{SSE})$ is

$$E[\sum_i \sum_j (y_{ij} - \bar{y})^2] = E[\sum_i (y_{i1} - \bar{y})^2] + E[\sum_i (y_{i2} - \bar{y})^2]$$
$$+ \cdots + E[\sum_i (y_{il} - \bar{y})^2].$$

Each quantity on the right of the equals sign has the same expected value,

$$E\{\sum_i (y_{ij} - \bar{y})^2\} = E\{\sum_i [(y_{ij} - \bar{y}_j) + (\bar{y}_j - \bar{y})]^2\}$$
$$= E\{\sum_i [(y_{ij} - \bar{y}_j)^2 + 2(y_{ij} - \bar{y}_j)(\bar{y}_j - \bar{y}) + (\bar{y}_j - \bar{y})^2]\}.$$

The middle quantity in this expression sums to zero, and

$$E[\sum_i (y_{ij} - \bar{y})^2] = E[\sum_i (y_{ij} - \bar{y}_j)^2] + bE[(\bar{y}_j - \bar{y})^2].$$

Looking at the two quantities on the right-hand side of the expression separately,

$$E[\sum_i (y_{ij} - \bar{y}_j)^2]$$

is the expectation of the sums of squares of deviations of a set of b random variables about their mean, and hence

$$E[\sum_i (y_{ij} - \bar{y}_j)^2] = (b - 1)V(y_{ij}) = (b - 1)(\sigma^2 + \sigma_b^2).$$

In the second quantity

$$(\bar{y}_j - \bar{y}) = (\mu + \tau_j + \bar{\beta} + \bar{\epsilon}_j) - (\mu + \bar{\beta} + \bar{\epsilon}) = \tau_j + \bar{\epsilon}_j - \bar{\epsilon},$$

where $\bar{\beta}$ is the average of the b random block components, $\bar{\epsilon}_j$ is the average of the random components (ϵ_{ij}) appearing in the total of observations receiving treatment j, and $\bar{\epsilon}$ is the average of all $n = bp$ random components. Squaring and taking expectations,

$$E[(\bar{y}_j - \bar{y})^2] = \tau_j^2 + \sigma^2\left(\frac{1}{b} - \frac{1}{n}\right).$$

Substituting these quantities into the original expression, we have

$$E[\sum_i \sum_j (y_{ij} - \bar{y})^2] = \sum_j E[\sum_i (y_{ij} - \bar{y})^2]$$
$$= \sum_j \{E[\sum_i (y_{ij} - \bar{y}_j)^2] + bE[(\bar{y}_j - \bar{y})^2]\}$$
$$= p(b - 1)(\sigma^2 + \sigma_b^2) + b\sum_j \tau_j^2 + bp\sigma^2\left(\frac{1}{b} - \frac{1}{n}\right)$$
$$= b\sum_j \tau_j^2 + p(b - 1)\sigma_b^2 + (pb - 1)\sigma^2,$$

where $b\sum_j \tau_j^2 = (p - 1)\theta_\tau$. Then

$$E(\text{SSE}) = E[\sum_i \sum_j (y_{ij} - \bar{y})^2] - E(\text{SSB}) - E(\text{SST})$$
$$= (bp - b - p + 1)\sigma^2.$$

And since SSE possesses $(bp - b - p + 1)$ degrees of freedom,

$$E(\text{MSE}) = \sigma^2.$$

Acquisition of the expected mean squares in the analysis of variance of a mixed or completely random model is essential in order that the proper mean squares be used to form the F-statistic for a particular test. They are also necessary for finding estimators of the variances of the random components of the linear model. Although they are not difficult to obtain, it is clear from the preceding that the derivation of the expected mean squares for various mixed models can be space-consuming and tedious. With this in mind, we will omit the actual derivation for the mixed models discussed in succeeding sections and leave these as exercises for the interested reader.

13.4 Two-Way Classification with Replication

The randomized block design of Sec. 13.2 represents a two-way classifica-cation of data with one qualitative variable, blocks, assumed to be randomly selected from a population and the other assumed to be fixed. We now consider an extension of this model to include r replications of each block-treatment combination.

The linear model for this experiment can then be modified to include a random element corresponding to block-treatment interaction. Thus a response, y_{ijk}, corresponding to the kth replication of treatment j in block i is assumed to be the sum of a general mean, μ, a random component β_i due to the ith block, a fixed effect τ_i due to treatment i, a random interaction term $(\beta\tau)_{ij}$, and a random component contributed by replication, ϵ_{ijk}.

$$y_{ijk} = \mu + \beta_i + \tau_j + (\beta\tau)_{ij} + \epsilon_{ijk}.$$

We will assume that fixed and random components β_i, τ_j, and ϵ_{ijk} satisfy the assumptions of Sec. 13.3 and will ascribe certain properties to the random interaction terms. These latter assumptions may vary considerably, with consequent variations in the distributional properties of the mean squares calculated in the analysis of variance. Hence to open our discussion of this mixed model, we will give the analysis of variance for the randomized block design with replication and then will consider different assumptions concerning the interaction terms and the resulting effect on the inferences to be derived from the data.

The analysis of variance is conducted in accordance with the formulas given in Chapter 8 for a k-way classification where, in this case, $k = 2$. The sums of squares, SST, SSB, and SS(BT) are calculated by the formulas of Sec. 8.7, and SSE is obtained by subtraction. This analysis is given in Table 13.3.

Table 13.3   Analysis of variance for a randomized block design with replication

Source	d.f.	SS	MS
Treatments	$p-1$	SST	$\text{SST}/(p-1)$
Blocks	$b-1$	SSB	$\text{SSB}/(b-1)$
Block $\times$ Treatment	$(b-1)(p-1)$	SS(BT)	$\text{SS(BT)}/(b-1)(p-1)$
Error	$bp(r-1)$	SSE	$\text{SSE}/bp(r-1)$
Total	$bpr-1$	$\sum_{i=1}^{n}(y_i-\bar{y})^2$	

Many models might be proposed for this experiment, but we will only consider those for which the major difference would concern the distributional properties of $(\beta\tau)_{ij}$. Two of these models as well as the respective analyses are outlined in the following discussion.

Model 1 $(\beta\tau)_{ij}$ *independently normally distributed with* $E[(\beta\tau)_{ij}] = 0$, $V[(\beta\tau)_{ij}] = \sigma_{bt}^2$ *and* $(\beta\tau)_{ij}$ *independent of the block effects* β_i *and the random components due to replication* ϵ_{ijk}.

The expected mean squares for this analysis are given in Table 13.4.

Table 13.4   Expected-mean-squares assumptions, Model 1

Source	d.f.	MS	E(MS)
Treatments	$p-1$	MST	$\sigma^2 + r\sigma_{bt}^2 + \theta_\tau$
Blocks	$b-1$	MSB	$\sigma^2 + rp\sigma_b^2 + r\sigma_{bt}^2$
Block $\times$ Treatment	$(b-1)(p-1)$	MS(BT)	$\sigma^2 + r\sigma_{bt}^2$
Error	$bp(r-1)$	MSE	σ^2
Total	$bpr-1$		

With each of the random components assumed to be normally distributed, the product of a ratio of a pair of mean squares by the ratio of the corresponding expected mean squares will form an F-statistic. For example,

$$F = \frac{\text{MST}}{\text{MS(BT)}} \cdot \frac{r\sigma_{bt}^2 + \sigma^2}{r\sigma_{bt}^2 + \sigma^2 + \theta_\tau}.$$

Under the null hypothesis that there is no difference between treatments, $\theta_\tau = 0$, the expected mean squares divide out and

$$F = \frac{\text{MST}}{\text{MS(BT)}}.$$

If θ_τ differs from zero, it can only be positive (since it is a multiple of the sum of squares of the treatment effects), and the F will tend to be larger than expected. The rejection region for probability of a type I error, α, will be

$$F \geq F_\alpha.$$

Examination of the expected mean squares in the analysis of variance indicates the appropriate mean-square ratio to use to test a given hypothesis. Thus to test $H_0: \sigma_b^2 = 0$ we would use

$$F = \frac{\text{MSB}}{\text{MS(BT)}}.$$

To test $H_0: \sigma_{bt}^2 = 0$ we use

$$F = \frac{\text{MS(BT)}}{\text{MSE}}.$$

The unbiased estimators of the expected response for treatment j and the difference between two treatments, i and j, are, respectively, $\bar{T}_j$ and $\bar{T}_i - \bar{T}_j$. The variance of $\bar{T}_j$ is

$$V(\bar{T}_j) = V[\mu + \bar{\beta} + \tau_j + (\overline{\beta\tau})_j + \bar{\epsilon}_j]$$

$$= \frac{\sigma_b^2}{b} + \frac{\sigma_{bt}^2}{b} + \frac{\sigma^2}{br} = \frac{1}{br}(r\sigma_b^2 + r\sigma_{bt}^2 + \sigma^2),$$

where $\bar{\beta}$ is the average of the b random block components, $(\overline{\beta\tau})_j$ is the average of the b interaction components in $\bar{T}_j$, and $\bar{\epsilon}_j$ is the average of the br error components in $\bar{T}_j$. Similarly,

$$V(\bar{T}_i - \bar{T}_j) = \frac{2}{br}(r\sigma_{bt}^2 + \sigma^2).$$

An unbiased estimate of $V(\bar{T}_j)$ can be obtained by using the appropriate linear combination of the mean squares, and an approximate $(1 - \alpha)$ confidence interval for $E(\bar{T}_j)$ can be constructed using

$$\bar{T}_j \pm t_{\alpha/2}\sqrt{\frac{1}{br}(r\hat{\sigma}_b^2 + r\hat{\sigma}_{bt}^2 + \hat{\sigma}^2)}.$$

The degrees of freedom for $t_{\alpha/2}$ will be based upon Satterthwaite's approximation, Sec. 12.7. Similarly, an exact $(1 - \alpha)$ confidence interval for $E(\bar{T}_i - \bar{T}_j)$ is

$$(\bar{T}_i - \bar{T}_j) \pm t_{\alpha/2}\sqrt{\frac{2}{br}(r\hat{\sigma}_{bt}^2 + \hat{\sigma}^2)}$$

or

$$(\bar{T}_i - \bar{T}_j) \pm t_{\alpha/2}\sqrt{\frac{2}{br}\text{MS(BT)}}.$$

The degrees of freedom associated with the $t_{\alpha/2}$ will be those attached to MS(BT), namely $(b - 1)(p - 1)$.

The major criticism of Model 1 concerns the assumption of independence of the $(\beta\tau)_{ij}$, since it is felt that these random elements within a given block will often be correlated. This point is undoubtedly well taken, but the real question is whether this correlation is large enough to substantially distort the properties of the statistical tests derived from Model 1. It is interesting to note that the same criticism could be leveled at the fixed-effect model for the randomized block design where the ϵ_{ij} are assumed to be independent. Correlation of the random errors within a block either exists or does not, and the manner in which the blocks are selected, fixed or random, will not change the status quo one bit.

Model 2 $(\beta\tau)_{ij}$ *normally distributed with* $E[(\beta\tau)_{ij}] = 0$,

$$V[(\beta\tau)_{ij}] = \frac{(p-1)}{p}\sigma_{bt}^2, \qquad \sum_j (\beta\tau)_{ij} = 0,$$

and

$$\text{Cov}\,[(\beta\tau)_{ij},\,(\beta\tau)_{kl}] = 0, \qquad i \neq k,$$
$$= -\frac{1}{p}\sigma_{bt}^2, \qquad i = k;\ j \neq l.$$

Model 2 is probably the most widely employed model for the two-way classification, blocks random and treatments fixed, and is described in detail in texts by Kempthorne (1952) and Graybill (1961). Thus, since treatments are assumed to be nonrandom with a coding such that

$$\sum_j \tau_j = 0,$$

it is argued that it is reasonable to assume that the summation of the interaction components, over all treatments *within* a given block, should equal zero. The variance of $(\beta\tau)_{ij}$ is defined as $[(p-1)/p]\sigma_{bt}^2$ rather than σ_{bt}^2 in order to simplify the form of the expected mean squares. The big difference between Models 2 and 1 is the assumption that random interaction elements within a given block sum to zero. This implies that they are correlated with a covariance equal to $-(1/p)\sigma_{bt}^2$ and that the covariance diminishes as the number of treatments increases.

The expected mean squares for Model 2 are given in Table 13.5.

Table 13.5   Expected-mean-squares assumptions, Model 2

Source	d.f.	MS	E(MS)
Treatments	$p-1$	MST	$\sigma^2 + r\sigma_{bt}^2 + \theta_\tau$
Blocks	$b-1$	MSB	$\sigma^2 + rp\sigma_b^2$
Block × Treatment	$(b-1)(p-1)$	MS(BT)	$\sigma^2 + r\sigma_{bt}^2$
Error	$bp(r-1)$	MSE	σ^2
Total	$bpr - 1$		

The only difference between the expected mean squares, Tables 13.4 and 13.5, is that σ_{bt}^2 does not appear in $E(\text{MSB})$. (Other minor differences actually occur due to the different definitions for $V[(\beta\tau)_{ij}]$ for Models 1 and 2, but these do not affect the analysis.) This would require the use of the mean-square ratio, $F = \text{MSB}/\text{MSE}$, to test the hypothesis $H_0: \sigma_b^2 = 0$, rather than $F = \text{MSB}/\text{MS(BT)}$ as indicated in the analysis for Model 1.

Unbiased estimators of the expected treatment yields and the difference between a pair of treatments will be as indicated for Model 1 but the estimators of σ_b^2 will differ. Actually, the estimators of $V[(\beta\tau)_{ij}]$ differ, but the slightly differing definitions for this quantity for the two models imply the same linear functions of mean squares as the estimators of σ_{bt}^2.

The variance of $\bar{T}_j$ will differ from that in Model 1. Thus

$$V(\bar{T}_j) = \frac{1}{b}\left(\sigma_b^2 + \frac{(p-1)}{p}\sigma_{bt}^2 + \frac{\sigma^2}{r}\right)$$

$$V(\bar{T}_i - \bar{T}_j) = \frac{2}{b}\left(\sigma_{bt}^2 + \frac{\sigma^2}{r}\right) = \frac{2}{br}(r\sigma_{bt}^2 + \sigma^2).$$

Actually, $V(\bar{T}_i - \bar{T}_j)$ differs, since σ_{bt}^2 does not possess the same meaning for the two models, but both use the same linear functions of the mean squares as estimators of $V(\bar{T}_i - \bar{T}_j)$.

We can construct large-sample confidence intervals for $E(\bar{T}_j)$ and $E(\bar{T}_i - \bar{T}_j)$ by using estimates of the variances given in the preceding paragraph and the same procedure indicated for Model 1.

Among other models proposed are those by Tukey (1949), Wilk and Kempthorne (1955), and Scheffe (1956). We will comment briefly on Scheffe's model, which is more general than Models 1 and 2 and hence more in agreement with the exact state of nature.

Scheffe defines the model for the kth response receiving treatment j in block i (Scheffe does not specifically refer to the second qualitative variables as "blocks," but we will do so in order to be consistent with earlier discussion) as

$$y_{ijk} = m_{ij} + \epsilon_{ijk},$$

where m_{ij} and ϵ_{ijk} are random variables. The ϵ_{ijk} are assumed to be mutually independent in repeated measurements and are equivalent to the quantities appearing in Models 1 and 2. The m_{ij} are independent of the ϵ_{ijk} and

$$m_{ij} = \mu + \tau_i + \beta_j + (\beta\tau)_{ij},$$

where

$$E(m_{ij}) = \mu_i, \ \mu_i = \mu + \tau_i,$$

$$\sum_i \tau_i = 0 \quad \text{and} \quad \beta_j = \frac{\sum_i m_{ij}}{b} - \mu.$$

Up to this point Scheffe's model is identical with Model 2, including the fact that $\sum_i (\beta\tau)_{ij} = 0$ for all j, which follows from the above assumptions.

The main difference now comes in establishing the variances and covariances of the random elements β_i and $(\beta\tau)_{ij}$. Rather than specify these quantities directly, Scheffe defines a variance-covariance matrix, V, for the random components m_{ij}, which possesses elements $\sigma_{i,i'}$. Then $V(\beta_i)$, Cov $[(\beta\tau)_{ij}, (\beta\tau)_{ik}]$, and Cov $[\beta_i, (\beta\tau)_{ij}]$ can be expressed in terms of the elements of V. Thus Model 2 represents a specific case of Scheffe's model.

With appropriate normality assumptions for the random components of the model, the F-tests for testing hypotheses $H_0: \sigma_b^2 = 0$ and $H_0: \sigma_{bt}^2$ (using the notation of Models 1 and 2) are exactly the same as for Model 2. Scheffe notes that a major difference in the analysis is the fact that MST/MS(BT) does not in general follow an F distribution when $H_0: \theta_\tau = 0$ is true.

The necessity for discarding the relatively simple estimation and test procedures of Models 1 and 2 in favor of those derived from Scheffe's model or one of comparable sophistication depends upon two things. First, to what extent does correlation between the random components of the linear model distort the derived characteristics of test and estimation procedures of Models 1 and 2? Second, is the degree of correlation between the random components large in many practical applications? The answer to the first question can be determined by empirical sampling studies, but the latter is difficult to assess.

As noted earlier, little difference exists between the methodologies derived from Models 1 and 2. The test of the hypothesis $H_0: \sigma_b^2 = 0$ will be more conservative for the procedure based on Model 1 because the denominator mean square, MS(BT), will generally be larger than MSE, which is used in the test for Model 2. Tests of hypotheses concerning θ_τ and σ_{bt}^2 utilize the same test statistics. Moreover, unbiased estimators of $V(\bar{T}_i - \bar{T}_j)$ employed in the large-sample confidence interval for the difference between a pair of treatment means are identical. The same is true for the unbiased estimator of $V(\bar{T}_j)$ and the associated confidence interval for a single treatment mean.

Which methodology should one use in analyzing data generated by this type of experimental situation? If correlations are not large, current preference of applied statisticians seems to favor the methodology associated with Model 2. If empirical studies tend to show that correlations seriously affect the methodology for Models 1 and 2 and if substantial correlations do exist in experimental data, then a shift to a methodology such as that implied by Scheffe's model will be necessary.

Example 13.2   An experiment was conducted to compare the length of time to assemble a device using four different assembly procedures, A, B, C, and

D. Five people were randomly selected to perform the assemblies and each person assembled two devices for each of the four methods. The sequence of assignment of method of assembly within a person was random. The data are shown in Table 13.6.

Table 13.6 Time to assemble a device (in minutes)

Assemblers

	1	2	3	4	5	*Totals*
A	17.20 19.62	19.67 21.19	19.09 18.87	18.21 19.03	17.57 18.00	188.45
B	24.24 23.56	32.95 33.39	26.50 27.83	26.65 25.47	23.72 23.77	268.08
C	19.52 19.44	22.99 23.07	22.44 21.49	12.38 12.00	19.80 21.38	194.51
D	15.29 13.91	21.79 21.37	16.15 17.37	14.98 15.34	23.46 21.98	181.64
Totals	152.78	196.42	169.74	144.06	169.68	832.68

(a) Do the data present sufficient evidence to indicate a difference in the mean responses for treatments?

(b) Do the data present sufficient evidence to indicate a difference in the mean response for assemblers?

(c) Find a 95 per cent confidence interval for the difference in the mean responses for treatments B and A.

Solution: The analysis of variance for the data in Table 13.6 is given below.

Source	d.f.	SS	MS	E(MS)
Treatments	3	486.85	162.28	$\sigma^2 + r\sigma_{bt}^2 + \theta_\tau$
Blocks	4	200.95	50.24	$\sigma^2 + rp\sigma_b^2$
BT Interaction	12	183.39	15.28	$\sigma^2 + r\sigma_{bt}^2$
Error	20	11.17	0.56	σ^2
Total	39	882.36		

(a) The test statistic for testing an hypothesis of "no difference between treatments" is

$$F = \frac{\text{MST}}{\text{MS(BT)}} = \frac{162.28}{15.28} = 10.62$$

based upon $\nu_1 = 3$ and $\nu_2 = 12$ degrees of freedom. Since the computed F exceeds the critical value, $F_{.05} = 3.49$, we conclude that a difference exists in the mean responses for treatments.

(b) The test statistic for testing the null hypothesis, $H_0: \sigma_b^2 = 0$, is

$$F = \frac{\text{MSB}}{\text{MSE}} = \frac{50.24}{.56} = 89.7,$$

where F is based upon $\nu_1 = 4$ and $\nu_2 = 20$ degrees of freedom. The test statistic greatly exceeds the critical value, $F_{.05} = 2.87$, and hence there is substantial evidence that σ_b^2 differs from zero. This would indicate person-to-person variability in the length of time to assemble the device.

(c) A 95 per cent confidence interval for $E(\bar{T}_A - \bar{T}_B)$ is

$$(\bar{T}_A - \bar{T}_B) \pm t_{\alpha/2} \sqrt{\frac{2}{br}(\hat{\sigma}^2 + r\hat{\sigma}_{bt}^2)}$$

or

$$(\bar{T}_A - \bar{T}_B) \pm t_{\alpha/2} \sqrt{\frac{2}{br}\text{MS(BT)}},$$

where $t_{\alpha/2}$ is based upon $\nu = 12$ degrees of freedom. Substituting,

$$(18.85 - 26.81) \pm (2.179)\sqrt{15.28}$$

or

$$-7.96 \pm 8.30.$$

13.5 A Split-Plot Design

A simple split-plot design is a two-factor factorial experiment with a very particular randomized assignment of the treatments within blocks of experimental material. Suppose, for example, that an experiment is conducted to compare two different types of soil preparation (factor A) and three different fertilizer applications (factor D). Four farming locations are selected (blocks) and two fields of equal area in each farm are randomly assigned to receive the two preparations of factor A. This is shown diagrammatically in Fig. 13.1. There we see that the large fields function as the experimental units (called *whole plots*) within a block, and factor A is randomly assigned to the whole plots to construct a complete randomized block design.

Figure 13.1 Assignment of levels of factor A to the whole plots

Farm (blocks)

1	2	3	4
A_1	A_2	A_1	A_2
A_2	A_1	A_2	A_1

After assignment of factor A, each whole plot is regarded as a small block and is partitioned into three *subplots* to receive a random assignment of the three levels of factor D. The complete split-plot design is shown in Fig. 13.2. Note that the assignment of factor levels to the experimental units creates small complete randomized blocks of the levels of D within the whole plots.

Figure 13.2 Assignment of treatments to plots in a split-plot design

Farms (blocks)

	1		2		3		4
	D_2		D_1		D_2		D_3
A_1	D_1	A_2	D_3	A_1	D_3	A_2	D_1
	D_3		D_2		D_1		D_2
	D_3		D_2		D_1		D_1
A_2	D_2	A_1	D_3	A_2	D_2	A_1	D_3
	D_1		D_1		D_3		D_2

In general, one may utilize any number of levels of factors A and D, denoted by the symbols a and d, respectively. The number of blocks, B, will be denoted by the symbol b and the total number of subplots in the experiment will be $n = abd$.

The split-plot design is employed in a situation where it is too costly or physically impossible to apply one set of treatments (factor A) to small experimental units. For example, it would be difficult and more costly to randomly assign the (ad) factor combinations of the complete factorial to the subplot experimental units of Fig. 13.2 because it would mean changing the soil preparation equipment as the experimenter moved from one small plot to another.

As a second example, suppose that an experimenter wishes to compare the effect of four types of chemical additives (A) and five types of steel reinforcing (D) on the strength of concrete beams. Further, suppose that it is difficult to add the additive after a batch of concrete has been mixed and that it is reasonable to insert the additive at the time of mixing and therefore regard a mix as the whole plot. The mixed concrete for a batch would then be partitioned into five parts, and test beams would be poured for each of the five methods of reinforcing.

The model for the split-plot design is

$$y_{ijk} = \mu + \alpha_i + \beta_j + \delta_k + (\alpha\beta)_{ij} + (\alpha\delta)_{ik} + \epsilon_{ijk},$$

where y_{ijk} is the measurement receiving the ith level of A and the kth level of D in the jth block. Treatment parameters associated with factor A, α_i, are assumed to be fixed and coded so that

$$\sum_i \alpha_i = 0.$$

Likewise, the remaining fixed factorial parameters associated with factor D and the interaction of A and D, δ_k and $(\alpha\delta)_{ik}$, respectively, are coded so that

$$\sum_k \delta_k = 0 \quad \text{and} \quad \sum_i (\alpha\delta)_{ik} = \sum_k (\alpha\delta)_{ik} = 0.$$

Blocks are assumed to be randomly selected from an infinitely large population so that the block effect, β_j, is regarded as random with $E(\beta_j) = 0$, $V(\beta_j) = \sigma_b^2$, and $\text{Cov}(\beta_j, \beta_k) = 0$, $j \neq k$. The random interaction terms, $(\alpha\beta)_{ij}$, are assumed to be independent of β_i and to possess mean and variance, $E(\alpha\beta)_{ij} = 0$ and $V[(\alpha\beta)_{ij}] = [(a-1)/a]\sigma_{ab}^2$, respectively, with

$$\sum_i (\alpha\beta)_{ij} = 0.$$

Consequently

$$\text{Cov}\,[(\alpha\beta)_{ij}, (\alpha\beta)_{kj}] = -\frac{1}{a}\sigma_{ab}^2, \quad i \neq k,$$

for observations in the same block and equals zero, otherwise. Finally, the random errors, ϵ_{ijk}, are assumed to be independent of β_i and $(\alpha\beta)_{ij}$ and mutually independent with $E(\epsilon_{ijk}) = 0$, $V(\epsilon_{ijk}) = \sigma^2$. The reader will note that the assumptions regarding the block effects and factor A are those for the two-way classification with replication, Model 2 (discussed in Sec. 13.4), if the assignment of factor D is ignored.

The analysis of variance for the split-plot design is given in Table 13.7, where the sums of squares are computed using the familiar formulas for a k-way classification (Sec. 8.7). Mean squares are obtained by dividing source sums of squares by their respective degrees of freedom; the expected mean squares are shown in column 5. The quantities θ_A, θ_D, and θ_{AD} are positive functions of the sums of squares of the parameters associated with factors A, D, and the AD interaction, respectively.

Table 13.7   Analysis of variance for a split-plot design

Source	d.f.	SS	MS	E(MS)
Blocks, B	$b - 1$	SSB	MSB	$\sigma^2 + ad\sigma_b^2$
A	$a - 1$	SSA	MSA	$\sigma^2 + d\sigma_{ab}^2 + \theta_A$
AB (Whole-plot error)	$(a-1)(b-1)$	SS(AB)	MS(AB)	$\sigma^2 + d\sigma_{ab}^2$
D	$d - 1$	SSD	MSD	$\sigma^2 + \theta_D$
AD	$(a-1)(d-1)$	SS(AD)	MS(AD)	$\sigma^2 + \theta_{AD}$
Subplot error	$a(b-1)(d-1)$	SSE	MSE	σ^2
Total	$abd - 1$			

Tests of hypotheses concerning θ_A, θ_D, θ_{AD}, σ_{ab}^2, and σ_b^2 can be conducted by comparing appropriate mean squares using the F-statistic when the random components of the model are assumed to be normally distributed. For example, to test the hypothesis $H_0 : \theta_A = 0$ we would use the test statistic $F = \mathrm{MS}A/\mathrm{MS}(AB)$. Similarly, a test of the hypothesis $H_0 : \theta_{AD} = 0$ would use the test statistic $F = \mathrm{MS}(AD)/\mathrm{MSE}$.

Since

$$\sum_k \delta_k = \sum_i (\alpha\delta)_{ik} = \sum_k (\alpha\delta)_{ik} = 0,$$

the variances of the mean response for a level of factor A or the difference between the mean responses for two levels of A will be exactly as given in the preceding section for a two-way classification with replication. Thus,

$$V(\bar{A}_i) = \frac{1}{b}\left(\sigma_b^2 + \frac{(a-1)}{a}\sigma_{ab}^2 + \frac{\sigma^2}{d}\right),$$

$$V(\bar{A}_i - \bar{A}_j) = \frac{2}{bd}(d\sigma_{ab}^2 + \sigma^2).$$

Other estimators of interest are those for the mean of a level of factor D, the difference between the means for two levels, the mean for a particular combination of A and D levels, say $(AD)_{ij}$, and a comparison of two of these means. The variances of these estimators are

$$V(\bar{D}_i) = \frac{1}{ab}(a\sigma_b^2 + \sigma^2),$$

$$V(\bar{D}_i - \bar{D}_j) = \frac{2\sigma^2}{ab}.$$

Letting $(\bar{AD})_{ij}$ represent the average of responses at the ith level of A and the jth level of D, we have

$$V(\bar{AD})_{ij} = \frac{1}{b}\left(\sigma_b^2 + \frac{a-1}{a}\sigma_{ab}^2 + \sigma^2\right).$$

And, for two different combinations of levels of A and D,

$$V[(\bar{AD})_{ij} - (\bar{AD})_{kl}] = \frac{2}{b}(\sigma_{ab}^2 + \sigma^2), \qquad i \neq k,$$

$$= \frac{2\sigma^2}{b}, \qquad i = k.$$

Approximations to the preceding variances can be obtained by substituting the estimates of $\hat{\sigma}_b^2$, $\hat{\sigma}_{ab}^2$, and $\hat{\sigma}^2$ into the above expressions, where

$$\hat{\sigma}_b^2 = \frac{\mathrm{MS}B - \mathrm{MSE}}{ad},$$

$$\hat{\sigma}_{ab}^2 = \frac{\mathrm{MS}(AB) - \mathrm{MSE}}{d},$$

$$\hat{\sigma}^2 = \mathrm{MSE}.$$

Approximate confidence intervals for the expected values of these means or the difference between a pair of means can be constructed using Student's t and Satterthwaite's approximation (Sec. 12.7) to the degrees of freedom. This procedure has been amply illustrated in earlier sections in this chapter.

Example 13.3 A new structural plastic is produced by baking plastic granules at a given temperature for a specified period of time. The application of high pressure on the newly produced plastic as well as the initial particle size were thought to affect the resulting compressive strength of the plastic. Hence, the following experiment was conducted to investigate the effects of these two variables. The ovens were of sufficient size to permit the baking of three plastic ingots and thus permit investigation of particle size (A) at three different levels. Oven temperatures vary somewhat, depending upon location within the oven. To eliminate this variability, the two pressure levels (D) were compared within each ingot by dividing each into two parts immediately after baking and randomly assigning one-half to each of the two pressure treatments. Thus each baking formed a block, and the ingots represent the whole plots. The subplots were the half-ingots, which were ultimately measured for compressive strength. Compressive-strength measurements for this two-factor split-plot design based on two bakings are shown in Fig. 13.8.

Table 13.8   Compressive-strength measurements on plastic

Baking (blocks)

		1		2	
		Pressure		Pressure	
		P_1	P_2	P_1	P_2
	S_1	5.0	5.7	5.4	5.8
Particle size	S_2	5.3	6.0	5.9	6.3
	S_3	5.8	6.5	6.4	6.6

(a) Give the analysis of variance for this experiment.
(b) Do the data present sufficient evidence to indicate an interaction between particle size and pressure treatment?
(c) Do the data present sufficient evidence to indicate a difference in the mean strength as a result of particle size?
(d) As a result of pressure treatment?
(e) Find a 95 per cent confidence interval for the difference in mean strength for the two pressure levels.

Solution: (a) The analysis of variance is tabulated below.

Source	d.f	SS	MS
Size (S)	2	1.4467	.7233
Blocks (B)	1	.3675	.3675
SB	2	.0200	.0100
Pressure (P)	1	.8009	.8009
SP	2	.0066	.0033
Subplot error	3	.1075	.0358
Total	11	2.7492	

(b) From the expected mean squares of Table 13.7, the test statistic for testing an hypothesis of "no size-pressure interaction" is

$$F = \frac{\text{MS}(SP)}{\text{MSE}} = \frac{.0033}{.0358} = .09$$

This F-value is so small that we need not bother to compare it with the tabulated critical value. It is clear that there is no evidence to indicate a size-pressure interaction.

(c) To test the hypothesis that there is no difference in mean strength for the levels of particle size, we will compare the particle-size mean square with the whole-plot mean square:

$$F = \frac{\text{MS}(S)}{\text{MS}(SB)} = \frac{.7233}{.0100} = 72.33.$$

Comparing with the critical value of $F_{.05} = 19.00$ based upon $\nu_1 = 2$ and $\nu_2 = 2$ degrees of freedom, we would reject the null hypothesis and conclude that a difference exists in the mean response for the three levels of particle size.

(d) To test an hypothesis of no difference in mean response due to pressure, we use the test statistic

$$F = \frac{\text{MS}(P)}{\text{MSE}} = \frac{.8009}{.0358} = 22.4$$

based on $\nu_1 = 1$ and $\nu_2 = 3$ degrees of freedom. Comparing with the critical value, $F_{.05} = 10.13$, we reject the null hypothesis and conclude that a difference exists in the mean response for the two pressure levels.

(e) A 95 per cent confidence interval for the difference in mean response for the two pressure levels is

$$(\bar{P}_2 - \bar{P}_1) \pm t_{.025} s \sqrt{\frac{1}{n_1} + \frac{1}{n_2}}.$$

Substituting, we obtain

$$(6.15 - 5.63) \pm (3.182)(.19)\sqrt{\tfrac{1}{6} + \tfrac{1}{6}}$$

or

$$.42 \pm .35.$$

The split-plot technique discussed in this section can be extended to include the study of a third factor by splitting each of the subplots into sub-subplots and randomly assigning the levels of the third factor within subplots. Indeed, the splitting can be done many times and in many different directions. The net effect is to focus more information on the main effects of the factors randomly assigned to the smaller subplots. Thus, $V(\bar{D}_i - \bar{D}_j)$ will always be less than or equal to $V(\bar{A}_i - \bar{A}_j)$ if for the sake of a fair comparison we assume that the numbers of measurements entering into the means, $\bar{A}_i$ and $\bar{B}_j$, are equal (that is, $a = d$).

The split-plot design can also be regarded as an incomplete block design, where the treatments are the (ad) factor combinations and the whole plots are the incomplete blocks. From this standpoint, the main effects for factor A are confounded with the whole-plot effects. Additional discussion of the split-plot design can be found in texts by Anderson and Bancroft (1952), Cochran and Cox (1957), Finney (1960), Kempthorne (1952), and Snedecor (1934). Scheffe (1959) does not refer specifically to a split-plot design but discusses a general mixed model that would include the split-plot as a special case.

13.6 A Mixed Model for a Calibration Study

Imagine a continuous manufacturing process where the product is a liquid with characteristic η_t which varies with time. For example, η_t might be the percentage of some impurity in the liquid at a particular point in time. The variable, η_t, cannot be monitored directly, but a gauge has been developed which is expected to give gauge readings, x, that are related to η_t subject to various errors of measurement. In this section we consider the problem of finding the calibration line and then establishing the error of predicting η_t for a specific gauge reading from the calibrated line.

In order to establish the relationship between η and x, a given amount of liquid is drained from the system at a particular point in time and the gauge reading, x, is observed. The liquid is then removed to the laboratory, thoroughly mixed, and partitioned into r subsamples; the subsamples are analyzed and the observed magnitude of the characteristic, which we will denote as y_t, is recorded. We will suppose that our experiment involves drawing k samples of liquid at k different points in time, where the gauge reading, x_i, is recorded for each of the $i = 1, 2, \ldots, k$ samples. Each sample is then partitioned into r subsamples, which are analyzed and yield the response measurements, y_{ij}, $i = 1, 2, \ldots, k, j = 1, 2, \ldots, r$. Thus y_{ij} is the measured magnitude of the characteristic on the jth analysis within sample i and differs from η_i by an error which we will postulate in a linear model. The plotted data might appear as indicated in Fig. 13.3.

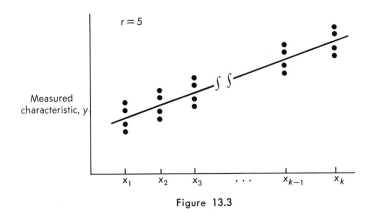

Figure 13.3

We will assume that an observed response, y_{ij} differs from η_i because of two sources of error. The first is due to the fact that the average amount of the characteristic (impurity) in the sampled liquid differs from the true amount in the process, η_i, by an amount, α_i. The second source of error is analytical or measurement error, which varies from one analysis to another and is represented by the quantity, ϵ_{ij}. Thus

$$y_{ij} = \eta_i + \alpha_i + \epsilon_{ij},$$

where $\eta_i = \beta_0 + \beta_1 x_i$. We will further assume that the sampling errors, α_i, are independent (for all practical purposes) with

$$E(\alpha_i) = 0, \qquad V(\alpha_i) = \sigma_\alpha^2,$$

and that the analytical errors are mutually independent with $E(\epsilon_{ij}) = 0$, $V(\epsilon_{ij}) = \sigma^2$, and $\text{Cov}\,(\alpha_i, \epsilon_{jk}) = 0$. Thus analytical errors are assumed to depend only on the method of analysis and on small errors due to the failure of the mixing to achieve homogeneity and are assumed to be independent of sampling error. We will not debate the merits of these assumptions but simply state that the following methodology is appropriate when the assumed model is a reasonable description of reality.

From the above assumptions,

$$E(y_{ij}) = \beta_0 + \beta_1 x_i,$$

so that all of the assumptions required for the unbiased estimation of β_0 and β_1 by the method of least squares are satisfied, except that the response measurements, y_{ij} and y_{il}, are correlated within sample i for $i = 1, 2, \ldots, k$. Thus

$$\text{Cov}\,(y_{ij}, y_{il}) = E[(\alpha_i + \epsilon_{ij})(\alpha_i + \epsilon_{il})] = \sigma_\alpha^2.$$

Actually this will cause no difficulty, as can be seen from the following argument. If the calibration line is determined using the means, $\bar{y}_i$, $i = 1, 2, \ldots, k$, for the k gauge readings,

$$\bar{y}_i = \beta_0 + \beta_1 x_i + \alpha_i + \bar{\epsilon}_i,$$

where

$$\bar{\epsilon}_i = \frac{\sum\limits_{j} \epsilon_{ij}}{r},$$

$E(\bar{y}_i) = \beta_0 + \beta_1 x$, and the random errors for $\bar{y}_i$ and $\bar{y}_j$, $i \neq j$, $(\alpha_i + \bar{\epsilon}_i)$ and $(\alpha_j + \bar{\epsilon}_j)$, are independent. Furthermore, if all $n = kr$ points are used to fit the line, it is well known that the least-squares estimators of β_0 and β_1 are

$$\hat{\beta}_1 = \frac{\sum\limits_{i} \sum\limits_{j} (y_{ij} - \bar{y})(x_i - \bar{x})}{\sum\limits_{i} \sum\limits_{j} (x_i - \bar{x})^2},$$

$$\hat{\beta}_0 = \bar{y} - \hat{\beta}_1 \bar{x}.$$

(Note: these estimators will not possess the same properties as in the case where all response measurements are independent.) These are exactly the same formulas as those obtained when $\bar{y}_i$, $i = 1, 2, \ldots, k$, is used as the response measurement. Hence the same least-squares line is obtained whether one employs all $n = kr$ measurements, y_{ij}, or just the k means, $\bar{y}_i$. This result will be useful in establishing the expected mean squares in the analysis of variance.

The analysis of variance for the calibration experiment will be obtained in exactly the same way as the analysis employed for a test of "lack of fit." Thus a sum of squares with $(r - 1)$ degrees of freedom can be computed within each sample and pooled to obtain an estimate of σ^2. This would give

$$\hat{\sigma}^2 = \frac{\text{SS(anal)}}{k(r - 1)} = \frac{\sum\limits_{i=1}^{k} \sum\limits_{j=1}^{r} (y_{ij} - \bar{y}_i)^2}{k(r - 1)}.$$

The remainder of the analysis of variance is shown in Table 13.9.

Table 13.9 Analysis of variance for the calibration experiment

Source	d.f.	SS	MS	E(MS)
Due to β_1	1			
Sample error	$k-2$	SSE	MSE $= \text{SSE}/(k-2)$	$\sigma_\alpha^2 + \dfrac{\sigma^2}{r}$
Analysis error	$k(r-1)$	SS (anal)	MSA $= \dfrac{\text{SS (anal)}}{k(r-1)}$	σ^2
Total	$kr-1$			

The quantity, SSE, appearing in Table 13.9 is the sum of squares of error using $\bar{y}_i$ as the response measurement. It would then follow that $\text{SSE}/(k-2)$ is an unbiased estimator of $V(\bar{y}_i)$, where

$$V(\bar{y}_i) = \sigma_\alpha^2 + \frac{\sigma^2}{r}.$$

Note that the sum of squares associated with β_1 is omitted because it is not needed in the following analysis. Secondly, even if this sum of squares were given, the sums of squares in Table 13.9 would not add to the total sum of squares because SSE is the sum of squares of deviations of the $\bar{y}_i$ about the fitted line (where each mean is based upon r observations). This sum of squares can be put on a single-observation basis by multiplying by r. Thus

$$\sum_{i=1}^{n} (y_i - \bar{y})^2 = \text{SS}(\beta_1) + r\text{SSE} + \text{SS(anal)},$$

and the appropriate sum of squares for "samples" is (rSSE).

If all random components in the linear model are assumed to be normally distributed, then

$$(k-2)\frac{r(\text{MSE})}{r\sigma_\alpha^2 + \sigma^2} = \chi_E^2,$$

$$k(r-1)\frac{\text{MSA}}{\sigma^2} = \chi_A^2$$

are independent chi-square variables with $(k-1)$ and $k(r-1)$ degrees of freedom, respectively. Then a test statistic to test the null hypothesis,

$$H_0: \sigma_\alpha^2 = 0,$$

would be

$$F = \frac{r(\text{MSE})}{\text{MSA}}.$$

An estimator of σ_α^2 is

$$\hat{\sigma}_\alpha^2 = \frac{r(\text{MSE}) - \text{MSA}}{r},$$

and an approximate confidence interval for σ_α^2 could be constructed using the method of Sec. 12.7.

The objective of a calibration study is to establish a calibration curve (in this case, a line) and to use this curve to predict $\eta = E(y)$ based on an observed value of x. This is the problem studied earlier in Sec. 7.8. Let

$$\hat{y} = \hat{\beta}_0 + \hat{\beta}_1 x$$

and let x_p denote the observed gauge reading. Then a $(1 - \alpha)$ confidence interval for $E(y)$ will be

$$\hat{y} \pm t_{\alpha/2}\sqrt{a'(X'X)^{-1}a(\text{MSE})}$$

where $\hat{y} = \hat{\beta}_0 + \hat{\beta}_1 x_p$,

$$X = \begin{bmatrix} 1 & x_1 \\ 1 & x_2 \\ 1 & x_3 \\ \cdot & \cdot \\ \cdot & \cdot \\ \cdot & \cdot \\ 1 & x_k \end{bmatrix} \quad \text{and} \quad a = \begin{bmatrix} 1 \\ x_p \end{bmatrix}$$

and $t_{\alpha/2}$ is based upon $(k - 2)$ degrees of freedom.

Example 13.4 Suppose that the response, y, measured in a calibration study is the per cent of a certain impurity in a 100-cc subsample of liquid. The independent variable, x, was measured at the time $k = 6$ samples were drawn from the process, and each sample was then mixed and partitioned into $r = 5$ 100-cc subsamples. The data are shown in Table 13.10.

Table 13.10 Per cent impurity in analyzed subsamples

x	1.3	2.1	3.5	3.9	5.2	5.9
y	4.6	6.0	7.4	7.2	8.5	8.8
	5.5	5.5	7.7	8.5	8.0	9.2
	4.3	5.8	6.9	8.0	8.9	10.0
	5.0	6.3	6.6	7.9	9.2	9.8
	4.2	6.6	7.5	7.5	8.6	9.6

(a) Find the calibration line.
(b) Do the data present sufficient evidence to indicate variation between samples?
(c) Use a 90 per cent confidence interval to estimate the true per cent impurity in the process when the gauge reads $x = 2.0$.

Solution: (a) Using the $\bar{y}_i$, $i = 1, 2, \ldots, 6$, as the response measurements and the method of least squares,

$$\bar{Y} = \begin{bmatrix} \bar{y}_1 \\ \bar{y}_2 \\ \bar{y}_3 \\ \bar{y}_4 \\ \bar{y}_5 \\ \bar{y}_6 \end{bmatrix}, \qquad X = \begin{bmatrix} 1 & 1.3 \\ 1 & 2.1 \\ 1 & 3.5 \\ 1 & 3.9 \\ 1 & 5.2 \\ 1 & 5.9 \end{bmatrix},$$

$$X'\bar{Y} = \begin{bmatrix} 43.92 \\ 175.448 \end{bmatrix}, \qquad (X'X)^{-1} = \begin{bmatrix} 1.02757 & -.23586 \\ -.23586 & .06462 \end{bmatrix},$$

and

$$\hat{\beta} = (X'X)^{-1}X'\bar{Y} = \begin{bmatrix} 3.7490 \\ .9784 \end{bmatrix},$$

Then $\hat{y} = 3.7490 + .9784x$.

(b) The "sum of squares for error" obtained when $\bar{y}_i$ is employed as the response is

$$\bar{Y}'\bar{Y} - \hat{\beta}'X'\bar{Y} = .2464.$$

The pooled sum of squares within each of the six groups is

$$\sum_{i=1}^{6} \sum_{j=1}^{5} (y_{ij} - \bar{y}_i)^2 = 5.436$$

and a table corresponding to Table 13.10 is shown below.

Source	d.f.	SSE	MS
Due to β_1	1		
Sample error	4	.2464	.0616
Analysis error	24	5.436	.2265
Total	29		

To test the hypothesis that $\sigma_\alpha^2 = 0$ we use the test statistic,

$$F = \frac{r\text{MSE}}{\text{MS(anal)}} = \frac{5(.0616)}{.2265} = 1.36,$$

where F is based upon $\nu_1 = 4$ and $\nu_2 = 24$ degrees of freedom. The computed F is less than the critical value, $F_{.05} = 2.78$, and hence there is no evidence that σ_α^2 is greater than zero. This, of course, does not mean that $\sigma_\alpha^2 = 0$. Additional experimentation with a consequent increase in information on σ_α^2 might reject H_0 and would permit a more accurate estimate of its value.

(c) When $x = 20$, $\hat{y} = 3.7490 + .9784(2.0) = 5.7058$ or, approximately, $\hat{y} = 5.71$. A 90 per cent confidence interval for $E(y)$ is

$$\hat{y} \pm t_{.05}\sqrt{a'(X'X)^{-1}a\text{MSE}}$$

where $a = \begin{bmatrix} 1 \\ 2.0 \end{bmatrix}$ and $a'(X'X)^{-1} = .343$; $\text{MSE} = .0616$ and $t_{.05} = 2.132$ (based on $\nu = 4$ degrees of freedom). Substituting, we obtain

$$5.71 \pm .31.$$

Note that the width of this interval would be reduced by increasing k, which means the inclusion of more samples in the experiment. This would certainly be done in a practical situation.

13.7 Summary

Experiments based upon a mixed model occur frequently and with a great deal of variety in all fields. These models are blends of the fixed-effect models of Chapters 1–11 and the completely random model of Chapter 12. Several of these models were presented in the preceding sections as examples of the mixed model, but they only scratch the surface of this interesting topic.

General principles can be established for the analysis of certain types of experiments based upon a mixed model. A good discussion of this topic may be found in Scheffe. At the same time, one might note that it is not difficult to encounter an experimental situation based upon a mixed model for which the explicit analysis is not readily available. Knowledge of the basic theory of statistics is rather essential in developing the appropriate method of analysis for these experiments.

Exercises

1. Refer to the study of uptake of digitalis by the heart muscle in Exercise 2, Chapter 8. Assume that the dogs were randomly selected from a population.
   (a) Write a mixed model for the experiment.
   (b) Find a 95 per cent confidence interval for $E(y)$ when digitalis level B is applied.
2. Refer to Exercise 5, Chapter 8.
   (a) Write a mixed model for the experiment assuming that the six locations were randomly selected from a population of locations.

(b) If variety 3 were recommended to farmers, what would you forecast as the expected yield? Answer this question by giving a 90 per cent confidence interval for $E(y)$.

(c) Give the variance of the difference in a pair of means.

3. Refer to Exercise 2.

    (a) Give the expected mean squares for this analysis of variance.

    (b) Find an approximate 90 per cent confidence interval for the variance component associated with locations.

4. Refer to Exercise 2. How many locations must be sampled in order to estimate the expected yield for a variety correct to within two bushels with probability equal to .95?

5. An experiment was conducted to compare the effect of five different drugs, A, B, C, D, and E, on the reduction of blood pressure of persons on a weight-reducing diet. Since the effect of the drugs will vary from person to person as well as day to day during the dieting period, a 5×5 Latin square design was employed. Five people randomly selected from an overweight population represent the columns of the Latin square. The test time, divided into five equal time periods, represents the rows, and an assignment of treatments, with drop in blood pressure measured at the end of each time period, might give the design shown below:

	Columns (People)				
	1	2	3	4	5
1	A	B	C	D	E
2	B	C	D	E	A
3	C	D	E	A	B
4	D	E	A	B	C
5	E	A	B	C	D

(Time Periods label for rows 1–5)

(a) Assume that people and time periods were randomly selected from respective populations. (This would imply that the test period was not long enough to produce a trend in the expected blood pressure). Write a mixed model for the experiment.

(b) Derive the expected mean squares for the experiment.

6. The data for Exercise 5 are shown below:

		People				
		1	2	3	4	5
Time Periods	1	A 53	B 49	C 39	D 52	E 56
	2	B 59	C 28	D 52	E 39	A 45
	3	C 33	D 49	E 32	A 24	B 57
	4	D 66	E 29	A 35	B 41	C 34
	5	E 40	A 26	B 49	C 23	D 59

(a) Do the data present evidence of a difference in the mean response for the drugs?

(b) For time periods?

(c) Find an approximate 90 per cent confidence interval for the variance component associated with people.

7. Refer to Exercises 5 and 6 and let $\bar{y}_i$ and $\bar{y}_j$ be two treatment means.
   (a) Find the expected value and variance of $(\bar{y}_i - \bar{y}_j)$.
   (b) Find the expected value and variance of $\bar{y}_i$.

8. Find a 90 per cent confidence interval for the difference in the expected response for treatments A and B, Exercise 6.

9. Find a 90 per cent confidence interval for the expected blood pressure of an overweight person treated with drug B. Use the data of Exercise 6.

10. Refer to the digitalis study, Exercise 2, Chapter 8. Suppose that six heart-muscle samples were obtained from each dog heart and that each treatment was replicated twice within a heart (block). The data are given on the next page.

Dogs

1	2	3	4
A 1342 1335	C 1698 1702	B 1296 1298	A 1150 1151
B 1608 1603	B 1387 1384	A 1029 1034	C 1579 1571
C 1881 1890	A 1140 1148	C 1549 1546	B 1319 1324

Use model 1, Section 13.4, and:

(a) Perform an analysis of variance for the data.

(b) Estimate the difference in mean response for digitalis levels A and B using a 90 per cent confidence interval.

(c) Estimate the mean response for digitalis level A using a 90 per cent confidence interval.

11. Derive the expected mean squares for the analysis of variance, Table 13.4, for the two-way classification with replication, Model 1.

12. Refer to the two-way classification model with replication in Section 13.4.

(a) What is the major difference in Models 1 and 2 for this experiment?

(b) How do the differences noted in (a) affect estimators and statistical tests associated with this experiment?

13. Answer parts (b) and (c) of Exercise 10 using Model 2 as a basis for the estimation procedures.

14. Refer to Model 2, Section 13.4, and show that the assumption

$$\sum_{j=1}^{t} (\beta\tau)_{ij} = 0$$

implies that

$$\text{Cov}\left[(\beta\tau)_{ij}, (\beta\tau)_{ik}\right] = -\frac{1}{p}\sigma_{bt}^2 \qquad \text{for } j \neq k.$$

15. Derive the expected mean squares, Table 13.5, using Model 2 for the two-way classification with replication.

16. Refer to the analysis of variance for a split-plot design, Table 13.7. What similarity does a test of "no difference in mean responses for treatments" assigned to whole plots have to a similar test for a randomized block design?

17. Refer to the split-plot model for the experiment, Table 13.7. Why are terms corresponding to $(\beta\delta)_{jk}$ and $(\alpha\beta\delta)_{ijk}$ not included in the model? If the sums of squares for the BD and ABD interactions were included in the model, how many degrees of freedom would be associated with each? Add the degrees of freedom for the BD and ABD interactions and note that this total is equal to the degrees of freedom associated with the subplot error.

18. Refer to Exercise 17. Why are the BD and ABD interaction sums of squares pooled to form the sums of squares for subplot error? How is this consistent with the analysis of a simple randomized block design?

19. Derive the expected mean squares, Table 13.7. You may use the derived mean squares for any designs discussed prior to Section 13.5 in your derivations.

20. Derive the variances of $\bar{A}_i$ and $(\bar{A}_i - \bar{A}_j)$ for the split-plot design, Table 13.7.

21. Derive the variances of $\bar{D}_i$ and $(\bar{D}_i - \bar{D}_j)$ for the split-plot design, Table 13.7.

22. The data for the split-plot design, Figure 13.2, are given below:

Farms (Blocks)

	1		2		3		4
	D_2 52		D_1 55		D_2 43		D_3 74
A_1	D_1 67	A_2	D_3 68	A_1	D_3 51	A_2	D_1 55
	D_3 58		D_2 54		D_1 64		D_2 62
	D_3 70		D_2 42		D_1 51		D_1 71
A_2	D_2 65	A_1	D_3 46	A_2	D_2 60	A_1	D_3 47
	D_1 62		D_1 56		D_3 68		D_2 46

(a) Do the data provide evidence to indicate a soil preparation by fertilizer interaction?

(b) What general recommendations would you make concerning the soil preparation and type of fertilizer that will achieve maximum yield?

23. Refer to Exercise 22. Find a 95 per cent confidence interval for the difference in mean responses for A_1D_1 and A_1D_3.

24. Refer to Exercise 22. Find an approximate 95 per cent confidence interval for the difference in mean response between A_1D_1 and A_2D_1.

25. Find an approximate 90 per cent confidence interval for the variance component due to samples, σ_α^2, in Example 13.4, Section 13.6.

26. A calibration curve was obtained by fixing the gauge reading and observing the response for an experiment similar to that described in Section 13.6. The calibration curve was assumed to be parabolic. Assumptions regarding the sampling and analysis errors are as given in Section 13.6. The data shown below indicate three analyses per sample.

x	1	2	3	4	5
	1.9	2.2	3.2	5.4	7.3
y	2.6	2.9	3.0	5.8	7.1
	2.8	2.4	3.5	6.2	7.0

(a) Write a mixed model for this experiment.
(b) Find the calibration curve.
(c) Estimate the variance components.
(d) Find $V(\hat{y})$.
(e) Find a 90 per cent confidence interval for $E(y)$ when $x = 2$. State assumptions necessary for method.

27. Refer to the sampling of radioactivity, Exercise 35, Chapter 12, and assume that n_1 locations are sampled and that it is desired to compare the mean radioactivity between locations. The mean radioactivity at location i is assumed to be μ_i, $i = 1, 2, \ldots, n_1$. Samples taken within location i are assumed to vary in their radioactivity from μ_i by the amount m_{ij}, where $E(m_{ij}) = 0$ and $V(m_{ij}) = \sigma_m^2$, $i = 1, 2, \ldots, n_1$ and the m_{ij} are assumed to be independent. Further assume that the radioactivity of the jth sample within location i is measured over n_3 one-minute time intervals and that the number of counts per minute follows a Poisson probability distribution with mean $(\mu_i + m_{ij})$. Thus the problem of Exercise 35, Chapter 12, has been expanded into a third stage.

(a) Write the mixed model for this experiment.
(b) Let $\bar{L}_i$ be the average number of counts per minute at location i and let $\bar{y}_{ij}$ be the average for the jth sample at location i. Show that the expected value of the mean squares, "between locations," is

$$\frac{n_3}{n_1} \sum_{i=1}^{n_1} V(\bar{y}_{ij}) + n_2 n_3 \sum_{i=1}^{n_1} \frac{(\mu_i - \bar{\mu})^2}{(n_1 - 1)},$$

where

$$\bar{\mu} = \frac{\sum_{i=1}^{n_1} \mu_i}{n_1}.$$

(c) Show that the pooled sum of squares of "samples within locations,"

$$n_3 \sum_i \sum_j (\bar{y}_{ij} - \bar{L}_i)^2,$$

has expected value $n_3(n_2 - 1) \sum_i V(\bar{y}_{ij})$. Find the expected mean square for "samples within location."

(d) Find the approximate probability distribution of the mean squares of (c) and (d). Use these results to form a test statistic to test an hypothesis of "no difference in mean radioactivity between locations."

References

Anderson, R. L., and T. A. Bancroft, *Statistical Theory in Research*. New York: McGraw-Hill Book Company, 1952.

Cochran, W. G., and G. Cox, *Experimental Designs*, 2nd ed. New York: John Wiley & Sons, Inc., 1957.

Graybill, F. A., *An Introduction to Linear Statistical Models*, Vol. I. New York: McGraw-Hill Book Company, 1961.

Kempthorne, O., *The Design and Analysis of Experiments*. New York: John Wiley & Sons, Inc., 1952.

Scheffe, H., "A Mixed Model for the Analysis of Variance," *Annals of Mathematical Statistics*, **27**, 23–36 (1956).

———, *The Analysis of Variance*. New York: John Wiley & Sons, Inc., 1959.

Tukey, J. W., *Interaction in a Row-By-Column Design*. Statistical Research Group, Princeton University. Memorandum Report 18, 1949.

Wilk, M. B., and O. Kempthorne, "Fixed, Mixed and Random Models in the Analysis of Variance," *Journal of the American Statistical Association*, **50**, 1144–1167 (1955).

14

A Brief Summary

The objective of many research projects is an experimental investigation
of the effect of a number of variables upon some response of interest. One of
the first requirements of this research is a thoughtful study of the phenomena
under investigation, an identification of important variables in the process,
and a specification of the manner in which experimental data will be collected. The design of the experiment is crucial because it determines the
quantity of information in the experiment relevant to the various unknown
parameters in the process. This text is concerned with the design and analysis
of experiments, with linear statistical models providing the key to an understanding of both of these topics.

After a review of some elementary concepts in Chapter 1, the introduction
to our study commenced in Chapter 2 where a substantial increase in information in a comparison of means was obtained by pairing (or blocking).
In contrast to a random assignment of treatments to the experimental
units, treatments A and B were assigned to pairs of units which were more
nearly homogeneous than all units as a whole. Then comparisons were made
between treatments within the relatively homogeneous conditions of the
pair of experimental units. An indication of the substantial gain in information over the completely randomized design was obtained by comparing

the widths of corresponding confidence intervals for the two methods of analysis, paired and unpaired. This particular example is important for several reasons. It indicated that a specified quantity of information could be obtained with a surprising reduction in cost (to approximately one-sixteenth the cost of the equivalent completely randomized design) by pairing (blocking) the treatments. It also pointed to the importance of correctly analyzing data. Some experimenters block their experiments as a matter of good experimental intuition—and then analyze the data as though they came from a completely randomized design. The increase in information by blocking is therefore lost by utilizing the wrong method of analysis. Thus this very simple experimental design illustrates the important role of the design of experiments in research.

In concluding Chapter 2, we drew an analogy between communication theory and the design of experiments in order to point to the two factors that control the quantity of information in an experimental design. Thus a voice signal is affected by background noise and the volume of the signal. The less the noise, or the louder the signal, the greater will be the amount of information received. In experimentation, nature is attempting to send a signal to us via experimental data to describe the true relationships existing in the phenomena under investigation. Unfortunately, the signal is partially obscured by experimental error, which is caused to a large extent by unknown and uncontrolled variables in the experiment. This is noise. The volume of nature's signal can be elevated by increasing the quantity of information collected in the experiment—that is, by increasing the sample size—and can also be increased by shifting information within an experiment by proper experimental design.

With the parallel between communications and experimentation in mind, we stated that experiments should be designed to reduce the noise or experimental error and to maximize the volume of nature's signal. Thus experimental designs were classified according to whether their primary contribution was noise reduction or the increase of volume.

Linear statistical models were introduced in Chapter 3. These models help the experimenter understand the relationship between the response and independent variables in the process as well as the manner in which experimental designs increase the quantity of information in an experiment. Furthermore, it is quite clear that they provide the basis for the analysis of all of the experimental data discussed in this text.

Linear statistical models, whether for blocked designs, factorial experiments, or data collected in an undesigned situation may be philosophically justified by a Taylor's series approximation to the true response function. Each model contains terms which are classified as main-effect or interaction terms corresponding to independent variables. These may be either quantitative or qualitative; the only difference between the two is the manner in which the terms are introduced in the model (qualitative variables using dummy variables). Qualitative variables imply multiple response surfaces which one would expect to be reasonably well-behaved and therefore satisfy the properties necessary for a converging Taylor's series approximation to the true response surface.

Some of the elementary block designs were presented in Chapter 4 along with their linear statistical models. Blocking in a single direction is an experimental filter that removes a source of noise to permit greater information to focus on the parameters of interest. Just as in electrical circuitry, filters may be constructed in several directions and in many different ways. Factorial experiments, presented in Chapter 5, are examples of volume-increasing designs which accomplish the increase by shifting information within the design to focus information on parameters of interest. Thus they are analogous to amplifier circuits in a communication network because they amplify information pertinent to the interaction and main-effect terms.

Linear statistical models fall in three categories: *fixed* with a single random component, *random* with a constant and multiple random components, and *mixed*—a combination of the fixed and random models. The fixed linear statistical model was implied for the experimental designs of Chapters 3 through 11. With knowledge of the theory of least squares (presented in Chapter 6) and the linear model appropriate for a design, this one single method can be used to fit the model to data derived from any of the designs discussed in Chapters 3 to 11 (and also to obtain the appropriate sums of squares for the random and mixed models of Chapters 12 and 13). Thus the theory of least squares provides a powerful method for fitting linear statistical models to data obtained from undesigned as well as designed experiments. The fitted model provides a predictor for the response as well as estimates of the model parameters, which may or may not possess practical interpretation.

Chapter 7 presents a theory of inference concerning the model parameters based upon normal distribution theory. Thus one is led to confidence intervals and tests of hypotheses utilizing Student's t. In addition, an estimator is given for any linear function of the model parameters, which would include $E(y)$ as a special case. A prediction interval for a particular value of y is also given.

Chapter 8 considers the problem of making inferences concerning sets of parameters, particularly the hypothesis that a set of parameters simultaneously equal zero. A test statistic based upon the drop in SSE from the reduced to the complete model leads to the F-statistic and an introduction to the analysis of variance. The analysis-of-variance formulas were given for common orthogonal designs but, more importantly, the fitting of the complete and reduced linear models provides the methodology by which all of these formulas may be derived. Thus an approach to the analysis of variance via linear models gives an intuitive justification for the analysis of variance as well as the basic procedure for calculating the adjusted sum of squares associated with any set of parameters for any design that employs a fixed-effect model.

The coefficient of determination as a measure of goodness of fit of a linear model was a natural outgrowth of a discussion of the analysis of variance. In addition, limitations to the practical conclusions derived from the analysis of variance were noted in Chapter 8, and Tukey's method of multiple comparison was given to show an alternative procedure for making inferences concerning the magnitude of treatment means. Procedures were also given for stabilizing the variance of the response measurements to satisfy the assumptions specified in Chapters 7 and 8.

Although it was not mentioned, this text departs from many others in the treatment of linear statistical models in that we always write linear models in which all of the parameters are estimable. (These are called models of *full rank*.) Thus all of the least-squares equations are linearly independent and $(X'X)$ possesses an inverse. Many models for experiments discussed in statistical literature contain one or more parameters that cannot be estimated and that result in $(X'X)$ matrices that do not possess an inverse. This procedure leads to an extensive amount of discussion and manipulation to circumvent the difficulty, and the result is the estimation of exactly the same set of estimable parameters (or a linear transformation of the parameters) as those contained in Chapters 3 through 13.

The comment above is related to the material of Chapter 9, which considers the effect of coding on the analysis of the experimental data. Particularly, we observe that one may estimate $(k + 1)$ linearly independent functions of $(k + 1)$ estimable parameters. Thus one may make a linear transformation on the model parameters (or, equivalently, the independent variables) to acquire a new set of parameters and a new X matrix. This principle was employed to obtain X matrices whose vectors formed a mutually orthogonal set, making $(X'X)$ diagonal and easy to invert. Thus Chapter 9 presents the general method for relating one system of coding to another and particularly deals with orthogonal systems to reduce the computational labor involved in the analysis of data.

All response functions of continuous independent variables may be regarded geometrically as response surfaces; consequently they have been discussed throughout the text. However, particular attention is given to techniques useful in locating a maximum or minimum response in Chapter 10 and also to various types of response-surface designs. Perhaps the most important topic in Chapter 10 concerns the characterization of designs in terms of constant variance (or information) contours, thus permitting their comparison.

The fractional factorial experiment, useful as a screening design, is presented in Chapter 11 along with a brief introduction to the incomplete block design. These designs possess a characteristic in common in that they may be employed to reduce block size when a substantial amount of variability occurs in the experimental material. Thus a complete factorial experiment may be blocked by assigning a fractional replicate to each block, thereby confounding defining contrasts with block contrasts. The incomplete block design permits the comparison of treatments with fewer than the total number appearing in each block.

Finally, an introduction to the design of experiments would not be complete without providing examples of the completely random and mixed models. The nested sampling design with an equal number of observations within samples at each level is considered in Chapter 12 along with its completely random model. Particular attention is given to the optimal selection of sample sizes for a specified quantity of information concerning $E(y)$. Several examples for mixed models were given in Chapter 12.

To conclude, we note that Chapters 2 through 8 cover the elementary designs and their analyses. Chapters 9 through 11 continue to deal with the fixed-effect model but concentrate on coding to reduce computational labor and on some new and very useful experimental designs appropriate for certain specific applications. Chapters 12 and 13 stand apart in that they provide an introduction to the random and mixed models.

Thus this text is aptly described by its title; it is an introduction to the very broad subject of the design and analysis of experiment. Many topics— for example, the incomplete block design—were only briefly introduced, and the reader is left to pursue them in texts or journals that deal with them more specifically. Finally, it should be quite apparent that many questions remain unanswered concerning the design of experiments. For example, response-surface designs should be selected which minimize both the variance and bias in estimating $E(y)$, perhaps using the mean-square error. Best strategies for selecting the experimental points in sequential experimentation also need to be investigated. We leave these problems, together with many others, to the reader.

Appendix I:
A Glossary of Symbols

α	Probability of a Type I error.
A'	The transpose of the matrix A.
A^{-1}	Denotes the inverse of A where A must be a square matrix.
β	Probability of a Type II error.
β_i	Refers to the ith parameter of a linear model.
$\hat{\beta}_i$	The estimator of β_i.
Cov (x, y)	The covariance of a pair of random variables, x and y.
$E[\quad]$	Symbol indicating the expected value of that which appears within the brackets.
$E(y)$	The expected value of a random variable, y.
F	The F-statistic (Chapter 8).
l	A linear function of random variables.
λ_i	A constant appearing in the ith orthogonal polynomial.
μ	Population mean.
MS	Denotes a mean square (Chapter 8).
p	The parameter of a binomial population.
$\hat{p}$	The estimator of p, the parameter of a binomial population.

ρ Population coefficient of correlation, $\rho = \dfrac{\text{Cov }(x, y)}{\sigma_x \sigma_y}$.

$q(r, v)$ The studentized range (Chapter 8).

r Sample coefficient of correlation.

R The number of runs in a sequence associated with the runs test.

s $\sqrt{s^2}$, usually called the "sample standard deviation."

s' Standard deviation of sample.

s^2 Unbiased estimator of σ^2 usually called the "sample variance."

σ^2 Population variance.

s'^2 Variance of sample measurements.

SS   Denotes a sum of squares associated with an analysis of variance (Chapter 8).

t Student's t.

u_i The ith orthogonal polynomial.

$V(y)$ The variance of a random variable, y.

X Upper case letters are used to denote a matrix.

$\mathbf{x}$ A column matrix, or vector.

χ^2 The chi-square random variable (Chapter 8).

$\bar{y}$ Sample mean.

$\hat{y}$ The estimator of $E(y)$; also the predictor of y.

z A normally distributed random variable with mean and variance equal to 0 and 1, respectively.

Appendix II:
Useful Statistical Tests and
Confidence Intervals

I. Inferences concerning the mean of a population.
1. Sample size, n, is large ($n > 30$).
   A. Test:
   Null hypothesis: $\mu = \mu_0$.
   Alternative hypothesis: $\mu \neq \mu_0$.
   Test statistic:

   $$z = \frac{\bar{y} - \mu_0}{\sigma/\sqrt{n}}.$$

   If σ is unknown and the sample is large use

   $$s = \sqrt{\frac{\sum\limits_{i=1}^{n} (y_i - \bar{y})^2}{n - 1}}$$

   as an estimate of σ.
   Rejection region:
   Reject if z is greater than 1.96 $\Big\}$ For $\alpha = .05$.
   Reject if z is less than -1.96

B. $(1 - \alpha)$ confidence interval:

$$\bar{y} \pm z_{\alpha/2}\sigma/\sqrt{n}\,.$$

2. Small samples, $n < 30$ and the observations are nearly normally distributed.

A. Test:

Null hypothesis: $\mu = \mu_0$.
Alternative hypothesis: $\mu \neq \mu_0$.
Test statistic:

$$t = \frac{\bar{y} - \mu_0}{s/\sqrt{n}}\,.$$

Rejection region: See t-tables.

B. $(1 - \alpha)$ confidence interval:

$$\bar{y} \pm t_{\alpha/2}s/\sqrt{n}\,.$$

II. Inferences concerning the difference between the means of two populations.

1. Large samples.

A. Assumptions:
   (a) Population I has mean equal to μ_1 and variance equal to σ_1^2.
   (b) Population II has mean equal to μ_2 and variance equal to σ_2^2.

B. Some results:
   (a) Let $\bar{y}_1$ be the mean of a random sample of n_1 observations from population I, and $\bar{y}_2$ be the mean of an independent and random sample of n_2 observations from population II. Consider the difference, $(\bar{y}_1 - \bar{y}_2)$.
   (b) It can be shown that the mean of $(\bar{y}_1 - \bar{y}_2)$ is $\mu_1 - \mu_2$ and its variance is $\dfrac{\sigma_1^2}{n_1} + \dfrac{\sigma_2^2}{n_2}$. Furthermore, for large samples, $\bar{y}_1 - \bar{y}_2$ will be approximately normally distributed.

C. Test:
   Null hypothesis: $\mu_1 - \mu_2 = D_0$. (Note: We are usually testing the hypothesis that $\mu_1 - \mu_2 = 0$, i.e., $\mu_1 = \mu_2$.) Alternative hypothesis: $\mu_1 - \mu_2 \neq D_0$.
   Test statistic:

$$z = \frac{(\bar{y}_1 - \bar{y}_2) - D_0}{\sqrt{\sigma_1^2/n_1 + \sigma_2^2/n_2}}\,.$$

If the null hypothesis is that $\mu_1 = \mu_2$, then $D_0 = 0$ and

$$z = \frac{\bar{y}_1 - \bar{y}_2}{\sqrt{\sigma_1^2/n_1 + \sigma_2^2/n_2}}.$$

If σ_1^2 and σ_2^2 are unknown and n is large, use s_1^2 and s_2^2 as estimates.
Rejection region:

$$\left.\begin{array}{c} \text{Reject if } z > \quad 1.96 \\ \text{or } z < -1.96 \end{array}\right\} \text{ For } \alpha = .05.$$

D. $(1 - \alpha)$ confidence interval:

$$(\bar{y}_1 - \bar{y}_2) \pm z_{\alpha/2}\sqrt{\frac{\sigma_1^2}{n_1} + \frac{\sigma_2^2}{n_2}}.$$

2. Small sample size.

   A. Assumptions: Both populations approximately normally distributed and

   $$\sigma_1^2 = \sigma_2^2.$$

   B. Test:

   Null hypothesis: $\mu_1 - \mu_2 = D_0$.
   Alternative hypothesis: $\mu_1 - \mu_2 \neq D_0$,

   $$t = \frac{\bar{y}_1 - \bar{y}_2 - D_0}{s\sqrt{\dfrac{1}{n_1} + \dfrac{1}{n_2}}},$$

   where s is a pooled estimate of σ.

   $$s = \sqrt{\frac{(n_1 - 1)s_1^2 + (n_2 - 1)s_2^2}{n_1 + n_2 - 2}}.$$

   Rejection region: See t-tables.

   C. $(1 - \alpha)$ confidence interval:

   $$(\bar{y}_1 - \bar{y}_2) \pm t_{\alpha/2}s\sqrt{\frac{1}{n_1} + \frac{1}{n_2}}.$$

III. Inferences concerning a probability, p.

1. Assumptions for a "binomial experiment":

   A. Experiment consists of n identical trials each resulting in one of two outcomes, say success or failure.

   B. The probability of success is equal to p and remains the same from trial to trial.

   C. The trials are independent of each other.

   D. The variable measured is $y =$ number of successes observed during the n trials.

2. Results:

A. The estimator of p is $\hat{p} = \dfrac{y}{n}$.

B. The average value of $\hat{p}$ is p.

C. The variance of $\hat{p}$ is equal to $\dfrac{pq}{n}$.

3. Test (n large):

Null hypothesis: $p = p_0$.

Alternative hypothesis: $p \neq p_0$ (two-tailed test).

Test statistic:

$$z = \frac{\dfrac{y}{n} - p_0}{\sqrt{\dfrac{p_0 q_0}{n}}}.$$

Rejection region: Reject if $|z| \geq 1.96$. Note: $\alpha = .05$.

4. $(1 - \alpha)$ confidence interval (n large):

$$\hat{p} \pm z_{\alpha/2}\sqrt{\frac{\hat{p}\hat{q}}{n}}.$$

IV. Inferences comparing two probabilities, p_1 and p_2.

1. Assumption: Independent random samples are drawn from each of two binomial populations.

	Pop. I	*Pop. II*
Probability of success $= p_1$		p_2
Sample size n_1		n_2
Observed success y_1		y_2

2. Results:

A. The estimated difference between p_1 and p_2 is

$$\hat{p}_1 - \hat{p}_2 = \frac{y_1}{n_1} - \frac{y_2}{n_2}.$$

B. The average value of $\hat{p}_1 - \hat{p}_2$ is $p_1 - p_2$.

C. The variance of $\hat{p}_1 - \hat{p}_2$ is

$$\frac{p_1 q_1}{n_1} + \frac{p_2 q_2}{n_2}.$$

3. Test (n_1 and n_2 large):

Null hypothesis: $p_1 = p_2 = p$.

Alternative hypothesis: $p_1 \neq p_2$ (two-tailed test).

Test statistic:

$$z = \frac{\dfrac{y_1}{n_1} - \dfrac{y_2}{n_2}}{\sqrt{\hat{p}\hat{q}\left(\dfrac{1}{n_1} + \dfrac{1}{n_2}\right)}} \quad \text{where} \quad \hat{p} = \frac{y_1 + y_2}{n_1 + n_2}.$$

Rejection region: Reject if $|z| \geq 1.96$. Note: $\alpha = .05$.

4. $(1 - \alpha)$ confidence interval (n_1 and n_2 large):

$$(\hat{p}_1 - \hat{p}_2) \pm z_{\alpha/z}\sqrt{\frac{\hat{p}_1\hat{q}_1}{n_1} + \frac{\hat{p}_2\hat{q}_2}{n_2}}.$$

V. Inferences concerning the variance of a population.

1. Assumption: Population measurements are normally distributed.

2. Test:

Null hypothesis: $\sigma^2 = \sigma_0^2$.
Alternative hypothesis: $\sigma^2 > \sigma_0^2$. (note that this implies a one-tailed test.)
Test statistic:

$$\chi^2 = \frac{(n - 1)s^2}{\sigma_0^2}.$$

Rejection region:
Reject if χ^2 is greater than or equal to χ_α^2 (see table of χ^2 values). For example, if $\alpha = .05$ and $n = 10$, reject if χ^2 is greater than 16.919.

3. $(1 - \alpha)$ confidence interval:

$$\frac{(n - 1)s^2}{\chi_U^2} < \sigma^2 < \frac{(n - 1)s^2}{\chi_L^2}.$$

VI. Tests for comparing the equality of two variances.

1. Assumptions:

A. Population I has a normal distribution with mean μ_1 and variance σ_1^2.

B. Population II has a normal distribution with mean μ_2 and variance σ_2^2.

C. Two independent random samples are drawn, n_1 measurements from population I, n_2 from population II.

2. Test:

Null hypothesis: $\sigma_1^2 = \sigma_2^2$.
Alternative hypothesis: $\sigma_1^2 > \sigma_2^2$.
   (one-tailed test)

Test statistic:

$$F = \frac{s_1^2}{s_2^2}.$$

Rejection region: Reject if F is greater than or equal to $F_\alpha(n_1 - 1, n_2 - 1)$.

3. $(1 - \alpha)$ confidence interval:

$$\frac{s_1^2}{s_2^2} \cdot \frac{1}{F_{v_1, v_2}} < \frac{\sigma_1^2}{\sigma_2^2} < \frac{s_1^2}{s_2^2} \cdot F_{v_2, v_1}$$

VII. Tests concerning the parameters, $\beta_0, \beta_1, \ldots, \beta_k$ that appear in the linear model.

  A. Assumptions and results:

   1. The random errors, $\epsilon_1, \epsilon_2, \ldots, \epsilon_n$ are independent and possess a normal probability distribution with $E(\epsilon) = 0$ and $V(\epsilon) = \sigma^2$ for given values of the independent variables, $x_1, x_2, \ldots, x_k$.

   2. Let c_{ij} be the element in the ith row and jth column of $(X'X)^{-1}$. Then it can be shown that

   $$V(\hat{\beta}_i) = c_{ii}\sigma^2$$
   $$\text{Cov}(\hat{\beta}_i, \hat{\beta}_j) = c_{ij}\sigma^2$$

   3. Let $l = a_0\hat{\beta}_0 + a_1\hat{\beta}_1 + \cdots + a_k\hat{\beta}_k = a'\hat{\beta}$ where $a' = [a_0, a_1, a_2, \ldots, a_k]$ and $\hat{\beta}' = [\hat{\beta}_0, \hat{\beta}_1, \hat{\beta}_2, \ldots, \hat{\beta}_k]$.

   4. An estimate of σ^2 based on $n - k - 1$ degrees of freedom can be computed as follows:

   $$s^2 = \frac{Y'Y - \hat{\beta}'X'Y}{n - k - 1}.$$

  B. Tests concerning a single parameter.

   1. *Null hypothesis:* $\beta_j = \beta_{j0}$.

   2. *Alternative hypothesis:* $\beta_j \neq \beta_{j0}$ (two-tailed test).

   3. *Test statistic:*

   $$t = \frac{\hat{\beta}_j - \beta_{j0}}{s\sqrt{c_{jj}}}.$$

   4. *Rejection region:* Reject the null hypothesis if $|t| \geq t_\alpha$ where t_α is based on $n - k - 1$ degrees of freedom.

  C. Tests concerning any linear function of parameters.

   1. Let $l = a'\hat{\beta}$ as defined in $A.3$. Then $E(l) = a'\beta$ where $\beta = [\beta_0, \beta_1, \beta_2, \ldots, \beta_k]$.

2. *Null hypothesis:* $E(l) = E_0(l)$

3. *Alternative hypothesis:* $E(l) \neq E_0(l)$

4. *Test statistic:*

$$t = \frac{l - E_0(l)}{s\sqrt{a'(X'X)^{-1}a}}.$$

5. *Rejection Region:* Reject the null hypothesis of $|t| \geq t_\alpha$ where t_α is based on $n - k - 1$ degrees of freedom.

Appendix III: Tables

Table 1: Normal Curve Areas

z	.00	.01	.02	.03	.04	.05	.06	.07	.08	.09
0.0	.0000	.0040	.0080	.0120	.0160	.0199	.0239	.0279	.0319	.0359
0.1	.0398	.0438	.0478	.0517	.0557	.0596	.0636	.0675	.0714	.0753
0.2	.0793	.0832	.0871	.0910	.0948	.0987	.1026	.1064	.1103	.1141
0.3	.1179	.1217	.1255	.1293	.1331	.1368	.1406	.1443	.1480	.1517
0.4	.1554	.1591	.1628	.1664	.1700	.1736	.1772	.1808	.1844	.1879
0.5	.1915	.1950	.1985	.2019	.2054	.2088	.2123	.2157	.2190	.2224
0.6	.2257	.2291	.2324	.2357	.2389	.2422	.2454	.2486	.2517	.2549
0.7	.2580	.2611	.2642	.2673	.2704	.2734	.2764	.2794	.2823	.2852
0.8	.2881	.2910	.2939	.2967	.2995	.3023	.3051	.3078	.3106	.3133
0.9	.3159	.3186	.3212	.3238	.3264	.3289	.3315	.3340	.3365	.3389
1.0	.3413	.3438	.3461	.3485	.3508	.3531	.3554	.3577	.3599	.3621
1.1	.3643	.3665	.3686	.3708	.3729	.3749	.3770	.3790	.3810	.3830
1.2	.3849	.3869	.3888	.3907	.3925	.3944	.3962	.3980	.3997	.4015
1.3	.4032	.4049	.4066	.4082	.4099	.4115	.4131	.4147	.4162	.4177
1.4	.4192	.4207	.4222	.4236	.4251	.4265	.4279	.4292	.4306	.4319
1.5	.4332	.4345	.4357	.4370	.4382	.4394	.4406	.4418	.4429	.4441
1.6	.4452	.4463	.4474	.4484	.4495	.4505	.4515	.4525	.4535	.4545
1.7	.4554	.4564	.4573	.4582	.4591	.4599	.4608	.4616	.4625	.4633
1.8	.4641	.4649	.4656	.4664	.4671	.4678	.4686	.4693	.4699	.4706
1.9	.4713	.4719	.4726	.4732	.4738	.4744	.4750	.4756	.4761	.4767
2.0	.4772	.4778	.4783	.4788	.4793	.4798	.4803	.4808	.4812	.4817
2.1	.4821	.4826	.4830	.4834	.4838	.4842	.4846	.4850	.4854	.4857
2.2	.4861	.4864	.4868	.4871	.4875	.4878	.4881	.4884	.4887	.4890
2.3	.4893	.4896	.4898	.4901	.4904	.4906	.4909	.4911	.4913	.4916
2.4	.4918	.4920	.4922	.4925	.4927	.4929	.4931	.4932	.4934	.4936
2.5	.4938	.4940	.4941	.4943	.4945	.4946	.4948	.4949	.4951	.4952
2.6	.4953	.4955	.4956	.4957	.4959	.4960	.4961	.4962	.4963	.4964
2.7	.4965	.4966	.4967	.4968	.4969	.4970	.4971	.4972	.4973	.4974
2.8	.4974	.4975	.4976	.4977	.4977	.4978	.4979	.4979	.4980	.4981
2.9	.4981	.4982	.4982	.4982	.4984	.4984	.4985	.4985	.4986	.4986
3.0	.4987	.4987	.4987	.4988	.4988	.4989	.4989	.4989	.4990	.4990

This table is abridged from Table I of *Statistical Tables and Formulas*, by A. Hald (New York: John Wiley & Sons, Inc., 1952). Reproduced by permission of A. Hald and the publishers, John Wiley & Sons, Inc.

Table 2: Critical Values of *t*

one - tail test

n	$t_{.100}$	$t_{.050}$	$t_{.025}$	$t_{.010}$	$t_{.005}$	d.f.
2	3.078	6.314	12.706	31.821	63.657	1
3	1.886	2.920	4.303	6.965	9.925	2
4	1.638	2.353	3.182	4.541	5.841	3
5	1.533	2.132	2.776	3.747	4.604	4
6	1.476	2.015	2.571	3.365	4.032	5
7	1.440	1.943	2.447	3.143	3.707	6
8	1.415	1.895	2.365	2.998	3.499	7
9	1.397	1.860	2.306	2.896	3.355	8
10	1.383	1.833	2.262	2.821	3.250	9
11	1.372	1.812	2.228	2.764	3.169	10
12	1.363	1.796	2.201	2.718	3.106	11
13	1.356	1.782	2.179	2.681	3.055	12
14	1.350	1.771	2.160	2.650	3.012	13
15	1.345	1.761	2.145	2.624	2.977	14
16	1.341	1.753	2.131	2.602	2.947	15
17	1.337	1.746	2.120	2.583	2.921	16
18	1.333	1.740	2.110	2.567	2.898	17
19	1.330	1.734	2.101	2.552	2.878	18
20	1.328	1.729	2.093	2.539	2.861	19
21	1.325	1.725	2.086	2.528	2.845	20
22	1.323	1.721	2.080	2.518	2.831	21
23	1.321	1.717	2.074	2.508	2.819	22
24	1.319	1.714	2.069	2.500	2.807	23
25	1.318	1.711	2.064	2.492	2.797	24
26	1.316	1.708	2.060	2.485	2.787	25
27	1.315	1.706	2.056	2.479	2.779	26
28	1.314	1.703	2.052	2.473	2.771	27
29	1.313	1.701	2.048	2.467	2.763	28
30	1.311	1.699	2.045	2.462	2.756	29
inf.	1.282	1.645	1.960	2.326	2.576	inf.

Table 3:   Percentage Points

ν_1 = numerator d. f.; ν_2 = denominator d. f.

ν_2 \ ν_1	1	2	3	4	5	6	7	8	9
1	39.86	49.50	53.59	55.83	57.24	58.20	58.91	59.44	59.86
2	8.53	9.00	9.16	9.24	9.29	9.33	9.35	9.37	9.38
3	5.54	5.46	5.39	5.34	5.31	5.28	5.27	5.25	5.24
4	4.54	4.32	4.19	4.11	4.05	4.01	3.98	3.95	3.94
5	4.06	3.78	3.62	3.52	3.45	3.40	3.37	3.34	3.32
6	3.78	3.46	3.29	3.18	3.11	3.05	3.01	2.98	2.96
7	3.59	3.26	3.07	2.96	2.88	2.83	2.78	2.75	2.72
8	3.46	3.11	2.92	2.81	2.73	2.67	2.62	2.59	2.56
9	3.36	3.01	2.81	2.69	2.61	2.55	2.51	2.47	2.44
10	3.39	2.92	2.73	2.61	2.52	2.46	2.41	2.38	2.35
11	3.23	2.86	2.66	2.54	2.45	2.39	2.34	2.30	2.27
12	3.18	2.81	2.61	2.48	2.39	2.33	2.28	2.24	2.21
13	3.14	2.76	2.56	2.43	2.35	2.28	2.23	2.20	2.16
14	3.10	2.73	2.52	2.39	2.31	2.24	2.19	2.15	2.12
15	3.07	2.70	2.49	2.36	2.27	2.21	2.16	2.12	2.09
16	3.05	2.67	2.46	2.33	2.24	2.18	2.13	2.09	2.06
17	3.03	2.64	2.44	2.31	2.22	2.15	2.10	2.06	2.03
18	3.01	2.62	2.42	2.29	2.20	2.13	2.08	2.04	2.00
19	2.99	2.61	2.40	2.27	2.18	2.11	2.06	2.02	1.98
20	2.97	2.59	2.38	2.25	2.16	2.09	2.04	2.00	1.96
21	2.96	2.57	2.36	2.23	2.14	2.08	2.02	1.98	1.95
22	2.95	2.56	2.35	2.22	2.13	2.06	2.01	1.97	1.93
23	2.94	2.55	2.34	2.21	2.11	2.05	1.99	1.95	1.92
24	2.93	2.54	2.33	2.19	2.10	2.04	1.98	1.94	1.91
25	2.92	2.53	2.32	2.18	2.09	2.02	1.97	1.93	1.89
26	2.91	2.52	2.31	2.17	2.08	2.01	1.96	1.92	1.88
27	2.90	2.51	2.30	2.17	2.07	2.00	1.95	1.91	1.87
28	2.89	2.50	2.29	2.16	2.06	2.00	1.94	1.90	1.87
29	2.89	2.50	2.28	2.15	2.06	1.99	1.93	1.89	1.86
30	2.88	2.49	2.28	2.14	2.05	1.98	1.93	1.88	1.85
40	2.84	2.44	2.23	2.09	2.00	1.93	1.87	1.83	1.79
60	2.79	2.39	2.18	2.04	1.95	1.87	1.82	1.77	1.74
120	2.75	2.35	2.13	1.99	1.90	1.82	1.77	1.72	1.68
∞	2.71	2.30	2.08	1.94	1.85	1.77	1.72	1.67	1.63

of the *F*-Distribution $(\alpha = .10)$

10	12	15	20	24	30	40	60	120	∞	ν_1 / ν_2
60.19	60.71	61.22	61.74	62.00	62.26	62.53	62.79	63.06	63.33	1
9.39	9.41	9.42	9.44	9.45	9.46	9.47	9.47	9.48	9.49	2
5.23	5.22	5.20	5.18	5.18	5.17	5.16	5.15	5.14	5.13	3
3.92	3.90	3.87	3.84	3.83	3.82	3.80	3.79	3.78	3.76	4
3.30	3.27	3.24	3.21	3.19	3.17	3.16	3.14	3.12	3.10	5
2.94	2.90	2.87	2.84	2.82	2.80	2.78	2.76	2.74	2.72	6
2.70	2.67	2.63	2.59	2.58	2.56	2.54	2.51	2.49	2.47	7
2.54	2.50	2.46	2.42	2.40	2.38	2.36	2.34	2.32	2.29	8
2.42	2.38	2.34	2.30	2.28	2.25	2.23	2.21	2.18	2.16	9
2.32	2.28	2.24	2.20	2.18	2.16	2.13	2.11	2.08	2.06	10
2.25	2.21	2.17	2.12	2.10	2.08	2.05	2.30	2.00	1.97	11
2.19	2.15	2.10	2.06	2.04	2.01	1.99	1.96	1.93	1.90	12
2.14	2.10	2.05	2.01	1.98	1.96	1.93	1.90	1.88	1.85	13
2.10	2.05	2.01	1.96	1.94	1.91	1.89	1.86	1.83	1.80	14
2.06	2.02	1.97	1.92	1.90	1.87	1.85	1.82	1.79	1.76	15
2.03	1.99	1.94	1.89	1.87	1.84	1.81	1.78	1.75	1.72	16
2.00	1.96	1.91	1.86	1.84	1.81	1.78	1.75	1.72	1.69	17
1.98	1.93	1.89	1.84	1.81	1.78	1.75	1.72	1.69	1.66	18
1.96	1.91	1.86	1.81	1.79	1.76	1.73	1.70	1.67	1.63	19
1.94	1.89	1.84	1.79	1.77	1.74	1.71	1.68	1.64	1.61	20
1.92	1.87	1.83	1.78	1.75	1.72	1.69	1.66	1.62	1.59	21
1.90	1.86	1.81	1.76	1.73	1.70	1.67	1.64	1.60	1.57	22
1.89	1.84	1.80	1.74	1.72	1.69	1.66	1.62	1.59	1.55	23
1.88	1.83	1.78	1.73	1.70	1.67	1.64	1.61	1.57	1.53	24
1.87	1.82	1.77	1.72	1.69	1.66	1.63	1.59	1.56	1.52	25
1.86	1.81	1.76	1.71	1.68	1.65	1.61	1.58	1.54	1.50	26
1.85	1.80	1.75	1.70	1.67	1.64	1.60	1.57	1.53	1.49	27
1.84	1.79	1.74	1.69	1.66	1.63	1.59	1.56	1.52	1.48	28
1.83	1.78	1.73	1.68	1.65	1.62	1.58	1.55	1.51	1.47	29
1.82	1.77	1.72	1.67	1.64	1.61	1.57	1.54	1.50	1.46	30
1.76	1.71	1.66	1.61	1.57	1.54	1.51	1.47	1.42	1.38	40
1.71	1.66	1.60	1.54	1.51	1.48	1.44	1.40	1.35	1.29	60
1.65	1.60	1.55	1.48	1.45	1.41	1.37	1.32	1.26	1.19	120
1.60	1.55	1.49	1.42	1.38	1.34	1.30	1.24	1.17	1.00	∞

Table 4:   Percentage Points

ν_1 = numerator d. f.; ν_2 = denominator d. f.

ν_2 \ ν_1	1	2	3	4	5	6	7	8	9
1	161.4	199.5	215.7	224.6	230.2	234.0	236.8	238.9	240.5
2	18.51	19.00	19.16	19.25	19.30	19.33	19.35	19.37	19.38
3	10.13	9.55	9.28	9.12	9.01	8.94	8.89	8.85	8.81
4	7.71	6.94	6.59	6.39	6.26	6.16	6.09	6.04	6.00
5	6.61	5.79	5.41	5.19	5.05	4.95	4.88	4.82	4.77
6	5.99	5.14	4.76	4.53	4.39	4.28	4.21	4.15	4.10
7	5.59	4.74	4.35	4.12	3.97	3.87	3.79	3.73	3.68
8	5.32	4.46	4.07	3.84	3.69	3.58	3.50	3.44	3.39
9	5.12	4.26	3.86	3.63	3.48	3.37	3.29	3.23	3.18
10	4.96	4.10	3.71	3.48	3.33	3.22	3.14	3.07	3.02
11	4.84	3.98	3.59	3.36	3.20	3.09	3.01	2.95	2.90
12	4.75	3.89	3.49	3.26	3.11	3.00	2.91	2.85	2.80
13	4.67	3.81	3.41	3.18	3.03	2.92	2.83	2.77	2.71
14	4.60	3.74	3.34	3.11	2.96	2.85	2.76	2.70	2.65
15	4.54	3.68	3.29	3.06	2.90	2.79	2.71	2.64	2.59
16	4.49	3.63	3.24	3.01	2.85	2.74	2.66	2.59	2.54
17	4.45	3.59	3.20	2.96	2.81	2.70	2.61	2.55	2.49
18	4.41	3.55	3.16	2.93	2.77	2.66	2.58	2.51	2.46
19	4.38	3.52	3.13	2.90	2.74	2.63	2.54	2.48	2.42
20	4.35	3.45	3.10	2.87	2.71	2.60	2.51	2.45	2.39
21	4.32	3.47	3.07	2.84	2.68	2.57	2.49	2.42	2.37
22	4.30	3.44	3.05	2.82	2.66	2.55	2.46	2.40	2.34
23	4.28	2.43	3.03	2.80	2.64	2.53	2.44	2.37	2.32
24	4.26	3.40	3.01	2.78	2.62	2.51	2.42	2.36	2.30
25	4.24	3.39	2.99	2.76	2.60	2.49	2.40	2.34	2.28
26	4.23	3.37	2.98	2.74	2.59	2.47	2.39	2.32	2.27
27	4.21	3.35	2.96	2.73	2.57	2.46	2.37	2.31	2.25
28	4.20	3.34	2.95	2.71	2.56	2.45	2.36	2.29	2.24
29	4.18	3.33	2.93	2.70	2.55	2.43	2.35	2.28	2.22
30	4.17	3.32	2.92	2.69	2.53	2.42	2.33	2.27	2.21
40	4.08	3.23	2.84	2.61	2.45	2.34	2.25	2.18	2.12
60	4.00	3.15	2.76	2.53	2.37	2.25	2.17	2.10	2.04
120	3.92	3.07	2.68	2.45	2.29	2.17	2.09	2.02	1.96
∞	3.84	3.00	2.60	2.37	2.21	2.10	2.01	1.94	1.88

of the F-Distribution $(\alpha = .05)$

10	12	15	20	24	30	40	60	120	∞	ν_1 \ ν_2
241.9	243.9	245.9	248.0	249.1	250.1	251.1	252.2	253.3	254.3	1
19.40	19.41	19.43	19.45	19.45	19.46	19.47	19.48	19.49	19.50	2
8.79	8.74	8.70	8.66	8.64	8.62	8.59	8.57	8.55	8.53	3
5.96	5.91	5.86	5.80	5.77	5.75	5.72	5.69	5.66	5.63	4
4.74	4.68	4.62	4.56	4.53	4.50	4.46	4.43	4.40	4.36	5
4.06	4.00	3.94	3.87	3.84	3.81	3.77	3.74	3.70	3.67	6
3.64	3.57	3.51	3.44	3.41	3.38	3.34	3.30	3.27	3.23	7
3.35	3.28	3.22	3.15	3.12	3.08	3.04	3.01	2.97	2.93	8
3.14	3.07	3.01	2.94	2.90	2.86	2.83	2.79	2.75	2.71	9
2.98	2.91	2.85	2.77	2.74	2.70	2.66	2.62	2.58	2.54	10
2.85	2.79	2.72	2.65	2.61	2.57	2.53	2.49	2.45	2.40	11
2.75	2.69	2.62	2.54	2.51	2.47	2.43	2.38	2.34	2.30	12
2.67	2.60	2.53	2.46	2.42	2.38	2.34	2.30	2.25	2.21	13
2.60	2.53	2.46	2.39	2.35	2.31	2.27	2.22	2.18	2.13	14
2.54	2.48	2.40	2.33	2.29	2.25	2.20	2.16	2.11	2.07	15
2.49	2.42	2.35	2.28	2.24	2.19	2.15	2.11	2.06	2.01	16
2.45	2.38	2.31	2.23	2.19	2.15	2.10	2.06	2.01	1.96	17
2.41	2.34	2.27	2.19	2.15	2.11	2.06	2.02	1.97	1.92	18
2.38	2.31	2.23	2.16	2.11	2.07	2.03	1.98	1.93	1.88	19
2.35	2.28	2.20	2.12	2.08	2.04	1.99	1.95	1.90	1.84	20
2.32	2.25	2.18	2.10	2.05	2.01	1.96	1.92	1.87	1.81	21
2.30	2.23	2.15	2.07	2.03	1.98	1.94	1.89	1.84	1.78	22
2.27	2.20	2.13	2.05	2.01	1.96	1.91	1.86	1.81	1.76	23
2.25	2.18	2.11	2.03	1.98	1.94	1.89	1.84	1.79	1.73	24
2.24	2.16	2.09	2.01	1.96	1.92	1.87	1.82	1.77	1.71	25
2.22	2.15	2.07	1.99	1.95	1.90	1.85	1.80	1.75	1.69	26
2.20	2.13	2.06	1.97	1.93	1.88	1.84	1.79	1.73	1.67	27
2.19	2.12	2.04	1.96	1.91	1.87	1.82	1.77	1.71	1.65	28
2.18	2.10	2.03	1.94	1.90	1.85	1.81	1.75	1.70	1.64	29
2.16	2.09	2.01	1.93	1.89	1.84	1.79	1.74	1.68	1.62	30
2.08	2.00	1.92	1.84	1.79	1.74	1.69	1.64	1.58	1.51	40
1.99	1.92	1.84	1.75	1.70	1.65	1.59	1.53	1.47	1.39	60
1.91	1.83	1.75	1.66	1.61	1.55	1.50	1.43	1.35	1.25	120
1.83	1.75	1.67	1.57	1.52	1.46	1.39	1.32	1.22	1.00	∞

Table 5: Percentage Points

$\nu_1 =$ numerator d. f.; $\nu_2 =$ denominator d. f.

ν_2 \ ν_1	1	2	3	4	5	6	7	8	9
1	4052	4999.5	5403	5625	5764	5859	5928	5982	6022
2	98.50	99.00	99.17	99.25	99.30	99.33	99.37	99.39	99.39
3	34.12	30.82	29.46	28.71	28.24	27.91	27.67	27.49	27.35
4	21.20	18.00	16.69	15.98	15.52	15.21	14.98	14.80	14.66
5	16.26	13.27	12.06	11.39	10.97	10.67	10.46	10.29	10.16
6	13.75	10.92	9.78	9.15	8.75	8.47	8.26	8.10	7.98
7	12.25	9.55	8.45	7.85	7.46	7.19	6.99	6.84	6.72
8	11.26	8.65	7.59	7.01	6.63	6.37	6.18	6.03	5.91
9	10.56	8.02	6.99	6.42	6.06	5.80	5.61	5.47	5.35
10	10.04	7.56	6.55	5.99	5.64	5.39	5.20	5.06	4.94
11	9.65	7.21	6.22	5.67	5.32	5.07	4.89	4.74	4.63
12	9.33	6.93	5.95	5.41	5.06	4.82	4.64	4.50	4.39
13	9.07	6.70	5.74	5.21	4.86	4.62	4.44	4.30	4.19
14	8.86	6.51	5.56	5.04	4.69	4.46	4.28	4.14	4.03
15	8.68	6.36	5.42	4.89	4.56	4.32	4.14	4.00	3.89
16	8.53	6.23	5.29	4.77	4.44	4.20	4.03	3.89	3.78
17	8.40	6.11	5.18	4.67	4.34	4.10	3.93	3.79	3.68
18	8.29	6.01	5.09	4.58	4.25	4.01	3.84	3.71	3.60
19	8.18	5.93	5.01	4.50	4.17	3.94	3.77	3.63	3.52
20	8.10	5.85	4.94	4.43	4.10	3.87	3.70	3.56	3.46
21	8.02	5.78	4.87	4.37	4.04	3.81	3.64	3.51	3.40
22	7.95	5.72	4.82	4.31	3.99	3.76	3.59	3.45	3.35
23	7.88	5.66	4.76	4.26	3.94	3.71	3.54	3.41	3.30
24	7.82	5.61	4.72	4.22	3.90	3.67	3.50	3.36	3.26
25	7.77	5.57	4.68	4.18	3.85	3.63	3.46	3.32	3.22
26	7.72	5.53	4.64	4.14	3.82	3.59	3.42	3.29	3.18
27	7.68	5.49	4.60	4.11	3.78	3.56	3.39	3.26	3.15
28	7.64	5.45	4.57	4.07	3.75	3.53	3.36	3.23	3.12
29	7.60	5.42	4.54	4.04	3.73	3.50	3.33	3.20	3.09
30	7.56	5.39	4.51	4.02	3.70	3.47	3.30	3.17	3.07
40	7.31	5.18	4.31	3.83	3.51	3.29	3.12	2.99	2.89
60	7.08	4.98	4.13	3.65	3.34	3.12	2.95	2.82	2.72
120	6.85	4.79	3.95	3.48	3.17	2.96	2.79	2.66	2.56
∞	6.63	4.61	3.78	3.32	3.02	2.80	2.64	2.51	2.41

of the F-Distribution $(\alpha = .01)$

10	12	15	20	24	30	40	60	120	∞	ν_1 / ν_2
6056	6106	6157	6209	6235	6261	6287	6313	6339	6366	1
99.40	99.42	99.43	99.45	99.46	99.47	99.47	99.48	99.49	99.50	2
27.23	27.05	26.87	26.69	26.60	26.50	26.41	26.32	26.22	26.13	3
14.55	14.37	14.20	14.02	13.93	13.84	13.75	13.65	13.56	13.46	4
10.05	9.89	9.72	9.55	9.47	9.38	9.29	9.20	9.11	9.02	5
7.87	7.72	7.56	7.40	7.31	7.23	7.14	7.06	6.97	6.88	6
6.62	6.47	6.31	6.16	6.07	5.99	5.91	5.82	5.74	5.65	7
5.81	5.67	5.52	5.36	5.28	5.20	5.12	5.03	4.95	4.86	8
5.26	5.11	4.96	4.81	4.73	4.65	4.57	4.48	4.40	4.31	9
4.85	4.71	4.56	4.41	4.33	4.25	4.17	4.08	4.00	3.91	10
4.54	4.40	4.25	4.10	4.02	3.94	3.86	3.78	3.69	3.60	11
4.30	4.16	4.01	3.86	3.78	3.70	3.62	3.54	3.45	3.36	12
4.10	3.96	3.82	3.66	3.59	3.51	3.43	3.34	3.25	3.17	13
3.94	3.80	3.66	3.51	3.43	3.35	3.27	3.18	3.09	3.00	14
3.80	3.67	3.52	3.37	3.29	3.21	3.13	3.05	2.96	2.87	15
3.69	3.55	3.41	3.26	3.18	3.10	3.02	2.93	2.84	2.75	16
3.59	3.46	3.31	3.16	3.08	3.00	2.92	2.83	2.75	2.65	17
3.51	3.37	3.23	3.08	3.00	2.92	2.84	2.75	2.66	2.57	18
3.43	3.30	3.15	3.00	2.92	2.84	2.76	2.67	2.58	2.49	19
3.37	3.23	3.09	2.94	2.86	2.78	2.69	2.61	2.52	2.42	20
3.31	3.17	3.03	2.88	2.80	2.72	2.64	2.55	2.46	2.36	21
3.26	3.12	2.98	2.83	2.75	2.67	2.58	2.50	2.40	2.31	22
3.21	3.07	2.93	2.78	2.70	2.62	2.54	2.45	2.35	2.26	23
3.17	3.03	2.89	2.74	2.66	2.58	2.49	2.40	2.31	2.21	24
3.13	2.99	2.85	2.70	2.62	2.54	2.45	2.36	2.27	2.17	25
3.09	2.96	2.81	2.66	2.58	2.50	2.42	2.33	2.23	2.13	26
3.06	2.93	2.78	2.63	2.55	2.47	2.38	2.29	2.20	2.10	27
3.03	2.90	2.75	2.60	2.52	2.44	2.35	2.26	2.17	2.06	28
3.00	2.87	2.73	2.57	2.49	2.41	2.33	2.23	2.14	2.03	29
2.98	2.84	2.70	2.55	2.47	2.39	2.30	2.21	2.11	2.01	30
2.80	2.66	2.52	2.37	2.29	2.20	2.11	2.02	1.92	1.80	40
2.63	2.50	2.35	2.20	2.12	2.03	1.94	1.84	1.73	1.60	60
2.47	2.34	2.19	2.03	1.95	1.86	1.76	1.66	1.53	1.38	120
2.32	2.18	2.04	1.88	1.79	1.70	1.59	1.47	1.32	1.00	∞

Table 6: Percentage Points of

Upper 5 %

ν \ p	2	3	4	5	6	7	8	9	10	11
1	17.97	26.98	32.82	37.08	40.41	43.12	45.40	47.36	49.07	50.59
2	6.08	8.33	9.80	10.88	11.74	12.44	13.03	13.54	13.99	14.39
3	4.50	5.91	6.82	7.50	8.04	8.48	8.85	9.18	9.46	9.72
4	3.93	5.04	5.76	6.29	6.71	7.05	7.35	7.60	7.83	8.03
5	3.64	4.60	5.22	5.67	6.03	6.33	6.58	6.80	6.99	7.17
6	3.46	4.34	4.90	5.30	5.63	5.90	6.12	6.32	6.49	6.65
7	3.34	4.16	4.68	5.06	5.36	5.61	5.82	6.00	6.16	6.30
8	3.26	4.04	4.53	4.89	5.17	5.40	5.60	5.77	5.92	6.05
9	3.20	3.95	4.41	4.76	5.02	5.24	5.43	5.59	5.74	5.87
10	3.15	3.88	4.33	4.65	4.91	5.12	5.30	5.46	5.60	5.72
11	3.11	3.82	4.26	4.57	4.82	5.03	5.20	5.35	5.49	5.61
12	3.08	3.77	4.20	4.51	4.75	4.95	5.12	5.27	5.39	5.51
13	3.06	3.73	4.15	4.45	4.69	4.88	5.05	5.19	5.32	5.43
14	3.03	3.70	4.11	4.41	4.64	4.83	4.99	5.13	5.25	5.36
15	3.01	3.67	4.08	4.37	4.60	4.78	4.94	5.08	5.20	5.31
16	3.00	3.65	4.05	4.33	4.56	4.74	4.90	5.03	5.15	5.26
17	2.98	3.63	4.02	4.30	4.52	4.70	4.86	4.99	5.11	5.21
18	2.97	3.61	4.00	4.28	4.49	4.67	4.82	4.96	5.07	5.17
19	2.96	3.59	3.98	4.25	4.47	4.65	4.79	4.92	5.04	5.14
20	2.95	3.58	3.96	4.23	4.45	4.62	4.77	4.90	5.01	5.11
24	2.92	3.53	3.90	4.17	4.37	4.54	4.68	4.81	4.92	5.01
30	2.89	3.49	3.85	4.10	4.30	4.46	4.60	4.72	4.82	4.92
40	2.86	3.44	3.79	4.04	4.23	4.39	4.52	4.63	4.73	4.82
60	2.83	3.40	3.74	3.98	4.16	4.31	4.44	4.55	4.65	4.73
120	2.80	3.36	3.68	3.92	4.10	4.24	4.36	4.47	4.56	4.64
∞	2.77	3.31	3.63	3.86	4.03	4.17	4.29	4.39	4.47	4.55

the Studentized Range, q(p, ν)

Points

12	13	14	15	16	17	18	19	20	p / ν
51.96	53.20	54.33	55.36	56.32	57.22	58.04	58.83	59.56	1
14.75	15.08	15.38	15.65	15.91	16.14	16.37	16.57	16.77	2
9.95	10.15	10.35	10.52	10.69	10.84	10.98	11.11	11.24	3
8.21	8.37	8.52	8.66	8.79	8.91	9.03	9.13	9.23	4
7.32	7.47	7.60	7.72	7.83	7.93	8.03	8.12	8.21	5
6.79	6.92	7.03	7.14	7.24	7.34	7.43	7.51	7.59	6
6.43	6.55	6.66	6.76	6.85	6.94	7.02	7.10	7.17	7
6.18	6.29	6.39	6.48	6.57	6.65	6.73	6.80	6.87	8
5.98	6.09	6.19	6.28	6.36	6.44	6.51	6.58	6.64	9
5.83	5.93	6.03	6.11	6.19	6.27	6.34	6.40	6.47	10
5.71	5.81	5.90	5.98	6.06	6.13	6.20	6.27	6.33	11
5.61	5.71	5.80	5.88	5.95	6.02	6.09	6.15	6.21	12
5.53	5.63	5.71	5.79	5.86	5.93	5.99	6.05	6.11	13
5.46	5.55	5.64	5.71	5.79	5.85	5.91	5.97	6.03	14
5.40	5.49	5.57	5.65	5.72	5.78	5.85	5.90	5.96	15
5.35	5.44	5.52	5.59	5.66	5.73	5.79	5.84	5.90	16
5.31	5.39	5.47	5.54	5.61	5.67	5.73	5.79	5.84	17
5.27	5.35	5.43	5.50	5.57	5.63	5.69	5.74	5.79	18
5.23	5.31	5.39	5.46	5.53	5.59	5.65	5.70	5.75	19
5.20	5.28	5.36	5.43	5.49	5.55	5.61	5.66	5.71	20
5.10	5.18	5.25	5.32	5.38	5.44	5.49	5.55	5.59	24
5.00	5.08	5.15	5.21	5.27	5.33	5.38	5.43	5.47	30
4.90	4.98	5.04	5.11	5.16	5.22	5.27	5.31	5.36	40
4.81	4.88	4.94	5.00	5.06	5.11	5.15	5.20	5.24	60
4.71	4.78	4.84	4.90	4.95	5.00	5.04	5.09	5.13	120
4.62	4.68	4.74	4.80	4.85	4.89	4.93	4.97	5.01	∞

Upper 1%

p ν	2	3	4	5	6	7	8	9	10	11
1	90.03	135.0	164.3	185.6	202.2	215.8	227.2	237.0	245.6	253.2
2	14.04	19.02	22.29	24.72	26.63	28.20	29.53	30.68	31.69	32.59
3	8.26	10.62	12.17	13.33	14.24	15.00	15.64	16.20	16.69	17.13
4	6.51	8.12	9.17	9.96	10.58	11.10	11.55	11.93	12.27	12.57
5	5.70	6.98	7.80	8.42	8.91	9.32	9.67	9.97	10.24	10.48
6	5.24	6.33	7.03	7.56	7.97	8.32	8.61	8.87	9.10	9.30
7	4.95	5.92	6.54	7.01	7.37	7.68	7.94	8.17	8.37	8.55
8	4.75	5.64	6.20	6.62	6.96	7.24	7.47	7.68	7.86	8.03
9	4.60	5.43	5.96	6.35	6.66	6.91	7.13	7.33	7.49	7.65
10	4.48	5.27	5.77	6.14	6.43	6.67	6.87	7.05	7.21	7.36
11	4.39	5.15	5.62	5.97	6.25	6.48	6.67	6.84	6.99	7.13
12	4.32	5.05	5.50	5.84	6.10	6.32	6.51	6.67	6.81	6.94
13	4.26	4.96	5.40	5.73	5.98	6.19	6.37	6.53	6.67	6.79
14	4.21	4.89	5.32	5.63	5.88	6.08	6.26	6.41	6.54	6.66
15	4.17	4.84	5.25	5.56	5.80	5.99	6.16	6.31	6.44	6.55
16	4.13	4.79	5.19	5.49	5.72	5.92	6.08	6.22	6.35	6.46
17	4.10	4.74	5.14	5.43	5.66	5.85	6.01	6.15	6.27	6.38
18	4.07	4.70	5.09	5.38	5.60	5.79	5.94	6.08	6.20	6.31
19	4.05	4.67	5.05	5.33	5.55	5.73	5.89	6.02	6.14	6.25
20	4.02	4.64	5.02	5.29	5.51	5.69	5.84	5.97	6.09	6.19
24	3.96	4.55	4.91	5.17	5.37	5.54	5.69	5.81	5.92	6.02
30	3.89	4.45	4.80	5.05	5.24	5.40	5.54	5.65	5.76	5.85
40	3.82	4.37	4.70	4.93	5.11	5.26	5.39	5.50	5.60	5.69
60	3.76	4.28	4.59	4.82	4.99	5.13	5.25	5.36	5.45	5.53
120	3.70	4.20	4.50	4.71	4.87	5.01	5.12	5.21	5.30	5.37
∞	3.64	4.12	4.40	4.60	4.76	4.88	4.99	5.08	5.16	5.23

Points

12	13	14	15	16	17	18	19	20	p / ν
260.0	266.2	271.8	277.0	281.8	286.3	290.0	294.3	298.0	1
33.40	34.13	34.81	35.43	36.00	36.53	37.03	37.50	37.95	2
17.53	17.89	18.22	18.52	18.81	19.07	19.32	19.55	19.77	3
12.84	13.09	13.32	13.53	13.73	13.91	14.08	14.24	14.40	4
10.70	10.89	11.08	11.24	11.40	11.55	11.68	11.81	11.93	5
9.48	9.65	9.81	9.95	10.08	10.21	10.32	10.43	10.54	6
8.71	8.86	9.00	9.12	9.24	9.35	9.46	9.55	9.65	7
8.18	8.31	8.44	8.55	8.66	8.76	8.85	8.94	9.03	8
7.78	7.91	8.03	8.13	8.23	8.33	8.41	8.49	8.57	9
7.49	7.60	7.71	7.81	7.91	7.99	8.08	8.15	8.23	10
7.25	7.36	7.46	7.56	7.65	7.73	7.81	7.88	7.95	11
7.06	7.17	7.26	7.36	7.44	7.52	7.59	7.66	7.73	12
6.90	7.01	7.10	7.19	7.27	7.35	7.42	7.48	7.55	13
6.77	6.87	6.96	7.05	7.13	7.20	7.27	7.33	7.39	14
6.66	6.76	6.84	6.93	7.00	7.07	7.14	7.20	7.26	15
6.56	6.66	6.74	6.82	6.90	6.97	7.03	7.09	7.15	16
6.48	6.57	6.66	6.73	6.81	6.87	6.94	7.00	7.05	17
6.41	6.50	6.58	6.65	6.72	6.79	6.85	6.91	6.97	18
6.34	6.43	6.51	6.58	6.65	6.72	6.78	6.84	6.89	19
6.28	6.37	6.45	6.52	6.59	6.65	6.71	6.77	6.82	20
6.11	6.19	6.26	6.33	6.39	6.45	6.51	6.56	6.61	24
5.93	6.01	6.08	6.14	6.20	6.26	6.31	6.36	6.41	30
5.76	5.83	5.90	5.96	6.02	6.07	6.12	6.16	6.21	40
5.60	5.67	5.73	5.78	5.84	5.89	5.93	5.97	6.01	60
5.44	5.50	5.56	5.61	5.66	5.71	5.75	5.79	5.83	120
5.29	5.35	5.40	5.45	5.49	5.54	5.57	5.61	5.65	∞

Table 7: Orthogonal Polynomials

See Section 9.9: x assumes values $1, 2, 3, \ldots, t$.
Tabulated values of $u_i, i = 1, 2, 3, 4$ were computed by substitution into the four orthogonal polynomials,

$$u_1 = \lambda_1(x - \bar{x})$$

$$u_2 = \lambda_2\left[(x - \bar{x})^2 - \frac{t^2 - 1}{12}\right]$$

$$u_3 = \lambda_3\left[(x - \bar{x})^3 - (x - \bar{x})\frac{3t^2 - 7}{20}\right]$$

$$u_4 = \lambda_4\left[(x - \bar{x})^4 - (x - \bar{x})^2\left(\frac{3t^2 - 13}{14}\right) + \frac{3(t^2 - 1)(t^2 - 9)}{560}\right]$$

Orthogonal polynomials for $t > 10$ and u_i; $i = 1, 2, \ldots, 6$, are given in the Biometrika Tables for Statisticians, Volume I, Third Edition.

$t = 3$

x	u_1	u_2
1	-1	1
2	0	-2
3	1	1
λ	1	3

$t = 4$

x	u_1	u_2	u_3
1	-3	1	-1
2	-1	-1	3
3	1	-1	-3
4	3	1	1
λ	2	1	$\frac{10}{3}$

$t = 5$

x	u_1	u_2	u_3	u_4
1	-2	2	-1	1
2	-1	-1	2	-4
3	0	-2	0	6
4	1	-1	-2	-4
5	2	2	1	1
λ	1	1	$\frac{5}{6}$	$\frac{35}{12}$

$t = 6$

x	u_1	u_2	u_3	u_4
1	-5	5	-5	1
2	-3	-1	7	-3
3	-1	-4	4	2
4	1	-4	-4	2
5	3	-1	-7	-3
6	5	5	5	1
λ	2	$\frac{3}{2}$	$\frac{5}{3}$	$\frac{7}{12}$

$t = 7$

x	u_1	u_2	u_3	u_4
1	-3	5	-1	3
2	-2	0	1	-7
3	-1	-3	1	1
4	0	-4	0	6
5	1	-3	-1	1
6	2	0	-1	-7
7	3	5	1	3
λ	1	1	$\frac{1}{6}$	$\frac{7}{12}$

$t = 8$

x	u_1	u_2	u_3	u_4
1	-7	7	-7	7
2	-5	1	5	-13
3	-3	-3	7	-3
4	-1	-5	3	9
5	1	-5	-3	9
6	3	-3	-7	-3
7	5	1	-5	-13
8	7	7	7	7
λ	2	1	$\frac{2}{3}$	$\frac{7}{12}$

$t = 9$

x	u_1	u_2	u_3	u_4
1	-4	28	-14	14
2	-3	7	7	-21
3	-2	-8	13	-11
4	-1	-17	9	9
5	0	-20	0	18
6	1	-17	-9	9
7	2	-8	-13	-11
8	3	7	-7	-21
9	4	28	14	14
λ	1	3	$\frac{5}{6}$	$\frac{7}{12}$

$t = 10$

x	u_1	u_2	u_3	u_4
1	-9	6	-42	18
2	-7	2	14	-22
3	-5	-1	35	-17
4	-3	-3	31	3
5	-1	-4	12	18
6	1	-4	-12	18
7	3	-3	-31	3
8	5	-1	-35	-17
9	7	2	-14	-22
10	9	6	42	18
λ	2	$\frac{1}{2}$	$\frac{5}{3}$	$\frac{5}{12}$

Table 8 : Critical Values of Chi-Square

d.f.	$\chi^2 0.995$	$\chi^2 0.990$	$\chi^2 0.975$	$\chi^2 0.950$	$\chi^2 0.900$	$\chi^2 0.100$	$\chi^2 0.050$	$\chi^2 0.025$	$\chi^2 0.010$	$\chi^2 0.005$
1	0.0000393	0.0001571	0.0009821	0.0039321	0.0157908	2.70554	3.84146	5.02389	6.63490	7.87944
2	0.0100251	0.0201007	0.0506356	0.102587	0.210720	4.60517	5.99147	7.37776	9.21034	10.5966
3	0.0717212	0.114832	0.215795	0.351846	0.584375	6.25139	7.81473	9.34840	11.3449	12.8381
4	0.206990	0.297110	0.484419	0.710721	1.063623	7.77944	9.48773	11.1433	13.2767	14.8602
5	0.411740	0.554300	0.831211	1.145476	1.61031	9.23635	11.0705	12.8325	15.0863	16.7496
6	0.675727	0.872085	1.237347	1.63539	2.20413	10.6446	12.5916	14.4494	16.8119	18.5476
7	0.989265	1.239043	1.68987	2.16735	2.83311	12.0170	14.0671	16.0128	18.4753	20.2777
8	1.344419	1.646482	2.17973	2.73264	3.48954	13.3616	15.5073	17.5346	20.0902	21.9550
9	1.734926	2.087912	2.70039	3.32511	4.16816	14.6837	16.9190	19.0228	21.6660	23.5893
10	2.15585	2.55821	3.24697	3.94030	4.86518	15.9871	18.3070	20.4831	23.2093	25.1882
11	2.60321	3.05347	3.81575	4.57481	5.57779	17.2750	19.6751	21.9200	24.7250	26.7569
12	3.07382	3.57056	4.40379	5.22603	6.30380	18.5494	21.0261	23.3367	26.2170	28.2995
13	3.56503	4.10691	5.00874	5.89186	7.04150	19.8119	22.3621	24.7356	27.6883	29.8194
14	4.07468	4.66043	5.62872	6.57063	7.78953	21.0642	23.6848	26.1190	29.1413	31.3193
15	4.60094	5.22935	6.26214	7.26094	8.54675	22.3072	24.9958	27.4884	30.5779	32.8013
16	5.14224	5.81221	6.90766	7.96164	9.31223	23.5418	26.2962	28.8454	31.9999	34.2672
17	5.69724	6.40776	7.56418	8.67176	10.0852	24.7690	27.5871	30.1910	33.4087	35.7185
18	6.26481	7.01491	8.23075	9.39046	10.8649	25.9894	28.8693	31.5264	34.8053	37.1564
19	6.84398	7.63273	8.90655	10.1170	11.6509	27.2036	30.1435	32.8523	36.1908	38.5822

d.f.	$\chi^2_{0.995}$	$\chi^2_{0.990}$	$\chi^2_{0.975}$	$\chi^2_{0.950}$	$\chi^2_{0.900}$	$\chi^2_{0.100}$	$\chi^2_{0.050}$	$\chi^2_{0.025}$	$\chi^2_{0.010}$	$\chi^2_{0.005}$
20	7.43386	8.26040	9.59083	10.8508	12.4426	28.4120	31.4104	34.1696	37.5662	39.9968
21	8.03366	8.89720	10.28293	11.5913	13.2396	29.6151	32.6705	35.4789	38.9321	41.4010
22	8.64272	9.54249	10.9823	12.3380	14.0415	30.8133	33.9244	36.7807	40.2894	42.7956
23	9.26042	10.19567	11.6885	13.0905	14.8479	32.0069	35.1725	38.0757	41.6384	44.1813
24	9.88623	10.8564	12.4011	13.8484	15.6587	33.1693	36.4151	39.3641	42.9798	45.5585
25	10.5197	11.5240	13.1197	14.6114	16.4734	34.3816	37.6525	40.6465	44.3141	46.9278
26	11.1603	12.1981	13.8439	15.3791	17.2919	35.5631	38.8852	41.9232	45.6417	48.2899
27	11.8076	12.8786	14.5733	16.1513	18.1138	36.7412	40.1133	43.1944	46.9630	49.6449
28	12.4613	13.5648	15.3079	16.9279	18.9392	37.9159	41.3372	44.4607	48.2782	50.9933
29	13.1211	14.2565	16.0471	17.7083	19.7677	39.0875	42.5569	45.7222	49.5879	52.3356
30	13.7867	14.9535	16.7908	18.4926	20.5992	40.2560	43.7729	46.9792	50.8922	53.6720
40	20.7065	22.1643	24.4331	26.5093	29.0505	51.8050	55.7585	59.3417	63.6907	66.7659
50	27.9907	29.7067	32.3574	34.7642	37.6886	63.1671	67.5048	71.4202	76.1539	79.4900
60	35.5346	37.4848	40.4817	43.1879	46.4589	74.3970	79.0819	83.2976	88.3794	91.9517
70	43.2752	45.4418	48.7576	51.7393	55.3290	85.5271	90.5312	95.0231	100.425	104.215
80	51.1720	53.5400	57.1532	60.3915	64.2778	96.5782	101.879	106.629	112.329	116.321
90	59.1963	61.7541	65.6466	69.1260	73.2912	107.565	113.145	118.136	124.116	128.299
100	67.3276	70.0648	74.2219	77.9295	82.3581	118.498	124.342	129.561	135.807	140.169

From "Tables of the Percentage Points of the χ^2-Distribution." *Biometrika*, Vol. 32 (1941), pp. 188–189, by Catherine M. Thompson. Reproduced by permission of Professor E. S. Pearson and the *Biometrika* Trustees.

Table 9: Squares and Roots

Roots of numbers other than those given directly may be found by the following relations: $\sqrt{100n} = 10\sqrt{n}$; $\sqrt{1000n} = 10\sqrt{10n}$; $\sqrt{\frac{1}{10}n} = \frac{1}{10}\sqrt{10n}$; $\sqrt{\frac{1}{100}n}$
$= \frac{1}{10}\sqrt{n}$; $\sqrt{\frac{1}{1000}n} = \frac{1}{100}\sqrt{10n}$.

n	n^2	$\sqrt{n}$	$\sqrt{10n}$	n	n^2	$\sqrt{n}$	$\sqrt{10n}$
				25	625	5.000 000	15.81139
1	1	1.000 000	3.162 278	26	676	5.099 020	16.12452
2	4	1.414 214	4.472 136	27	729	5.196 152	16.43168
3	9	1.732 051	5.477 226	28	784	5.291 503	16.73320
4	16	2.000 000	6.324 555	29	841	5.385 165	17.02939
5	25	2.236 068	7.071 068	30	900	5.477 226	17.32051
6	36	2.449 490	7.745 967	31	961	5.567 764	17.60682
7	49	2.645 751	8.366 600	32	1 024	5.656 854	17.88854
8	64	2.828 427	8.944 272	33	1 089	5.744 563	18.16590
9	81	3.000 000	9.486 833	34	1 156	5.830 952	18.43909
10	100	3.162 278	10.00000	35	1 225	5.916 080	18.70829
11	121	3.316 625	10.48809	36	1 296	6.000 000	18.97367
12	144	3.464 102	10.95445	37	1 369	6.082 763	19.23538
13	169	3.605 551	11.40175	38	1 444	6.164 414	19.49359
14	196	3.741 657	11.83216	39	1 521	6.244 998	19.74842
15	225	3.872 983	12.24745	40	1 600	6.324 555	20.00000
16	256	4.000 000	12.64911	41	1 681	6.403 124	20.24846
17	289	4.123 106	13.03840	42	1 764	6.480 741	20.49390
18	324	4.242 641	13.41641	43	1 849	6.557 439	20.73644
19	361	4.358 899	13.78405	44	1 936	6.633 250	20.97618
20	400	4.472 136	14.14214	45	2 025	6.708 204	21.21320
21	441	4.582 576	14.49138	46	2 116	6.782 330	21.44761
22	484	4.690 416	14.83240	47	2 209	6.855 655	21.67948
23	529	4.795 832	15.16575	48	2 304	6.928 203	21.90890
24	576	4.898 979	15.49193	49	2 401	7.000 000	22.13594

From "Handbook of Tables for Probability and Statistics," edited by William H. Beyer (Cleveland: The Chemical Rubber Company, 1966). Reproduced by permission of Professor W. H. Beyer and the publishers, The Chemical Rubber Company.

n	n^2	$\sqrt{n}$	$\sqrt{10n}$	n	n^2	$\sqrt{n}$	$\sqrt{10n}$
50	2 500	7.071 068	22.36068	90	8 100	9.486 833	30.00000
51	2 601	7.141 428	22.58318	91	8 281	9.539 392	30.16621
52	2 704	7.211 103	22.80351	92	8 464	9.591 663	30.33150
53	2 809	7.280 110	23.02173	93	8 649	9.643 651	30.49590
54	2 916	7.348 469	23.23790	94	8 836	9.695 360	30.65942
55	3 025	7.416 198	23.45208	95	9 025	9.746 794	30.82207
56	3 136	7.483 315	23.66432	96	9 216	9.797 959	30.98387
57	3 249	7.549 834	23.87467	97	9 409	9.848 858	31.14482
58	3 364	7.615 773	24.08319	98	9 604	9.899 495	31.30495
59	3 481	7.681 146	24.28992	99	9 801	9.949 874	31.46427
60	3 600	7.745 967	24.49490	100	10 000	10.00000	31.62278
61	3 721	7.810 250	24.69818	101	10 201	10.04988	31.78050
62	3 844	7.874 008	24.89980	102	10 404	10.09950	31.93744
63	3 969	7.937 254	25.09980	103	10 609	10.14889	32.09361
64	4 096	8.000 000	25.29822	104	10 816	10.19804	32.24903
65	4 225	8.062 258	25.49510	105	11 025	10.24695	32.40370
66	4 356	8.124 038	25.69047	106	11 236	10.29563	32.55764
67	4 489	8.185 353	25.88436	107	11 449	10.34408	32.71085
68	4 624	8.246 211	26.07681	108	11 664	10.39230	32.86335
69	4 761	8.306 624	26.26785	109	11 881	10.44031	33.01515
70	4 900	8.366 600	26.45751	110	12 100	10.48809	33.16625
71	5 041	8.426 150	26.64583	111	12 321	10.53565	33.31666
72	5 184	8.485 281	26.83282	112	12 544	10.58301	33.46640
73	5 329	8.544 004	27.01851	113	12 769	10.63015	33.61547
74	5 476	8.602 325	27.20294	114	12 996	10.67708	33.76389
75	5 625	8.660 254	27.38613	115	13 225	10.72381	33.91165
76	5 776	8.717 798	27.56810	116	13 456	10.77033	34.05877
77	5 929	8.774 964	27.74887	117	13 689	10.81665	34.20526
78	6 084	8.831 761	27.92848	118	13 924	10.86278	34.35113
79	6 241	8.888 194	28.10694	119	14 161	10.90871	34.49638
80	6 400	8.944 272	28.28427	120	14 400	10.95445	34.64102
81	6 561	9.000 000	28.46050	121	14 641	11.00000	34.78505
82	6 724	9.055 385	28.63564	122	14 884	11.04536	34.92850
83	6 889	9.110 434	28.80972	123	15 129	11.09054	35.07136
84	7 056	9.165 151	28.98275	124	15 376	11.13553	35.21363
85	7 225	9.219 544	29.15476	125	15 625	11.18034	35.35534
86	7 396	9.273 618	29.32576	126	15 876	11.22497	35.49648
87	7 569	9.327 379	29.49576	127	16 129	11.26943	35.63706
88	7 744	9.380 832	29.66479	128	16 384	11.31371	35.77709
89	7 921	9.433 981	29.83287	129	16 641	11.35782	35.91657

n	n^2	$\sqrt{n}$	$\sqrt{10n}$	n	n^2	$\sqrt{n}$	$\sqrt{10n}$
130	16 900	11.40175	36.05551	170	28 900	13.03840	41.23106
131	17 161	11.44552	36.19392	171	29 241	13.07670	41.35215
132	17 424	11.48913	36.33180	172	29 584	13.11488	41.47288
133	17 689	11.53256	36.46917	173	29 929	13.15295	41.59327
134	17 956	11.57584	36.60601	174	30 276	13.19091	41.71331
135	18 225	11.61895	36.74235	175	30 625	13.22876	41.83300
136	18 496	11.66190	36.87818	176	30 976	13.26650	41.95235
137	18 769	11.70470	37.01351	177	31 329	13.30413	42.07137
138	19 044	11.74734	37.14835	178	31 684	13.34166	42.19005
139	19 321	11.78983	37.28270	179	32 041	13.37909	42.30839
140	19 600	11.83216	37.41657	180	32 400	13.41641	42.42641
141	19 881	11.87434	37.54997	181	32 761	13.45362	42.54409
142	20 164	11.91638	37.68289	182	33 124	13.49074	42.66146
143	20 449	11.95826	37.81534	183	33 489	13.52775	42.77850
144	20 736	12.00000	37.94733	184	33 856	13.56466	42.89522
145	21 025	12.04159	38.07887	185	34 225	13.60147	43.01163
146	21 316	12.08305	38.20995	186	34 596	13.63818	43.12772
147	21 609	12.12436	38.34058	187	34 969	13.67479	43.24350
148	21 904	12.16553	38.47077	188	35 344	13.71131	43.35897
149	22 201	12.20656	38.60052	189	35 721	13.74773	43.47413
150	22 500	12.24745	38.72983	190	36 100	13.78405	43.58899
151	22 801	12.28821	38.85872	191	36 481	13.82027	43.70355
152	23 104	12.32883	38.98718	192	36 864	13.85641	43.81780
153	23 409	12.36932	39.11521	193	37 249	13.89244	43.93177
154	23 716	12.40967	39.24283	194	37 636	13.92839	44.04543
155	24 025	12.44990	39.37004	195	38 025	13.96424	44.15880
156	24 336	12.49000	39.49684	196	38 416	14.00000	44.27189
157	24 649	12.52996	39.62323	197	38 809	14.03567	44.38468
158	24 964	12.56981	39.74921	198	39 204	14.07125	44.49719
159	25 281	12.60952	39.87480	199	39 601	14.10674	44.60942
160	25 600	12.64911	40.00000	200	40 000	14.14214	44.72136
161	25 921	12.68858	40.12481	201	40 401	14.17745	44.83302
162	26 244	12.72792	40.24922	202	40 804	14.21267	44.94441
163	26 569	12.76715	40.37326	203	41 209	14.24781	45.05552
164	26 896	12.80625	40.49691	204	41 616	14.28286	45.16636
165	27 225	12.84523	40.62019	205	42 025	14.31782	45.27693
166	27 556	12.88410	40.74310	206	42 436	14.35270	45.38722
167	27 889	12.92285	40.86563	207	42 849	14.38749	45.49725
168	28 224	12.96148	40.98780	208	43 264	14.42221	45.60702
169	28 561	13.00000	41.10961	209	43 681	14.45683	45.71652

n	n^2	$\sqrt{n}$	$\sqrt{10n}$	n	n^2	$\sqrt{n}$	$\sqrt{10n}$
210	44 100	14.49138	45.82576	250	62 500	15.81139	50.00000
211	44 521	14.52584	45.93474	251	63 001	15.84298	50.09990
212	44 944	14.56022	46.04346	252	63 504	15.87451	50.19960
213	45 369	14.59452	46.15192	253	64 009	15.90597	50.29911
214	45 796	14.62874	46.26013	254	64 516	15.93738	50.39841
215	46 225	14.66288	46.36809	255	65 025	15.96872	50.49752
216	46 656	14.69694	46.47580	256	65 536	16.00000	50.59644
217	47 089	14.73092	46.58326	257	66 049	16.03122	50.69517
218	47 524	14.76482	46.69047	258	66 564	16.06238	50.79370
219	47 961	14.79865	46.79744	259	67 081	16.09348	50.89204
220	48 400	14.83240	46.90416	260	67 600	16.12452	50.99020
221	48 841	14.86607	47.01064	261	68 121	16.15549	51.08816
222	49 284	14.89966	47.11688	262	68 644	16.18641	51.18594
223	49 729	14.93318	47.22288	263	69 169	16.21727	51.28353
224	50 176	14.96663	47.32864	264	69 696	16.24808	51.38093
225	50 625	15.00000	47.43416	265	70 225	16.27882	51.47815
226	51 076	15.03330	47.53946	266	70 756	16.30951	51.57519
227	51 529	15.06652	47.64452	267	71 289	16.34013	51.67204
228	51 984	15.09967	47.74935	268	71 824	16.37071	51.76872
229	52 441	15.13275	47.85394	269	72 361	16.40122	51.86521
230	52 900	15.16575	47.95832	270	72 900	16.43168	51.96152
231	53 361	15.19868	48.06246	271	73 441	16.46208	52.05766
232	53 824	15.23155	48.16638	272	73 984	16.49242	52.15362
233	54 289	15.26434	48.27007	273	74 529	16.52271	52.24940
234	54 756	15.29706	48.37355	274	75 076	16.55295	52.34501
235	55 225	15.32971	48.47680	275	75 625	16.58312	52.44044
236	55 696	15.36229	48.57983	276	76 176	16.61325	52.53570
237	56 169	15.39480	48.68265	277	76 729	16.64332	52.63079
238	56 644	15.42725	48.78524	278	77 284	16.67333	52.72571
239	57 121	15.45962	48.88763	279	77 841	16.70329	52.82045
240	57 600	15.49193	48.98979	280	78 400	16.73320	52.91503
241	58 081	15.52417	49.09175	281	78 961	16.76305	53.00943
242	58 564	15.55635	49.19350	282	79 524	16.79286	53.10367
243	59 049	15.58846	49.29503	283	80 089	16.82260	53.19774
244	59 536	15.62050	49.39636	284	80 656	16.85230	53.29165
245	60 025	15.65248	49.49747	285	81 225	16.88194	53.38539
246	60 516	15.68439	49.59839	286	81 796	16.91153	53.47897
247	61 009	15.71623	49.69909	287	82 369	16.94107	53.57238
248	61 504	15.74802	49.79960	288	82 944	16.97056	53.66563
249	62 001	15.77973	49.89990	289	83 521	17.00000	53.75872

n	n^2	$\sqrt{n}$	$\sqrt{10n}$	n	n^2	$\sqrt{n}$	$\sqrt{10n}$
290	84 100	17.02939	53.85165	330	108 900	18.16590	57.44563
291	84 681	17.05872	53.94442	331	109 561	18.19341	57.53260
292	85 264	17.08801	54.03702	332	110 224	18.22087	57.61944
293	85 849	17.11724	54.12947	333	110 889	18.24829	57.70615
294	86 436	17.14643	54.22177	334	111 556	18.27567	57.79273
295	87 025	17.17556	54.31390	335	112 225	18.30301	57.87918
296	87 616	17.20465	54.40588	336	112 896	18.33030	57.96551
297	88 209	17.23369	54.49771	337	113 569	18.35756	58.05170
298	88 804	17.26268	54.58938	338	114 244	18.38478	58.13777
299	89 401	17.29162	54.68089	339	114 921	18.41195	58.22371
300	90 000	17.32051	54.77226	340	115 600	18.43909	58.30952
301	90 601	17.34935	54.86347	341	116 281	18.46619	58.39521
302	91 204	17.37815	54.95453	342	116 964	18.49324	58.48077
303	91 809	17.40690	55.04544	343	117 649	18.52026	58.56620
304	92 416	17.43560	55.13620	344	118 336	18.54724	58.65151
305	93 025	17.46425	55.22681	345	119 025	18.57418	58.73670
306	93 636	17.49286	55.31727	346	119 716	18.60108	58.82176
307	94 249	17.52142	55.40758	347	120 409	18.62794	58.90671
308	94 864	17.54993	55.49775	348	121 104	18.65476	58.99152
309	95 481	17.57840	55.58777	349	121 801	18.68154	59.07622
310	96 100	17.60682	55.67764	350	122 500	18.70829	59.16080
311	96 721	17.63519	55.76737	351	123 201	18.73499	59.24525
312	97 344	17.66352	55.85696	352	123 904	18.76166	59.32959
313	97 969	17.69181	55.94640	353	124 609	18.78829	59.41380
314	98 596	17.72005	56.03570	354	125 316	18.81489	59.40790
315	99 225	17.74824	56.12486	355	126 025	18.84144	59.58188
316	99 856	17.77639	56.21388	356	126 736	18.86796	59.66574
317	100 489	17.80449	56.30275	357	127 449	18.89444	59.74948
318	101 124	17.83255	56.39149	358	128 164	18.92089	59.83310
319	101 761	17.86057	56.48008	359	128 881	18.94730	59.91661
320	102 400	17.88854	56.56854	360	129 600	18.97367	60.00000
321	103 041	17.91647	56.65686	361	130 321	19.00000	60.08328
322	103 684	17.94436	56.74504	362	131 044	19.02630	60.16644
323	104 329	17.97220	56.83309	363	131 769	19.05256	60.24948
324	104 976	18.00000	56.92100	364	132 496	19.07878	60.33241
325	105 625	18.02776	57.00877	365	133 225	19.10497	60.41523
326	106 276	18.05547	57.09641	366	133 956	19.13113	60.49793
327	106 929	18.08314	57.18391	367	134 689	19.15724	60.58052
328	107 584	18.11077	57.27128	368	135 424	19.18333	60.66300
329	108 241	18.13836	57.35852	369	136 161	19.20937	60.74537

n	n^2	$\sqrt{n}$	$\sqrt{10n}$	n	n^2	$\sqrt{n}$	$\sqrt{10n}$
370	136 900	19.23538	60.82763	410	168 100	20.24846	64.03124
371	137 641	19.26136	60.90977	411	168 921	20.27313	64.10928
372	138 384	19.28730	60.99180	412	169 744	20.29778	64.18723
373	139 129	19.31321	61.07373	413	170 569	20.32240	64.26508
374	139 876	19.33908	61.15554	414	171 396	20.34699	64.34283
375	140 625	19.36492	61.23724	415	172 225	20.37155	64.42049
376	141 376	19.39072	61.31884	416	173 056	20.39608	64.49806
377	142 129	19.41649	61.40033	417	173 889	20.42058	64.57554
378	142 184	19.44222	61.48170	418	174 724	20.44505	64.65292
379	143 641	19.46792	61.56298	419	175 561	20.46949	64.73021
380	144 400	19.49359	61.64414	420	176 400	20.49390	64.80741
381	145 161	19.51922	61.72520	421	177 241	20.51828	64.88451
382	145 924	19.54482	61.80615	422	178 084	20.54264	64.96153
383	146 689	19.57039	61.88699	423	178 929	20.56696	65.03845
384	147 456	19.59592	61.96773	424	179 776	20.59126	65.11528
385	148 225	19.62142	62.04837	425	180 625	20.61553	65.19202
386	148 996	19.64688	62.12890	426	181 476	20.63977	65.26868
387	149 769	19.67232	62.20932	427	182 329	20.66398	65.34524
388	150 544	19.69772	62.28965	428	183 184	20.68816	65.42171
389	151 321	19.72308	62.36986	429	184 041	20.71232	65.49809
390	152 100	19.74842	62.44998	430	184 900	20.73644	65.57439
391	152 881	19.77372	62.52999	431	185 761	20.76054	65.65059
392	153 664	19.79899	62.60990	432	186 624	20.78461	65.72671
393	154 449	19.82423	62.68971	433	187 489	20.80865	65.80274
394	155 236	19.84943	62.76942	434	188 356	20.83267	65.87868
395	156 025	19.87461	62.84903	435	189 225	20.85665	65.95453
396	156 816	19.89975	62.92853	436	190 096	20.88061	66.03030
397	157 609	19.92486	63.00794	437	190 969	20.90454	66.10598
398	158 404	19.94994	63.08724	438	191 844	20.92845	66.18157
399	159 201	19.97498	63.16645	439	192 721	20.95233	66.25708
400	160 000	20.00000	63.24555	440	193 600	20.97618	66.33250
401	160 801	20.02498	63.32456	441	194 481	21.00000	66.40783
402	161 604	20.04994	63.40347	442	195 224	21.02380	66.48308
403	162 409	20.07486	63.48228	443	196 249	21.04757	66.55825
404	163 216	20.09975	63.56099	444	197 136	21.07131	66.63332
405	164 025	20.12461	63.63961	445	198 025	21.09502	66.70832
406	164 836	20.14944	63.71813	446	198 916	21.11871	66.78323
407	165 649	20.17424	63.79655	447	199 809	21.14237	66.85806
408	166 464	20.19901	63.87488	448	200 704	21.16601	66.93280
409	167 281	20.22375	63.95311	449	201 601	21.18962	67.00746

n	n^2	$\sqrt{n}$	$\sqrt{10n}$	n	n^2	$\sqrt{n}$	$\sqrt{10n}$
450	202 500	21.21320	67.08204	490	240 100	22.13594	70.00000
451	203 401	21.23676	67.15653	491	241 081	22.15852	70.07139
452	204 304	21.26029	67.23095	492	242 064	22.18107	70.14271
453	205 209	21.28380	67.30527	493	243 049	22.20360	70.21396
454	206 116	21.30728	67.37952	494	244 036	22.22611	70.28513
455	207 025	21.33073	67.45369	495	245 025	22.24860	70.35624
456	207 936	21.35416	67.52777	496	246 016	22.27106	70.42727
457	208 849	21.37756	67.60178	497	247 009	22.29350	70.49823
458	209 764	21.40093	67.67570	498	248 004	22.31591	70.56912
459	210 681	21.42429	67.74954	499	249 001	22.33831	70.63993
460	211 600	21.44761	67.82330	500	250 000	22.36068	70.71068
461	212 521	21.47091	67.89698	501	251 001	22.38303	70.78135
462	213 444	21.49419	67.97058	502	252 004	22.40536	70.85196
463	214 369	21.51743	68.04410	503	253 009	22.42766	70.92249
464	215 296	21.54066	68.11755	504	254 016	22.44994	70.99296
465	216 225	21.56386	68.19091	505	255 025	22.47221	71.06335
466	217 156	21.58703	68.26419	506	256 036	22.49444	71.13368
467	218 089	21.61018	68.33740	507	257 049	22.51666	71.20393
468	219 024	21.63331	68.41053	508	258 064	22.53886	71.27412
469	219 961	21.45641	68.48357	509	259 081	22.56103	71.34424
470	220 900	21.67948	68.55655	510	260 100	22.58318	71.41428
471	221 841	21.70253	68.62944	511	261 121	22.60531	71.48426
472	222 784	21.72556	68.70226	512	262 144	22.62742	71.55418
473	223 729	21.74856	68.77500	513	263 169	22.64950	71.62402
474	224 676	21.77154	68.84766	514	264 196	22.67157	71.69379
475	225 625	21.79449	68.92024	515	265 225	22.69861	71.76350
476	226 576	21.81742	68.99275	516	266 256	22.71563	71.83314
477	227 529	21.84033	69.06519	517	267 289	22.73763	71.90271
478	228 484	21.86321	69.13754	518	268 324	22.75961	71.97222
479	229 441	21.88607	69.20983	519	269 361	22.78157	72.04165
480	230 400	21.90890	69.28203	520	270 400	22.80351	72.11103
481	213 361	21.93171	69.35416	521	271 441	22.82542	72.18033
482	232 324	21.95450	69.42622	522	272 484	22.84732	72.24957
483	233 289	21.97726	69.49820	523	273 529	22.86919	72.31874
484	234 256	22.00000	69.57011	524	274 576	22.89105	72.38784
485	235 225	22.02272	69.64194	525	275 625	22.91288	72.45688
486	236 196	22.04541	69.71370	526	276 676	22.93469	72.52586
487	237 169	22.06808	69.78539	527	277 729	22.95648	72.59477
488	238 144	22.09072	69.85700	528	278 784	22.97825	72.66361
489	239 121	22.11334	69.92853	529	279 841	23.00000	72.73239

n	n^2	$\sqrt{n}$	$\sqrt{10n}$	n	n^2	$\sqrt{n}$	$\sqrt{10n}$
530	280 900	23.02173	72.80110	570	324 900	23.87467	75.49834
531	281 961	23.04344	72.86075	571	326 041	23.89561	75.56454
532	283 024	23.06513	72.93833	572	327 184	23.91652	75.63068
533	284 089	23.08679	73.00685	573	328 329	23.93742	75.69676
534	185 156	23.10844	73.07530	574	329 476	23.95830	75.76279
535	286 225	23.13007	73.14369	575	330 625	23.97916	75.82875
536	287 296	23.15167	73.21202	576	331 776	24.00000	75.89466
537	288 369	23.17326	73.28028	577	332 929	24.02082	75.96052
538	289 444	23.19483	73.34848	578	334 084	24.04163	76.02631
539	290 521	23.21637	73.41662	579	335 241	24.06242	76.09205
540	291 600	23.23790	73.48469	580	336 400	24.08319	76.15773
541	292 681	23.25941	73.55270	581	337 561	24.10394	76.22336
542	293 764	23.28089	73.62065	582	338 724	24.12468	76.28892
543	294 849	23.30236	73.68853	583	339 889	24.14539	76.35444
544	295 936	23.32381	73.75636	584	341 056	24.16609	76.41989
545	297 025	23.34524	73.82412	585	342 225	24.18677	76.48529
546	298 116	23.36664	73.89181	586	343 396	24.20744	76.55064
547	299 209	23.38803	73.95945	587	344 569	24.22808	76.61593
548	300 304	23.40940	74.02702	588	345 744	24.24871	76.68116
549	301 401	23.43075	74.09453	589	346 921	24.26932	76.74634
550	302 500	23.45208	74.16198	590	348 100	24.28992	76.81146
551	303 601	23.47339	74.22937	591	349 281	24.31049	76.87652
552	304 704	23.49468	74.29670	592	350 464	24.33105	76.94154
553	305 809	23.51595	74.36397	593	351 649	24.35159	77.00649
554	306 916	23.53720	74.43118	594	352 836	24.37212	77.07140
555	308 025	23.55844	74.49832	595	354 025	24.39262	77.13624
556	309 136	23.57965	74.56541	596	355 216	24.41311	77.20104
557	310 249	23.60085	74.63243	597	356 409	24.43358	77.26578
558	311 364	23.62202	74.69940	598	357 604	24.45404	77.33046
559	312 481	23.64318	74.76630	599	358 801	24.47448	77.39509
560	313 600	23.66432	74.83315	600	360 000	24.49490	77.45967
561	314 721	23.68544	74.89993	601	361 201	24.51530	77.52419
562	315 844	23.70654	74.96666	602	362 404	24.53569	77.58866
563	316 969	23.72762	75.03333	603	363 609	24.55606	77.65307
564	318 096	23.74868	75.09993	604	364 816	24.57641	77.71744
565	319 225	23.76973	75.16648	605	366 025	24.59675	77.78175
566	320 356	23.79075	75.23297	606	367 236	24.61707	77.84600
567	321 489	23.81176	75.29940	607	368 449	24.63737	77.91020
568	322 624	23.83275	75.36577	608	369 664	24.65766	77.97435
569	323 761	23.85372	75.43209	609	370 881	24.67793	78.03845

n	n^2	$\sqrt{n}$	$\sqrt{10n}$	n	n^2	$\sqrt{n}$	$\sqrt{10n}$
610	372 100	24.69818	78.10250	650	422 500	25.49510	80.62258
611	373 321	24.71841	78.16649	651	423 801	25.51470	80.68457
612	374 544	24.73863	78.23043	652	425 104	25.53429	80.74652
613	375 769	24.75884	78.29432	653	426 409	25.55386	80.80842
614	376 996	24.77902	78.35815	654	427 716	25.57342	80.87027
615	378 225	24.79919	78.42194	655	429 025	25.59297	80.93207
616	379 456	24.81935	78.48567	656	430 336	25.61250	80.00383
617	380 689	24.83948	78.54935	657	431 649	25.63201	81.05554
618	381 924	24.85961	78.61298	658	432 964	25.65151	81.11720
619	383 161	24.87971	78.67655	659	434 281	35.67100	81.17881
620	384 400	24.89980	78.74008	660	435 600	25.69047	81.24038
621	385 641	24.91987	78.80355	661	436 921	25.70992	81.30191
622	386 884	24.93993	78.86698	662	438 244	25.72936	81.36338
623	388 129	24.95997	78.93035	663	439 569	25.74879	81.42481
624	389 376	24.97999	78.99367	664	440 896	25.76820	81.48620
625	390 625	25.00000	79.05694	665	442 225	25.78759	81.54753
626	391 876	25.01999	79.12016	666	443 556	25.80698	81.60882
627	393 129	25.03997	79.18333	667	444 889	25.82634	81.67007
628	394 384	25.05993	79.24645	668	446 224	25.84570	81.73127
629	395 641	25.07987	79.30952	669	447 561	25.86503	81.79242
630	396 900	25.09980	79.37254	670	448 900	25.88436	81.85353
631	398 161	25.11971	79.43551	671	450 241	25.90367	81.91459
632	399 424	25.13961	79.49843	672	451 584	25.92296	81.97561
633	400 689	25.15949	79.56130	673	452 929	25.94224	82.03658
634	401 956	25.17936	79.62412	674	454 276	25.96151	82.09750
635	403 225	25.19921	79.68689	675	455 625	25.98076	82.15838
636	404 496	25.21904	79.74961	676	456 976	26.00000	82.21922
637	405 769	25.23886	79.81228	677	458 329	26.01922	82.28001
638	407 044	25.25866	79.87490	678	459 684	26.03843	82.34076
639	408 321	25.27845	79.93748	679	461 041	26.05763	82.40146
640	409 600	25.29822	80.00000	680	462 400	26.07681	82.46211
641	410 881	25.31798	80.06248	681	463 761	26.09598	82.52272
642	412 164	25.33772	80.12490	682	465 124	26.11513	82.58329
643	413 449	25.35744	80.18728	683	466 489	26.13427	82.64381
644	414 736	25.37716	80.24961	684	467 856	26.15339	82.70429
645	416 025	25.39685	80.31189	685	469 225	26.17250	82.76473
646	417 316	25.41653	80.37413	686	470 596	26.19160	82.82512
647	418 609	25.43619	80.43631	687	471 969	26.21068	82.88546
648	419 904	25.45584	80.49845	688	473 344	26.22975	82.94577
649	421 201	25.47548	80.56054	689	474 721	26.24881	83.00602

n	n^2	$\sqrt{n}$	$\sqrt{10n}$	n	n^2	$\sqrt{n}$	$\sqrt{10n}$
690	476 100	26.26785	83.06624	730	532 900	27.01851	85.44004
691	477 481	26.28688	83.12641	731	534 361	27.03701	85.49854
692	478 864	26.30589	83.18654	732	535 824	27.05550	85.55700
693	480 249	26.32489	83.24662	733	537 289	27.07397	85.61542
694	481 636	26.34388	83.30666	734	538 756	27.09243	85.67380
695	483 025	26.36285	83.36666	735	540 225	27.11088	85.73214
696	484 416	26.38181	83.42661	736	541 696	27.12932	85.79044
697	485 809	26.40076	83.48653	737	543 169	27.14774	85.84870
698	487 204	26.41969	83.54639	738	544 644	27.16616	85.90693
699	488 601	26.43861	83.60622	739	546 121	27.18455	85.96511
700	490 000	26.45751	83.66600	740	547 600	27.20294	86.02325
701	491 401	26.47640	83.72574	741	549 081	27.22132	86.08136
702	492 804	26.49528	83.78544	742	550 564	27.23968	86.13942
703	494 209	26.51415	83.84510	743	552 049	27.25803	86.19745
704	495 616	26.53300	83.90471	744	553 536	27.27636	86.25543
705	497 025	26.55184	83.96428	745	555 025	27.29469	86.31338
706	498 436	26.57066	84.02381	746	556 516	27.31300	86.37129
707	499 849	26.58947	84.08329	747	558 009	27.33130	86.42916
708	501 264	26.60827	84.14274	748	559 504	27.34959	86.48699
709	502 681	26.62705	84.20214	749	561 001	27.36786	86.54479
710	504 100	26.64583	84.26150	750	562 500	27.38613	86.60254
711	505 521	26.66458	84.32082	751	564 001	27.40438	86.66026
712	506 944	26.68333	84.38009	752	565 504	27.42262	86.71793
713	508 369	26.70206	84.43933	753	567 009	27.44085	86.77557
714	509 796	26.72078	84.49852	754	568 516	27.45906	86.83317
715	511 225	26.73948	84.55767	755	570 025	27.47726	86.89074
716	512 656	26.75818	84.61678	756	571 536	27.49545	86.94826
717	514 089	26.77686	84.67585	757	573 049	27.51363	87.00575
718	515 524	26.79552	84.73488	758	574 564	27.53180	87.06320
719	516 961	26.81418	84.79387	759	576 081	27.54995	87.12061
720	518 400	26.83282	84.85281	760	577 600	27.56810	87.17798
721	519 841	26.85144	84.91172	761	579 121	27.58623	87.23531
722	521 284	26.87006	84.97058	762	580 644	27.60435	87.29261
723	522 729	26.88866	85.02941	763	582 169	27.62245	87.34987
724	524 176	26.90725	85.08819	764	583 696	27.64055	87.40709
725	525 625	26.92582	85.14693	765	585 225	27.65863	87.46428
726	527 076	26.94439	85.20563	766	586 756	27.67671	87.52143
727	528 529	26.96294	85.26429	767	588 289	27.69476	87.57854
728	529 984	26.98148	85.32292	768	589 824	27.71281	87.63561
729	531 441	27.00000	85.38150	769	591 361	27.73085	87.69265

n	n^2	$\sqrt{n}$	$\sqrt{10n}$	n	n^2	$\sqrt{n}$	$\sqrt{10n}$
770	592 900	27.74887	87.74964	810	656 100	28.46050	90.00000
771	594 441	27.76689	87.80661	811	657 721	28.47806	90.05554
772	595 984	27.78489	87.86353	812	659 344	28.49561	90.11104
773	597 529	27.80288	87.92042	813	660 969	28.51315	90.16651
774	599 076	27.82086	87.97727	814	662 596	28.53069	90.22195
775	600 625	27.83882	88.03408	815	664 225	28.54820	90.27735
776	602 176	27.85678	88.09086	816	665 856	28.56571	90.33272
777	603 729	27.87472	88.14760	817	667 489	28.58321	90.38805.
778	605 284	27.89265	88.20431	818	669 124	28.60070	90.44335
779	606 841	27.91057	88.26098	819	670 761	28.61818	90.49862
780	608 400	27.92848	88.31761	820	672 400	28.63564	90.55385
781	609 961	27.94638	88.37420	821	674 041	28.65310	90.60905
782	611 524	27.96426	88.43076	822	675 684	28.67054	90.66422
783	613 089	27.98214	88.48729	823	677 329	28.68798	90.71935
784	614 656	28.00000	88.54377	824	678 976	28.70540	90.77445
785	616 225	28.01785	88.60023	825	680 625	28.72281	90.82951
786	617 796	28.03569	88.65664	826	682 276	28.74022	90.88354
787	619 369	28.05352	88.71302	827	683 929	28.75761	90.93954
788	620 944	28.07134	88.76936	828	685 584	28.77499	90.99451
789	622 521	28.08914	88.82567	829	687 241	28.79236	91.04944
790	624 100	28.10694	88.88194	830	688 900	28.80972	91.10434
791	625 681	28.12472	88.93818	831	690 561	28.82707	91.15920
792	627 264	28.14249	88.99438	832	692 224	28.84441	91.21403
793	628 849	28.16026	89.05055	833	693 889	28.86174	91.26883
794	630 436	28.17801	89.10668	834	695 556	28.87906	91.32360
795	632 025	28.19574	89.16277	835	697 225	28.89637	91.37833
796	633 616	28.21347	89.21883	836	698 896	28.91366	91.43304
797	635 209	28.23119	89.27486	837	700 569	28.93095	91.48770
798	636 804	28.24889	89.33085	838	702 244	28.94823	91.54234
799	638 401	28.26659	89.38680	839	703 921	28.96550	91.59694
800	640 000	28.28427	89.44272	840	705 600	28.98275	91.65151
801	641 601	28.30194	89.49860	841	707 281	29.00000	91.70605
802	643 204	28.31960	89.55445	842	708 964	29.01724	91.76056
803	644 809	28.33725	89.61027	843	710 649	29.03446	91.81503
804	646 416	28.35489	89.66605	844	712 336	29.05168	91.86947
805	648 025	28.37252	89.72179	345	714 025	29.06888	91.92388
806	649 636	28.39014	89.77750	846	715 716	29.08608	91.97826
807	651 249	28.40775	89.83318	847	717 409	29.10326	92.03260
808	652 864	28.42534	89.88882	848	719 104	29.12044	92.08692
809	654 481	28.44293	89.94443	849	720 801	29.13760	92.14120

n	n^2	$\sqrt{n}$	$\sqrt{10n}$	n	n^2	$\sqrt{n}$	$\sqrt{10n}$
850	722 500	29.15476	92.19544	890	792 100	29.83287	94.33981
851	724 201	29.17190	92.24966	891	793 881	29.84962	94.39280
852	725 904	29.18904	92.30385	892	795 664	29.86637	94.44575
853	727 609	29.20616	92.35800	893	797 449	29.88311	94.49868
854	729 316	29.22328	92.41212	894	799 236	29.89983	94.55157
855	731 025	29.24038	92.46621	895	801 025	29.91655	94.60444
856	732 736	29.25748	92.52027	896	802 816	29.93326	94.65728
857	734 449	29.27456	92.57429	897	804 609	29.94996	94.71008
858	736 164	29.29164	92.62829	898	806 404	29.96665	94.76286
859	737 881	29.30870	92.68225	899	808 201	29.98333	94.81561
860	739 600	29.32576	92.73618	900	810 000	30.00000	94.86833
861	741 321	29.34280	92.79009	901	811 801	30.01666	94.92102
862	743 044	29.35984	92.84396	902	813 604	30.03331	94.97368
863	744 769	29.37686	92.89779	903	815 409	30.04996	95.02631
864	746 496	29.39388	92.95160	904	817 216	30.06659	95.07891
865	748 225	29.41088	93.00538	905	819 025	30.08322	95.13149
866	749 956	29.42788	93.05912	906	820 836	30.09983	95.18403
867	751 689	29.44486	93.11283	907	822 649	30.11644	95.23655
868	753 424	29.46184	93.16652	908	824 464	30.13304	95.28903
869	755 161	29.47881	93.22017	909	826 281	30.14963	95.34149
870	756 900	29.49576	93.27379	910	828 100	30.16621	95.39392
871	758 641	29.51271	93.32738	911	829 921	30.18278	95.44632
872	760 384	29.52965	93.38094	912	831 744	30.19934	95.49869
873	762 129	29.54657	93.43447	913	833 569	30.21589	95.55103
874	763 876	29.56349	93.48797	914	835 396	30.23243	95.60335
875	765 625	29.58040	93.54143	915	837 225	30.24897	95.65563
876	767 376	29.59730	93.59487	916	839 056	30.26549	95.70789
877	769 129	29.61419	93.64828	917	840 889	30.28201	95.76012
878	770 884	29.63106	93.70165	918	842 724	30.29851	95.81232
879	772 641	29.64793	93.75500	919	844 561	30.31501	95.86449
880	774 400	29.66479	93.80832	920	846 400	30.33150	95.91663
881	776 161	29.68164	93.86160	921	848 241	30.34798	95.96874
882	777 924	29.69848	93.91486	922	850 084	30.36445	96.02083
883	779 689	29.71532	93.96808	923	851 929	30.38092	96.07289
884	781 456	29.73214	94.02127	924	853 776	30.39737	96.12492
885	783 225	29.74895	94.07444	925	855 625	30.41381	96.17692
886	784 996	29.76575	94.12757	926	857 476	30.43025	96.22889
887	786 769	29.78255	94.18068	927	859 329	30.44667	96.28084
888	788 544	29.79933	94.23375	928	861 184	30.46309	96.33276
889	790 321	29.81610	94.28680	929	863 041	30.47950	96.38465

n	n^2	$\sqrt{n}$	$\sqrt{10n}$	n	n^2	$\sqrt{n}$	$\sqrt{10n}$
930	864 900	30.49590	96.43651	965	931 225	31.06445	98.23441
931	866 761	30.51229	96.48834	966	933 156	31.08054	98.28530
932	868 624	30.52868	96.54015	967	935 089	31.09662	98.33616
933	870 489	30.54505	96.59193	968	937 024	31.11270	98.38699
934	872 356	30.56141	96.64368	969	938 961	31.12876	98.43780
935	874 225	30.57777	96.69540	970	940 900	31.14482	98.48858
936	876 096	30.59412	96.74709	971	942 841	31.16087	98.53933
937	877 969	30.61046	96.79876	972	944 784	31.17691	98.59006
938	879 844	30.62679	96.85040	973	946 729	31.19295	98.64076
939	881 721	30.64311	96.90201	974	948 676	31.20897	98.69144
940	883 600	30.65942	96.95360	975	950 625	31.22499	98.74209
941	885 481	30.67572	97.00515	976	952 576	31.24100	98.79271
942	887 364	30.69202	97.05668	977	954 529	31.25700	98.84331
943	889 249	30.70831	97.10819	978	956 484	31.27299	98.89388
944	891 136	30.72458	97.15966	979	958 441	31.28898	98.94443
945	893 025	30.74085	97.21111	980	960 400	31.30495	98.99495
946	894 916	30.75711	97.26253	981	962 361	31.32092	99.04544
947	896 809	30.77337	97.31393	982	964 324	31.33688	99.09591
948	898 704	30.78961	97.36529	983	966 289	31.35283	99.14636
949	900 601	30.80584	97.41663	984	968 256	31.36877	99.19677
950	902 500	30.82207	97.46794	985	970 225	31.38471	99.24717
951	904 401	30.83829	97.51923	986	972 196	31.40064	99.29753
952	906 304	30.85450	97.57049	987	974 169	31.41656	99.34787
953	908 209	30.87070	97.62172	988	976 144	31.43247	99.39819
954	910 116	30.88689	97.67292	989	978 121	31.44837	99.44848
955	912 025	30.90307	97.72410	990	980 100	31.46427	99.49874
956	913 936	30.91925	97.77525	991	982 081	31.48015	99.54898
957	915 849	30.93542	97.82638	992	984 064	31.49603	99.59920
958	917 764	30.95158	97.87747	993	986 049	31.51190	99.64939
959	919 681	30.96773	97.92855	994	988 036	31.52777	99.69955
960	921 600	30.98387	97.97959	995	990 025	31.54362	99.74969
961	923 521	31.00000	98.03061	996	992 016	31.55947	99.79980
962	925 444	31.01612	98.08160	997	994 009	31.57531	99.84989
963	927 369	31.03224	98.13256	998	996 004	31.59114	99.89995
964	929 296	31.04835	98.18350	999	998 001	31.60966	99.94999
				1000	1000 000	31.62278	100.00000

Answers

Chapter 1

1. (a) 4.5, (b) $s = 4.15$, (c) $\bar{y} \pm s = 7.20 \pm 4.15$, (d) 4.34
2. (a) 4.34, (b) 8.5, (c) 2.0
3. (a) 14.5, (b) $\bar{y} = 74.9$, $s^2 = 281.4$, $s = 16.78$
5. $E(y) = 7/4$
   $\sigma_y^2 = 15/16$
6. 19/32
7. .507
8. (a) 5;3, (b) -1;15, (c) 3;59
9. 12;28
10. 3μ; 3/2
11. 800 hrs.; 8 hrs.
13. 0.0087; 0.0287
14. .03115

15. 0.2112
16. $74.014 < \mu < 77.986$
17. $-.097 < p < .430$
18. $t = 2.65$
19. $z = -2.81$
20. $.014 < p_1 - p_2 < .256$
21. $z = 1.29$
22. $t = -1.359$
23. $1.26 < \mu_1 - \mu_2 < 26.74$
24. $z = 3.0$
25. (a) at least 5/9, (b) at least 40/49, (c) at most 1/4
26. 0.966
27. $z = -1.38$
28. $-1.21 < \mu_1 - \mu_2 < 1.41$
29. $t = .17$
30. $z = 2.31$
31. $t = -2.91$
32. $98.04 < \mu < 98.48$
33. $z = 4.099$
34. 0.0164 if correction factor is used
    0.0128 if correction factor is not used
35. $-20, 83.5$
36. $z = .320$
37. $z = 17.64$

Chapter 2

1. $n = 167$
2. $n_1 = n_2 = 40$
3. $n = 2435$
   $n = 3600$
4. $n = 31$
5. $n = 2300$
6. $n = 60$
   $n = 89$

7. $n = 21$

8. $n = 1,000,000$

9. $z = 1.61$ do not reject
   $n = 494$

15. $1.42 \pm .405$

16. $n = 282$

17. $n = 20$

18. $t = 1.64$ do not reject

19. 1.02 ± 1.429

20. $n = 69$

21. $n = 154$

22. $n = 10,000$

Chapter 3

3. $y = 1 + \frac{3}{2}x$

4. $y = 6 - 4x + x^2$

5. $(k + 1)$; same number

8. $y = \beta_0 + \beta_1 x_1 + \beta_2 x_2 + \epsilon$

11. $(p - 1)$ terms

12. $(p - 1)$ terms

15. $y = \beta_0 + \beta_1 x_1 + \beta_2 x_2 + \beta_3 x_3 + \beta_4 x_4 + \epsilon$

$x_1 = 1$ if paint B	$x_2 = 1$ if C	$x_3 = 1$ if D	$x_4 = 1$ if E
$x_1 = 0$ if not	$x_2 = 0$ if not	$x_3 = 0$ if not	$x_4 = 0$ if not

Chapter 4

3. $y = \beta_0 + \beta_1 x_1 + \beta_2 x_2 + \beta_3 x_3 + \epsilon$

$x_1 = 1$ if block 2	$x_2 = 1$ if treatment B	$x_3 = 1$ if treatment C
$x_1 = 0$ if block 1	$x_2 = 0$ if not	$x_3 = 0$ if not

6. 2 d.f.

7. 3 d.f.

8. Randomized block — 10 d.f.

19. 12 d.f. with all 25 measurements
    11 d.f. with one lost

20. 17 d.f.; no

Chapter 5

7. $y = \beta_0 + \beta_1 x_1 + \beta_2 x_2 + \beta_3 x_1 x_2 + \epsilon;\ (\beta_1 + \beta_3 x_2)$
8. $y = \beta_0 + \beta_1 x_1 + \beta_2 x_2 + \beta_3 x_3 + \beta_4 x_1 x_2 + \beta_5 x_1 x_3 + \beta_6 x_2 x_3 + \beta_7 x_1 x_2 x_3$
$+ \epsilon;\ (\beta_1 + \beta_4 x_2 + \beta_5 x_3 + \beta_7 x_2 x_3)$
9. 3 parameters
10. 5 main effect
    8 2-way interactions
    4 3-way interactions
11. 5 main effect
    8 2-way interactions
    4 3-way interactions
15. 6 main effect
    15 2-way interactions
    20 3-way interactions
    15 4-way interactions
    6 5-way interactions
    1 6-way interaction
16. 0 d.f.
    22 d.f.
21. 6 d.f.
22. Latin square design
23. (a) bacteria types (qualitative) and time (quantitative)
    (b) 2×5 factorial
    (c) $y = \beta_0 + \beta_1 x_1 + \beta_2 x_2 + \epsilon;\ x_1 = 1$ if B, $x_1 = 0$ if not; $x_2 = $ time
    (d) β_2
    (e) 7
24. $\beta_3 x_1 x_2;\ 6$
25. (d) 9 d.f.
26. (b) 16 responses
    (c) 6 d.f.
28. Unable to estimate and test for factor interactions.

Chapter 6

1. SSE $= .00024,\ \hat{\beta}_0 = .498$
2. $\hat{y} = 1.5 - .6x_1$

3. $\hat{y} = 3.9 - .95x$

4. $\hat{y} = 2.1 - .6x_1$

5. $\hat{y} = -.71 - 0.14x + .14x^2$

6. (a) $\hat{y} = .9524 + 1.0833x + .1190x^2 - .0833x^3$
   (b) $x = 1,\ \hat{y} = 2.0714$

7. (a) $\hat{y} = 1.4285 + .5000x_1 + .1190x_2 - .5000x_3$
   (b) $\hat{y} = 2.0715$

12. (a) $y = \beta_0 + \beta_1 x_1 + \epsilon$; $(0, 1$ coding)
    (b) $\hat{y} = 7.933 + 0.1x_1$

13. (a) $y = \beta_0 + \beta_1 x_1 + \beta_2 x_2 + \beta_3 x_3 + \cdots + \beta_9 x_9 + \epsilon$
    (b) $\hat{y} = 327.628 - .056x_1 + .1x_2 + .05x_3 + .25x_4 - .2x_5 + .05x_6$
    $\qquad + .2x_7 + .15x_8 - .25x_9$

14. (a) $x_1 = \dfrac{T_1 - 60}{10},\ x_2 = \dfrac{P - 15}{5},\ x_3 = \dfrac{C - 1.5}{.5},\ x_4 = \dfrac{T_2 - 150}{50}$
    (b) $y = \beta_0 + \beta_1 x_1 + \beta_2 x_2 + \beta_3 x_3 + \beta_4 x_4 + \epsilon$
    (c) $\hat{y} = 20.50 - 2.5125x_1 - 1.8375x_2 - .7875x_3 + .650x_4$

15. (a) $y = \beta_0 + \beta_1 x_1 + \beta_2 x_2 + \beta_3 x_3 + \beta_4 x_4 + \beta_5 x_1 x_2 + \beta_6 x_1 x_3 + \beta_7 x_1 x_4$
    $\qquad + \beta_8 x_2 x_3 + \beta_9 x_2 x_4 + \beta_{10} x_3 x_4 + \epsilon$
    (b) $\hat{y} = 20.5000 - 2.5125x_1 - 1.8375x_2 - .7875x_3 + .650x_4 - .600x_1 x_2$
    $\qquad - 1.000x_1 x_3 + .1875x_1 x_4 - .0750x_2 x_3 + .4125x_2 x_4 - 1.1625x_3 x_4$
    (c) $\hat{y} = 23.675$

16. $x = \dfrac{t - 50}{15}$; $-2, -1, 0, 1, 2$

17. $x = \dfrac{t - 157.5}{12.5}$; $-3, -1, 1, 3$

22. $\hat{y} = 1.1138 + .5428 x_1 + 3.4132 x_2$

23. $\hat{y} = 9.34 + 2.46x_1 + .60x_2 + .41x_1 x_2$

24. $y = \beta_0 + \beta_1 x_1 + \beta_2 x_2 + \beta_3 x_3 + \beta_4 x_1 x_2 + \beta_5 x_1 x_3 + \beta_6 x_2 x_3 + \beta_7 x_1 x_2 x_3$
    $\qquad + \beta_8 x_4 + \beta_9 x_5 + \epsilon$

$$\begin{bmatrix} 3.000 \\ 1.667 \\ -\ .500 \\ 2.333 \\ -\ .083 \\ .917 \\ -\ .083 \\ .167 \\ .500 \\ .250 \end{bmatrix}$$

Chapter 7

1. (a) $SSE = .46$
   (c) $s^2 = .23$
   (d) 2 d.f.
2. (a) $SSE = 1.0$
   (c) $s^2 = .5$
   (d) 2 d.f.
3. $SSE = .40$
   $s^2 = .133$
   3 d.f.
4. $t = -5.20$; reject H_0
5. $-.6 \pm .367$
6. $t = 3.46$; reject H_0
7. $.14 \pm .089$
8. $t = -13.7$; reject H_0
9. $k = 1$ replication
10. $k = 1$ replication
11. $.9 \pm .64$
12. $.9 \pm 1.31$
13. $2.07 \pm .19$
14. $2.07 \pm .34$
15. $t = -3.66$; reject
    $t = -2.68$; reject
    $t = -1.15$; do not reject
    $t = .95$; do not reject
16. -2.51 ± 1.51
17. $k = 2$ replications
18. 22.61 ± 2.75
19. 22.61 ± 5.64
20. $\hat{\beta}' = [20.5, -2.52, -1.84, -.788, .65, -.60, -1.0, .1875, .075, .413, 1.163]$
    do not reject any H_0
21. $1 - (.95)^6 \approx .267$
22. 3.75 ± 1.03
23. $t = 2.62$; reject
24. $.41 \pm .38$
25. $12.81 \pm .43$
26. $12.81 \pm .80$

27. $k = 5$ replications
28. (a) $t = 6.35$ for $T \times D$ ∴ reject
    $t = -.58$ for $T \times T$ ∴ do not reject
   (b) $t = 16.1$ for linear effect ∴ reject
29. $\hat{\beta}_i \pm .31$
30. $k = 9$ replications
31. $\left. \begin{array}{l} .5 \pm .759 \\ .25 \pm .759 \end{array} \right\} = $ no difference indicated
32. (b) $\hat{y} = 2.3642 + .9518x_1 - 1.651x_2$ (c) -1.651 ± 1.31
33. $t = 5.858$; reject
34. no, $t = -.76$
35. $k = 68$ replications
36. $12.134 \pm .952$
37. 12.134 ± 1.962
38. (c) 9 d.f.   (e) SSE $= .864$ (f) $.08 \pm .314$; $-.28 \pm .314$
39. (b) SSE $= 2.17$ (c) $t = 1.27$; do not reject (d) $t = 3.672$; reject
40. $27.417 \pm .713$
41. 27.417 ± 1.272
42. $k = 7$ replications

Chapter 8

1. SSB $= 7.1717$
2. (a) ANOVA

Source	d.f.	SS	MS
Blocks	3	173,415.00	57,805.00
Treatment	2	524,177.17	262,088.59
Error	6	6,089.50	1,014.92
Total	11	703,681.67	

   (c) yes
   (d) yes
   (e) $\sigma_{\bar{T}_i - \bar{T}_j} = \dfrac{\sigma}{\sqrt{2}}$
   (f) 237.25 ± 55.13
3. $n = 61$
4. (a) SSE $= 394.0$ with 6 d.f.   (e) no
5. (a) SSE $= 38.33$ with 20 d.f.   (b) yes   (c) yes   (d) 30.7 ± 2.39
   (e) 5.1 ± 1.668
6. $k = 3$ replicates

7. (a) SSE $= 36.05$ with 5 d.f. (f) no evidence

8. (a) SSE $= 0.214$ with 4 d.f. (c) yes

9. (a) SSE $= 13.8678$ with 8 d.f. (c) no (d) yes

10. (a) SSE $= 2.00$ with 6 d.f. (c) no (e) no (f) no (g) yes

11. (a) SSE $= 1.0$ with 3 d.f. (c) yes

13. (a) SSE $= .1638$ with 3 d.f. (b) yes
 (c) about 13 times as much information (d) $n = 22$

14. SSE $= 32.66$ with 4 d.f. (a) yes (b) yes

15. (a) 8 d.f. (b) $t = 1.2$, do not reject (c) $k = 13$ replicates

17. $F = 6.033$, reject

19. $r^2 = .954$

20. $r^2 = .346$

21. $r^2 = .966$

22. $\omega = 2.325$ ($\alpha = .05$)

23. (a) SSE $= 7.00$ with 14 d.f. (b) yes (c) ANOVA

Source	d.f.	SS
Paint	7	224.5
Blocks	2	1.0
Error	14	7.0
Total	23	232.5

24. $F = .332$; do not reject

26. $r^2 = .971$

28. $\omega = 2.39$

29. $\omega = 19.8$

32. (a) $E(s^2) = \sigma^2$ $V(s^2) = \dfrac{2\sigma^4}{n-1}$ (b) $y^* = \ln y$

33. (a) $\hat{y} = 79.875 - 2.25x_1 + 6.25x_2 + 3.25x_1x_2$
 (b) $F = 21.01$; yes, reject (c) $r^2 = .476$

34. (a) ANOVA

Source	d.f.	SS	MS
Paint	2	539.583	
Location	2	377.083	
Exposure	1	550.013	
P × L	4	108.584	
P × E	2	55.029	
L × E	2	55.362	
P × L × E	4	34.971	
Error	54	61.250	1.134
Total	71	1781.875	

(b) $\sigma_{\overline{P_iL_j} - \overline{P_{i1}L_{j1}}} = \dfrac{\sigma}{2}$ (c) $r^2 = .97$

35. (a) $\text{SST} = \sum_i \dfrac{T_i^2}{n_i} - CM$

ANOVA

Source	d.f.	SS	MS
Treatment	2	6.207	3.103
Error	4	8.087	2.022
Total	6	14.294	

(b) no   (c) no   (e) $r^2 = .435$

37. $\omega = 2.041$

38. (a) ANOVA

Source	d.f.	SS	MS
Treatment	1	4	4
Row	1	1	1
Column	1	4	4
Error	0	0	
Total	3	9	

(b) χ^2 and z (c) $\chi^2 = \frac{4}{1}$ is greater than $\chi^2_{.05} = 3.84$; (c) yes for treatments

Chapter 9

1. independent, constant variance

2. $\sum_i^n a_i b_i = 0$ (a_i) coefficients of l_1; (b_i) coefficients of l_2; $i = 1, 2, \ldots, n$,

5. $\sum_1^4 a_i = 0$; linear contrast

9. $a'b = 0$

10. no; no

11. $l_0, l_1, \ldots, l_k$ must be mutually orthogonal; $c_i = \dfrac{1}{\mathbf{x}_i'\mathbf{x}_i}$

13. 2

15. $\text{SSE} = 6.88$

17. ANOVA

Source	d.f.	SS	MS	F	$F_{.05} = 19.0$
Rows	2	21.56	10.78	3.13	Do not reject
Cols.	2	37.56	18.78	5.45	
Treatments	2	48.22	24.11	7.00	
Error	2	6.88	3.44		
Total	8	114.22			

18. (a) Impossible with blocks assumed nonrandom.

    (b) 5.67 ± 6.54

20. SSE $= 32.67$

21. (a) SSE $= .87$

    (b) .71

    (c) no

    (d) $13.34 \pm .46$

22. 2.57

23. (a) ANOVA

Source	d.f.	SS
Treatments	2	1.39
Error	9	.92
Total	11	2.31

    (b) yes

    (c) yes; SS(Covariate) $= .79$

24. (b) SS $= .044$

25. (a) yes; SS(Treatments) $= 4.68$

    (b) no, SS(Covariate) $= .60$

26. (b) $2.85 \pm .35$

    (c) no

28. (a) yes

    (b) 19.29 ± 12.09

    (c) 6

29. (b) no

    (c) 103.32 ± 4.19

30. (b) $\beta_i^* = \frac{1}{2}\beta_i \qquad i = 1, 2, 3, 4, 5$

    $\beta_0^* = \beta_0 + \frac{1}{2}(\beta_1 + \beta_2 + \beta_3 + \beta_4 + \beta_5)$

    (c)
    $$A = \begin{bmatrix} 1 & \frac{1}{2} & \frac{1}{2} & \frac{1}{2} & \frac{1}{2} & \frac{1}{2} \\ 0 & \frac{1}{2} & 0 & 0 & 0 & 0 \\ 0 & 0 & \frac{1}{2} & 0 & 0 & 0 \\ 0 & 0 & 0 & \frac{1}{2} & 0 & 0 \\ 0 & 0 & 0 & 0 & \frac{1}{2} & 0 \\ 0 & 0 & 0 & 0 & 0 & \frac{1}{2} \end{bmatrix}$$

31. $\sigma^2/2$, $\sigma^2/8$

32. (a) $x_i = \dfrac{x_i^* + 1}{2}$, $i = 1, 2, 3, 4, 5$

(b)
$$A = \begin{bmatrix} 1 & 0 & 0 & 0 & 0 & 0 \\ -1 & 2 & 0 & 0 & 0 & 0 \\ -1 & 0 & 2 & 0 & 0 & 0 \\ -1 & 0 & 0 & 2 & 0 & 0 \\ -1 & 0 & 0 & 0 & 2 & 0 \\ -1 & 0 & 0 & 0 & 0 & 2 \end{bmatrix}$$

34.
$$A = \begin{bmatrix} 1 & 0 & 0 & 0 & 0 & 0 & 0 & 0 & 0 \\ 0 & 1 & 0 & 0 & 0 & 0 & 0 & 0 & 0 \\ 0 & 0 & 1 & 0 & 0 & 0 & 0 & 0 & 0 \\ \frac{1}{2} & 0 & 0 & \frac{1}{2} & 0 & 0 & 0 & 0 & 0 \\ \frac{1}{2} & 0 & 0 & 0 & \frac{1}{2} & 0 & 0 & 0 & 0 \\ 0 & 0 & 0 & 0 & 0 & 1 & 0 & 0 & 0 \\ 0 & \frac{1}{2} & 0 & 0 & 0 & 0 & \frac{1}{2} & 0 & 0 \\ 0 & 0 & \frac{1}{2} & 0 & 0 & 0 & 0 & \frac{1}{2} & 0 \\ 0 & 0 & 0 & 0 & 0 & \frac{1}{2} & 0 & 0 & \frac{1}{2} \end{bmatrix}$$

35.
$$A = \begin{bmatrix} 1 & 0 & 0 & -1 & -1 & 0 & 0 & 0 & 0 \\ 0 & 1 & 0 & 0 & 0 & 0 & -1 & 0 & 0 \\ 0 & 0 & 1 & 0 & 0 & 0 & 0 & -1 & 0 \\ 0 & 0 & 0 & 2 & 0 & 0 & 0 & 0 & 0 \\ 0 & 0 & 0 & 0 & 2 & 0 & 0 & 0 & 0 \\ 0 & 0 & 0 & 0 & 0 & 1 & 0 & 0 & -1 \\ 0 & 0 & 0 & 0 & 0 & 0 & 2 & 0 & 0 \\ 0 & 0 & 0 & 0 & 0 & 0 & 0 & 2 & 0 \\ 0 & 0 & 0 & 0 & 0 & 0 & 0 & 0 & 2 \end{bmatrix}$$

Chapter 10

4. approximate maximum in lower right corner of square bounded by $x_1 = \pm 1$, $x_2 = \pm 1$
5. perpendicular to lines of constant response
6. proportional to $\beta_1 = 1$ and $\beta_2 = -.5$
11. 0
15. no; SSE $= 18.0$

16. no

17. no

18. no lack of fit

19. design is first order orthogonal

20. $V(\hat{y}) = \frac{1}{5} + \frac{2}{5}(x_1^2 + x_2^2)$

23. design is first order orthogonal

24. $V(\hat{y}) = V(\hat{\beta}_0) + \dfrac{d^2}{\frac{3}{2}(1 + r^2)}\sigma^2$

25. $r = 1$

31. (a) $V(\hat{y}) = \sigma^2(.167 + 1.259x_1^2 + 1.259x_2^2 + 5.926x_1^2x_2^2 + 2.667x_1^{*2}$
$+ 2.667x_2^{*2} + 4.148x_1^2x_2 + 2.074x_1^*x_2 - 2.074x_2x_2^* - .592x_1^*x_2^*)$

where $x_i^* = x_i^2 - \dfrac{\sum\limits_{j=1}^{n} x_{ij}^2}{n}$

(b) no

32. (a) no

33. (a) $\hat{y} = 9.83 - 1.156x_1 + .444x_2 - 4.622x_1x_2 - 4.622x_1^* + 2.223x_2^*$

where $x_i^* = x_i^2 - \dfrac{\sum\limits_{j=1}^{n} x_{ij}^2}{n}$

(b) $11.778 \pm .494$

35. $\hat{y} = 77.057 + 1.533x_1 + 5.555x_2 + .223x_3 + .115x_4 - 2.578x_1^* -$
$6.619x_2^* - 1.705x_3^* - .231x_4^* - .2x_2x_3 + .4x_2x_4 + 2.9x_3x_4$ where
$x_i^* = x_i^2 - \dfrac{\sum x_i^2}{n} = x_i^2 - .68618$

39. add 8 axial points; $\alpha = 1.3537$

40. 8 factorial points
6 axial points
6 center points

Chapter 11

9. SSE $= 2.47$; effects of
x_2 and x_3 are significant

11. $x_1x_2x_4x_5$, $x_1x_2x_3x_5x_6x_7$, $x_3x_4x_6x_7$, $x_1x_2x_4x_6x_7$, $x_1x_2x_3$, $x_3x_4x_5$, $x_5x_6x_7$

14. $\frac{1}{4}$ rep.

18. $E(\hat{\beta}_1) = \beta_1 + \beta_{23}$

19. (a) x_2x_3
(b) $x_1x_2x_3x_4$
(c) $x_1x_3x_4$

(d) $x_1 x_2 x_3 x_4 x_5$

20. (a) $x_2 x_3$, $x_1 x_3 x_4 x_5$, $x_2 x_4 x_5$
    (b) $x_1 x_2$, $x_4 x_5$, $x_1 x_2 x_3 x_4 x_5$
    (c) $x_1 x_3 x_4$, $x_2 x_3 x_5$, $x_1 x_5$
    (d) $x_2 x_3 x_4$, $x_1 x_3 x_5$, $x_2 x_5$
    (e) $x_2 x_4$, $x_1 x_5$, $x_2 x_3 x_5$

21. $E(\hat{\beta}_1) = \beta_1 + \beta_2 + \beta_{134} + \beta_{234}$

22. yes

24. 10 blocks; $\lambda = 3$

25. (b) yes; SSE $= 1.24$
    (c) -3.0 ± 1.11

26. (b) ANOVA

Source	d.f.	SS	MS
Mixes	3	45.00	15.00
Blocks	7	12.40	1.77
Error	13	3.74	.29
Total	23	61.14	

(c) yes   (d) $-4.70 \pm .71$

27. $\beta_0 + \frac{1}{4}(\beta_4 + \beta_5 + \beta_6)$; $\beta_4, \beta_5, \beta_6$ block parameters

28. $-\beta_1 = \mu_A - \mu_B$

29. $-\beta_1 - \dfrac{\beta_6}{3}$

30. $r = 3$

31. (a) $\lambda = 2$
    (b) yes
    (c) $1.48 \pm .66$

32. (a) $\lambda = 4$
    (b) yes
    (c) $y^* = \sqrt{y}$
    (e) 14
    (f) yes

34. no

35. (a) ANOVA

Source	d.f.	SS	MS
Mixes	3	45.00	15.00
Reps	1	3.60	3.60
Blocks in Reps	6	8.80	1.47
Error	13	3.74	.29
Total	23	61.14	

(e) yes

Chapter 12

4. ANOVA

Source	d.f.	SS	MS
Paper Samples	9	2348.30	260.92**
Within	20	174.67	8.73
Total	29	2522.97	

5. ANOVA

Source	d.f.	MS
Subjects	9	164.48
Time/subject	20	16.95
Reps/time	30	3.72
Total	59	

7. $E(\text{MS Resistors}) = \sigma^2 + 3\sigma_R^2$
   $E(\text{MSE}) = \sigma^2$

8. $E(\text{MS Subjects}) = \sigma^2 + 2\sigma_T^2 + 6\sigma_S^2$
   $E(\text{MS Time/Subjects}) = \sigma^2 + 2\sigma_T^2$
   $E(\text{MSE}) = \sigma^2$

11. yes

12. yes; yes

14. (123.4, 869.6)

15. (5.1, 18.2)

16. (991.3, 1004.6)

17. (39.8, 279.1)

19. $3.4 < \sigma_B^2 < 18.0$
    $10.8 < \sigma_A^2 < 101.8$
    $2.4 < \sigma^2 < 6.6$

20. (32.9, 40.4)

21. $n_1 = 4,\ n_2 = 2$
    cost \$208

22. $n_1 = 13,\ n_2 = 2,\ n_3 = 4$, cost \$3944

23. (b) (17.7, 63.2)
    (c) (15.6, 27.0)
    (d) (14.9, 17.3)

24. (37.8, 42.2)

25. $n_1 = 7,\ n_2 = 2,\ n_3 = 2$

26. (a) $y = \mu + \alpha_i + \gamma_{ij} + \delta_{ijk} + \epsilon_{ijkl}$

(b) $V(\bar{y}) = \dfrac{\sigma_\alpha^2}{n_1} + \dfrac{\sigma_\gamma^2}{n_1 n_2} + \dfrac{\sigma_\delta^2}{n_1 n_2 n_3} + \dfrac{\sigma^2}{n_1 n_2 n_3 n_4}$

(c) $V(\bar{y}_i) = \sigma_\alpha^2 + \dfrac{\sigma_\gamma^2}{n_2} + \dfrac{\sigma_\delta^2}{n_2 n_3} + \dfrac{\sigma^2}{n_2 n_3 n_4}$

27. ANOVA

Source	d.f.	E(MS)
A	$n_1 - 1$	$n_2 n_3 n_4 \sigma_\alpha^2 + n_3 n_4 \sigma_\gamma^2 + n_4 \sigma_\delta^2 + \sigma^2$
B in A	$n_1(n_2 - 1)$	$n_3 n_4 \sigma_\gamma^2 + n_4 \sigma_\delta^2 + \sigma^2$
C in B	$n_1 n_2(n_3 - 1)$	$n_4 \sigma_\delta^2 + \sigma^2$
D in C	$n_1 n_2 n_3(n_4 - 1)$	σ^2

29. (a) Let $y_{ij} = \mu + \alpha_i + \epsilon_{ij}$ where α_i is a random component for days and ϵ_{ij} is a random component for estimators. Then

$$\sum_{i=1}^{n_1} \bar{y}_i = n_1 \mu + \sum_{i=1}^{n_1} \alpha_i + \frac{\sum_{i=1}^{n_1} \sum_{j=1}^{3} \epsilon_{ij}}{3}$$

(b) ANOVA

Source	d.f.	SS	MS
Days	6	386.310	64.385
Estimate/days	14	19.073	1.362
Total	20	405.383	

30. (a) $E(\bar{y}_{n_1}) = \mu$

$V(\bar{y}_{n_1}) = \dfrac{\sigma_\alpha^2}{n_1} + \dfrac{\sigma^2}{3n_1}$

(b) $E(\bar{y}_{n_1+d} - \bar{y}_{n_1}) = 0$

$V(\bar{y}_{n_1+d} - \bar{y}_{n_1}) = \dfrac{d\sigma_\alpha^2}{n_1(n_1 + d)} + \dfrac{d\sigma^2}{3n_1(n_1 + d)}$

31. $(n_1 + d)\bar{y}_{n_1} \pm t_{\alpha/2}\sqrt{\dfrac{d(n_1 + d)}{n_1}\left(\hat{\sigma}_\alpha^2 + \dfrac{\hat{\sigma}^2}{3}\right)}$

32. 1035.7 ± 23.3

33. $E(\bar{y}_{n_1} - \bar{y}_{n_2}) = 0$

$V(\bar{y}_{n_1} - \bar{y}_{n_2}) = \left(\sigma_\alpha^2 + \dfrac{\sigma^2}{3}\right)\left(\dfrac{1}{n_1} + \dfrac{1}{n_2}\right)$

40. $n_1 = 7$
$n_2 = 6$

42. (a) $6.74 < \sigma^2 < 16.37$
$11.47 < \sigma_\alpha^2 < 53.23 \ (\nu = 14)$

43. $Y_{ij} = \mu + \alpha_i + \beta_j + \epsilon_{ij}$
α_i = random component for the ith day
β_j = random component for the jth estimator
ϵ_{ij} = random error

All random components are assumed to be mutually independent with zero expectations and variances, σ_α^2, σ_β^2 and σ^2, respectively.

Analyze as a two-way classification.

$E(\text{MS Days}) = n_2 \sigma_\alpha^2 + \sigma^2$

$E(\text{MS Est.}) = n_1 \sigma_\beta^2 + \sigma^2$

$E(\text{MSE}) = \sigma^2$

where n_1 = number of days

n_2 = number of estimators

Chapter 13

1. (b) 1402.5 ± 224.65

2. (b) 36.3 ± 1.5

  (c) $\dfrac{\sigma^2}{3}$

3. (a) $E(\text{MST}) = \sigma^2 + \theta_\tau$

   $E(\text{MSB}) = \sigma^2 + 5\sigma_b^2$

   $E(\text{MSE}) = \sigma^2$

  (b) $.99 < \sigma_b^2 < 13.18$ $(\nu \approx 4)$

4. choose $b = 5$

6. (a) $F = 36.203 > F_{.05}$; reject (SSE $= 170.88$)

  (b) $F = 7.1516 > F_{.05}$; reject

  (c) $20.3 < \sigma_c^2 < 271.0$ $(\nu \approx 4)$

7. (a) $\tau_i - \tau_j$; $\dfrac{2\sigma^2}{5}$

  (b) $\mu + \tau_i$; $\frac{1}{5}(\sigma_R^2 + \sigma_c^2 + \sigma^2)$

8. 14.4 ± 4.25

9. 51 ± 7.3 $(\nu \approx 9)$

10. (a) SSE $= 186$

  (b) 236.3 ± 45.3

  (c) 1166.1 ± 165.9

13. see No. 10. (b) and (c)

22. (a) $F = 38.2 > F_{.05} = 3.89$; reject (SSE $= 142.7$)

23. 14 ± 5.32

24. 8.75 ± 4.75 $(\nu \approx 16)$

25. $.004 < \sigma_\alpha^2 < 4.2$ $(\nu \approx 1)$

26. (b) $\hat{y} = 2.59 - .60x + .31x^2$

  (c) $\hat{\sigma}^2 = .124$

   $\hat{\sigma}_\alpha^2 = .27$

  (e) $2.63 \pm .99$

Index